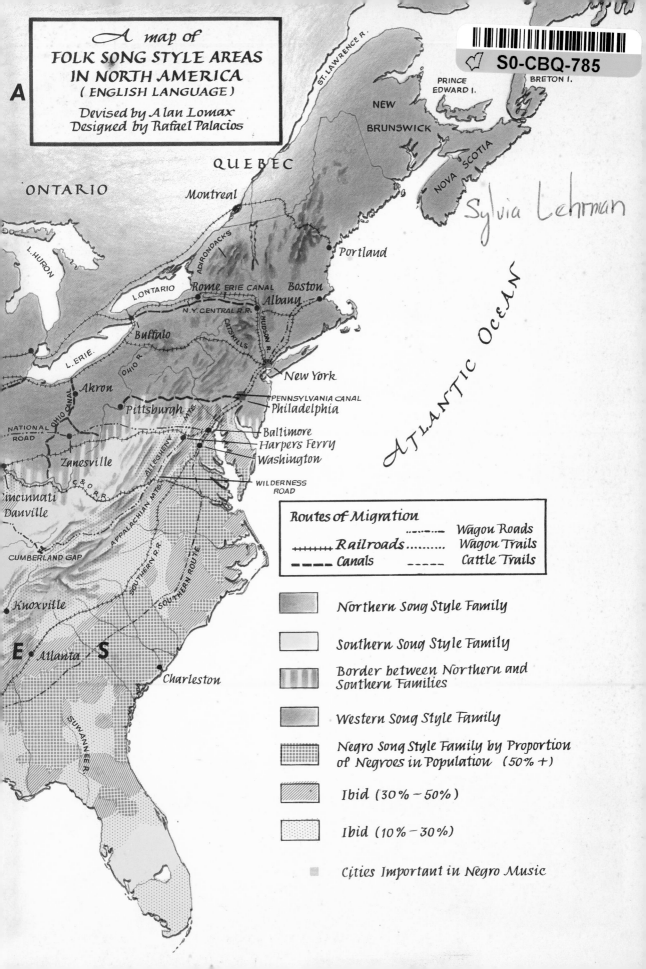

A map of FOLK SONG STYLE AREAS IN NORTH AMERICA
(ENGLISH LANGUAGE)

Devised by Alan Lomax
Designed by Rafael Palacios

Sylvia Lehrman

ATLANTIC OCEAN

QUEBEC

ONTARIO

ST. LAWRENCE R.

NEW BRUNSWICK

PRINCE EDWARD I.

BRETON I.

NOVA SCOTIA

Montreal

Portland

L. HURON

ADIRONDACKS

L. ONTARIO

Rome   ERIE CANAL   Boston
Albany
N.Y. CENTRAL R.R.
CATSKILLS
HUDSON R.

Buffalo

L. ERIE

OHIO R.

New York

Akron

OHIO CANAL

PENNSYLVANIA CANAL
Philadelphia

Pittsburgh   ALLEGHENY MTS.

NATIONAL ROAD

Baltimore
Harpers Ferry
Washington

Zanesville

C. & O. R.R.

WILDERNESS ROAD

Cincinnati
Danville

APPALACHIAN MTS.

CUMBERLAND GAP

SOUTHERN R.R.

SOUTHERN ROUTE

Knoxville

Atlanta

Charleston

SUWANNEE R.

Routes of Migration

·–··–··–	Wagon Roads
+++++++ Railroads	·········· Wagon Trails
▬ ▬ ▬ Canals	– – – Cattle Trails

Northern Song Style Family

Southern Song Style Family

Border between Northern and Southern Families

Western Song Style Family

Negro Song Style Family by Proportion of Negroes in Population (50% +)

Ibid (30% – 50%)

Ibid (10% – 30%)

Cities Important in Negro Music

THE FOLK SONGS
OF NORTH AMERICA

THE FOLK SONGS OF NORTH AMERICA

IN THE ENGLISH LANGUAGE

BY

ALAN LOMAX

Melodies and guitar chords transcribed by
PEGGY SEEGER

With one hundred piano arrangements by
MATYAS SEIBER and DON BANKS

Illustrated by
MICHAEL LEONARD

Editorial Assistant
SHIRLEY COLLINS

DOUBLEDAY & COMPANY, INC.
GARDEN CITY, NEW YORK

Library of Congress Catalog Card Number 60-15185
© Alan Lomax 1960
Piano Arrangements by Matyas Seiber and Don Banks in this anthology
© Cassell & Co., Ltd. 1960

To My Father
JOHN A. LOMAX
who broke the trail

CONTENTS

The references below indicate the page on which the music and words of individual songs are to be found. To find the note relating to a specific song the reader should consult the index of song titles on p.617.

PART I. THE NORTH

PART II. THE SOUTHERN MOUNTAINS AND BACKWOODS

PART III. THE WEST

PART IV. THE NEGRO SOUTH

APPENDIXES

MAPS

INTRODUCTION

A Folk Song Map

The map sings. The chanteys surge along the rocky Atlantic seaboard, across the Great Lakes and round the moon-curve of the Gulf of Mexico. The paddling songs of the French-Canadians ring out along the Saint Lawrence and west past the Rockies. Beside them, from Newfoundland, Nova Scotia, and New England, the ballads, straight and tall as spruce, march towards the West.

Inland from the Sea Islands, slave melodies sweep across the whole South from the Carolinas to Texas. And out on the shadows of the Smoky and Blue Ridge mountains the old ballads, lonesome love songs, and hoedowns echo through the upland South into the hills of Arkansas and Oklahoma. There in the Ozarks the Northern and Southern song families swap tunes and make a marriage.

The Texas cowboys roll the little doughies north to Montana, singing Northern ballads with a Southern accent. New roads and steel rails lace the Southern backwoods to the growl and thunder of Negro chants of labour—the axe songs, the hammer songs, and the railroad songs. These blend with the lonesome hollers of levee-camp mule-skinners to create the blues, and the blues, America's *cante hondo*, uncoils its subtle, sensual melancholy in the ear of all the states, then all the world.

The blues roll down the Mississippi to New Orleans, where the Creoles mix the musical gumbo of jazz—once a dirty word, but now a symbol of musical freedom for the West. The Creoles add Spanish pepper and French sauce and blue notes to the rowdy tantara of their reconstruction-happy brass bands, stir up the hot music of New Orleans and warm the weary heart of humanity. . . . These are the broad outlines of America's folk-song map. The saga of American folk song, the story of the complex forces that shaped these traditions, follows presently.

The Melting Pot

The first function of music, especially of folk music, is to produce a feeling of security for the listener by voicing the particular quality of a land and the life of its people. To the traveller, a line from a familiar song may bring back all the familiar emotions of home, for music is a magical summing-up of the patterns of family, of love, of conflict, and of work which give a community its special feel and which shape the personalities of its members. Folk song calls the native back to his roots and prepares him emotionally to dance, worship, work, fight, or make love in ways normal to his place.

Each group of settlers in the New World tried to establish a musical community like the one they had left in Europe. They dotted the map with little Swedens, little Lithuanias, little Italies, and so on, while the music of Spain, Portugal, France, Great Britain, and

West Africa spread over domains in the western hemisphere. Everywhere in the New World we find songs that were popular in the days when the colonists set sail from their homelands. Thus American folk song is, in one aspect, a museum of musical antiques from many lands. On the other hand, some European folk traditions, particularly those rooted in village ceremonial, did not long survive in the American melting pot. More will be said of this, but first a word about a tendency for which America is particularly notable—the mixing and blending of various folk-strains to produce new forms.

The isolation of colonial and frontier life sometimes had a benign effect upon the traditional arts, which are normally slow to ripen. Here and there in the wilderness circumstances permitted a cultural pocket to form, where regional or tribal song families could slowly combine to produce a sturdy new breed. The music of Haiti, for instance, shows the mingling of several West African tribal strains; the music of the Southern Appalachians is an Anglo-Scots-Irish synthesis, more British than anything to be heard on those for ever disparate isles. Indeed, the pedant may search in vain for a ' pure ' American folk song. ' There just ain't no such animal.' Our best songs and dances are hybrids of hybrids, mixtures of mixtures, and this may be the source of their great appeal to a cosmopolitan age and the cause for their extremely rapid development. Folk music, like other arts and sciences, blooms hard by the crossroads.

Singing Democrats

On the American frontier men worked and sang together on terms of amity and equality impossible in the Old World. A man was judged not by his accent or his origins, but by his character and capacities. A song was treasured for its suitability to frontier life. Inherited regional patterns of speech and song broke down beneath this pragmatic, democratic pressure. However, the materials for new folk-song traditions were at hand. The mass of the colonists were poor country folk, carriers of traditional melodies. Many were rebels, fleeing from political persecution and longing to express their feelings openly. Thus a note of social protest rang through native American balladry, and the lives and problems of the common people became its main concern. What in Britain had been a tendency to heroize the sailor lad and the kitchen-maid became the dominant theme of the American ballad maker.

' A man ain't nothin' but a man . . .' sings John Henry for all these free-born working-men, busy with the job of taming a continent. In the ballads the men bawl out their complaints about bad working conditions, and in the love songs the women keen their discontent with patriarchal conventions of love and marriage.

The common man, the individual, is everything in American folk song. The folk spirituals—in contrast to older types of hymns—sing mainly of personal salvation, while in the worldly ballads and lyrics, the first person singular steadily replaces the impersonal narrator. What cantankerous individualists were these frontiersmen!

> I'll buy my own whiskey, I'll drink my own dram,
> And for them that don't like me I don't give a damn!

Not only personal eccentricity, but musical non-conformity was relished. An historian tells of a Rocky Mountain hunter on his yearly spree in St. Louis, who lay on the bar-room floor and drummed out an accompaniment to his song on his bare belly. The stubby little Kentucky farmer bragged, ' When I was a-singin' in my cornfield, my folks could hear me on the front porch a mile and a half down the holler.' Southern hymn composers deliberately broke the rules of conventional harmony by writing series of parallel fourth and fifth chords. The New Orleans jazz men brought new sounds out of the trumpet by playing ' dirty ', that is, with as much of the forbidden vibrato as possible. . . . From the time of the ' nigger minstrels ' to the pelvic beat of rock and roll, Americans have welcomed every musical innovation of the Negro.

The saying was, ' It's a big country.' If a man failed in one town, he could make a fresh start in a new one. Social and geographical mobility became a main feature of American life, and moving to new pastures or to a new apartment, a fixed national habit.

> . . . I think I'll settle down, and I says, says I,
> I'll never wander further till the day I die.
> But the wind it sorta chuckles—Why of course you will,
> For once you git the habit, you just can't keep still . . .

These restless Americans scattered certain folk songs from Maine to California, while others were left behind, half-finished, like so many ghost towns, when the work camps moved west or ' culture ' invaded frontier outposts. We are fortunate that the collectors have rescued these ' ghost-songs ' from oblivion. Their very rawness lends them the impact of truth, for they speak in the unvarnished language of the pioneer worker. Yet the ' moving habit ' gave Americans a rootless, lonesome feeling. Where the freedom of the wilderness was the breath of life to such bold spirits as Boone and Crockett, gentler folk were sometimes troubled by the vast landscapes and the awesome solitudes that surrounded their little cabins. The mountaineer speaks of his old songs as ' lonesome tunes ' ; the pioneer sings of himself as a poor, wayfaring stranger—a poor, lonesome cowboy—a poor boy lookin' for a home—travellin' down a ' lonesome road '.

' Every jug stood on its own bottom ' in America. In Europe the established churches had imposed an official code of conduct on a population which often had a pagan tradition. When this churchly authority was finally broken by the American Revolution and every man won the freedom to live according to the dictates of his own conscience, a new situation prevailed. The church was no longer a buffer between man and God. Calvinist morality became a self-imposed creed. Thus the religious freedom won by fighting Protestants in the Revolution left every man naked and alone, to come to terms with an angry and demanding God and with his own alerted, sin-ridden conscience. The American Protestant burdened his heart with the ethical and moral conflicts which had riven church and state in Europe for many centuries. The gains for the human spirit were magnificent, but the cost has been great, as our history and our folk songs show.

Troubled in Mind

The moral precepts of Puritans and Calvinists became the folk mores of pioneer America. No idea in the young democracy ante-dated or outweighed the conviction that the pleasures of the world were steps on the road to business failure and eternal damnation. The Protestant catalogue of sin included love-making, drinking, gambling, playing the fiddle, singing worldly songs, dancing, fishing on Sunday, and anything else an hysterical preacher could think of. A ' bad ' or ' wild ' girl had few good offers of marriage. A rogue male could go west and blow off steam, but even then he had to look Hell in the face when he died.

This ' folklore of sin ' put iron in the backbone of the pioneer; it made him sober and hardworking; but it left him with an inner sense of guilt and shame which no one in nineteenth-century America could really escape. Today the psychoanalyst copes with its aftermath at one level of society, juvenile and divorce courts at another, while the folk singers continue to echo the convictions of ' old-time religion ' . . .

> I've told you once and I've told you twice,
> There's sinners in Hell for shootin' dice . . .

In Great Britain Christian bigots hammered away for centuries at the ingrained paganism of the people, but even where they succeeded in stamping out the ancient festivals of May and Midsummer and Christmas, the *feeling* of festival remains and, in spite of surface conformity, the old permissive patterns keep their potency to this day. Below the reserved and often dour exterior of the Briton, one discovers an easy and natural acceptance of the pleasures of the flesh and the bed, foreign to folk psychology in America, where a sense of sin is at the marrow of folklore. Few traces of the paganism of Britain are found in the United States. The great mass of gently erotic ditties still common and broadcastable (!) in England and Scotland live in America mainly in the nether-world of ' dirty songs '.

After many years of collecting in both countries, I am profoundly impressed by the comparative paganism and resignation of Britain, as contrasted with the Puritanism and free aggressiveness of America. The British song-tradition in America has been censored, both conscientiously and consciously.* Religious folk in the backwoods rigidly applied Calvinist distinction between sacred and sinful songs—that is between songs with religious texts and all other songs whatsoever. I once asked a Mississippi guitarist what he thought would happen to him if he were killed while playing the blues. ' I'd go to hell,' he replied, and he meant this, literally. A country preacher thundered: ' The Lord fixed a gulf between Heaven and Hell, between the saints and the sinners—and when the Lord fixes something, brother, it's *fixed* ! '

In the popular mind a gulf was fixed between pleasure and righteousness, thus inflaming the old wound of guilt and sexual anxiety which has so often characterized our civilization. Although the young democracy gave women more political rights and social status than they had known for centuries, nineteenth century prudery designed to rob them of sexual pleasure. A majority of our ancestors believed that only bad women enjoyed sex : a dutiful wife suffered it for the sake of her husband. Thus the women of the frontier, whose lives were hard, lonely, and comfortless at best, found solace in romantic or vengeful fantasies. Their favourite ballads and love songs were shrouded in gloom, drowned in melancholy, and poisoned by sado-masochism.

Love, they say, means sorrow, invites betrayal, leads to long separation and brings true lovers to the grave. This melancholy view of love probably came to the West from the Orient, where a jealous and patriarchal family system prevails; but in all Europe, notably in Britain, pagan notes of joy sound in the gloom. In English songs the maiden is very pleasantly seduced before she is betrayed. In Scots songs she is very often raped but, if she has pluck, she may win a fine, noble husband. But our pioneer folk censor struck these pleasurable realities from the songs, and, as far as possible, from life, leaving Americans the sad moral to sing . . .

> The grave will decay you and turn you to dust,
> There's not one boy in fifty that a poor girl can trust . . .

* For an example of the effect of this folk censorship, compare the British and American versions of *The Foggy Dew* (pp. 89, 90).

The full weight of Puritanism did not fall upon the Negroes, who came largely from cultures which placed a high value on erotic and aggressive behaviour and which provided vivid outlets for them in song, dance, and ceremonial. As slaves and later, as second-class citizens in the South, they were not expected to conform rigidly to the conventions that harrassed the whites. Even the country Baptist preachers looked on sex as one thing and sin as another. At the folk level, especially, the Negro escaped some of the anxieties and conflicts that plagued white Americans, and his often joyous, always sensuous music shows it. Not until the twentieth century, when the group had thoroughly assimilated Western ascetic morality and was beset by discrimination and social dislocation, did Negroes begin to sing the ' careless love ' blues.

White Solo—Black Chorus

Two principal traditions gave rise to our hybrid music—the British and the West African. The folk-song map shows dark and fertile islands of Afro-American songs rising out of a sea of Anglo-American music. Today these islands are slowly subsiding, but they have indelibly coloured the surrounding ocean.

For centuries, most British folk songs have been sung in solo with occasional unison choruses, although in remoter parts of the islands there are clear traces of an older choral style. The pioneer white in America retained scarcely any ability to make music in groups. When he and his fellows sang together in church, there was little blending and no harmony unless a singing teacher was there to instruct them. White pioneers sang long ballads, slow lyric pieces with highly decorated melodies, or lilting dance tunes—largely in solo, often in a high-pitched, sometimes ' womanish ' nasal tone. A tense throat allowed little variation in vocal colour, but great delicacy in ornamentation. The effect was a mournful wailing sound, like an oriental oboe, suitable to the inner melancholy and conflict of the songs. A singer sat stiffly erect, his body rigid, the muscles of his throat and face tense, gazing into the distance or with his eyes closed—an impersonal, though highly charged story-teller. For him the words and tune were separate entities and the words more important than the tune. Song rhythm conformed, normally, to the demands of the text; in the older pieces it wandered and wavered and gathered pace again as the verse demanded. The fiddle was the most widely used instrument and, as played, it was another high-pitched, reedy, wailing voice, seconding and matching the singer or lilting the dance tunes. Such were the characteristics of white folk music, North, South, and West during the pioneer period. Indeed, the modern crooner still sings in this style—with a trace of Neapolitan and a touch of the tarbrush.

The sounds that came from the dark islands of Negro song were a stimulating contrast. Most of the American Negro slaves came from West Africa, where music-making was largely a group activity, the creation of a many-voiced, dancing throng. Typically, a leader raised the song and was answered by a chorus of blended voices, often singing simple chords, the whole accompanied in polyrhythm by an orchestra of drums, shakers, hand-clapping, etc. (Soloists singing highly decorated melodies were more characteristic of Arab-influenced cultures in the north near the Sahara.)

Few African instruments survived in North America, but African musical habits did.* The slaves continued to sing in leader-chorus style, with a more relaxed throat than the whites, and in deeper-pitched, mellower voices, which blended richly. The faces of the

---

* Marshall Stearns in *The Story of Jazz* (Oxford University Press, 1956 ; Mentor Books, 1958) tells the instrumental side of this story.

singers were animated and expressive; the voices playful. They used simple European chords to create harmony of a distinctive colour. If not actually dancing as they sang, they patted their feet, swayed their bodies, and clapped out the subtle rhythms of their songs. A strong, surging beat underlay most of their American creations, and this was accompanied in an increasingly complex style as they improvised or acquired instruments. Words and tunes were intimately and playfully united, and 'sense' was often subordinated to the demands of rhythm and melody. Community songs of labour and worship and dance songs far outnumbered narrative pieces, and the emotion of the songs was, on the whole, joyfully erotic, deeply tragic, allusive, playful, or ironic rather than nostalgic withdrawn, factual, or aggressively comic — as among white folk singers.

For more than two hundred years these two contrasting musical cultures dwelt side by side in America in a state of continually stimulating exchange and competition. Song material passed back and forth across the racial line so that it becomes increasingly difficult to say which group has contributed most to a song. As in the West Indies and parts of South America, true Afro-European songs, and especially dances, developed, which gained continental, then world-wide popularity. Indeed, it seems very likely that one day all American music will be *café-au-lait* in colour.

The Folk-Song Regions

Although Afro-American folk music has its regional peculiarities, it expresses the same feelings and speaks the same basic language everywhere. It has changed with each advance of the Negro people and in accord with an African trait, by which new songs and new types are constantly developed out of stock material and are preferred to older music. Anglo-American folk music, on the other hand, is conservative in practice. However, it was split by history and geography into three principal regional families, all closely akin, but self-consistent and self-perpetuating to a considerable degree: *The Northern*, relatively more permissive and open-voiced; *The Southern*, more guilt-ridden, pinched-voiced, and violent; and *The Western*, a blend of the two.* Of course, these regions do not have sharply defined boundaries, but rather wide border zones in which styles mingle. The four regions (the fourth being the *Negro South*), which are treated in detail in separate parts of this book, provide the historical framework within which many of the elements in our rich and confusing folk heritage fall into place. (See pp. 1, 153, 299, and 447).

Folk Songs and History

The intention of this volume is to put a choice selection of our folk songs into their historical and social setting so that they tell the story of the people who made and sang them — to compose, in a word, a folk history, or a history of the folk of America. However, few folk songs have a direct connexion with political events. They may reflect economic developments that open up opportunities or place fresh burdens on the common man. Some songs hint at a deep ground swell of response to major social changes. Here one may see why certain songs are forgotten and new ballads appear. But normally folk songs change slowly and mysteriously, rooted as they are in fundamental social and psychological patterns that resist alteration. New versions and variants arise ceaselessly as the songs are passed on by word of mouth, and the study of these versions has fascinated scholars. To my way of thinking, however, we do not yet understand enough about the unconscious processes at work in the slow emergence of versions to control such studies.

* This book deals only with songs in the English language, with nothing to say about the aboriginal and other minority music traditions which splash our folk-song map with colour.

The most one can say at present is that folk songs, even the seemingly factual ones, are expressions of feeling, and many of them, in our guilt-ridden and repressive culture, provide outlets for all sorts of unconscious fantasies. They are ' the stuff that dreams are made on '; they murmur of wishes and emotional conflicts too disturbing to be more openly stated by the singer and his community. Because these songs are passively accepted as favoured fantasies by whole human families over long periods of time, they can be taken as the signposts of persistent patterns of community feeling and can throw light into many dark corners of our past and our present. An ideal folk-song study could be a history of popular feeling. In this volume I have tried to suggest what such a study could reveal about our people.

British Ballads in America

What happened to the old narrative songs, like *Edward* and *Barbara Allen*, when they crossed the Atlantic? Almost one hundred of these three hundred ' classic ' ballads, many with old-style modal tunes, have been recently found in North America, a much larger number than in the living tradition of Great Britain. Here is an instance of the conservatism of a colonial people, continuing to sing the songs that were popular in their homeland at the time they left it. But conservatism is not the only principle at work here. The folk are selective. One has only to compare the full list of British popular ballads with the American list to see that the settlers cast out whole categories of ballads.

Most of the ballads which gained wide popularity in America have to do with sexual conflict viewed through feminine eyes. The pride of *Barbara Allen* kills sweet William. The cupidity of *Lord Thomas's* mother brings on the death of *Fair Ellender* and her rival, the *Brown Girl*. The married woman, who leaves her *House Carpenter* and her children, is soon drowned together with her *Daemon Lover*. Another gayer lady prefers to stay in the cold fields with the *Gypsy Laddie* rather than return to her husband's castle. *Pretty Polly* turns the tables on her seducer, the *Elfin Knight*, and pushes him over a cliff. Devoted *Lady Nancy Belle* pines away to the grave when *Lord Lovel* leaves her for a year and a day. *Jimmy Randall* dies in his mother's arms, poisoned by a wicked sweetheart. *Lord Barnard* runs through *Little Musgrove*, his wife's lover, then beheads the guilty woman. The pitiful ghosts of her babes return to haunt the *Cruel Mother*, who has stabbed them. Such are the themes of ballads cherished by the women of the backwoods, for whom love and marriage meant gruelling labour, endless childbearing, and subservience. In the ballads one can see the women turning to thoughts of revenge, to morbid death wishes, to guilt-ridden fantasies of escape. Always the sorrows of women bring violence and death to those around them.

Similar emotions find comic outlet in our two favourite humorous narratives. *The Farmer's Curst Wife*, packed off to Hell, trounces the Devil and his whole family and returns to earth to give her old husband another drubbing. In *Our Goodman*, the wandering husband is told that the man in bed with his wife is a cabbage head or a baby.

Little sung in America are the British ballads in which men play a hero's part. Censored out and gone are the merry Scots ballads of rape and pregnancy, as well as the languorous seduction songs of southern England. In their place stand a host of later broadside pieces— *Lily Monroe*, *William Riley*, *The Broken Token*, *The Little Mohee*, and a dozen more—all stories of the faithful and virtuous maiden who gets her man ; but this romantic theme of virtue rewarded has a darker twin in the sadistic and punishing *Cruel Ship's Carpenter* theme—the story of the pregnant girl murdered by her treacherous lover, which has given rise to more than half of the ballads composed by white folk singers in America !*

* *Omie Wise*; *Rose Connelly*; *Tom Dula*; *The Lone Green Valley*, etc. (*See* pp. 268, 267, 269, 93)

In one story about his Nova Scotia singers, Mackenzie gives us a glimpse into the depths of murderous feeling that stir below the surface of these violent fantasies:

John was a man of superb and preternatural solemnity. On three occasions only have I seen him writhing in the clutches of laughter. The first was when, leaning on his garden rake, he told the circumstantial narrative of a gross insult to his own wife. The second was when he described with equal faithfulness the tragic death of his beloved dog. The third was when he told me the story of the mutiny on the Saladin . . .

> O first we killed our captain,
> And then we killed our mate,
> Then overboard the bos'n threw
> Together in the deep . . .

' Just think of that deck,' John entreated. ' Just think of that deck with dead bodies strewed on it an' all red an' slippery with blood! ' Then for some reason which it would be idle to explain, he burst into a fit of monstrous laughter . . .

It is easy to understand why the common people of Great Britain, ridden into the ditch for centuries, pushed off their rich commons into city slums and then shipped abroad to colonize hostile lands, had a fund of vengeful laughter to spend. Like all voyagers they had dreamed of discovering gold and pleasure in the New World. Instead they found a land where hard work was the first article of religion, and the rest a catalogue of the sins of the flesh. Weak and sensual mortals were condemned to the cold hell of failure on this earth and Calvin's burning hell in the next. To the religious, death became a friend who freed them from continual struggle, and to the rebellious, death was a final break with a painful morality. The morbid hymns and bloody ballads expressed their unconscious wishes.

The American Come-All-Ye

The way of escape lay west along the skidways of the lumberjacks, the dim wagon trails of the pioneers, and the watery tracks of the keelboatmen into the pathless plains. The rewards and the dangers of the monstrous wilderness were endless; the sky was the limit; and every working day tested a man's hardihood and courage. Out west, the wilderness hunter, the raftsman, the lumberjack, the prospector, and the plainsman cussed, drank, whored, killed, and grabbed land from the Indians with a satisfying freedom from restraint. Their rough campfire balladry is the best account we have of the feelings of the men who tamed the continent, and its quietly factual, humorous, or sentimental tone indicates that they found plenty of aggressive outlets in everyday life. These men admired a song because it was ' as true as steel ', and a singer because ' he spoke his words out plain '. If they seem preoccupied with death, perhaps it is because death stared them in the face every day.

Darn Fool Ditties

Yet a broad, sunny streak of laughter runs through the creations of the song-makers who followed the western star. The fiddlers, banjo singers, and rhymesters were rebels, bound and determined to get some fun out of life in spite of the disapproval of respectable folk. They were kin to little Cindy. . . .

> Cindy got religion, she'd had it once before,
> But when she hears my old banjo, she's the first one on the floor . . .

They belonged to the wild and godless breed that once inhabited the town of Songo Locks in Maine. A missionary visited that place in the early days, and, when he returned, he was asked whether he had saved any souls. ' Well,' he said, ruefully, ' I had some success, I believe.   Anyway, I left Jesus Christ with them.   But I've been worried sick ever since for fear they'd crucify Him again.'

To American humorists nothing was sacred.   Anyone who put on airs had his pants kidded off.   A man who couldn't take a joke and tell one couldn't get elected dog-catcher. The very marvels and dangers of the wilderness were exaggerated until they seemed ridiculous and thus terrifying no longer.   Finding laughter the great leveller, Americans poured out a flood of jokes, quips, and wisecracks that swept the class system into the dustbin of the past.   They were the first people in history to win free of superstition and tyranny, and the pent-up laughter of centuries burst out of them.   America became a laughing nation.   Indeed, as Lincoln saw, America's pioneer philosophy is summed up in its comic anecdotes.

American comic songs range over the social scale from banker to bum, but songs of awkward lovers and comic courtships hit Americans especially hard on the funny bone.   Love was something you laughed at or died of.   In part this is the rude laughter of the *shivaree*, expressing a crude, voyeur eroticism ;   yet small, bitter notes sound through the mirth . . . of women disappointed in awkward lovers . . . of men rebelling against the wearisome tyranny of romantic and frightened women . . . of the feelings of shame and fear impressed upon both sexes by a repressive Paulian code.   The one batch of white songs which catch sounds of untramelled, earthy pleasure are the lyrics for the hoedown fiddle and the banjo.   I suspect that many of these rowdy and joyous songs were created in settlements far out on the frontier, beyond the reach of the preacher and his board of joy-killing deacons.   They were kept alive by the reckless crew who roistered and drank, even though they were dancing beyond the pale of respectability.   Their rhymes ring like a cock crowing at the dawning of an American day . . .

> Chickens a-crowin' on Sourwood Mountain,
> So many pretty girls I can't count 'em . . .
> Girls on the Cripple Creek 'bout half grown,
> Jump on a boy like a dog on a bone . . .

Compared with the mouth music of Scotland, American dancing rhymes were cryptic and allusive, relying on wild, zany images to convey hidden erotic meaning.   Here they were met more than half-way by the songs of the Negroes, which concealed beneath their surface innocence a world of irony and protest, and by the funny songs of the blackface minstrels, which were silly, but sometimes amusing parodies on the Negro jingles.   All were rooted in an old Celtic type which turned the world upside down and inside out . . .

> You should have seen the eel with his pipes, playing a broadside,
> The lark with its nest in the gander's beard,
> The water-hen crooning and playing the Jew's harp,
> The church leaping and dancing all over the valley . . .

Americans have created many such darn-fool ditties out of non-sequiturs and splintered images—songs which, like surrealist paintings, mirror the swift turbulence of modern life. They recall that mythical bird, the Kansas jay-hawk ' that flies backwards because he doesn't care where he's goin' but wants to know where he's been.   When you hear the old jay-hawk squawlin', you know that if somethin' ain't happened, it's goin' to.'

The Devil's Music

To give the fiddler a rest or just to liven a crowd up, American square dance callers improvised haywire rhymes in dance rhythms which were often called ' Devil's ditties ', because the Devil was generally held to be the king and principal instructor of fiddlers. Behind this superstition lay the old Gaelic tales of the gift of music coming from the fairies, and Scots and American yarns of the fiddler who takes lessons from Satan in the graveyard at midnight. Folklore continually hints at a real connexion between folk musicians and survivals of the witch cult and Satanism in America.

As part of his initiation into the American *vaudou* cult, the Negro novice must learn to play the guitar. He goes to the cross-roads at midnight armed with a black cat bone, and as he sits in the dark playing the blues, the Devil approaches, cuts the player's nails to the quick, and swaps guitars. Thus the *vaudouist* sells his soul to the Devil and in return receives the gift of invisibility and the mastery of his instrument. These practices may explain why the religious often call an expert Negro folk musician ' a child of the Devil ' or ' the Devil's son-in-law '. Jelly Roll Morton, the king of jazz pianists, believed that his godmother had sold him to Satan, and poor Jelly died screaming about hell-fire and calling for holy oil. Among the humble and declassed, musical skill brings power and money and the love of women, gifts for which men have always been willing to pay the highest price.

Swing Your Partner

A full account of a frontier shindig is given on pages 224-5. The opening lines of the story catch the mood of joyous riot . . .

You may talk about your bar hunts and knottin' tigers' tails through the bung holes of barrels, but if a frolic in the Knobs of old Knox(ville) don't beat 'em all for fun, then I'm no judge of fun—from a kiss that cracks like a waggon whip to a fight that rouses all outdoors, and as to laughin', why, they invented laughin' . . .

By the 1930's when I visited the Kentucky mountains, square dancing had almost disappeared because so many folks had been killed during jealous, drunken quarrels at these Saturday night blowouts!

The dance callers who gradually worked out the many forms of the American country dance, knew how to handle our jealous and cantankerous forefathers. Their dance inventions are characterized by ' progressive activity ' (every couple visiting every other couple in turn to perform the same figures), by *promenades* in which every boy partners every girl and finally returns to his partner, and by *changes* that deftly re-shuffle all the couples. The caller became far more important in America than in Europe because a heterogeneous American crowd needed a leader to unify them. His talent for ' mixing up the figures ' appealed to their love of novelty, and brought British country dancing to a fresh boil.

A separate volume would be needed to describe American folk dances and their music. However, their story is roughly the same as that of the songs. The frontier preserved things forgotten in the mother country, as Sharp observed when he discovered in the Kentucky running set ' the sole survival of a type of country dance which preceded the Playford dance ' . . . But, as usual, the frontier shook the bag, and American square dances are a mosaic of figures and steps from England, Scotland, and Ireland, roughly conforming in their areas of distribution to the song regions mentioned earlier.

The fiddlers played tunes from all round the British Isles along with many American originals. Again, the American versions are often more primitive and more antique in style than those found in Britain today, and markedly wilder and more aggressive. The hoedown fiddler plays with less polish and tunefulness than his Scotch-Irish brothers, but his stronger beat, his more rhythmic attack, his syncopations, and his rapid, heavy bowing make the old reels fairly sizzle.   His motive is to play ' music as hot as a hen in a basket of wool trying to lay a goose egg . . . as hot as a blistered man running through a pepper patch '.   Indeed, it is ' hot ' rhythm that every year more emphatically marks all American popular music.   ' Hot ' music swept America after World War I, and hit every European capital, Moscow included, after World War II, permitting a repressed urban population to express sexual and aggressive drives of almost psychotic violence.   You can hear this in the hillbilly boogies, in rock and roll, and the cacophonic Bronx cheer of be-bop, and you can see it in the faces of the Holiness singer, the blues shouter, and the skiffler.

Negro Improvisers

The founders and the carriers of American hot music were, of course, the Negroes. Their West African culture encouraged songs and dances which gave a pleasurable community outlet to sexual and aggressive behaviour.   Such release of tension probably accounts for the exquisite rhythmic ability and the vocal relaxation and freedom of good Negro singers, as compared with those of other cultures.   At any rate, the slaves continued to sing, dance, and play this way in America, and in the next hundred and fifty years their descendants were to teach white Americans how to play every instrument from the banjo to the xylophone in hot style.

Few, if any, white singers have mastered the playful 'swinging' vocal style of the Negro. When a Negro sings, the bridle is off.   His voice tells you plainly whether he is melancholy or happy or angry.   As a slave or a share-cropper he had to temper his language for safety's sake, but his music voiced his feelings without the equivocating restraints of the white tradition and with unashamed feeling.

This is no primitive trait.   Both the Negro and his songs are complex and civilized.   The folk Negro in Africa and America, as a child and as an adult, can *play* at being hostile or sexy in singing and in conversation, and no one thinks the worse of him.   So he can *play* with a melody, shaping it to his changing moods, gracing it with all the colour of a relaxed voice.

A folk song is actually a continuum of performances, each one varying in great or slight degree, and thus it grows as it lives, acquiring fresh material or losing bits of the old, and spawning variant forms, which continue to evolve. Every conceivable cultural, social, and psychological factor can come to bear upon this process. In the folk song of the West, for instance, there has been a continual interplay between the written and the oral streams of culture—the former fixed eternally in print, the latter living mainly in the bodies of a community of carriers and subject to slips of memory and to group emotion.

Since the majority of Negro songs are not only polyrhythmic but choral, each version is a group re-creation, and the song grows as it lives, as a continuum of varying group performances.   Anyone who has ever sung with Negroes knows how wonderful it feels to be ' backed up ' by such an inventive and sympathetic group.   Each participant contributes a bit of harmony, a small rhythmic device, a shade of vocal colour, which, if heard separately, may seem slight and unmusical, but when performed in concert, produces a bewitching effect.   The composer is hard to distinguish from the song leader, and often he does no more than suggest a new line or refrain to his congregation, who will then orchestrate it and later alter it in an enormous number of performances.

The singers do not weary with the repetition of a simple bit of song because they are always improvising in concert. An eight-bar tune may be sung for half an hour in church and then all week by members of the congregation. Thus a new song can acquire a high folk polish in a short time, each phrase having been worked on and approved of by a sizeable group of talented singers. This new bit now joins a repertoire of closely similar songs that may be easily recombined to create fresh variants. Indeed, since Negroes love to improvise, this is precisely what happens. A good leader gathers floating material from various sources, gives his own twists to tune and rhythm, so that no two renditions are ever quite the same. Not even in solo performance does the songmaker lose his identity with the group, for he continually reproduces the harmony parts of the chorus and claps and dances out the rhythm. Even long solo ballads like *John Henry* and *Frankie* are antiphonal in structure, and the solo blues are so organized that the guitar or piano can make rhythmic and harmonic responses to the singer.

This habit of improvisation within a choral framework produces many skilled leaders and solo-singers. ' You have to really go ' to hold a Negro audience. So it is that every country preacher has his own ' moan ', every dancer his own ' move ', and every mule-skinner his own ' holler '. So it is that among Negroes, songs and styles of songs rise to popularity and are discarded, frequently with every decade.

White Bards

If the Negro emphasis is on the improviser and his chorus, the white is upon the solo song rememberer and his silent audience. For the Negro, song is a natural part of life's activities ; for the white a self-conscious moment of communication. The white singer carefully tunes his voice, for his latent emotions must be kept under control. His long and often exquisite solo piece is a demanding act of memory, almost ritualistic in character, for he aims to reproduce the poem and the melody precisely as he heard them. The accepted convention is that he is not personally involved, but passing on a story about someone else —

a good story which will only be spoiled by alteration. If he forgets a line he will say, ' I messed up that song '; but if he remembers a song vividly, he will argue and even fight another singer over the ' rightness ' of his version. Thus, although the white tradition preserves the glorious big tunes and ballads of the ancient bards, which the Negro style would have long ago altered and perhaps forgotten, it sometimes lacks flexibility and verve.

The text of a white ballad is its fixed point, but change can come in several ways, most of them *apparently* negative. A singer may forget one bit or find it meaningless, and thereupon substitute a phrase of his own. Often this is a piece of gibberish for which a later singer will insert words that seem to him to make better sense. In this way an extraneous element may enter a stanza and will alter it completely, as successive singers try to rationalize the irrational element. This is one of the processes of *creative forgetting* by which folk singers slowly modernize and protect the valued old songs.

As text and tune are separable items for white singers, new marriages are continually arranged between them. The same air often appears as a dance tune, a ballad, a hymn, or a march, though the most fertile source of new tunes is the dance tradition, where the Devil's children are at work inventing new snares for the unwary. Traditional singers also feel free to vary a tune, saying, ' Every person's got a born right to sing a tune his own way.' What this means in practice is that a singer will apply his stock of flourishes, slides, holds, tremolos, and other ornaments to dress up a tune and alter it from stanza to stanza, so that it matches the verses and relieves the monotony of a long song. However, this technique of ornamentation is traditional and may not exceed certain limits without offending the true country singer of any one region. In my opinion ornamentation is the backbone of the white folk-song tradition, indicating its ancient derivation from the Orient, allowing the singer subtle ways of expressing his personal emotion, and providing the source and the materials for new tunes.

In America, the white song repertory grew in a number of ways. Sometimes popular hits were taken over by folk singers, though such songs were not usually varied and diffused unless, like *Dan Tucker* and *O Susannah*, they were initially folky. . . . Sometimes a closely knit group—anywhere from a cow camp to a college fraternity—was inspired by a common experience to compose a ballad, and this was gradually rhymed into shape out of verses contributed by several composers and approved of by the company. These collective songs continue to grow by accretion, as have *The Chisholm Trail* and *Mademoiselle from Armentières*. . . . Revivalists from the time of Luther onward made religious parodies of sinful songs, and these the folk felt free to change to suit themselves. . . . Often the ballad press and the newspaper poet put songs into circulation—see *Captain Kidd* and *Fair Charlotte*. In recent times ·the most important medium for the circulation of folk songs has been records, which distribute them more efficiently, if less happily, than the strolling minstrels of the past.

However, most of our frontier ballads were composed by local bards—humble and modest men who preferred to remain anonymous. (For the story of a modern folk bard, *see* pp. 426-30.) Normally, the poet was steeped in the song lore of his region, and was passionately identified with the group for whom he sang. In composing a new ballad, he took a well-known traditional song that told as nearly as possible the story he wished to tell, and altered it only as far as his theme demanded. In the opening stanzas he gave the old story its fresh topical setting and for the rest confined himself to changing names or adding new lines here or there. Even these new lines generally came from the traditional stock. Thus some of our ballads set out from Britain, served their time on deep water, lived in lumberjack bunk-houses, rode the western ranges and now fly with the jet pilots. The folk poet is a conservative, building solidly out of his tradition, for both he and his audience find the old songs hard to improve upon.

The Hard Rock

So, slowly, our folk songs grew, part dream and part reality, part past and part present. Each phrase rose from the deeps of the heart or was carved out of the rock of experience. Each line was sung smooth by many singers, who tested it against the American reality, until the language became apt and truthful and as tough as cured hickory. Here lies the secret of their beauty. They evoke the feeling of the place and of belonging to a particular branch of the human family. They honestly describe or protest against the deepest ills that afflict us—the colour bar, our repressed sexuality, our love of violence, and our lone-liness. Finally, they have been cared for and reshaped by so many hands that they have acquired the patina of art, and reflect the tenderest and most creative impulses of the human heart, casting upon our often harsh and melancholy tradition a lustre of true beauty.

No wonder then that a part of the captive audience of the entertainment industry is turning to folk song. These young skifflers and banjo pickers are sick of listening passively. They want to make music of their own. Some know that it is dangerous for them to express their discontent in a political direction, and so, for the moment, the tuneful complaints of their forebears voice their rebellious feelings. Having identified themselves with the democratic musical traditions of their country, they go on to make their own topical songs, and some of these modern ballads may have the staying power of the old.

What is more important, however, is that a whole generation of creative young people are becoming expert practitioners of our native folk song and thus are coming to grips with the profoundest American emotional problems. These have not changed as much as we like to suppose. The crimes and follies committed, and the wounds sustained by our people in conquering a continent still trouble us all. Behind the façade of success, the old conflicts are still unresolved, and our folk songs are the symbols of these problems. In them the young people discover the source of their own malaise and by singing them, they begin to face these problems with increased maturity.

This lonesome, raucous, hard-hitting music truly represents us. Only when it has been played and sung and thoroughly accepted will we be ready to create art forms which express the whole of what we wish to be. So long as these keys to our past lie rusty and unused, we will repeat the old stereotypes and half-truths in glossy and increasingly superficial guises—in comic books, records, films, and advertisements ; new legends and new art forms will not arise and we will continue to play, like children, in the sunny forecourt of creation.

How to Sing

It is most important to sing, and, especially, to try to feel these songs as they were intended to be sung and felt. The way in which a country singer handles his voice is neither accidental nor unpremeditated. He is conforming to one of several inherited traditions of singing, all of which are at least as old, as highly cultivated, and as difficult to master as the *bel canto* of our opera singers. True, some of the voices we hear on field recordings are cracked with age and harsh living, but they have everything to teach us if we wish to learn to sing folk songs well. Style is half of folk song, as it is of all music, and it can be acquired as art is acquired, first by imitation, second by absorption, and finally by understanding. Therefore, the student cannot spend too much time at first listening to the authentic recordings now available. When he has the hang of these, he can apply what he knows to printed songs.

There are many aids for the singer in the expression marks Miss Seeger has used in her notation, but a few additional remarks may be helpful. To the white singer the metre of the verse dominates the tune. In a long ballad it reshapes the melodic rhythm from stanza to stanza. If you recall this and run into the tune the held notes and the pauses which the *verse* demands, the charming irregularities of these songs will come easy to you. In the faster hillbilly tunes, set up an undeviating lick on your instrument and let the song phrase itself without too much reference to the regular spacing of the accompaniment. The voice should be hard, tight, impersonal, and nasal (if you like)—a narrator's voice. Any attempt to sing ' expressively ' and with ' good vocal technique ' reduces the effectiveness of these pieces.

Negro songs are another matter entirely. Words, tune, and accompaniment must flow together in a pulsing, sensuous whole, while the musical rhythm plays tricks with verbal accent. The best approach is to sing one stanza or chorus many times to a strong off-beat rhythm until you can begin to improvise a bit. When you go on to other stanzas, you will find that the beat will force you to introduce syncopations into the text. Use a rich voice with a lot of vibrato. Study the recommended records and learn how to reproduce the moans, whoops, slides, and falsetto leaps of the country Negro. One of the master folk singers is Louis Armstrong, who attacks pop songs as if he were a Baptist preacher from the Deep South.

The five-string banjo, guitar, or mandolin are the favoured accompanying instruments among folk singers. To guide the stringed accompanist, letter indications (C for C major, G7 for G seventh major, Em for E minor, etc.) are printed over each melody line. Instructions for how to play American folk guitar and banjo appear in Appendix II, and alongside the tempo indications for each melody Peggy Seeger and I have noted the strokes or ' licks ' most appropriate for that song. (Example: *GUITAR*—1A—strummed chords). Directions for playing these licks are given in the numbered headings in the Appendix.

These stringed instrument settings do not always match the piano chords. Good piano arrangements must often take another path than the folk player would choose. Matyas Seiber, out of his wide knowledge of European folk tunes, has devised simple, yet subtle accompaniments for some of the older tunes in this book. Don Banks, an old hand at jazz, has, at my suggestion, treated many of the Negro songs as if they were primitive jazz or the blues. He has cleverly applied ragtime style to some hoedowd tunes, and in one or two cases (*Fourth Day of July*) has transcribed a banjo accompaniment for the piano. *How Long Blues*, copied from a Jimmy Yancey recording by Miss Seeger, provides the rudiments of slow blues piano. Thus, when you have mastered all the different accompanying styles in this book, you should, with the aid of the chord letters, be able to improvise settings for the remainder of the songs.

Acknowledgements

In a very real sense, this volume is an anthology of anthologies, drawing upon the Lomax compilations as well as the regional collections of my colleagues. I was profoundly touched by their generosity in permitting me to reprint numerous songs. Due acknowledgement is made, and warning is hereby given that *most of the songs in this volume are protected by copyright*—the Lomax material by Essex in Great Britain and Ludlow, Inc. in New York, and the remainder by the publishers or sources indicated. Under the title of every song there is a *headnote* which gives the sources of the variants published in this volume. In addition, each headnote contains a small number of references to other volumes where parallel versions of the same song can be found, and in these volumes there are lengthy lists of citations, so that the reader is quickly led to a large number of versions of any song in which he is particularly interested. Each collection cited is designated by the surname of its principal editor or by a condensation of its title, viz., Botkin, Sharp, etc. The full titles will be found in an alphabetical list of useful reference books in Appendix I.

Phil Miller, Sally Jackson, Rae Korson, Ewan MacColl, Robin Roberts, Herb Greer, and Dolly Collins were all extremely helpful in the work of compilation. Anne Lomax, Elizabeth Harold, and Herbert Sturz read the manuscript and made valuable suggestions. Ed Waters, the Australian ballad student, spent several months with me on the original compilation. A. L. Lloyd and Russell Ames gave me the benefit of their expert advice on the whole book and Peter Kennedy helped with the discography. Margot Mayo and her sisters, Hally Wood and Joan Robbins, helped read the proofs. But it is to Peggy Seeger and Shirley Collins, two of the finest singers of folk songs, that my principal debts are owed. Their handiwork appears on every page.

ALAN LOMAX

PART I. THE NORTH

THE NORTH

. . . includes the Maritime Provinces of Canada . . . New England and the Middle Atlantic States . . . the area between the Ohio River and the Great Lakes . . . and the western American-Canadian border regions. A rich folk-song culture developed in the North-East during the colonial period and was carried West by the lumberjacks and the settlers who fanned out across the Midwest. In the Ohio valley it is found in conjunction with the Southern Backwoods tradition, but west of the Mississippi the two families merged to produce the western ballad types.

In general, the North was an area of unaccompanied solo singing in a hard, clear tone, less pinched and nasal than that used in the Southern backwoods, and with harsh unison on the refrains. Though the polyphonic singing school movement began in New England and spread into the South, the harmony was always book-learnt, never improvised. The fiddle was the principal instrument at pioneer dances, though fife and drum bands were common in the early nineteenth century. The table dulcimer, probably a Scandinavian importation, was popular among the lumberjacks of the Lake States, and recently the piano has become the centre of the modern New England square dance orchestra.

The traditional ballads of the North-East are closer to British originals than those of the South, for contact with the British Isles has been constantly refreshed by new waves of immigrants, especially from Scotland and Ireland. These new-comers also brought with them the topical ballads of the eighteenth and nineteenth centuries, firmly establishing the come-all-ye style as the model for Northern ballad composers. Their narrative ballads, which celebrated the achievements of the common man at work, in their turn inspired most of the new songs of the unfolding frontier. During the nineteenth century the American come-all-ye was subject to fresh Irish influences as refugees poured across the Atlantic from impoverished Ireland.

In spite of their rigorous code, the Puritan congregations gave women more independence and were perhaps less stringent in their sexual code than the Non-conformist churches that dominated the Southern backwoods. And, when the power of the Puritans declined, the churches of the new revival never gained ascendancy over the lives of the people they did further South. The rigours of American Protestantism were further palliated by the growth of the practical and worldly Yankee culture, by the cosmopolitan influences of seaports and large cities, and by the constant flow of travel through the North-East. This

1

sophistication permitted the public performance of songs which were sung behind closed doors in the South; but, by the middle of the nineteenth century, it brought an end to the making and singing of folk songs in the North-East. Only among the lumberjacks, or in isolated communities in the Maritime Provinces, has Northern folk-song tradition remained alive.

OLD COLONY TIMES

1. IN GOOD OLD COLONY TIMES

AMONG THE FIRST SETTLERS to come to the region which John Smith had christened New England, was one man who looked at the wilderness land with the eyes of a poet . . .

In the month of June, Anno Salutis 1622, it was my chance to arrive in the parts of New England, and when I had more seriously considered of the bewty of the place, I did not think that in all the knowne world it could be paralleled . . . For so many goodly groves of trees . . . Dainty fine round-raising hillocks . . . Delicate fair plaines, sweet crystal fountaines and cleare running streames . . . Fowle in abundance, Fish in multitude, and besides, millions of Turtle doves on the green boughs, which sate pecking of the full, ripe grapes. Here and there dispersed, you might see Lillies, which made the Land to me seem paradise. In mine eye, 'twas Nature's masterpiece, her chieftest magazine of all where lives her store . . . If this land be not rich, then is the whole world poore . . .

The feeling of exalted confidence that inspired this New England rhapsody has never entirely departed from American life. The green wilderness continent offered such abundance and independence to the settlers as no men had ever enjoyed, and it was soon to fulfil its promise. After a few hard winters, the Puritan settlements began to prosper; the leaders fell upon their knees, thanked God and vowed they would make a fresh beginning for all men. Crowded, corrupt, caste-ridden England lay far away over the Atlantic, and the New England colonists set out to found a new society based on equality, sobriety, reverence, and hard work, and to plant the feet of their children on this straight and narrow road.

The Puritans were rebels against a social system in which the amusements of the aristocracy counted for more than the hunger of the commons and the stability of the country. They set their faces against all worldly diversions. Singing, dancing, feasting, playing games, and a hundred more innocent follies of mankind fell under their interdict. One Puritan recalled with shame how, in his youth, he hid behind a door to whittle, in order to conceal this sin from his father. Ministers, who were otherwise men of intelligence and ability, preached hysterically against ' playbooks, romances, filthy songs and ballads'. Emotional tension in the colony rose to such a pitch that, seventy years after the jubilant settler described New England as nature's masterpiece, a frenzy of witch-hunting broke out in New Salem. During the terrible summer of 1692, fourteen women and five men were publicly hanged as witches on the testimony of five adolescent girls. These young women, one might say, were running berserk at an adult world that deprived them of the normal diversions of youth.

Until recently it was believed that early New England had no folk songs. According to the historians, Puritan music consisted of a ' crude form of barbarously sung, simple psalmody ', and as the cultural life of these self-enclosed and bigoted villages declined,

3

even the psalms degenerated. The number of tunes in the psalm books diminished from forty to thirteen within a century, and no two congregations, indeed, no two individuals, sang the tunes in the same way. In the 1720's Puritan ministers lamented that . . .

. . . the tunes are now miserably tortured, twisted and quavered into a horrid medley of confused and disorderly noises . . . Left to the mercy of every unskilful Throat to chop and alter, twist and change, according to their odd Humours and Fancies, they sound like Five Hundred different tunes roared out at the same time . . .

However, doleful psalm singing was not the whole of New England folk music, for not all the colonists were Puritans, nor were all the Puritans ' puritanical '. The sternest ministers loved the bottle; indeed, when a new man was ordained, the deacons often had to be carried home from the ceremony. On weekdays these hearty seventeenth century Englishmen frequented the village tavern, where ' drunken, carnal poets ' sang their ' carnal sonnets ' (folk songs) in spite of the bigots.

In fact, recent research has shown that the colonial North-East was rich in folk music. A greater variety of British ballads has been recovered there than in any other area on the continent. During the eighteenth and early nineteenth centuries, Yankees composed numbers of topical songs, which circulated orally, or were printed on cheap broadsheets and hawked by wandering pedlars or fiddlers. Benjamin Franklin did extremely good business with the ballads he published in Philadelphia. One of them called ' Lovewell's Fight . . . being a true account of the bloody fight which happen'd between Captain Lovewell's company, and the Indians at Pigwocket, an excellent new song . . ' appeared in 1725 and was still being sung in New England a century later. Franklin's account was somewhat one-sided . . .

These rebels lay in ambush this very place hard by,
So that an English soldier did one of them espy,
And cried out, ' Here's an Indian '—and with that they started out,
As fiercely as old lions, and hideously did shout.
Thus up spake Captain Lovewell when first the fight began,
' Fight on, my gallant heroes, you see they fall like rain.'
For as we are informed, the Indians were so thick,
A man could scarce fire a gun and not some of them hit . . .

Probably many more such songs would have been published in the North-East if the presses had not been controlled by the clergy. The preachers, however, did not intimidate the seamen, trappers, and woodsmen. With a few drinks under their belts, they sang ballads that peeled the paint right off the tavern walls. ' On the frontier of Maine,' wrote Mrs. Eckstorm, ' Every man was his own poet.' One sawmill worker recalled . . .

' Uster have a lot of fun with my partner; uster make up songs together. He'd make up a verse and sing it in my ear—for the saws were shrieking—and then I'd make up a verse or so and sing it in his ear. We reckoned at one time to have seventy-nine verses to that song, seventy-eight of which would burn the paper they was writ on . . .'

The Yankee singer was a good deal less censorious than any folk singer has been in America since his time. His repertoire was huge, sometimes including four or five hundred pieces, and the lusty unaccompanied singing of ballads was a favourite diversion. Indeed, the eighteenth century drinking song speaks true when it says . . .

In good old colony times,
When we lived under the king,
Three roguish chaps fell into mishaps
Because they could not sing.

4

2. CAPE ANN

THOUGH THE NEW WORLD teemed with natural wonders, Puritan story-tellers were not content with the facts, but embroidered them with legends imported from the Old World. Thus they made themselves at home with less familiar terrors. Hubbard and Increase Mather, in a report to the Royal Society, spoke of a hill in Maine which ' was carried some eight rods over the tree tops and set upside down in the Kennebunk River '. John Josselyn, perhaps the first English tourist to visit America, had an adventure with a Triton or ' Mere-man in Casco Bay, who laying his hands on the side of the canoe, had one of them chopt off with a hatchet . . . It was in all respects like the hand of a man. The Triton sunk, dyeing the water with his purple blood.'

Thus encouraged by men of repute, New Englanders began to spin their local yarns. With time there developed the Yankee poker-faced liar, the predecessor of all American tall story tellers and humorists, from Davy Crockett to Mark Twain and James Thurber. These Yankee yarn spinners were ' not mere liars,' as Ben Botkin so aptly puts it, ' they were artists in ascertaining the limits of their victim's capacity for being deceived. If these limits could not be found, so much the better.' About one such Yankee it was said, ' When he wants his pigs to come to be fed, he has to get somebody else to call them.'

The Yankee liars enjoyed improving on nature. According to Amasa Abbey, for instance . .

. . . the trees were so large where he came from in Massachusetts, that one day he started to cut one down, and after chopping for two weeks he started to go round it to see how large it was. He found a man on the other side who had been chopping for three weeks, and neither had heard the noise of the other's axe . . .

The old British ballad of the three fools found new roots in this American setting. Originally of Celtic derivation (*see* p. 253), the song had been used in an Elizabethan drama, *The Two Noble Kinsmen*, in which Shakespeare may have had a hand . . .

> There were three fools fell out about an howlet,
> One said it was an owl,
> The other sed nay,
> The third he sed it was a hawk
> And her bels were cut away . . .

Trimmed out with New England fancies, the song became widely popular in the North-East when the Hutchinson family sang it on their tours, along with that New England perennial, *Springfield Mountain*.

QUOTES: (a) Dorson, p. 26. *John Josselyn writes his voyages*, 1638-67. (b) Dorson, p. 103. ' Proceedings of the Orleans County Historical Society, Nov. 1889—Jan. 1891.'

3. SPRINGFIELD MOUNTAIN

' WILDE BEASTES and venimous sarpints ' abounded in the American wilderness. To these real perils the settlers added imaginary reptiles—the hoopsnake that seized its tail in its mouth and rolled swiftly after its prey—the coach-whip that beat its victims to death with its long, black, flexible tail—the hornsnake that carried a stinger in its tail six inches long and sharp as a needle; but right from the start the rattlesnake has played the lead in American tall tales. Cotton Mather, the fire-and-brimstone Puritan preacher and an antediluvian New England literary figure, set down the earliest known American snake story in a letter to the Secretary of the Royal Society, dated 1712 . . .

> At Cape Fear, one of our people, Sporting with a Rattlesnake, provoked him and suffered him to bite the edge of a Good Broad Ax; whereupon, immediately Ye colour of the Steel Iron changed, and at the first blow he gave, when he went after to use his Ax, ye discoloured part of ye bitten iron broke off without any more ado.

The first flag of the American Revolutionary Army bore the image of an angry rattle-snake and the motto—DON'T TREAD ON ME; and the first indigenous folk ballad to gain national currency tells of the death by snake-bite of young Timothy Myrick of Spring-field Mountain (now Wilbraham), Massachusetts, on 7 August, 1761. The original song was serious, even lugubrious in tone, for many New Englanders must have died this way, and many more pioneers were to die of snake-bite on the way west. Then a Yankee comic impersonator, by the name of Spear, invented a parody called ' Love and Pizen ', introduc-ing Timothy's fiancée, Sally. Sally died when she tried to suck the poison out of the snake-bit heel, and the vaudeville version concluded with the double-entendre moral . . .

> And mind, when you're in love, don't pass
> Too near to patches of high grass . . .

This song struck America's funny bone and it has turned up in many variants all across the country (see songs 212 and 213 for the western cowboy form). Here, however, is a rare version of the original elegy, recorded from the singing of J. C. Kennison, an itinerant Vermont scissor-grinder, in 1939.

4. BILLY BROKE LOCKS

PHILLIPS BARRY believes that, about the year 1700, a new wave of colonists from Britain brought a group of ballads into New England which did not reach the southern states. Among these he cites *Captain Kidd*, and the Scots *Archie o' Cawfield*, upon which the present ballad is based, and whose story runs as follows . . .

Archie Hall of Liddesdale, one of three reiving (cattle rustling) brothers, lies prisoner in Dumfries jail. Dickie and Jockie Hall ride to his rescue. Jockie, a man of Homeric stature and strength, bursts the iron bolts of the dungeon with a blow, and though the prisoner has ' fifteen weight of good Spanish iron on his fair bodie ', picks him up in his arms, observing, ' I count him lighter than a flea.' The three brothers make good their escape by swimming their horses across a river that daunts their English pursuers. In the Scots ballad they refer to each other affectionately as ' billie '. In Scots dialect ' billie ' meant comrade or buddy; thus, in our ballad, ' Billy ' takes the place of ' Jockie '.

Very likely *Archie o' Cawfield* was one of the ballads Cotton Mather had in mind when in 1713 he lamented ' the vogue of the foolish Songs and Ballads which hawkers and pedlars carry into all portions of the Country '. There is no doubt that it served as the model for *Billy Broke Locks*, composed around 1737, when the colonists of Massachusetts became involved in a currency dispute with the crown.

At that time exchange in the colonies was based upon Spanish coinage, which brought a different price in the various colonial capitals. Parliament attempted to resolve this confusion by several issues of paper money called 'tenors'; but when the 'new tenor' replaced the 'old tenor', disturbances broke out in Massachusetts, and two satirical broadsides entitled *The Death of Old Tenor* and *The Dying Speech of Old Tenor* were published— and suppressed. John Webb (or Webber) then mint-master of Salem, Massachusetts, apparently stuck to 'Old Tenor' and for this offence was sent to prison. When his friends broke into jail and rescued Webb, someone celebrated the event by re-making *Archie o' Cawfield* to tell the story of the escape of the man who had stood up for 'Old Tenor', and so is identified with 'Old Tenor' in the chorus.

Thus the rebellious fire of a sixteenth-century Scots border rant passed into a new song of social conflict, producing what is certainly the best of our early colonial ballads. *Billy Broke Locks* must have been extremely popular in New England for Barry found five good versions of it, two hundred years after the event.

5. CAPTAIN KIDD—1

ALTHOUGH ENGLISH BY BIRTH, Captain Kidd became an American folk hero by adoption. He committed his piratical acts in American waters and left legends of buried treasure on lonely beaches all along the Atlantic Coast.

When he was brought to Execution Dock in London, 9 May, 1701, there to be hung in the gibbets between high and low tides for two weeks, a ballad seller was probably hawking this song among the crowds of the curious. On the occasion of any spectacular execution, a Grub Street poet generally composed 'the criminal's last good night' several days in advance of his demise. As one ballad seller said—

We prints it several days afore it comes off, and goes and stands with it right under the drop, and many's the penny I've turned away when I've been asked for an account of the whole business before it happened . . .

The tune Captain Kidd may have heard at his own execution was a favourite one with the ballad coiner. A few months previously, the thieving chimney sweep, Jack Hall, had been hung at the same spot to the tune of a similar ballad . . .

> Up the ladder I did grope,
> That's no joke, that's no joke,
> Up the ladder I did grope
> And the hangman spread the rope,
> And never a word I spoke
> Coming down, coming down . . .

Next year saw the same formula used to celebrate the deeds of that old sea-dog, Admiral Benbow . . .

> Brave Benbow he set sail
> For to fight, for to fight,
> He fought them up and down
> Till the blood came trickling down,
> Where he lay, where he lay . . .

There were Jacobite settings, like *Aiken Drum*, and love songs, such as . . .

7

For weel he kenned the way
O the way, o the way . . .

During the next two centuries, there were at least a dozen new songs to the Kidd tune, including two ballads about John Paul Jones and a number of hymns, among them *Wondrous Love* and the song on page 70 of this volume.

But Dr. Jackson, that assiduous tune detective, in his ' Odyssey of Captain Kidd ' (Southern Folklore Quarterly XV), shows that this tune has been producing new songs for at least four hundred years. Lovers in Scotland in the sixteenth century knew . . .

My lufe is lyand seik,
Send him joy, send him joy . . . (Complaynt of Scotland—1549)

and a century later were singing . . .

My love's in Germany,
Send him hame, send him hame . . .

In the 1650's, the early social and religious reformers, the Levellers, defied the gentry with . . .

The gentry are all around,
Stand up now, stand up now . . .

Ravenscroft's ' Melismata ' (1611) contained the hymn . . .

Remember, o thou man,
O thou man, o thou man . . .

. . . and from this comes a song popular among American Sacred Harpers almost three centuries afterwards . . .

Remember, sinful youth,
You must die, you must die . . .

The Captain Kidd ballad, set to this tune, was a prime favourite among these a-going folk of the North-East. Harriet Beecher Stowe, in one of her sketches, tells how and why it was sung . . .

' Wal, boys, that 'are history o' Kidd's is a warnin' to fellers. Why, Kidd had pious parents and Bible and sanctuary priveliges when he was a boy, and yet come to be hanged. It's all in this 'ere song I'm a-goin' to sing ye.' A most minor-keyed tune was doled forth, which seemed quite refreshing to Sam's pathetic vein as he sang in his most lugubrious tones . . .

My name was Robert Kidd,
As I sailed, as I sailed . . .

6. WHISKY IN THE JAR

NEW ENGLAND BRED more privateers than highwaymen, yet from stage-coach days comes the yarn of Tom the Leveller, a true colonial Robin Hood. Tom's career began when he lay sick almost to death. His old mother summoned the Devil and agreed that he could have Tom's soul if he would save his life. The Devil restored the lad to health and, after some years had passed, came to claim Tom for his own. Tom drawled, ' Wait,

8

won't you, till I jest get these galluses on.' The Satanic gentleman agreed, whereupon the quick-witted Yankee threw his braces in the fire and the Devil withdrew, discomfited.

Tom then took to the roads, robbing the rich and giving to the poor, until he became known as ' the honest thief ', or in his own words, ' the Leveller '. He lifted roasts from the hearths of the well-fed and left them in the kitchens of the hungry. He rifled the nurseries of pampered children and distributed their toys among the poor tykes he met on his travels. He once found a poor sick woman lying on the floor of her cabin, without a bed, and he promptly climbed in the back window of a fine house, absconded with the best feather mattress, and made the old lady comfortable. Children adored him, women sympathized with him, and the poor of New England heroized him. When he was finally nabbed roasting a stolen goose, Tom was let off with a good whipping, after which he disappeared from history, if not from legend.

The best outlaw ballad found in the North is an importation from Ireland. The folk of seventeenth century Britain liked and admired their local highwaymen; and in Ireland (or Scotland) where the gentlemen of the roads robbed the English landlords, they were regarded as national patriots. Such feelings inspired this rollicking ballad, still sung today in Scotland and Ireland, and twice or thrice found in backwoods New England. The Massachusetts version about Alan McCollister, the valiant soldier, seems to be the oldest so far recorded. Its end is tragic and patriotic . . .

> As McCollister was walking up the gallows ladder,
> He called to the sheriff for his Irish cap and feather,
> Saying, ' I have robbed many a man, but I never killed any,
> And now I must be hung for the taking of their money . . .

There is a close connection between this ballad and John Gay's *Beggar's Opera* (1728). One must certainly have inspired the other. Because of the wide distribution of the ballad in the Celtic world and its rarity in England, I tend to believe that Gay got the idea for MacHeath and Polly when he heard a strolling Irish ballad-monger sing *Whisky in the Jar* in the streets of London.

SOURCE: *Stagecoach and Tavern Days*, A. M. Earle (Macmillan Co., 1900), p. 381.

7. STRAWBERRY LANE

THE DEMURE YOUNG WOMEN of New England, strolling down Strawberry Lane, moved through a garden of charmingly feminine erotic fantasies and Freudian symbols. Indeed, this song may well have been composed by women (for there were female bards in early Britain) at a time when women more openly expressed their natural longings. The old ballad tells of a maiden in her castle bower who hears the faraway blast of the elfin horn and wishes the fairy knight were in her bed. The fairy (in ancient belief a man of medium stature) appears straightaway at her bedside, but he demands the answers to his riddles before he will consent to be her lover.

The riddling contest between mortal and demon is a folk motif older than the Sphinx, and this part of the ballad still survives, even though the girl and her elfin lover were long ago censored out of the story. Its ancient, half-understood symbols pleased the women and girls of Britain and the American frontier, and the song travelled all the way to the Pacific coast. In the old days, a girl who made a shirt for a man meant to marry him. The

9

wells, thorns, horns, eggshells, ploughs, and thimbles are all familiar erotic images. The refrain unfailingly points out that every rose (woman) grows merry and fine, a consoling idea to women living in a Puritanical society. The burden of one North Carolina version, in fact, provides a dramatic answer to the problems of a shy country girl who says, ' A-rose Mary in time!'

8. LADY ISABEL AND THE ELF-KNIGHT

THE CAREER of John Christie and the works of the Marquis de Sade are sufficient to remind one that the Bluebeard legend, common to all the west, is based on fact as well as fancy, on practice as well as impulse. Folk singers in every part of Europe and America know the popular ballad form of the Bluebeard story, in which a plucky girl kills the monster who has done away with a number of women. The Nordic heroine lulls the villain to sleep by delousing him and then stabs him as he lies with his head in her lap. A lively French Jeanneton kicks him into the river when he kneels down to strip off her costly silk stockings.

Our American Pretty Polly is likewise a decisive girl, but obsessed by the fear of being caught out after bedtime by her pa. Always modest, she insists that her seducer turn away before she disrobes, explaining that ' A naked woman is a sinful sight, For a man to see . . . '

Even more prudish singers have Polly put forth the excuse that she ' wishes to say her prayers ' or ' must clear away some briars '. Normally, however, the main emphasis in American versions falls upon the last scene, in which Polly bribes her parrot not to tell on her. One thinks of the flapper of the 1920's crawling through the back window of her college dormitory, her virtue intact after an all-night party. Polly, too, has preserved her chastity during her evening's escapade, and no one but the parrot is any the wiser. Indeed, this carefully underscored moral conclusion may explain why this ballad, alone of all the merry Scots songs of rape and seduction, was common to the whole frontier.

This girl was the perfect fantasy heroine for Puritan, nonconformist America, for she and her parrot were both named Polly, and thus the debate with Polly and the bribing of Polly was a debate with Polly's own conscience—the Puritan's principal ally in a struggle with sin.

1. IN GOOD OLD COLONY TIMES

SEE: Belden, 268; Botkin III, 841; Brown II, 458; Randolph I, 416. Known from Lancashire south in England; as far west as Nebraska in U.S.
Piano arrangement by DON BANKS

1 In good old colony times,
  When we lived under the king,
  Three roguish chaps fell into mishaps
  Because they could not sing,
  Because they could not sing,
  Because they could not sing,
  Three roguish chaps fell into mishaps
  Because they could not sing.

2 O the first, he was a miller
  And the second, he was a weaver,
  And the third, he was a little tailor,
  Three roguish chaps together, *etc.*

3 O the miller, he stole corn,
  And the weaver, he stole yarn,
  And the little tailor ran right away
  With the broadcloth under his arm, *etc.*

4 The miller was drowned in his dam,
  And the weaver got hung in his yarn,
  And the Devil clapped his claws on the little tailor
  With the broadcloth under his arm, *etc.*

2. CAPE ANN

FROM: *Songs of the Hutchinson Family* (Firth & Hall, N.Y.C., 1843). SEE: Belden, 246; Botkin III, 839; Opie, 421. Found England; Maritime Canada; New England; South; Middle West.

Gaily ♩=138

GUITAR— 6A or 2A
BANJO— 1 or 4B

We hunt-ed and we hal-loed, And the first thing that we found Was a barn in the mea-dow And that we left be-hind. Look ye there! One said it was a barn, But the o-ther said nay; He said it was a meet-ing house With the stee-ple blown a-way. Look ye there!

1 We hunted and we halloed,
  And the first thing that we found
  Was a barn in the meadow
  And that we left behind.
  Look ye there!
  One said it was a barn,
  But the other said nay;
  He said it was a meeting house
  With the steeple blown away.
  Look ye there!

2 So we hunted and we halloed,
  And the next thing we did find
  Was the moon in the element
  And that we left behind.
  Look ye there!
  One said it was the moon,
  But the other said nay,
  He said it was a Yankee cheese
  With the one half cut away.
  Look ye there!

3 So we hunted and we halloed,
  And the next thing we did find
  Was the lighthouse in Cape Ann
  And that we left behind.
  Look ye there!
  One said it was the lighthouse
  But the other said nay,
  He said it was a sugar loaf
  With the paper blown away.
  Look ye there!

4 So we hunted and we halloed,
  And the last thing we did find
  Was the owl in the olive bush
  And that we left behind.
  Look ye there!
  One said it was an owl,
  The other said nay,
  He said it was the Evil One
  And we all three ran away.
  Look ye there!

3. SPRINGFIELD MOUNTAIN

Recorded by Alan Lomax from J. C. Kennison, Townshend, Vt., 1939. SEE: Belden, 299; Brown II, 489; Flanders I, 159; Flanders III, 15; Laws, 213. *Vermont Songs and Ballads*, H. Flanders, p. 35. Tragic form rare; comic form in many variants throughout U.S.

1 On Springfield Mountain there did dwell
  A handsome youth was known full well,
  Lieutenant Merrill's only son,
  A likely youth, full twenty-one.

2 On Friday morning he did go
  Down to the meadows for to mow,
  He mowed, he mowed all round the field
  With a poisonous serpent at his heel.

3 When he received his deathly wound
  He laid his scythe upon the ground,
  For to return was his intent,
  Calling aloud long as he went.

4 His calls were heard both far and near,
  But no friend to him did appear.
  They thought he did some workman call,
  Alas, poor man, alone did fall.

5 Day being past, night coming on,
  The father went to seek his son,
  And there he found his only son,
  Cold as a stone, dead on the ground.

6 He took him up and he carried him home,
  And on the way did lament and mourn,
  Saying, ' I heard, but did not come,
  And now I'm left alone to mourn.'

7 In the month of August, the twenty-first,
  When this sad accident was done,
  May this be a warning to you all
  To be prepared when God shall call.

4. BILLY BROKE LOCKS

FROM: p. 393 of *British Ballads from Maine*, Phillips Barry (Yale U.P., 1929).
Used by permission. As sung by Mrs. S. S. Thornton, South West Harbor, and
Mrs. F. P. Barker, Brewer, Maine, from a Massachusetts grandmother, early
nineteenth century.

Smoothly ♩ = 144

GUITAR– 3C
BANJO– 1 & 2

1 There were nine to hold the British ranks,
And five to guard the town about,
And two to stand at either hand,
And one to let the Old Tenor out.
CHORUS:
Billy broke locks and Billy broke bolts,
And Billy broke all that he came nigh,
Until he came to the dungeon door,
And that he broke right manfully.

2 There was eighty weight of good Spanish iron
Between his neck-bone and his knee,
But Billy took Johnny up under his arm
And lugged him away right manfully. (CHO.)

3 They mounted their horses and away did ride,
And who but they rode manfully,
Until they came to the river bank
And there they alighted right manfully. (CHO.)

4 And then they called for a room to dance,
And who but they danced merrily,
And the best dancer amongst them all
Was old John Webb who was just set free. (CHO)

5. CAPTAIN KIDD—1

FROM: *Sam Lawson's Old Town Stories*, Harriet Beecher Stowe, 1872. SEE: Brown II, 350; Flanders II, 16; Mackenzie, 278; Reeves, 132; Whall, 9.

Powerfully ♩ = 96   GUITAR—1

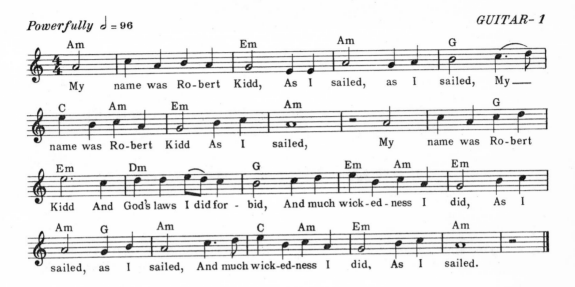

My name was Robert Kidd, As I sailed, as I sailed, My — name was Robert Kidd As I sailed, My name was Robert Kidd And God's laws I did for-bid, And much wick-ed-ness I did, As I sailed, as I sailed, And much wick-ed-ness I did, As I sailed.

1 My name was Robert Kidd,
As I sailed, as I sailed,
My name was Robert Kidd,
As I sailed,
My name was Robert Kidd
And God's laws I did forbid,
And much wickedness I did,
As I sailed, as I sailed,
And much wickedness I did,
As I sailed.

Now ye see, boys, he's a-goin' to tell how he abused his religious privileges, just hear now . . .

2 My father taught me well,
As I sailed, as I sailed . . .
My father taught me well,
To shun the gates of Hell,
But yet I did rebel
As I sailed, as I sailed . . .

3 He put a Bible in my hand,
As I sailed, as I sailed . . .
He put a Bible in my hand,
And I sunk it in the sand,
Before I left the strand,
As I sailed, as I sailed . . .

Did ye ever hear o' such a hardened, contrary critter, boys? It's awful to think on. Wal, ye see that 'ere's the ways fellers allers begin the ways o' sin, by turnin' their backs on the Bible and the advice o' pious parents. Now hear what he come to.

4 Then I murdered William More
As I sailed, as I sailed . . .
I murdered William More
And left him in his gore,
Not many leagues from shore,
As I sailed, as I sailed . . .

5 To Execution Dock
I must go, I must go . . .
To Execution Dock
While thousands round me flock
To see me on the block,
I must go, I must go . . .

He was an officer in the British Navy, and he got to bein' a pirate; used to take ships and sink 'em, and murder the folks, and so they say he got no end of money—gold and silver and precious stones, as many as the wise men in the east.

15

6 I steered from sound to sound
  As I sailed, as I sailed . . .
  I steered from sound to sound
  And many ships I found
  And most of them I burned,
  As I sailed, as I sailed . . .

8 I had eighty bars of gold,
  As I sailed, as I sailed . . .
  I had eighty bars of gold
  And riches uncontrolled
  And dollars in my hold
  As I sailed, as I sailed . . .

7 I spied three ships from Spain,
  As I sailed, as I sailed . . .
  I spied three ships from Spain,
  I fired on them amain
  Till all their crews were slain,
  As I sailed, as I sailed . . .

9 Take warning now by me,
  For I must die, I must die . . .
  Take warning now by me,
  And shun bad company
  Lest you go to hell like me,
  When you die, when you die . . .

6. WHISKY IN THE JAR

Collected, arranged and used by permission of Frank Warner. SEE: Flanders I, 245,
III, 139; Ord, 368.

Strongly accented ♩ = 116

GUITAR- *1 or 2A*
BANJO- *FREE STRUM*

1 As I was going over Gilgarra Mountain,
  I met Colonel Pepper and his money he was counting.
  I drew forth my pistols and I rattled my sabre
  Saying ' Stand and deliver, for I am a bold deceiver.'
  CHORUS:
  Musha ringum duram da,
  Whack! fol de daddy-o,
  Whack! fol de daddy-o,
  There's whisky in the jar.

2 The shining golden coins did sure look bright and jolly,
I took the money home and I gave it to my Molly,
She promised and she vowed that she never would deceive me,
But the Divil's in the women and they never can be easy. (CHO.)

3 Now when I awakened between the hours of six and seven,
Guards were standing round me in numbers odd and even,
I flew to my pistols, but, alas, I was mistaken,
For I fired off my pistols and a prisoner was taken. (CHO.)

4 They put me in jail without judge or writing,
For robbing Colonel Pepper on Gilgarra Mountain,
But they didn't take my fists, so I knocked down the sentry
And I bid a long farewell to the Judge in Sligo town. (CHO.)

5 Some take delight in fishing and bowling,
Others take delight in the carriage a-rolling,
But I take delight in the juice of the barley,
Courting pretty girls in the morning so early. (CHO.)

7. STRAWBERRY LANE

FROM: p. 284 of *Journal of American Folklore*, XXX. As sung by W. H. Banks,
Maine, born 1834. SEE: Barry, 3; Belden, 1; Brown II, 13; Child, No. 2;
Coffin, 30; Flanders I, 8, III, 194; Greig, 1; Opie, 108; Randolph I, 38; Sharp
I, 1. Also Guide (*Elfin Knight*).

Smoothly and quietly ♩=144 *or faster*

GUITAR- 2A
BANJO- 4B or 1

1 As I was a-walking up Strawberry Lane,
  Every rose grows merry and fine,
I chanced for to meet a pretty fair maid
  Who wanted to be a true lover of mine.

2 ' You'll have for to make me a cambric shirt,
And every stitch must be finicle work.'

3 ' You'll have for to wash it in a deep well
Where water never was nor rain ever fell.'

4 ' You'll have for to hang it on yonder green thorn
That never bore a bud since Adam was born.'

5 ' Now since you have been so hard with me,
Perhaps I can be as hard as thee.'

6 ' You'll have for to buy me an acre of land
Between the salt water and the sea sand.'

7 ' You'll have for to plough it with a deer's horn,
And plant it all over with one grain of corn.'

8 ' You'll have for to thrash it in an egg-shell,
And bring it to market in a thimble.'

8. LADY ISABEL AND THE ELF KNIGHT

Reprinted from *Traditional Songs of Nova Scotia*, Helen Creighton and Doreen
Senior (Ryerson Press, Toronto, 1950). Used by permission. SEE: Barry, 14;
Belden, 5; Brown II, 15; Child, No. 4; Coffin, 32; Greenleaf, 3; Greig, 2;
Guide and Index (*Outlandish Knight*); Mackenzie I, 3; Randolph I, 414; Sharp I, 5.
Piano arrangement by MATYAS SEIBER

1 There was a lord in London town,
  He courted a lady gay,
  And all that he courted this lady for
  Was to take her sweet life away.

2 'Come give to me of your father's gold,
  Likewise your mother's fee,
  And two of the best horses in your father's stable,
  For there stand thirty and three.'

3 She mounted on her milk-white steed
  And he the fast travelling grey,
  They rode till he came to the seashore side,
  Three hours before it was day.

4 'Alight, alight, my pretty Polly,
  Alight, alight,' said he,
  'For six pretty maids I have drownded here,
  And you the seventh shall be.

5 'Now take off your silken dress,
  Likewise your golden stay,
  For I think your clothing too rich and too gay
  To rot all in the salt sea.'

6 'Yes, I'll take off my silken dress,
  Likewise my golden stay,
  But before I do so, you false young man,
  You must face yon willow tree.'

7 Then he turned his back around
  And faced yon willow tree,
  She caught him around the middle so small
  And throwed him into the sea.

8 And as he rose and as he sank
  And as he rose, said he,
  'O give me your hand, my pretty Polly,
  My bride forever you'll be.'

9 'Lie there, lie there, you false young man,
  Lie there instead of me,
  For six pretty maids you've drownded here,
  And the seventh one has drownded thee.'

10 She lighted on her milk-white steed
   And led the fast travelling grey,
   And rode till she came to her father's outside
   One hour before it was day.

11 The parrot in the garret so high
   And unto pretty Polly did say,
   'What's the matter, my pretty Polly,
   You're driving before it is day?'

12 'No tales, no tales, my pretty Polly,
   No tales, no tales,' said she,
   'Your cage will be made of the glittering gold
   And yours of ivory.'

13 'No tales, no tales, my pretty Polly,
   No tales, no tales,' said she,
   'Your cage will be made of the glittering gold
   And hung on yon willow tree.'

9. EDWARD

To the child of New England, his father was often the frightening representative of a punishing, patriarchal God. Cotton Mather writes: ' I took my little daughter, Katy, into my study and sett before her the sinful condition of her Nature, and I charged her to pray in secret places every day.'

Only now can we appreciate the fires of terror and of violent revengeful feelings that must have been burning in the breast of the Puritan lad who ' never ventured to make a boy's simple request of his father, to offer so much as a petition for a knife or a ball, without putting it into writing in due form '.

The father frequently plays the tyrant's role in the old ballads, when he interferes between two lovers, but the mother generally appears as the more important figure, often as an evil witch (*see* p. 173). In ballad after ballad the son comes home to die in his mother's arms, or to confess a horrible crime, and in the classic British form of *Edward*, the crime is patricide. The hair-raising climax of this 'finest of ballads ' discloses that the deed was done on the mother's advice and hints at an incestuous relationship between mother and son. This motif occurs in New England, but not elsewhere in America, though the ballad has been widely recorded—North, South, Midwest, and the Pacific coast. In the more usual form, the hero has killed his own brother, as he did in the parent Scandinavian narrative, and sentences himself to the ancient Scandinavian punishment for this crime— to be set adrift in an open boat.

Ballads with an incestuous undercurrent are found less frequently in the South than in New England, where O'Neill found the setting for his dramas of incest. The old sea-ports produced stern fathers and cold, righteous husbands, whose feelings for their wives are caricatured in an anecdote from Nova Scotia.

A fishing captain, visiting away from home, receives a wire from his first mate: ' Your wife fell over-board and was drowned. We pulled her up with eight lobsters attached. What shall we do?' The captain wired right back: ' Ship me the lobsters and set her again.'

QUOTE: Calhoun.

10. FATHER GRUMBLE

Calhoun, in his extensive study of the American family, points out that ' the Plymouth colony was the very first place in this country, if not in the whole world, to recognize and honour woman. From the very first she had her rightful place at her husband's side as her children's head. Women were co-equal with men in social life and held a superior position to that held by them in England . . .' While this observation would hardly pass muster with an anthropologist, still it draws attention to the advance achieved by women in American colonies.

New England women practised many trades, including blacksmithing. They partici-pated in trading ventures and published newspapers. The names of six women appeared on the list of the Salem conspirators against taxation. In several communities women had the vote. Their normal activity, however, was running the home, and in the Northern colonies this meant a busy life, as an affectionate Philadelphia husband noted in his diary in the year 1778 . . .

(My wife) did the baking and the cooking; made twenty large cheeses from one cow; was gardener and apple butter maker; kept the house clean; cut and dried apples; made cider without tools for the constant drink of the family; attended to the washing and ironing; sewed and knit for us all . . . I think she hath not been four times, since her residence here, to visit the neighbors. When one is sick, she is a faithful nurse, night and day. She rose at day-break, at her age, and went to the wharves to buy wood. The horse would have died in the war if she had not skirmished for hay for him. Beyond all this she suffers and instructs Poll, our pestiferous hired girl . . .

Father Grumble has his come-uppance when he underestimates the power of a woman. His story dramatizes the triumph of women over men, and suggests, as does the following story, the direction sexual conflict was to take in the U.S.

Two old critters lived together thirty year, but by an' by they fell out, and they'd mump around all day without speaking, and when it come night, they'd turn their backs on one another an' snore, and pretend to be asleep, each one wishing the other would speak, but nary one would speak first. So it went on, till one night in the fall, they heared a terrible rumpus among the sheep in the yard, and he ups an' dresses him an' goes out. After quite a spell an' he didn't come back, she slips on her gown and shoes and out she goes. There he was, clinched with an almighty great bear, the bear a-chawin' at him an' him a-huggin' as hard as the bear to keep him from gettin' his hind claws into his innards, which is unpleasant as I know. ' Go to it, ol' man, go it, bear,' says she. ' It's the fust fight I ever see that I didn't keer which licked.'

She stood lookin' on a little spell, with her fists on her hips, till she see the ol' man was gettin' tired, and the bear havin' the best of it, and then she up with a sled stake and gave the bear such a wallop on the head it knocked him stiffer than a last, and then they had a huggin' match over the carcass of the bear, and lived together as folks oughter to the end of their days.

QUOTES: Calhoun, and *Danves Folks*, R. B. Robinson (Houghton Mifflin, 1894), p. 297. From Botkin III.

11. I'LL GIVE MY LOVE AN APPLE

. . . Jacob Minline went into the room where Sarah Tuttel was. They sat down together; his arm being around her; and her arm upon his shoulder or about his neck, and he kissed her and she kissed him or they kissed one another, continuing in this posture about a half an hour . . .

This episode from the Massachusetts Bay colony in the year 1660 indicates that New Englanders were not always so ' puritanical ' as they have been painted. Indeed, it was not until the latter part of the eighteenth century that the respectable folk managed to outlaw the North European custom of bundling in New England. Then a local poet gave voice to the feminine protests . . .

It shan't be so, they rage and storm,
And country girls in clusters swarm,
And fly and buzz like angry bees,
And vow they'll bundle when they please.
Some mothers, too, will plead their cause,
And give their daughters great applause,
And tell them 'tis no sin nor shame
For we, your mothers did the same.
' If I won't take my sparks to bed

21

> A laughing stock I shall be made.'
> But last of all, up speaks romp Moll,
> And pleads to be excused,
> For how can she e'er married be
> If bundling be refused?

Courtship in New England was decidedly more fun than in the South and West, and there were several reasons for this. Immigrants from rural Britain refreshed old permissive folk attitudes. After the decline of the Puritans, new Protestant cults never gained the general influence they had in the South and Midwest. Calvinist morality, to be sure, became a rooted part of the popular life, but it was a Scots Calvinism, which had never won a complete victory over Scots pagan folkways. And then, the North-East was growing increasingly cosmopolitan.

Thus North-Easterners sang a number of the merry old Scots marriage-by-rape or marriage-after-pregnancy ballads that are seldom heard in the Southern mountains. The lusty Scots tale of *Captain Wedderburn's Courtship*, for example, is a favourite in the North-East, but, so far as I am aware, is unknown in Southern tradition in its complete form. The story begins as . . .

> The Lord of Rosslyn's daughter gaed through the wood her lane,
> And there she met Captain Wedderburn, a servant to the King.
> He said unto his livery man, ' Were't na agen the law,
> I wad take her to my ain bed, and lay her at the wa'.'

Then the bold captain, in the fashion common to many Scots ballads, attempts marriage by rape. He carries off the young lady forcibly and demands, pleads, promises anything. ' So we'll baith lie in ae bed, an' ye'll lie at the wa'.' For fourteen stanzas the braw Scots lass rejects him, then agrees to be his if he can answer six riddles. The captain proves a master riddler, answering in perfect rhyme, and the ballad concludes . . .

> There's na into the king's realm to be found in blither twa,
> Now she is Mrs. Wedderburn and she lies at the wa' . . .

In both England and America this ballad has often been shorn of its rowdy plot and reduced to the present lullaby form—a prime example of how the ballad singers themselves have censored their songs in recent centuries. Southerners, however, were pretty consistently more prudish than northern singers, an observation that is borne out by comparison of the well-known southern *I Gave My Love a Cherry* with this variant of the lullaby, collected in Nova Scotia.

QUOTE: Calhoun.

12. THE QUAKER'S COURTSHIP

THE LIVELY GIRLS of New England enjoyed this seventeenth century satire of the solemn Quakerish swain who behaved as if courtship was a religious duty instead of a pleasurable pastime. Unmarried women were scarce in old New England, and the hot-blooded Puritans often did their wooing on the run. One morning, a young Puritan knocked at the house of a family where he was not known. He introduced himself to the head of the house, and asked permission to pay court to his daughter. After lunch he proposed to the young lady and was accepted. That same afternoon he obtained the marriage licence, and directly after supper he married the girl.

13. SAILING IN THE BOAT

IN THE YEAR 1769 at a wedding in New London, ninety-two jigs, fifty contra-dances, forty-three minuets and seventeen hornpipes were danced, and the party broke up at a quarter of one in the morning—at what time could it have begun?

The savages themselves were not more fond of dancing than were the colonists who came after them. Dancing schools were forbidden in New England by the authorities, but dancing could not be repressed in an age in which the range of conversation was necessarily narrow and the appetite for physical activity and excitement almost insatiable . . .

In spite of Puritan disapproval, the rural sports of old England gradually came to life again in the colonies, together with new customs that suited the country. The people amused themselves at quilting bees, apple-parings, shooting matches, sugaring-off parties in maple sugar time, and husking bees where the fellow that found the red ear of corn could kiss his favourite girl. They danced to the music of the fiddle and, later on, to orchestras of mouth harps, banjos, pianos, drums, and combs. In communities that disapproved of instrumental music, young people played games at their evening parties, and in rural Connecticut game-songs such as *Sailing in the Boat* continued to be popular until about 1870.

These entertainments were called ' kitchen junkets ' in certain part of rural New England. On Saturday evenings the kitchen of some large farmhouse was cleared and swept, the floor was sprinkled with cornmeal, a jug or two of hard cider was set outside in the dark for the men, and the young people danced and frolicked until midnight refreshments were served. Afterwards the party might go on until four or five in the morning, when it was time to see the girls home. Then there was a long, pleasant walk through the fields to the scattered homesteads, ending with a final embrace at the door. A young lady had to be careful not to walk home with too many boys or she might get the name of ' liking the fellers '. In that case, a respectable young man would think twice about marrying her.

QUOTE: *Customs and Fashions in Old New England*, Alice Morse Earle (Scribner & Sons, 1893), p. 74.

14. AS I ROVED OUT

FOR THE YANKEE, the land was no more than ' a shelter from the storm—a perch on which he built his eyries and hid his young, while he skimmed the surface of the waves and hunted the deeps of the oceans '. Long before the Revolution, British politicians complained that small, swift vessels, made of American timber and manned by reckless American seamen, threatened English trade. American fishermen were crowding the British off the New-foundland fishing banks, and the whalers of Cape Cod and Nantucket were taking ' British ' whales in the Arctic.

A boy of coastal New England, ' weaned on Jamaica rum and teethed on hardtack and salt horse,' could rise to be captain before he was twenty and retire with a fortune after five or ten years of hard sailing and hard trading.

The romance of sea-life, in those days, was not just recruiting officers' talk; and the tanned lad with the roll to his walk was more than romantic, he was an excellent catch. This little Canadian ditty is cousin to a thousand other songs of the eighteenth and early nineteenth centuries, in which susceptible young ladies sighed for, pined for, hopped in bed with, ran away to sea with, followed across the main, scorned richer suitors for—in a word, tried anything—to marry their 'sweet sailor boys'. Later on, the feminine folk singer, being no more nor less fickle than history, turned to the pursuit of lumberjacks, cowboys, and railroaders (*see* song 215).

15. THE SOW TOOK THE MEASLES

A NEW BREED of men was developing out of the pioneer Puritan stock. Puritan sobriety and thrift remained the fundamentals of their code, but, as practical men of affairs, they could dispense with their ancestors' finicking concern over moral and religious questions. About one old Unitarian deacon, who kept a store, this story is told.

> He calls to his shop assistant 'John, have you sanded the sugar?' 'Yessir.' 'Have you watered the rum?' 'Yessir.' 'Well, boy, then come to prayers . . .'

New England pedlars loaded their packs with ribbons and notions and wooden nutmegs and made the whole frontier their market. New England merchant sailors bought and sold in every port in the world. Seizing upon the unlimited opportunities of the New World, many of these men quickly rose to become merchant princes, able to finance and direct the American Revolution. So, towards the end of the eighteenth century, the Yankee stepped on the world's stage.

Close cousin to the shrewd Yorkshireman, this witty rustic, turned trader-inventor-statesman, was America's first folk hero. He set the stamp of his humour and his philosophy upon every phase of America's development and reappears again and again in our folk history—as Davy Crockett, Abe Lincoln, Paul Bunyan, Henry Ford, and—wearing striped trousers and a beaver hat—as Uncle Sam himself. The New England humorist, Josh Billings, has written the classic description of this shrewd, bumptious, and amusing New England type.

> Live Yankees are chuck full of karakter and sissing hot with enterprize and curiosity. In bild we find them az lean az a hunter's dorg, pashunt bekauze cunning; ever watchful; slo to anger; avoiding a fight; but resolute at bay. The oil of their langwidge iz their desire tew pleze, and their greasy words forshadder a profitt.

> They are natural mechanicks; the history ov man's necessitys iz the history ov their invenshuns. The Live Yankee has no hum; his luv of invenshun breeds luv of change, and wherever a human trail shows itself, we find him pantin on the trak. He looks at a marble pyramid, guesses its height, calkulates the stone by the perch and sells the magnifisent relic in Boston at a profit.

> Go where you will, from the numb palsied North tew the swetting limberness of the South, and the everlastin' Yankee you will find, either vehement in an argue or purswazive in a swop. His religion is praktikal. He luvs liberty with red pepper enthusiasm and fully beleafs Nu England kan whip the universe . . . If his religion iz sometimes only the severities of the Sabbath, it iz becauze his bias iz the thursting impulse of a creatin' genius chained tew the more sordid pashun for lucre . . .

Such was the nature of the practical idealist who fired the shot at Concord, Mass., that was heard round the world. This man, who could make a silk purse out of a sow's ear, transformed the old English *My Jolly Herring* into his own image in *The Sow Took the Measles*.

QUOTE: *Josh Billings on Ice* (Carlton Publishers, N.Y., 1870).

9. EDWARD

FROM: *Ballads Migrant in New England*, Helen Hartness Flanders (Farrar, Strauss & Young, N.Y., 1953). Used by permission. SEE: Brown II, 42; Child, No. 13; Coffin, 45; Randolph I, 67; Sharp I, 47-54. Also L.C. Record 57 B-2.
Piano arrangement by MATYAS SEIBER

Free ballad style ♩ = 63

GUITAR- *1 or 3A*
BANJO- *4B OR FREE STRUM*

1. 'How came that blood on your shirt sleeve? O dear love, tell me, me, me.' 'It is the blood of my old grey-hound, That traced the fox for me, me, me, That traced the fox for me.'

2. 'It—

1. ' How came that blood on your shirt sleeve?
   O dear love, tell me, me, me.'
   ' It is the blood of my old greyhound,
   That traced the fox for me, me, me,
   That traced the fox for me.'

2. ' It does look too pale for the old greyhound,
   O dear love, tell me, me, me,
   It does look too pale for the old greyhound,
   That traced the fox for thee, thee, thee. . .

3. ' How came that blood on your shirt sleeve?
   O dear love, tell me, me, me.'
   ' It is the blood of my old grey mare,
   That ploughed the field for me, me, me . . . '

4. ' It does look too pale for the old grey mare,
   O dear son, tell me, me, me,
   It does look too pale for the old grey mare,
   That ploughed the field for thee, thee, thee . . .

5. ' How came this blood on your shirt sleeve?
   O dear love tell me, me, me.'
   ' It is the blood of my brother-in-law,
   That went away with me, me, me . . . '

6. ' And what did you fall out about?
   O dear love, tell me, me, me.'
   ' About a little bit of bush
   That never would-a growed to a tree, tree, tree . . . '

7. ' And it's what will you do now, my son?
   O dear love, tell me, me, me!'
   ' I'll set my foot on yonder ship
   And sail across the sea, sea, sea . . . '

8. ' And it's when will you come back again?
   O dear love, tell me, me, me!'
   ' When the sun sets into yonder sycamore tree,
   And that will never be, be, be . . . '

10. FATHER GRUMBLE

FROM: p. 248 of *Folk Songs of Old New England*, Eloise Linscott (Macmillan, 1939).
Used by permission. SEE: Belden, 225; Brown II, 445; Guide (*Old Man and Wife*);
JAFL XXVI, 364. Probably derived from Scots *John Grumley*.
Known Scotland, Ireland, England; common New England, South, Mid-West.
Probably print-transmitted.

Lilting ♩.=108

GUITAR- 2B & 6B
BANJO- 4A

1 There was an old man that lived in a wood,
   As you can plainly see,
   Who said he could do more work in a day
   Than his wife could do in three.
   'If that be so,' the old woman said,
   'Why this you must allow,
   That you shall do my work for a day
   While I go drive the plough.

2 'But you must milk the tiny cow
   For fear she should go dry,
   And you must feed the little pigs
   That are within the sty,
   And you must watch the bracket hen
   Lest she should lay astray,
   And you must wind the reel of yarn
   That I spun yesterday.'

3 The old woman took the staff in her hand
   And went to drive the plough;
   The old man took the pail in his hand
   And went to milk the cow;
   But Tiny hinched and Tiny flinched
   And Tiny cocked her nose
   And Tiny hit the old man such a kick
   That the blood ran down to his toes.

4 'Twas, 'Hey my good cow,' and 'How, my good
   And 'Now, my good cow, stand still.   [cow,'
   If ever I milk this cow again,
   'Twill be against my will.'
   And when he'd milked the tiny cow
   For fear she should go dry,
   Why, then he fed the little pigs
   That were within the sty.

5 And then he watched the bracket hen,
   Lest she should lay astray,
   But he forgot the reel of yarn
   His wife spun yesterday.
   He swore by all the leaves on the tree,
   And all the stars in heaven,
   That his wife could do more work in a day
   Than he could do in seven.

11. I'LL GIVE MY LOVE AN APPLE

FROM: p. 163 of *Traditional Songs of Nova Scotia*, Helen Creighton and Doreen Senior (Ryerson Press, Toronto, 1950). Used by permission. With stanzas from the southern variants. For *Captain Wedderburn's Courtship*, see Brown II, 48; Child, 46; Creighton II, 21; Sharp II, 190.

1 I'll give my love an apple without e'er a core,
   I'll give my love a dwelling without e'er a door,
   I'll give my love a palace wherein she might be,
   That she might unlock it without e'er a key.

2 How can there be an apple without e'er a core?
      etc. through verse.

3 My head is an apple without e'er a core,
   My mind is the dwelling without e'er a door,
   My heart is a palace wherein she might be,
   That she might unlock it without e'er a key.

4 I'll give my love a cherry without e'er a stone,
   I'll give my love a chicken without e'er a bone,
   I'll tell my love a story without any end,
   I'll give my love a baby and no cryin'.

5 How can there be a cherry without e'er a stone?
      etc. through verse

6 When the cherry's in blossom it has no stone,
   When the chicken's in the egg it has no bone,
   The story of ' I love you ' will never end,
   When the baby is a-gettin', there's no cryin'.

12. THE QUAKER'S COURTSHIP

From singing of Richard Dyer Bennett, with two final stanzas from Newell, 95.
SEE: Belden, 265; Brown III, 16; Creighton II, 199; Newell, 94; Randolph III,
58 and 258. Related to *Paper of Pins*. Known in different forms in England.
This American variant found New England, South, Mid-West. SEE ALSO: *I'm Goin'
Away to Texas*—this volume.

1 *Man:* Once there was a Quaker lover,
     O dear, O dear me,
  Courted a Pres-by-terian's daughter,
     O dear, O dear me.
  ' Here's a ring worth many a shilling,
     O dear, O dear me,
  Take it and wear it, if thou art willing,
     O dear, O dear me.'
Woman: ' What do I care for you and your money?
     Tee-i-dinktum, tee-i-day,
  Want a man to call me honey,
     Tee-i-dinktum, tee-i-day.'

2 *Man:* ' Madam, I have both home and land,
  And both shall be at thy command.'
Woman: ' What do I care for your home and land?
  All I want's a handsome man.'

3 *Man:* ' Madam, I have come a-courtin',
  'Tis not for pleasure, nor for sportin'.'
Woman: ' What do I care for your desire?
  If you come, you'll court the fire.'

4 *Man:* ' I'll go home and tell my mother,
  She'll go straight and find me another.'
Woman: ' What do I care for you and your mother?
  She's an old Quaker and you're another.'

5 *Man:* ' Must I give up my religion?
  Must I be a Presbyterian?'
Woman: ' Cheer up, cheer up, loving brother,
  If you can't catch one fish, catch another.'

13. SAILING IN THE BOAT

FROM: *Games and Songs of American Children*, W. W. Newell (Harper Bros. N.Y., 1883). Known also in England and the Bahamas.

Rollicking ♩ = 208

GUITAR- *4 or 5A*
BANJO- *1 or 2*

Sail-ing in the boat when the tide runs high, Sail-ing in the boat when the tide runs high, Sail-ing in the boat when the tide runs high, Wait-ing for the pret-ty girl to come by'm by. Here she comes, so fresh and fair, Sky-blue eyes and cur-ly hair, Ro-sy in cheek, dim-ple in her chin, Say, young man, but you can't come in.

1 Sailing in the boat when the tide runs high, (3)
Waiting for the pretty girl to come by'm by.
CHORUS:
Here she comes, so fresh and fair,
Sky-blue eyes and curly hair,
Rosy in cheek, dimple in her chin,
Say, young man, but you can't come in.

2 Rose in the garden for you, young man, (2)
Rose in the garden, get it if you can,
But take care not a frost-bitten one. (CHO.)

3 Choose your partner, stay till day, (3)
And don't never mind what the old folks say.
(CHO.)

4 Old folks say 'tis the very best way (3)
To court all night and sleep all day. (CHO.)

14. AS I ROVED OUT

FROM: p. 69 of *Ballads and Sea Songs of Newfoundland*, Elizabeth Greenleaf (Harvard U.P., 1933). Used by permission. As sung by Charles Willis, Fogo, Newfoundland, 1929. SEE: Creighton, 212; Guide (*Tarry Trousers*); Sharp's *Folk Songs of Somerset* II, 30 (an Irish air); Sharp II, 168. Many southern English variants.
Piano arrangement by MATYAS SEIBER

1 As I roved out one fine summer s evening
To view the flowers and take the air,
'Twas there I spied a tender mother
Talking to her daughter dear.

2 Saying, ' Daughter, O daughter, I'll have you
                 to marry,
No longer to lead a sweet single life.'
' O mother, O mother, I'd rather tarry
To be some brave young sailor's wife.'

3 ' O a sailor boy likes all for to wander,
He will prove your overthrow.
O daughter, you are better to wed with a farmer,
For to the seas he ne'er do go.'

4 ' O mother, I cannot wed with a farmer,
Though he decks me with diamonds bright,
I'll wait for my love with the tarry, tarry
                     trousers,
For he's my darling and my heart's delight.'

5 Now Polly is the wife of some jolly sailor,
  See how neat and trim she goes,
  See how neatly he maintains her,
  Dressed in silks from top to toe.

6 She leans her head on her true love's shoulder,
  Tears down from her eyes do flow.
  ' O stay with me, my dearest Willie,
  And to the seas no more don't go.'

15. THE SOW TOOK THE MEASLES

SEE: Brown III, 218; Guide and Index (*Red Herring Song*); Randolph, 149; Reeves, 179. Found New England, Ozarks. Derived from *The Red Herring Song*, common in southern England, also found Ireland.

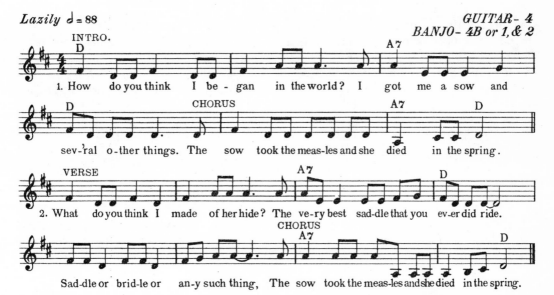

Lazily ♩ = 88

GUITAR- 4
BANJO- 4B or 1, & 2

1. How do you think I be-gan in the world? I got me a sow and sev'ral o-ther things. The sow took the meas-les and she died in the spring.

2. What do you think I made of her hide? The ve-ry best sad-dle that you ev-er did ride. Sad-dle or brid-le or an-y such thing, The sow took the meas-les and she died in the spring.

1 How do you think I began in the world?
  I got me a sow and sev'ral other things.
  CHORUS:
  The sow took the measles and she died in the spring.

2 What do you think I made of her hide?
  The very best saddle that you ever did ride.
  Saddle or bridle or any such thing, (CHO.)

3 What do you think I made of her nose?
  The very best thimble that ever sewed clothes,
  Thimble or thread or any such thing, (CHO.)

4 What do you think I made of her tail?
  The best whup that ever sought sail.
  Whup or whup socket, any such thing, (CHO.)

5 What do you think I made of her feet?
  The very best pickles you ever did eat.
  Pickles or glue or any such thing, (CHO.)

31

YANKEE SOLDIERS AND SAILORS

16. BRAVE WOLFE

JAMES WOLFE, known as the most gallant gentleman of his age, was perfect ballad material. King George III said of him, ' If the man is mad, I wish he would bite all my generals.' The taking of Quebec from the French in 1759 was an operation of magnificent coolness. His troops landed at night under walls heavily armed with cannon, and clambered up an almost perpendicular cliff before they could engage the enemy. Both Wolfe and the French commander, Montcalm, were killed the next day in the open fields before the city, but Wolfe died smiling when he heard that his British and colonial forces had won. The French power in America was broken; the French and Indian wars were over; and the colonists were free to move west and to settle their differences with the English. Soon the army, then the whole world, learned that Wolfe had left one of the loveliest young women in England disconsolate.

Some unknown colonial bard published this piece in Boston in 1759, not long after ' the bad news came to town '. The pocket songsters, those palm-sized booklets of song verses that travelled in the pockets and knapsacks of Americans from coast to coast, kept the ballad in print for almost a hundred years; and collectors have since found it among the people in Canada and New England, and as far south as West Virginia.

17. THE WARS OF AMERICA
18. FELIX THE SOLDIER

My brother Pat, he is a brisk young soldier,
He carries his firelock all over his left shoulder,
And on the field of battle, by me soul, he's never daunted,
For he'll fight like the Devil or some fairy that is haunted.

IF SOLDIER folk songs were the only evidence, it would seem that the armies that fought in early American wars were composed entirely of Irishmen. The finest folk ballads of the Indian Wars, the American Revolution, the Mexican War, the Civil War, and the Plains Indian War, all had Irish tunes; and perhaps our best soldiers' folk songs are these two pieces, sung by Irish recruits who marched with the redcoats in the French and Indian Wars. They speak for the many poor Irish lads forced by privation to become mercenary soldiers.

Ireland lost so many of her boys in the French and English wars that the recruiting sergeant became a dreaded figure in the western counties. He would treat an ignorant boy to drinks and then press the loan of a shilling on him. Once the poor dupe accepted the King's shilling, he was as good as in the army, and the sergeant could haul him off to the barracks. The Irish version of *The Wars of America* begins . . .

' O, Mrs. McGrath, ' the sergeant said,
' Would you like to make a soldier out of your son, Ted?
With his shining sword and his big, cocked hat?
O, Mrs. McGrath, wouldn't you like that?'

The cycle of songs which apparently gave rise to *Felix the Soldier* takes a more cheerful view of military life. A related song, common in both Ireland and the United States, is a satire on the raw Irish recruit.

The first thing they gave me, it was a big gun,
And under the trigger they planted me thumb,
Placed me finger on the trigger and the thing begin to smoke,
And it give me poor shoulder a hell of a poke.

Now I says to McGuire, ' You may think it's quite grand
To place such a tool in any man's hands.
No, Mister McGuire, I think I shall retire,
For the thing is running mad; can't you see her spitting fire?'

Under gallant General Wolfe, there was no way that a brave man could retire. The Irish recruit ' scaled the wall ' at Quebec and marched on through the smoke of the battle to learn the realities of war and greatly to improve the ballad.

19. IN THE DAYS OF '76

WHEN THE War of Independence broke out between England and the thirteen colonies in 1776, the ballad press poured out a volume of political and patriotic pieces, which reflected the fighting spirit of the colonists, but bore small resemblance to folk songs. This literary ballad, for example, was composed when eight hundred Vermont villagers routed a wing of Burgoyne's army . . .

Why come ye hither, Redcoats? Your mind, what madness fills?
In our valleys there is danger and there's danger in our hills.
Oh, hear ye not the singing of the bugle wild and free?
Soon you'll know the ringing of the rifle from the tree.
O the rifle, O the rifle, in our hands will prove no trifle!

In the Days of '76 is one of the best of these pseudo-ballads from the music-hall tradition, but we know surprisingly few of the campfire songs of the ragged Continentals who fought for America's independence. Most of the soldier's songs of that day have disappeared, or else the raw country militia never established sufficient esprit-de-corps to create its own songs. Many of the skirmishes of the Revolutionary War were as casually begun and terminated as this one . . .

I remember that day we were plowing, when we heard the sound of a cannon toward New Haven. ' Whoa,' said Uncle Benton; stopped team, off harness, mounted Old Sorrel, bareback, shouldered the old musket and rode off to New Haven. Deacon Bartlett went, too; and Sam Bartlett said he never saw father more keen after deer than he was to get a shot at the Regulars. He had a large-bored, long old shot-gun, that I bought afterwards for ducks.

So father took the old firelock and went out with them. But the British proved too strong for them, and the word came for each one to look out for himself. Father happened to see a scout; he raised his gun and stood deliberating whether he could kill a fellow-being. The click of a trigger nearby turned his head towards a British marksman who had no such scruples, but was aiming straight at his head. He popped down into a ravine, losing his gun and hat, and wandered about all that hot July day bare-headed, and got sunstroke, from which he never fully recovered . . .

20. JOHNNY HAS GONE FOR A SOLDIER

Shule Agrah—the Irish meaning is ' Come with me, my love '—comes from the period after the Treaty of Limerick in 1691, when ' like a flight of wild geese ', many young Irish patriots fled to France and served in the armies of the French King. The girl dyes her petticoat red to show that she is engaged and loyal to her absent Johnny.

> I'll dye my petticoat, yes, dye it red,
> And through the world I'll beg my bread,
> Until my people will wish me dead,
> *Is do bhillidh tu a muirnin slan.*
> (May you return safe, my love.)

Garbling the Irish refrain in such fantastic ways as . . .

> Shoo lie, shoo lie, shoo lie roo,
> Shoo lie, shoo lie, sacka babba coo,
> When I return to the sally babba coo,
> Shiver an a boo shi lory . . .

American singers have used the tune for a sea chantey (*see* p. 56), a lumberman's complaint, a play-party song, a Cherokee Indian chant, and this, the finest soldier song of the American Revolutionary War.

Close to one-third of the three million colonists were descendants of folks who had left hungry and oppressed Ireland, singing . . .

> With me knapsack on me shoulder sure there's no one could be bolder,
> And I'm leavin' dear old Ireland without warning,
> For of late I've took a notion for to cross the briny ocean,
> And I'm off to Philadelphia in the mornin' . . .

As soon as his foot struck American soil, the Irish emigrant became an ardent American patriot, hot in his support of the colonial, indeed, any cause against the King. Between thirty-five and fifty per cent of Washington's army were ex-Hibernians, and in 1778, Sir Henry Clinton wrote from America to Lord George Germain that ' the emigrants from Ireland were in general to be looked upon as our most serious antagonists '. Sir Henry's opinion is confirmed by the record.

John Paul Jones and other Irish-born privateers preyed on British shipping. General Washington had three Irish aide-de-camps, and James McHenry was his Secretary of War. Another Irishman, Francis Scott Key, wrote *The Star-spangled Banner*. Tim Murphy, reputedly the best shot in the American Army, saved the day at the Battle of Saratoga by picking off the British commanding general. The Irish took Fort William and Mary, led the Liberty Boys at Golden Hill, and won recognition for their valour at the Battle of Bunker Hill.

A century later, when anti-Irish sentiment reached a peak in America, one Michael O'Brien successfully challenged dignified Senator Lodge of Boston to produce any record of Cabots or Lodges in the Revolution to match the seventy-five O'Briens on the muster roll of the Massachusetts regiments, and the two hundred and thirty-six listed by all the states.

21. YANKEE DOODLE DANDY-0

THE TREATY OF PEACE signed between Great Britain and her victorious thirteen colonies in 1783 did not end their quarrels. The British Navy, locked in a life and death struggle with Napoleon, was seizing American ships and impressing American seamen. In the far West shots were fired and scalps were taken in the battle for the fur trade. War was formally declared in 1812.

For a year, to English astonishment, America was victorious on the sea. Her navy consisted of only sixteen ships, but her swift Baltimore and Boston privateers in seven months took seven hundred British prizes worth a total of 25 million dollars. One privateer captain had a notice posted in Lloyd's declaring the British Isles in a state of blockade.

Such a situation could not long endure. By the end of 1813 the huge British Navy had bottled the American privateers up in port, and the British *Shannon* forced Captain ' Don't-give-up-the-ship ' Lawrence to strike his colours on America's *Chesapeake*. Then true-blue Britons everywhere roared with delight over their version of *Yankee Doodle Dandy-o*, still popular among old sea-dogs in the Maritime Provinces.

> Brooks and all his crew,
> In courage stout and true
> They worked the Yankee frigate neat and handy-o,
> O may they ever prove,
> In fighting and in love,
> That bold British tars can lick a Yankee-doodle-dandy-o.

In 1815 this rather pointless and inconclusive war came to an end, but the Yankees, now free of British red-tape, launched a fleet of swift packets and clippers which soon challenged the English merchant marine on every ocean.

22. THE FISH OF THE SEA

OFF CAPE COD lies George's Bank, 8,500 square miles of sea shelf where feed cod, hake, halibut, bluefish, and mackerel. From Nantucket these shallows run on north for a thousand miles to the Grand Banks off Newfoundland—37,000 square miles of the fishiest sea in the world. Here, in spite of fogs, storms, and collisions that once took eighty vessels and four hundred men a year, the North Americans harvested the grey-green North

Atlantic. Here they tested radical designs that later produced the packets and the clippers. Here they, themselves, became superlative seamen.

When their holds were full of fish, they raced for home, their halliards made fast aloft so that sail could not be taken in. A Cape schooner sailed best, they claimed, with her lee rail under water and her cabin dragging. They tell of a race down from the Banks which was won by a captain who kept his schooner's sail level with the water and his crew, well-liquored up, clinging on to the keel. This ancient fisherman's ballad, which I heard recently among the bargemen of the Suffolk coast, was sung by the old salts of New England on such happy occasions.

23. CAPE COD GIRLS

ONCE THE WARS were won and the blockade lifted, the Yankee trader set out to capture the trade of the world. The *Old Farmer's Almanac* summed up the impression he made upon his age . . .

Place the Yankee upon a rock in the middle of the ocean, and, with his penknife and a bunch of shingles, he would work his way on shore. He sells salmon from the Kennebec to the people of Charleston; raises coffee in Cuba; swaps mules and horses in Porto Rico; retails ice from Alden's pond, Connecticutt to the East Indies; starts in a cockleshell craft of fifteen tons, loaded with onions, mackerel, and notions for Valparaiso; baits his traps on the Columbia river; prescribes sarsparilla and eyewash to the mandarins of China; builds railroads for the autocrat of Russia; is schoolmaster for his country and missionary to the whole heathen world. If perpetual motion is ever to be discovered, he will surely be the lucky contriver, for he is the factotum for the world . . .

Thus the young women of New England came to be celebrated upon all the seas and in all the ports of the world, where their young men heaved up the anchor to this ditty.

QUOTE: *Old Farmer's Almanac*, Boston, 1851.

24. SALLY BROWN

THE VIGOROUS COSMOPOLITANS of Salem and Boston did not turn up their noses at the slave trade. They swapped dried codfish in Europe for cheap cotton goods—cotton goods for slaves on the west coast of Africa—and slaves for rum in the West Indies; then they sold the rum at quadrupled prices in Boston Harbour. This was a way for a captain to get rich quick—if he could stomach the smell that rose from the holds where the naked blacks were packed in belly to back, or if he could throw the sick overboard and enter 'jettisoned cargo' in his log.

The whole story reminds one of the observation that one old salt made about Sally Brown, the heroine of this chantey. ' Now some folks might think Sally was immoral,' he said, ' but that was the way of the world in them days.'

This capstan chantey can be sung in rollicking style; yet, as one authority on the subject points out, the song is really nostalgic and ' should be sung fairly slowly, its lightness tinged with sadness and regret '.

36

25. SHENANDOAH

THE PRIMITIVE work chant, which some historians of music believe was the primordial ancestor of all song, comes into life wherever men have to do hard labour with nothing but their bare hands and their co-operative spirit to help them.

Francisco Fabri, a fifteenth century Venetian Friar, was the first person to write about chanteying . . . ' There are others who sing when work is going on, because work at sea is very heavy, and is only carried on by a concert between one who sings out orders and the laborers who sing in response . . . ' Chanteying was again described in the sixteenth-century poem ' Complaynt of Scotland '; and there is evidence that two chanteys, popular in the nineteenth century (*Bowline* and *Amsterdam Maid*), livened up the work on Queen Elizabeth's carracks. Yet chanteying almost certainly antedates the Renaissance; the work songs of the Sicilian tuna fishers are said to go back to pre-Christian times.

I think it should be a matter of some pride to Americans that we have contributed to such an ancient and honourable practice. *Sally Brown*, *A Long Time Ago*, *Santy Anno*, *Let the Bullgine Run*, *Away Rio*, and other fine chanteys either originated among American seamen or assumed their present shape on board American ships. *Shenandoah*, the most beautiful of all sea songs in English, probably began as a voyageur song on the rivers west of the Mississippi, taking its title from the Indians for whom the great valley of Virginia was named. It became, somehow, a capstan chantey and then a favourite song of the regular cavalry who sometimes fought the Indians out west, but also fell in love with and married Indian women.

SOURCE: Whall.

26. SANTY ANNO

No ONE will ever know the why and wherefore of the heroes of the chanteys, like *Stormalong* and *Reuben Ranzo*. Nor can anyone explain why these particular figures of fantasy pleased the sea-washed, underfed, dog-tired sailor, and made him pull his hands raw on a tarry rope. These secrets have gone down over the horizon with the white-winged clippers. Gone, too, is the reason that General Santyanna, whom the Texans whipped in their war for independence, should be the hero of the finest halliard chantey. Captain Rasmussen, a Norwegian chanteyman who sailed before the mast on the square-riggers, learned this version along the coast of Mexico in the great days of the mahogany trade.

The chanteys arose among the despised common seamen, as they fought the drag of line and anchor and bawled out whatever wild cries, oaths, and barbarities would help them in their struggle with wind and sea. Of all folk music, these work songs of the sea most clearly belong to the unlearned, unwashed common labourer, and are, most certainly, communal creations. Of all songs in English, they are perhaps the noblest, the most vigorous, the most stirring, and the hardest to imitate.

Recent research indicates that chanteying fell into disuse on English ships during the eighteenth century, and emerged again at full bawl in the rising American merchant marine about 1815. English naval discipline did not permit the singing of chanteys, nor did the near-military regulations on board the heavily armed East Indiamen encourage it. These vessels carried large crews which could handle the work aboard ship without the spur of the chanteyman, though sometimes a fiddler or a piper played while the men tramped round the capstan. Chanteying continued on smaller English vessels, but it was probably not until the American packets began their regular trans-Atlantic runs in 1817 and American clippers began to show their heels to the rest of the world, that these songs came into their own. They were essential to the handling of a fast American ship which carried a great spread of canvas and a small crew; without them, the work on such a vessel simply could not be done.

The chanteys roared into life again on board British vessels in the 1830's, when English seamen began to replace Americans aboard the packets and, later still, in the 1860's when the British merchant marine once more dominated all the seas.

Meantime, Yankee singers had put their stamp upon these songs, and they had become truly Anglo-American.

27. BLOOD RED ROSES

To COMPREHEND precisely how the chanteys functioned, one would have to take a cruise aboard a square-rigger, or study the rigging plan of a nineteenth-century barque with its dozens of sails, its miles of line, hundreds of blocks, etc. It will suffice us to know little more than that a chantey was an extra hand on a rope or capstan bar. Truly, that extra hand was needed to raise yards of wet or frozen half-inch thick canvas in the teeth of a sixty-mile gale, or to hoist an upper topsail-yard, sixty feet long and as thick as a man's waist in the middle!

The chanteyman stood close to the mast, grasping the topsail halliard—a line that ran through blocks to the topsail yard aloft. The gang laid hold of the tail of the rope. He pulled down to the block; they hauled out from the block along the deck. First he gave a long, wild cry—a savage sound that was old when Columbus sailed—and the gang came taut on the rope. Then he sang his first line—something he was composing about the mate, the shipping master, or a girl of the port—always to a traditional tune. Then all hauled and sung together on the chorus line—with a pull on the first syllable and perhaps another on the tail of the verse. Thus:

> Chanteyman: Whisky's drivin' the cap'n blind,
> Gang: WHISky, JOHNny!

By now the chanteyman had his wind again and his rhyme between his teeth.

> Chanteyman: The damned old mate has lost 'is mind,
> Gang: WHISky for my JOHNny-o.

28. A LONG TIME AGO

RELIABLE WITNESSES from the American fleet say that the best of all chanteymen were the Negroes and, after them, the Irish. Certainly Negroes originated many chanteys and contributed to others, for the work song has long been the special province of the Negro, both in Africa and in the Americas. Under slavery and afterwards, Negroes composed many songs for handling small boats (*see* song 281), and this and other Negro work songs were adapted by chanteymen for ship-board jobs.

Many blue-water men spent the winter months as long-shoremen along the Gulf Coast, with Negroes in the gangs. Heaving at the bars of the huge screws that could compress a bale of cotton to a quarter of its size, these ' screwmen chawed more tobacco, cussed harder, sweated faster and sang louder than any men in the world '. Sometimes they heaved so hard that the seams of the ship were torn apart and the decks lifted off their stanchions. *A Long Time Ago*, born in this environment, sailed out of Mobile Bay, round the Horn, to become one of the favourite sailor work songs in all climes.

William Doerflinger, in his superb book *Shantymen and Shantyboys* (Macmillan, 1951), states that the term ' chantey ' first came into use in the late 1840's in the dialect of the Gulf Coast; earlier writers, describing the custom in other parts of the world, had not used the word ' chantey '. Doerflinger does not agree that it was the term for the Negro or lumberman's ' shantey ' or dwelling, but argues plausibly that it was the French root ' chant ', given a final diminutive ' y '. My guess is that round New Orleans, French-speaking roustabouts once encouraged each other to ' chantez ' (pronounced ' shantay ').

29. THE BULLGINE RUN

THE FOLLOWING advertisement appeared in a New York newspaper in 1817 . . .
LINE OF AMERICAN PACKETS BETWEEN NEW YORK AND LIVERPOOL. In order to furnish frequent and regular conveyance for GOODS and PASSENGERS, the subscribers have undertaken to establish a line of vessels between NEW YORK and LIVERPOOL, on a certain day of every month of the year. One shall sail from New York on the fifth and one from Liverpool on the first of every month. These ships have all been built in New York of the very best materials. They are remarkably fast sailers and their accommodations for passengers are uncommonly extensive and comfortable . . .

So began one of the major maritime revolutions, for this was the first time that trans-oceanic shipping had guaranteed to stick to a schedule in spite of wind and tide. The American packet lines lived up to their promises. They sailed in fair weather or foul, with or without a full cargo, and every trip was an attempt to break a record. Between five and six weeks had been the normal time taken to cross the Atlantic. The American packets now did the easterly trip in seventeen or eighteen days and made the difficult westerly passage in twenty-three. Ralph Waldo Emerson recalls an uncomfortable record-breaking passage when the captain slept in the cable locker when he was off watch to prevent the terrified first mate from taking in sail.

SOURCE: Davidson.

30. ROW, BULLIES, ROW
31. THE BANKS OF NEWFOUNDLAND

WITHIN A GENERATION after 1816 American packets had captured the transatlantic trade—a business too profitable to permit the survival of the old share system of privateering days. At the same time, the lines of the ships had grown sharper, and their small crews were driven harder and harder at their work. It became normal to keep all hands employed on deck from dawn till dusk, in addition to the night-watch required of every man aboard. The blue-nose Yankee mate appeared, proud of his reputation as a ' blower and striker '.

More and more Americans left the sea, turning inland to seek their fortunes on the expanding frontier. The crews of the packet ships were recruited from the riff-raff of the world's waterfronts—shanghaied, tricked into signing papers by crimps and boarding-house masters who operated in every port. The packet-rat travelled light, coming aboard to make a mid-winter Atlantic crossing in a cotton shirt and a pair of dungarees. He was proud of his ability to take punishment. ' I can sail any man's ship,' he bragged.

Mates boasted that they killed a man every trip. It became normal to carry four or five able seamen in a crew of thirty. The remainder were green hands, drunks and criminals, who had to be cowed by beating and torture. The third mate was a cross ' between a New Orleans mule and a wildcat '; the second mate bragged that he was ' a tiger who bloodied his whiskers every change of watch ', and the first mate bawled, ' It's my habit to spread the toughest packet-rat on a ship's biscuit and eat him before the voyage gets under way.'

Accommodation for the first-class passengers was as luxurious as money could provide, but for the tens of thousands of poor Irish, Scots, and German immigrants the packets were hell-holes. Often three hundred men, women, and children occupied a single steerage compartment, seventy by thirty feet, which also accommodated pigs, sheep, cows, and chickens. A few tiny portholes threw faint beams of light into the gloomy, stinking apartment. If anyone fell ill, the ship's carpenter could provide surgery or a coffin. Under such conditions, a shy, red-faced seaman often picked some bashful, immigrant girl, pale with sea-sickness, and a love affair began that would plant a new family somewhere upon the burgeoning frontier. The second ballad shares its haunting Irish tune with the Australian deportation song, *Van Diemen's Land*.

32. THE GREENLAND WHALE FISHERY

THE FOLLOWING EXTRACT from a sailor's journal testifies to the realism of this favourite ballad of British and American whalemen . . .

. . . On the seventh day after our departure from the coast, at 2 p.m. a whale was seen from the mast head, and the cheering cry of ' there she blows ' resounded through the ship. Our captain the day before had put a new boat upon his cranes of which my brother was steersman. At the time of raising the whale, the wind blew fresh and caused a heavy sea. The whale being to leeward at no great distance, we hauled back our main yard, lowered away our boats and made the best of our way for the whale. The monster lay fore and aft in the trough of sea. The captain's boat was ahead and going with great speed before the wind and the sea. As the boat approached, the boat steerer put himself in the attitude to strike; the captain, fearing danger, cried to him to ' hold his hand '; but he disregarded the captain's orders and threw both irons, plunging them to the socket in the monster's side. For this rashness they were all made bitterly to repent. At one instant, the motion of his gigantic fluke cut our boat completely in two . . .

QUOTE: Reuben Delano's *Wanderings and Adventures* (T. Drew, Jr., Worcester, Mass., 1843). Narrative of twelve years' life in whale ships.

33. GET UP, JACK

JACK TAR, whom poets and after-dinner speakers toasted as the very backbone of British and American commerce, met an indifferent reception when he came ashore. Ladies mistook his rolling gait for a drunken stagger and hastily crossed to the other side of the road as he approached. His windy voice, salty speech, and shipboard manners marked him off from prim landsmen; and pious folk, hearing far off the echoes of his quayside frolics, forgot that he had lived an ascetic life for weeks or months aboard ship, and concluded that Jack was an entirely depraved character.

By and large, therefore, the common seaman was left no choice as to his friends ashore. Barmen, bawds, and boarding-house keepers welcomed him to port, and with these venal companions Jack, hero of many a battle with the monster ocean, flung his gold about, and then took his hangover quietly to sea. Not unnaturally, he grew cynical about the people who stayed behind and profited from his hard life, and he registered this hard-bought cynicism in ballads like *Get Up, Jack*, which paints a true picture of the penniless or ageing sailor turned into the cold street. As the nineteenth century wore on and conditions for the sailor worsened, the moral of this ballad became more and more apparent to American seamen, and New England Yankees, preferring the role of John to that of Jack, turned their backs on the sea and headed for the West.

16. BRAVE WOLFE

From singing of Frank Warner and Yankee John Galusha. Used by permission of Frank Warner. SEE: Flanders III, 55; Greenleaf, 96; Guide and Index (*General Wolfe*); Laws, 118; Mackenzie, 198.

1 ' Bad news has come to town, bad news is carried,
   Some say my love is dead, some say he's married.
   As I was a-ponderin' on this, I took to weepin',
   They stole my love away while I was sleepin'.'

2 Then away went this brave youth and embarked on the ocean,
   To free Amerikay was his intention,
   He landed in Quebec with all his party,
   The city to attack, being brave and hearty.

3 He drew his army up in lines so pretty,
   On the plains of Abraham, back of the city.
   At a distance from the town where the French would meet him,
   In double numbers there resolved to beat him.

4 Montcalm and this brave youth together walkèd,
   Between two armies they, like brothers, talkèd,
   Till each one took his post and did retire,
   It was then these numerous hosts commenced their fire.

5 Little did he think death was so near him,
   Yes, little did he think death was so near him,
   When shot down from his horse was this, our hero,
   We'll long lament his loss in tears of sorrow.

6 He raisèd up his head where the cannons did rattle
   And to his aide he said, ' How goes the battle?'
   His aide-de-camp replied, ' It's ended in our favour.'
   Then says this brave youth, ' I quit this earth with pleasure.'

7 ' Bad news has come to town, bad news is carried,
Some say my love is dead, some say he's married.
As I was a-ponderin' on this, I took to weepin',
They stole my love away while I was sleepin'.'

17. THE WARS OF AMERICA

Collected and arranged by Alan Lomax from singing of Elmer George, Calais,
Vt., 1939. SEE: Lomax IV, 198. A common ballad in Northern Ireland.
Piano arrangement by MATYAS SEIBER

1 I have two sons and a son-in-law, ⎱ (2)
  Fightin' in the wars of America. ⎰
  But I don't know if I'll see them more,
  Or whether they'll visit old Ireland's shore.
  CHORUS:
  To the rum-die-ah, fa-da-diddle-ah,
  Whacks to the lady to the rum-die-ah.

2 I spied two ships a-comin' on the sea, ⎱ (2)
  Hulliloo, bubiloo! and I think 'tis he. ⎰
  ' O ships, O ships, will you wait for a while,
  Till I find Terry, my own child? (CHO.)

3 ' My son, Terry, is neat and trim, ⎱ (2)
  To every leg he has one shin. ⎰
  He's mama's pet and darlin' boy,
  He's the ladies toy and the girls' own joy.' (CHO.)

4 ' O wasn't you cunnin', wasn't you cute, ⎱ (2)
  You didn't get away from the Frenchman's shoot. ⎰
  'Tis not a devilish shin or leg you have at all,
  They was all shot away at the Frenchman's ball.' (CHO.)

5 ' Mother dear, why don't you know ⎱ (2)
  When the boys enlist, they've got to go? ⎰
  There stands old Bonyparte, stalks all round,
  It's fight or die or stand your ground.' (CHO.)

6 *Repeat stanza 3.*
  CHORUS:
  To the rum-die-ah, fa-da-diddle-ah,
  Aye—de rather rather rum-die-ah.

18. FELIX THE SOLDIER

Collected, arranged, and used by permission of Frank Warner. SEE: Lomax IV, 200; Sharp II, 228. Seamus Ennis says it is one-half of a standard 18th-century Irish jig.

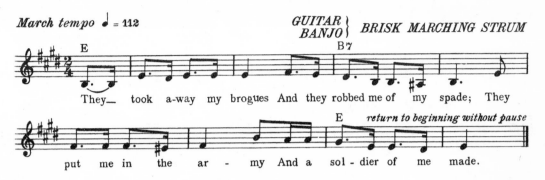

1 They took away my brogues
   And they robbed me of my spade;
   They put me in the army
   And a soldier of me made.

2 But I couldn't beat the drum,
   And I couldn't play the flute,
   So they handed me a musket
   And taught me how to shoot.

3 We had a bloody fight
   After we had scaled the wall,
   And the Divil a bit of mercy
   Did the Frenchies have at all.

4 But the Injuns they were sly,
   And the Frenchies, they were coy,
   So they shot off the left leg
   Of this poor Irish boy.

5 Then they put me on a ship
   And they sent me home again,
   With all my army training
   After battle's strife and din.

6 I will bid my spade adieu,
   For I cannot dig the bog,
   But I still can play a fiddle
   And I still can drink my grog.

7 I have learned to smoke a pipe
   And have learned to fire a gun,
   To the Divil with the fighting,
   I am glad the war is done.

19. IN THE DAYS OF '76

From the collection of Wallace House. Folkways 'American Songs from 1776-1812'. Used by his permission.
Piano arrangement by MATYAS SEIBER

1 The days of seventy-six, my boys,
We ever must revere,
Our fathers took their muskets then
To fight for freedom dear.
Upon the plains of Lexington
They made the foe look queer.
CHORUS:
O 'tis great delight to march and fight
As a Yankee volunteer.
Spoken: READY! AIM! FIRE!

2 Through snow and ice at Trenton, boys,
They crossed the Delaware,
Led on by immortal Washington
No danger did they fear.
They gave the foe a drubbing, boys,
Then back to town did steer. (CHO.)

3 At Saratoga next, my boys,
Burgoyne they beat severe;
And at the siege of Yorktown
They gained their cause so dear;
Cornwallis there gave up his sword,
Whilst Freedom's sons did cheer. (CHO.)

4 And should a foeman e'er again
Upon our coast appear,
There's hearts around me, brave and true,
Who'd quickly volunteer
To drive invaders from the soil
Columbia's sons hold dear.
CHORUS:
O they'd each delight to march and fight
Like Yankee volunteers.
Spoken: READY! AIM! FIRE!

20. JOHNNY HAS GONE FOR A SOLDIER

From the collection of Wallace House, ibid. SEE: Belden, 281; Index and Guide
(*Shule Agrah, Shule Aroon*); JEFSS V, 29, 180-3; Joyce, No. 425; Lomax II, 299;
Randolph, I, 400, III, 209; Sharp II, 50.
Piano arrangement by MATYAS SEIBER

Smoothly ♩ = 112

GUITAR- 6A
BANJO- 4B

1. O John - ny dear has gone a - way, He has gone a - far a - cross the bay, O my
2. I'll dye my dress I'll dye it red, And through the streets I'll beg my bread, And

p dolce

Arp. *Arp.*

heart is sad and wea - ry to - day, John - ny has gone for a sol - dier.
through the streets I'll beg my bread,

Arp.

Shule, shule, shule a-grah, Time can on-ly heal my woe, Since the lad of my heart from me did go, O John-ny has gone for a sol-dier.

1 O Johnny dear has gone away,
He has gone afar across the bay,
O my heart is sad and weary today,
Johnny has gone for a soldier.
CHORUS:
Shule, shule, shule agrah,
Time can only heal my woe,
Since the lad of my heart from me did go,
O Johnny has gone for a soldier.

2 I'll dye my dress, I'll dye it red,
And through the streets I'll beg my bread,
And through the streets I'll beg my bread,
Johnny has gone for a soldier.   (CHO.)

3 I'll sell my clock, I'll sell my reel,
I'll sell my flax and spinning wheel,
To buy my true love a sword of steel,
Johnny has gone for a soldier.   (CHO.)

4 Me, O my, I love him so,
Broke my heart to see him go,
Only time can heal my woe,
Johnny has gone for a soldier.   (CHO.)

21. YANKEE DOODLE DANDY-O

SEE: Colcord, 130; Index and Guide (*Chesapeake* and *Shanon*); Laws, 121; Mackenzie, 208; Whall, 61. Melody is Scots: *Bonnie Lass o' Fyvie-o*.

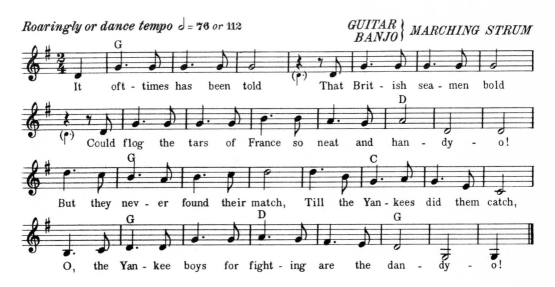

Roaringly or dance tempo ♩ = 76 or 112

GUITAR BANJO } MARCHING STRUM

It oft - times has been told That Brit - ish sea - men bold

Could flog the tars of France so neat and han - dy - o!

But they nev - er found their match, Till the Yan - kees did them catch,

O, the Yan - kee boys for fight - ing are the dan - dy - o!

1 It ofttimes has been told
That British seamen bold
Could flog the tars of France so neat and handy-o!
But they never found their match,
Till the Yankees did them catch,
O, the Yankee boys for fighting are the dandy-o!

2 The *Guerriere*, a frigate bold,
On the foaming ocean rolled,
Commanded by proud Dacres, the grandee-o!
With as choice a British crew
As a rammer ever drew,
They could flog the French at two to one so
        handy-o!

3 When this frigate bore in view,
Said proud Dacres to his crew,
' Come, clear the ship for action and be handy-o!
To the weather gauge, boys, get her.'
And to make his men fight better
He mixed a drink of gunpowder and brandy-o!

4 The British shot flew hot,
Which the Yankees answered not,
Till they got within the distance they call
' Now,' says Hull unto his crew,   [handy-o!
' Boys, let's see what we can do,
If we take this boasting Briton, we're the dandy-o!'

5 The first broadside we poured
Carried her mainmast by the board,
Which made this lofty frigate look abandon'd-o!
Then Dacres shook his head,
And to his crew he said,
' Lord, I didn't think these Yankees were so
        handy-o!'

6 Then Dacres came on board
To deliver up his sword,
He wanted not to part with it so handy-o!
' O keep your sword,' says Hull,
' For it only makes you dull,
So cheer up, sir, and take a double brandy-o!'

7 Come, fill your glasses full,
And we'll drink to Captain Hull,
And so merrily we'll push about the brandy-o!
John Bull may toast his fill,
Let the world say what it will,
But the Yankee boys for fighting are the dandy-o!

22. THE FISH OF THE SEA

FROM: p. 188 of *Songs of American Sailormen*, Joanna Colcord (W. W. Norton, N.Y., 1938). Used by permission. SEE: Creighton II, 232; Guide; Whall, 97. Recently collected from Bob Roberts in Suffolk, England. Chorus as *Blow Ye Winds Southerly* often sung in England.
Piano arrangement by MATYAS SEIBER

Steadily and smoothly ♩ = 144

GUITAR- 4 & 5A
BANJO- 1

Come all ye young sail-or-men, lis-ten to me, I'll sing you a
song of the fish of the sea. Then blow, ye winds, west-er-ly, west-er-ly
blow, We're bound to the south-'ard, so stead-y she goes.

1 Come all ye young sailormen, listen to me,
  I'll sing you a song of the fish of the sea.
  CHORUS:
  Then blow, ye winds, westerly, westerly blow,
  We're bound to the south-'ard, so steady she goes.

2 First come the whale, the biggest of all,
  He clumb up aloft and let every sail fall. (CHO.)

3 And next come the mackerel with his striped back.
   He hauled aft the sheets and boarded each tack.   (CHO.)

4 Then come the porpoise with his little blue snout,
   He went to the wheel, calling ' Ready about.'   (CHO.)

5 Then come the smelt, the smallest of all,
   He jumped to the poop. ' Lower topsails,' he bawled.   (CHO.)

6 Next come the cod with his old chucklehead,
   Swung by the forechains, a-heavin' the lead.   (CHO.)

7 Then come the flounder, as flat as the ground,
   ' Damn your eyes, chucklehead, mind how you sound.'   (CHO.)

8 The herring called out, ' I'm the king of the seas,
   If you want any wind, why, I'll blow you a breeze.'   (CHO.)

23. CAPE COD GIRLS

FROM: p. 91 of *Songs of American Sailormen*, Joanna Colcord (W. W. Norton, N.Y., 1938). Used by permission. SEE: Doerflinger, 71.
Piano arrangement by MATYAS SEIBER

1 O Cape Cod girls they have no combs,
    Heave away, heave away!
They comb their hair with codfish bones,
    Heave away, heave away!
CHORUS:
Heave away, you bully, bully boys!
Heave away, heave away!
Heave away, and don't you make a noise,
For we're bound for Australia.

2 O Cape Cod boys they have no sleds,
    They slide downhill on codfish heads. (CHO.)

3 O Cape Cod cats they have no tails,
    They blew away in heavy gales. (CHO.)

24. SALLY BROWN

Stanzas from *Shantymen and Shantyboys*, William Doerflinger (Macmillan Co., N.Y., 1951), p. 74. Used by permission. SEE: Colcord, 61; Mackenzie, 275; Whall, 64.

Vigorously ♩ = 126

GUITAR– 2A & 3A
BANJO– 5

Sal - ly Brown was a Cre-ole la-dy, Way___ ay,___ roll and go! O
Sal - ly Brown was a Cre-ole la-dy, Spend my mo-ney on Sal-ly Brown.

1 Sally Brown was a Creole lady,
  Way-ay, roll and go!
  O Sally Brown was a Creole lady,
  Spend my money on Sally Brown.

2 She had a farm in the isle of Jamaicer,
  Where she raised sugar cane and terbaccer.

3 Also she had a fine young daughter,
  And that's the gal that I was arter.

4 For seven long years I courted Sally,
  And when I asked her if she'd marry . . .

5 ' These lily-white hands and slender wais',
  A tarry sailor will ne'er embrace.'

6 So then she married a Cuban soldier,
  Who beat her up and stole her money.

7 One night she was taken with a pain in her belly,
  And they sent for the doctor whose name was
                                            Kelly.

8 And from her took a little tar baby,
  O Sally dear, why didn't you have me?

25. SHENANDOAH

SEE: Colcord, 83; Doerflinger, 77; Index; Lomax II, 546.

Powerfully ♩=72

GUITAR-⎫
BANJO-⎬ *FREE STRUM*
REFRAIN

O Shen-an-doah, I love your daugh-ter, A-way you roll-ing riv-er, For her I've crossed the roll-ing wa-ter, A-way we're bound a-way, A-cross the wide Mis-sour-i.

1 O Shenandoah, I love your daughter,
  Away, you rolling river,
  For her I've crossed the rolling water,
  Away, we're bound away,
  Across the wide Missouri.

2 The trader loved this Indian maiden,
  With presents his canoe was laden.

3 O Shenandoah, I'm bound to leave you,
  O Shenandoah, I'll not deceive you.

4 O Shenandoah, I long to hear you,
  O Shenandoah, I long to hear you.

26. SANTY ANNO

Collected by Alan Lomax and Peter Kennedy from Captain Rasmussen. SEE:
Colcord, 84; Doerflinger, 78; Index; Mackenzie, 262.
Piano arrangement by MATYAS SEIBER

1 Maximilian's daughter has my love,
   Heave away for Santy Anno!
Maximilian's daughter has my love,
   Heave away, my lads, for Mexico!

2 And I left my love in Laguna town,
   And I left my love in Laguna town.

3 And when will I see Laguna's shore?
   And when will I see my love once more?

27. BLOOD RED ROSES

As sung by A. L. Lloyd and Paul Clayton, rarely published. SEE: Doerflinger, 22.
Heard among Negro crew on American ship in the 1820's.

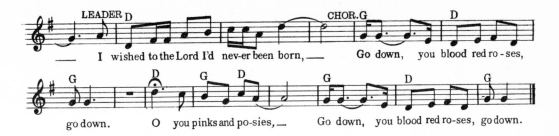

I wished to the Lord I'd nev-er been born, ___ Go down, you blood red ro-ses, go down. O you pinks and po-sies, ___ Go down, you blood red ro-ses, go down.

1 As I was going round Cape Horn,
  Go down, you blood red roses, go down.
I wished to the Lord I'd never been born,
  Go down, you blood red roses, go down.

CHORUS:
O you pinks and posies,
Go down, you blood red roses, go down.

2 Around that Cape in heavy gales,
  And it's all for the sake of them sperm-whales.

3 Around Cape Horn in frost and snow,
  Around the Cape we all must go.

4 O yes, my lads, we're all a-lee,
  We'll soon be far away from sea.

5 Just one more pull and that'll do,
  And we're the boys to pull her through.

28. A LONG TIME AGO

SEE: Colcord, 65; Doerflinger, 37; Mackenzie, 264.

Slowly and powerfully ♩.=54

GUITAR— 3A
BANJO— 4A

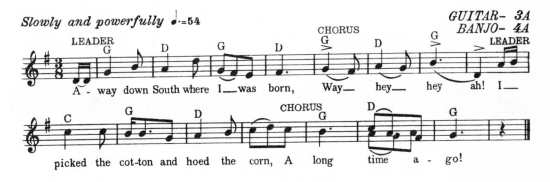

A-way down South where I ___ was born, Way ___ hey ___ hey ah! I ___ picked the cot-ton and hoed the corn, A long time a-go!

1 Away down South where I was born,
  Way-hey-hey-ah!
I picked the cotton and hoed the corn,
  A long time ago!

2 I'm going away to Mobile Bay,
  Where they screw cotton by the day.

3 Five dollars a day's a white man's pay,
  And a dollar and a half is a black man's pay.

4 O rock them blocks and make them cry,
  The gol-durn topmast sheave is dry.

5 O stretch your backs and haul away.
  An' make your port an' take your pay.

6 I wish I had a drink of rum,
  I'd sing you a song if I had one.

7 The wind from the north a-blowin' a gale,
  The blamed old captain crowdin' on sail.

8 I wish to God I'd never been born,
  To go a-ramblin' round Cape Horn.

29. THE BULLGINE RUN

FROM: p. 99 of *Songs of American Sailormen*, Joanna Colcord (W. W. Norton, N.Y., 1938). Used by permission. SEE: Index. To tune of *Shule Agrah* (see *Johnny's Gone for a Soldier*).

Piano arrangement by MATYAS SEIBER

clear a-way the track, let the bull-gine run! bull-gine run!

1 O the smartest clipper you can find,
    Ah hee, ah ho, are you most done?
Is the *Marg'ret Evans* of the Blue Cross line,
    So clear away the track, let the bullgine run!
CHORUS:
To my hey rig-a-jig in a low-back car,
    Ah hee, ah ho, are you most done?
With Liza Lee all on my knee,
    So clear away the track, let the bullgine run!

2 O the *Marg'ret Evans* of the Blue Cross line,
    She's never a day behind her time.   (CHO.)

3 O when I come home across the sea,
    It's Liza, will you marry me?   (CHO.)

30. ROW, BULLIES, ROW

Collected and adapted by Alan Lomax, partly from the singing of Ewan Maccoll.
SEE: Colcord, 176; Doerflinger, 106. Mentioned by Dana in his *Cruise off California* in the 1830's. Song still known in Liverpool.

CHORUS:
Singing row, row, bullies, row,
Them sweet Frisco girls, they have got us in tow. } (2)

1 From Liverpool to Frisco, a-roving I went,
To stay in that country it was my intent,
But by drinking bad whisky, like other damn fools,
I soon was transported back to Liverpool. (CHO.)

2 The clipper ship, *Comet*, lies out in the bay,
A-waiting for a fair wind to get under way,
The sailors on board are so sick and so sore
For their liquor's all gone and they can't get no more. (CHO.)

3 Then up steps the first mate in his jacket of blue,
He's hunting up work for the sailors to do,
Then it's ' Up topsail halliards,' he loudly does roar,
' Lay aloft, Paddy, you son of a whore!' (CHO.)

4 That night off Cape Horn I won't soon forget,
It gives me the horrors to think of it yet.
We were diving bows under and all of us wet,
A-making twelve knots with the skysails all set. (CHO.)

5 Here's to our captain, where'er he may be,
He's a friend to a sailor on land or on sea,
But as for the first mate, that dirty old brute,
I hope, when he dies, straight to Hell he'll skyhoot. (CHO.)

31. THE BANKS OF NEWFOUNDLAND

FROM: p. 173 of *Songs of American Sailormen*, Joanna Colcord (W. W. Norton, N.Y., 1938). Used by permission. SEE: Doerflinger, 123; Greenleaf, 230; Guide; JEFSS I, 142; Mackenzie, 304, 385. A western ocean version of the Australian deportation song *Van Diemen's Land* (see Guide; Reeves, 217).
Piano arrangement by MATYAS SEIBER

You ram-blin' boys of Li-ver-pool, I'll have you to be-ware,___ When you go in a Yan-kee pack-et ship, no dun-ga-rees to wear,___ But__ have your mon-key jack-et al-ways at your com-mand,___ For be-ware of the cold nor' west - ers on the Banks of New-found - land.___ We'll wash her and we'll scrub her with ho-ly stone and

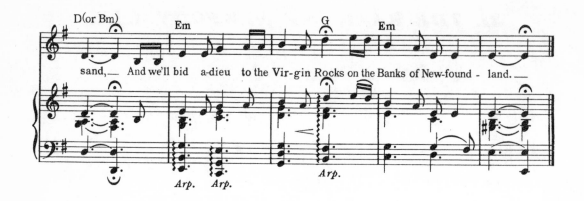

sand,___ And we'll bid a-dieu to the Vir-gin Rocks on the Banks of New-found - land. ___

1 You ramblin' boys of Liverpool, I'll have you to beware,
  When you go in a Yankee packet ship, no dungarees to wear,
  But have your monkey jacket always at your command,
  For beware of the cold nor'westers on the Banks of Newfoundland.
  CHORUS:
  We'll wash her and we'll scrub her with holystone and sand,
  And we'll bid adieu to the Virgin Rocks on the Banks of Newfoundland.

2 We had some Irishmen on board, Jim Doyle and Michael Moore,
  'Twas in the winter of '56 our sailors suffered sore,
  They pawned their clothes in Liverpool and sold them out of hand,
  Not thinking of those cruel winds on the Banks of Newfoundland.

3 One night as I lay on my bed a-dreaming of my home,
  I dreamt I was in Liverpool way down in Marabone,
  With my true love beside me and a jug of ale in hand—
  But I woke quite broken-hearted on the Banks of Newfoundland.

4 We had one female kind on board, Mary Murphy was her name,
  To her I promised marriage, on me she had a claim,
  She tore her flannel petticoats to make mittens for my hands,
  Saying, ' I can't see my true love freeze on the Banks of Newfoundland.'   (CHO.)

5 It's now we're passing Sandy Hook and the cold winds, they still blow,
  The tug-boat she's ahead of us, to New York we will go,
  We'll fill our glasses brimming full with a jug of rum in hand
  And bid adieu to the hardships on the Banks of Newfoundland.
  CHORUS:
  So, boys, fill up your glasses, and merrily they'll go round,
  And we'll drink a health to the captain and the girls of New York Town.

32. THE GREENLAND WHALE FISHERY

FROM: p. 214 of *Our Singing Country*, John and Alan Lomax (Macmillan, N.Y., 1941). As sung by Asel Trueblood, St. Ignace, Michigan. SEE: Colcord, 151; Guide; Sharp, *Folk Songs of Somerset* III, 55; Whall, 99. Still sung in Norfolk, England. Peter Kennedy says: common in England.

1 In eighteen hundred and forty-nine,
   On March the seventeenth day,
   We h'isted our colours to our topmast high
   And for Greenland bore away, brave boys,
   And for Greenland bore away.

2 And when we reached that icy shore
   With our gallant ship in full fold,
   We wished ourselves back safe at home again,
   With our friends all on the shore, brave boys . . .

3 Our captain stood on the fo'cas'le head
   With his spyglass in his hand.
   'There's a whale, there's a whale, there's a whale,' cries he,
   'And it blows on every span, brave boys' . . .

4 And when this whale we did harpoon,
   He gave one slap with his tail.
   He upset the boat, we lost five of our crew,
   Neither did we catch that whale, brave boys . . .

5 'Bad news, bad news,' our captain, he cried,
   For it grieved his heart in full store,
   But the losing of that hundred barrel whale,
   It grieved him ten times more, brave boys . . .

6 'Then h'ist your anchors and away,' cries he,
   'Let us leave this cold counteree,
   Where the whalefish does grow and the stormy winds do blow,
   And daylight's seldom seen, brave boys' . . .

33. GET UP, JACK

Collected, arranged, and used by permission of Frank Warner. SEE: Guide and
Index (*Green Beds*); Lomax II, 493.
Piano arrangement by MATYAS SEIBER

1. Ships may come and ships may go, as long as the sea does roll, Each sail-or lad, like-
2. When Jack's a-shore he beats his way to some board-ing house, He's wel-comed in with

-wise his dad, he loves that flow-ing bowl. A lass a-shore he does a-dore,
rum and gin, like-wise with port and souse. He'll spend and spend and nev-er of-fend,

one that is plump and round, But when his money is gone, it's the same old song,—'Get
till he lies drunk on the ground, But when his money is gone, it's the same old song,—'Get

up, Jack! John, sit down!'} Come a-long, come a-long, my jol-ly brave tars, There's
up, Jack! John, sit down!'}

CHORUS *Rhythmically*

lots of grog in the jar, We'll plough the brin-y o-cean With those jol-ly rov-ing tars. tars.

1 Ships may come and ships may go, as long as the sea does roll,
Each sailor lad, likewise his dad, he loves that flowing bowl.
A lass ashore he does adore, one that is plump and round,
But when his money is gone, it's the same old song—
' Get up, Jack! John, sit down!'
CHORUS:
Come along, come along, my jolly brave tars,
There's lots of grog in the jar,
We'll plough the briny ocean
With those jolly roving tars.

2 When Jack's ashore, he beats his way to some boarding-house,
He's welcomed in with rum and gin, likewise with port and souse,
He'll spend and spend and never offend, till he lies drunk on the ground,
But when his money is gone, it's the same old song—
' Get up, Jack! John, sit down!'

3 Now when Jack is old and weather-beat, too old to knock about,
In some grogshop they'll let him stop, till eight bells he's turned out.
Then he cries and he sighs right up to the skies: ' Good Lord, I'm homeward bound,'
For when your money is gone, it's the same old song—
' Get up, Jack! John, sit down!'

SHOUTERS AND SHAKERS

34. CAPTAIN KIDD – II
(An early shape-note version)

AT THE FOLK LEVEL, the American Revolution was a move towards religious and musical liberty as well as political and economic independence. The musical radicals of that age played an active part in the struggle—men like the New England blacksmith-composer, William Billings, who wrote the anthem of the Minute Men . . .

> Let tyrants shake their iron rod,
> And slavery clink her galling chains,
> We'll fear them not, but trust in God:
> New England's God forever reigns.

Taking advantage of their hard-won emancipation, these men set about supplying the new nation with suitable songs. Billings, himself, composed pieces in the fugal style, some of which are still performed just as he wrote them in Southern singing conventions. Other American musicians decided to rescue their countrymen from the musical doldrums by teaching them how to sing in parts. They invented a new type of notation, in which the positions of the notes of the scale were signalized by four shapes, easily distinguishable by eye. One of the earliest of many such ' Easy Instructors ', published in 1798 in Philadelphia, announced itself as ' A New Method of Teaching Sacred Harmony, containing the rudiments of music on an improved plan, wherein the naming and timing of the notes are familiarized to the weakest capacity '.

FA   SOL   LA   FA   SOL   LA   MI

Armed with these ' instructors ', which contained lively religious songs in three and four parts, the Yankee singing master sold music to rural America. His ' singin' school ' was the first and probably the soundest of America's ' culture-in-ten-painless-lessons ' courses. Following the easy-to-read sol-fa system of shaped notes, whole congregations of Americans of ' weak capacity ' were taught to sing in counterpoint, and very capably, too. if we may believe this contemporary account . . .

The wool was also spun in the family, partly by my sisters, and partly by Molly Gregory, daughter of our neighbor, the town carpenter. I remember her well as she sang and spun aloft in the attic. In those days (the 1830's) church-singing was one of the fine arts—the only one, indeed, which flourished in Ridgefield, except the music of the drum and fife. The choir was divided into four parts, ranging on three sides of the meeting-house gallery. The tenor, led by Deacon Hawley, was in front of the pulpit, the bass to the left, and the treble and counter to the right—the whole being set into motion by a pitch-pipe, made by the deacon himself, who was a cabinet maker.

Molly took upon herself the entire counter, for she had excellent lungs. The fugueing tunes, which had then run a little mad, were her delight, and of all these, *Montgomery* was the general favorite. In her solitary operations aloft, I have often heard her send forth from the attic windows the droning hum of her wheel, with fitful snatches of a hymn, in which the bass began, the tenor followed, then the treble, and finally the counter—winding up with irresistible pathos. Molly, singing to herself and all unconscious of eavesdroppers, carried on all the parts.

As the frontier moved west and south, the ' singin' school ' movement spread through the American backwoods, growing steadily more popular as it got away from the centres of polite culture . . .

> Some think there's nothing half so good
> As oysters roasted, fried or stewed,
> While others think there's pleasure more
> In sliding down a cellar door,
> While some think this, and some think that,
> They all agree there's greater sat—
> Isfaction to be always had
> In the singing school, as I have said . . .

These country get-togethers, where boy met girl, where greybeards and children, men and women were equals in the world of music, became immensely popular. The teachers did not, thank heaven, have time or inclination to interfere with the way their pupils sang. They left them to shrill away in their hard, pure voices, decorating the written notes with typical country quavers. The part-writing, devised by rural geniuses who were unhampered by the prejudices of conventional training, abound in parallel fourths and fifths, and harmonies in seconds (*see* p. 238). Their hymns ran to lively tempos. Hearing these shape-note singers today, one thinks of a cross between a steam calliope and a Ukrainian peasant choir. Naturally, this sound did not please urban musicians.

A Miss Augusta Brown in the *Cincinnati Musician and Intelligence* of the 1840's writes:

Hundreds of country idlers, too lazy or too stupid for farmers and mechanics, ' go to singing school for a spell ', get their diplomas from others scarcely better qualified than themselves, and then with their brethren, the far-famed ' Yankee Pedlars ', itinerate to all parts of the land, to corrupt the taste and pervert the judgement of the unfortunate people who, for want of better, have to put up with them. We have heard of one of these cute geniuses who ' set up ' in a town way down east as a cobbler! On his sign, under the announcement of his profession, as a provider for the wants of bodily understanding, was the following choice couplet . . .

> Delightful task! to mend the boot
> And teach the young idea how to flute.

Cobbling and music! We just ask how any musical nerve can stand that?

Nonetheless, these musical cobblers knew what the people wanted. Following Jeremiah Ingall's *Christian Harmony* in 1805 came *Kentucky Harmony*, *Missouri Harmony* (used by Lincoln), *Columbian Harmony*, *The Western Lyre*, *The Sacred Harp*, *Southern Harmony*, and a score of song-books, all using the four-shape system. They were on sale in country stores that often distributed no other books. ' Singin' Billy Walker ', the South Carolina mountain editor of *Southern Harmony*, claimed that his book sold six hundred thousand copies before 1854. Perhaps the reason for the almost incredible success of these books among a barely literate audience was that they were packed with folk-tunes.

Motivated by a democratic wish to please their audience and by their own interest in spreading the gospel and selling song-books, these backwoods compilers filled their pages with the popular tunes of the frontier—*Turkey in the Straw*, *Lord Lovel*, *Barbara Allen*, *O Susannah*, *The Irish Washerwoman*, etc. Indeed a good proportion of the secular tunes in this volume were also published in the *Sacred Harp*—' Devil's ditties ' with sacred texts. A people, barred by their ministers from dancing and singing profane songs, could thus enjoy the carnal tunes in religious disguise. This habit of ' robbing the Devil of his best tunes ' goes back at least to the time of Luther, but it was never so marked as in nineteenth-century America. There, where pirates and frontier bullies got religion and sobbed out their guilt at public revivals, any musical stratagem was allowable.

QUOTE: *Yankee Life by Those who Lived It* Ed. June B. Mussey (A. Knopf, N.Y., 1947). Entire note based on Jackson I-IV.

35. WICKED POLLY

COTTON MATHER, the New England theologian, witch-burner, and local patriot, bragged that New England had the deadliest serpents, the most enterprising devils, and the most remarkably painful preachers of any spot of God's kingdom. Yankee yarns bear him witness.

A man who had gone to sleep during a particularly long sermon awakened and enquired of a neighbor how long the minister had been preaching. Mistaking the question, the man replied, ' Thirty or forty years.' ' Well,' said the sleeper, ' I reckon I'll stay on till the end. He must be about through.'

In fact, the old dissenting sects—the Puritans, Lutherans, Congregationalists, etc.—which removed to the colonies to find freedom in worship, had become established and conservative in their turn. They frowned upon the emotionalism that has always been essential to the success of Protestantism at the popular level.

Meanwhile, the folk of Great Britain and America continued their religious revolt against the established church. The Shaking Quakers, shouting Methodists, New Light Baptists, and Pacifist Mennonites, preached salvation for all through faith and baptism by total immersion, and prophesied that the hottest seats in Hell waited for the rich, the powerful, and the worldly. This sort of doctrine appealed to the wrong people—to the poor and politically powerless. Harvard professors of divinity were shocked when dissenting preachers of the Great Awakening of the 1740's shouted, ' Now, now, now you are going right into the bottom of Hell!' and raised a commotion among the women. Police broke up the meetings and jailed the speakers.

The great preachers of the period, like Whitfield and Edwards, did not yet realize the need for a new style of music for their popular religion; but here and there, humbler revivalists began to introduce folky songs into their services. The hamlet of Little Rest, Rhode Island, long before the Revolution, was the birthplace of one of the first American religious folk songs. A giddy young woman named Polly died after a brief illness and the country revivalist who preached her funeral service, intoned a ballad about her. ' The venerable man was assisted to the pulpit and, as with quavering voice he uttered the words of *Wicked Polly*, the people listened with breathless attention.' For these people Hell was a place, headquarters for a real Satan—how real can be felt in the diary of ' Crazy ' Lorenzo Dow, the wildest Bible-thumper of them all.

October 20, 1796 . . . Satan pursues me from place to place. Oh! how can people dispute there being a Devil! If they underwent as much as I do with his buffetings, they would dispute it no more. He, throwing his fiery darts, my mind is harrassed like punching the body with forks and clubs . . .'

This was the Devil who dragged Wicked Polly screaming down to Hell. Her story, set to an old ballad air, caught the imagination of folk. It was reprinted in a score of rural song-books, was carried as far south as Jamaica and as far west as Iowa, and it is still sung by Southern Hard Shell Baptists as a warning to their gallivanting granddaughters.

QUOTE: Jackson I, p. 192.

36. SATAN'S KINGDOM

THERE IS AN AMUSING Yankee yarn of a ship's crew that arrived in port on a Sunday and, as there was nothing better to do, they decided to go in a body to church. The minister straightway directed his sermon to the tough old salts in the balcony . . .

He compared a sinner in this life, without religion, to a ship of war in a violent gale, without sufficient strength to enable her to ride it out. The first was as surely on his course to Hell as the ship was to be wrecked. He then proceeded to describe a ship in this condition—her rigging broken—her rudder unshipped and the unmanageable vessel drifting at the mercy of the wind and waves. ' What appalling cry is that which now rises on the blast, benumbing us all with the fear of death? Hark! '' We're lost—the ship is running on a lee shore, and in a few minutes—'' '

' Avast there,' cried the boatswain, being so much carried away by the excitement of the moment, that, fancying himself on shipboard, he blew his whistle with tremendous energy and cried out in a stentorian voice, ' Tumble up, tumble up, my lads, and furl every damned rag, loose the foretop-mast-staysail, double reef the mizzen topsail, jump into the chains, one of you with the lead—cheerily, men, cheerily, and we'll weather Hell in spite of damnation!'

Scenes like this launched a new type of spiritual, that encouraged the maximum of group participation. Unlike the majority of the shape-note hymns, which had been written by known authors, they were collections of anonymous authorship, which wandered from song to song and were fitted together according to the inclinations of the singers. *Satan's Kingdom*, which Jackson ascribes to the 1790's, has a considerable historical importance, since it shows the early use of stanzas that, subsequently, provided the matter for dozens of spirituals, Negro and white.

SOURCE: Jackson III, 232. QUOTE: *The Old American Comic Almanac*, Samuel Dickinson (Boston, 1839).

37. COME, LIFE, SHAKER LIFE

At Manchester, in England, this blessed fire began,
And like a flame in stubble, from house to house it ran;
A few at first received it and did their lusts forsake,
And soon their inward power brought on a mighty shake . . .

The first Shaker colony, consisting of nine members led by the prophetess, Mother Ann Lee, was established near Watervliet, New York, in 1776. Ann Lee worked in English mills as a child, married a blacksmith in her teens, and gave birth to four children, all of whom died in their infancy. A member of the visionary Shaking Quakers, she was subject to hysterical seizures, during which she talked to heavenly visitors, who informed her that sex and private property were the roots of all evil. Preaching to crowds in the Manchester streets, she told of witnessing the act which caused the fall of Adam and Eve. The police promptly jailed her for disturbing the Sabbath and advocating total celibacy.

After the Revolution, the Shakers entered into the religious ferment boiling up in the thirteen states. In spite of their radical doctrines, which enshrined a dual or masculine-feminine concept of the Godhead, they made many converts. Their strict abstention from all fleshly pleasures attracted the ascetics and neurotics of the Baptist and Puritan groups. Other converts were drawn to the Shakers by the orderliness and tranquillity that reigned in their communities. The superb Shaker handicraft and their fascinating songs and dances, which induced a state of euphoria in the participants, appealed to persons who were seeking a creative outlet in that harsh age.

I used to dance before the Lord, which grieved Michael sorely,
I'll dance and dance and dance again, his pride shall never hold me,
I'll not be bound by any man nor yet by woman's fancies,
I am a merry, merry soul, I'm lovely in the dances.

In the early years Shaker dances were chaotic and individualistic—' a perpetual scene of trembling, quivering, shaking, sighing, crying, groaning, screaming, jumping, singing, dancing and turning ', the men and women dancing in separate rooms. The motive of these spontaneous rhythmic movements, which the Shakers called ' labouring ', was mortification of the flesh; and this was induced by ' a perpetual springing from the house floor, about four inches up and down ', until the dancers became hysterical. After the zeal of the first years had worn off, orderly forms of dancing came into use at Shaker meetings and their choreography became one of the wonders of America.

The worshippers (were) capering around the room in a double circle, the females whirling round the inner ring, the males describing the outward one. After reversing their positions in this movement, they converted the two smaller circles into a single one, each sex following the other by alternate evolutions; and by a skilful manœuvre, which I never saw executed but in the army, the men suddenly faced about, slipped on one side, so as to let the women pass, and met them at the opposite end of the room . . .

The dances were performed to rollicking mouth music like *Come, Life*, which is taken, together with the material for these notes, from that remarkable book *The Gift to be Simple*, by Edward Andrews (J. J. Augustin, 1940).

38. SHAKER FUNERAL HYMN

THE SHAKERS saw the Kentucky revival of the early nineteenth century (*see* pp. 238-43) as a heaven-sent opportunity. They sent missionaries south and made many converts among the shouting Methodists and Baptists. Flourishing new Shaker colonies were established in Kentucky, Ohio, and Indiana. At the peak of its growth the sect numbered around six thousand members and owned large and well-developed properties in several states. In 1837 the Shakers experienced their own revival which swept their settlements with a flame of strange, somewhat childish mysticism.

It began when a fourteen-year-old girl received a song from the deceased Mother Ann Lee in a vision. As the news of this ' gift ' from the Shakers in the spirit world spread abroad, other ' gifts of song ' were given to other visionaries, and at such a pace that there was scarcely time to record them all. Tribes of exotic spirits, who had been converted by Mother Ann Lee in Heaven, camped on the borders of their green fields and taught the Shakers songs in gibberish tongues believed to be various dialects of Indian, Turkish, Chinese, Hottentot, and ' braid Scots '. Others were given draughts of spiritual wine by departed Shaker prophets and reeled round the meeting-houses, ranting drunken ditties. The women received spiritual presents, worldly gewgaws which Shaker doctrine forbade them to possess—golden chains, boxes of pearls, golden tiaras, and dresses of silvered silk. The spirits of the mighty dead declared that they had been converted to Shakerism in the other world; and Julius Caesar, Napoleon, Mahomet, George Washington, and Artaxerxes delivered messages of childish joy through the lips of Shakers in trance.

Spiritual Eskimos drove their sledges across the Shaker dance floors; Laplanders skated sedately among the sledges; Arabs stole things; while Abyssinians leapt about with strange cries. Thus the Shaker revival poured out new ceremonials, new dances, and new songs for more than ten years, and then subsided, as the interest of the nation was drawn to the issues of the Civil War. After 1864 the movement slowly declined, until today there are only a handful of old people left who still remember what it was like to be shaken with the celibate joy of Mother Ann's teachings.

Despite its strangeness, however, the Shaker movement was the most successful and longest-lived Utopian Communist experiment of modern times. It left behind a body of strangely beautiful songs, some like familiar children's games, some members of the Baptist white spiritual family, but some having a vagrant, childish charm which is quite their own—another witness to the indefatigable creativity of the human spirit under every circumstance.

34. CAPTAIN KIDD–II

(Set in the Sacred Harp style)

FROM: *Columbian Harmony*, William More (Cincinnati, 1825). SEE: Jackson II, 159. First sung in Maryland, early 19th century.
Piano arrangement by MATYAS SEIBER

GUITAR– 1
BANJO– STRUM

1 Through all the world below
   God is seen all around,
   Search hills and valleys through,
   There He's found.
   The growing of the corn,
   The lily and the thorn,
   The pleasant and forlorn,
   All declare, God is there,
   In meadows drest in green,
   God is seen.

2 See springing waters rise,
   Fountains flow, rivers run,
   The mist that veils the sky
   Hides the sun.
   Then down the rain doth pour,
   The ocean, it doth roar
   And beat upon the shore,
   And all praise, in their ways,
   The God who ne'er declines
   His designs.

3 The sun with all his rays
   Speaks of God as he flies,
   The comet in her blaze
   ' God,' she cries;
   The shining of the stars,
   The moon, when she appears,
   His awful name declares;
   See them fly through the sky,
   And join the solemn sound
   All around.

35. WICKED POLLY

SEE: Belden, 460; Brown III, 92; Jackson I, 189; Jackson II, 55; Randolph IV, 16.
Pieces of this type often sung at mountain funerals.

1 Young people, who delight in sin,
  I'll tell you what has lately been;
  A woman who was young and fair,
  Died in sin and deep despair.

2 She went to frolics, dance and play,
  In spite of all her friends could say—
  'I'll turn to God when I get old,
  And he will then receive my soul.'

3 On Friday morning she took sick,
  Her stubborn heart began to break,
  She called her mother to her bed,
  Her eyes were rolling in her head.

4 'O mother, mother, fare you well,
  Your wicked Polly's doomed to Hell,
  The tears are lost you shed for me,
  My soul is lost I plainly see.

5 'My earthly father, fare you well,
  Your wicked Polly's doomed to hell,
  The flaming wrath begins to roll,
  I am a lost and ruined soul.'

6 She gnawed her tongue before she died,
  She rolled, she groaned, she screamed and cried,
  'O must I burn for evermore
  Till thousand, thousand years are o'er?'

7 Young people, lest this be your case,
  O turn to God and trust His grace,
  Down on your knees for mercies cry,
  Lest you in sin, like Polly, die.

36. SATAN'S KINGDOM

FROM: *Revival Hymns* (H. W. Day, Boston, 1842). SEE: Brown III, 661.
Piano arrangement by MATYAS SEIBER

1 This night my soul has caught new fire,
    Halle-hallelujah!
I feel that heav'n is drawing nigh'r,
    Glory hallelujah!
I long to drop this cumbrous clay,
    Halle-hallelujah!
And shout with saints in endless day,
    Glory hallelujah!
CHORUS:
Shout, shout, we are gaining ground,
Halle-hallelujah!
Satan's kingdom is tumbling down,
Glory hallelujah!

2 Ye little Samsons, up and fight,
  Put the Philistine host to flight;
  The troops of Hell are must'ring round,
  But Zion's sons, maintain your ground.   (CHO.)

3 The heavenly flame is now begun
  And soon the victory will be won.
  Some foes are wounded, others fell,
  The Lord is saving souls from Hell.   (CHO.)

4 When Israel came to Jericho,
  Began to pray and shout and blow,
  The tottering walls came tumbling down.
  The noise, like thunder, shook the ground. (CHO.)

5 Saint Paul and Silas bound in jail,
  Would pray and sing in spite of Hell;
  They made the prison loudly ring,
  Although opposed by Hell's dark king.   (CHO.)

6 All glory, glory to the Lamb,
  Bless, O my soul, His wondrous name,
  On angel's wings I soon shall rise
  And shout His glories in the skies.   (CHO.)

37. COME, LIFE, SHAKER LIFE

FROM: p. 103 of *The Gift To Be Simple*, Edward D. Andrews (Augustin, N.Y., 1940).
Used by permission. Seamus Ennis says this tune resembles a 12/8 Irish jig.

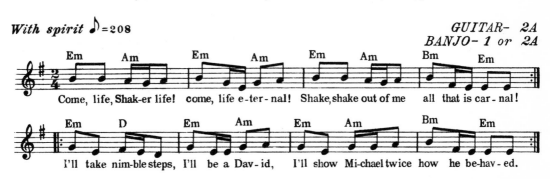

1 Come, life, Shaker life, come, life eternal!   } (2)
  Shake, shake out of me all that is carnal!

2 I'll take nimble steps, I'll be a David,   } (2)
  I'll show Michael twice how he behavéd.

3 *Repeat first stanza.*

38. SHAKER FUNERAL HYMN

FROM: p. 102 of *The Gift To Be Simple*, Edward D. Andrews (Augustin, N.Y., 1940).
Used by permission.

Piano arrangement by MATYAS SEIBER

Our brother's gone, he is no more,
He's quit our coast, he's left our shore,
He's burst the bonds of mortal clay,
The spirit's fled and soars away.

We now may hear the solemn call:
' Be ye prepared, both great and small.'
The call excludes no sex nor age,
For all must quit this mortal stage.

Then let the righteous sing,
When from corruption they get free;
O death, where is thy sting?
O grave, where is thy victory?

74

PIONEERS

39. THE LOVELY OHIO

IN 1795 no more than thirty thousand people dwelt in the vast stretch of forest and prairie between New York State and the Mississippi River. Within three generations, the best land in the territory had been put under the plough, hundreds of new towns dotted the prairie and the new states of the Midwest had sent many regiments to fight for the Union cause. This rapid process of settlement was well begun by 1817. The people of the thirteen states were turning their backs on the sea, and the old America was breaking up. The once fertile land of New England could no longer support her sons . . .

I was drivin' stage through this piece of woods some years ago, when I came all to once on a rabbit settin' on the brush fence and cryin' as if his heart would break. I stopped the horse and said, ' What ails ye there?' The rabbit wiped his eyes with his tail as well as he could, and said to me, ' Stranger, my father died last week, and left me two hundred acres of this land, an' I've got to get my livin' off on it.' An' then he bust out crying again. ' G'lang,' said I to me hoss. ' Can't do a thing to help ye if it's as bad as that ' . . .

Arguments over the wisdom of western migration went on in thousands of households.

The husband: Away to Wisconsin a journey I'll go,
For to double my fortune as other men do,
While here I must labor each day in the field,
And the winter consumes all the summer doth yield.

The wife: O husband, remember those lands of delight
Are surrounded by Indians who murder by night.
Your house will be plundered and burnt to the ground,
While your wife and your children lie mangled around.

Nevertheless, in spite of Indians and doubts and domesticity, the people moved west on foot, by canal boat, horseback, and in covered wagons. They said, ' If Hell was west of us, we'd leave Heaven to get there.'

' We were worth nothing when we landed,' wrote one Indiana pioneer. ' Now we have oxen, a cow, some hogs. While I write this letter my wife is eating preserved peaches on home-made bread, and washing them down with our own whiskey, mixed with fresh spring water.'

Mrs. Grundy and the excisemen had not yet reached ' the banks of the lovely O-hi-o '.

QUOTE: Vol. I, *Yankee Life by Those who Lived It* Ed. June B. Mussey (A. Knopf, N.Y., 1947).

40. HUDSON RIVER STEAMBOAT

WHEN ROBERT FULTON perfected the steamboat in 1807, Tom Paine, the ageing revolutionary, suggested that the inventor should hire a whale to pull his contraption. Somebody else described the vessel as ' a backwoods saw-mill mounted on a scow and set afire '. The Scots engineer on the *Clermont* got so jubilantly drunk that he was fired when the vessel touched shore. While Fulton and Livingstone quietly acquired a monopoly on all steamboat building and travel, the people of the fat Hudson valley went steamboat crazy. These stay-at-homes were bitten by the travel bug, and now they could satisfy their yearnings to go west by a comfortable cruise up the Hudson on a ' monster that moves on the waters defying winds and tide '.

So popular did steamboat races become that ministers denounced them for emptying the churches on Sunday. Rival captains took these contests to heart. During one race, the captain of the *Swallow Express* stoked his furnaces with the ship's fine mahogany furniture; the commander of the *Aetna* tied down the safety valves on his boilers and his boat lived up to her name by exploding. The craze for steamboat racing on the Hudson continued until 1852 when in the contest between the *America* and the *Henry Clay* (306 feet long and costing 35,000 dollars), the latter boat caught fire and eighty passengers were killed. Further racing was banned, and the white-and-gold steamboats took up the peaceful course they still pursue in the quiet, golden valley.

SOURCE: *The Hudson*, Carl Carmer (Farrar & Rinehart, 1939).

41. EL-A-NOY

EVERY AMERICAN PIONEER had a touch of the real-estate agent in him. The place he found to settle became, in his telling, a veritable Eden, a natural paradise—' all creation biled down and distilled in all its virtues '. During the eighteenth century the Yankee held the centre of the stage, boosting New England as the wonderland of the universe, but Jonathan had to take a back seat and sing mum when his Hoosier and Sucker and Badger cousins bragged about the glories of the new West along the Lakes.

' Wal now, stranger,' said the Yankee, ' suppose you tell us about your own country; you're the only man I ever seen from west, that didn't die of fever 'n agur.'

' Well, old Yankee, I'll just tell you all about it. If a farmer in our country plants his ground with corn and takes first rate care of it, he'll git a hundred bushels to the acre; if he takes middlin' care of it he'll get seventy-five bushels to the acre; and if he don't plant at all he'll get fifty.'

' I have heard tell, yet somewhat doubt *that* story, that the Ohio parsnips have sometimes grown clean through the earth and have been pulled through by people on the other side.'

' Wal now,' says the Yankee, ' I rather guess as how you've told enough, stranger, for the present. How'd you like to trade for some clocks to sell out west?'

' Never use 'em—we keep time altogether with pumpkin vines. You know, they grow just five feet an hour, and that's an inch a minute. Don't use clocks at all.'

Such tales as these, such songs as *El-a-noy*, moved many people to pull up stakes and head for Illinois. However, it was a two-way stream, for many settlers bought estates in Eden only to discover that their acres lay beneath the water or in malarial swamps. A cartoon of the day showed a healthy family bound for Illinois, meeting a wagon-full of haggard ragamuffins coming back, a legend on the wagon sheet reading, ' I have been to Illinois.'

42. OLEANA

DICKENS, in the American adventures of *Martin Chuzzlewit*, satirized the land-sharks who preyed upon naive folk during the midwestern land-rush. Of all these nineteenth-century swindles, perhaps the most heartless was that perpetrated on Ole Bull, the famous Norwegian fiddler. Having grown rich from his American tours, Ole invested his money in an enormous tract of land in Pennsylvania where land-starved Norwegians could support themselves until they had set up their homesteads. Many Norwegian admirers read his advertisements and set out confidently for ' Oleana '.

Disillusionment came quickly. The emigrants found that ' Oleana ' was far from the railroad in the roughest Pennsylvania hill country—in fact, ' it was nothing but woods, high mountains, and narrow valleys ' which would require many years to prepare for cultivation. When pay day rolled around, no money was forthcoming. It developed that the man who had sold Ole the land did not even own most of it. Ole had been bilked of his fortune, and was forced to spend a season playing benefit concerts for his stranded colonists.

When poor Ole's bubble burst, Ditmar Meidell, a clever Norwegian newspaper-man, wrote *Oleana*, provoking ripples of mirth on both sides of the Atlantic. He was poking fun, not so much at Ole Bull's mistaken philanthropy, as at the Norwegians who had dreamed of an easy life in America, won at no cost to themselves. Meidell wove into his ballad motifs from the medieval legends of the Land of Cockaigne, or, as the Germans called it, *Schlaraffenland*, ' where roast pigs trotted about with knives and forks in their backs squealing '' Eat me ''—where rivers ran with beer, hens laid eggs as big as houses, cakes rained from the skies, the moon was full every night, where they paid you more if you did no work, and the poorest man was a Count '.

This satirical ballad is still popular among Norwegians in America and in the old country; it may have given Ibsen the idea for *Peer Gynt* and *Gyntiana*. Perhaps it was a Norwegian hobo, with *Oleana* in his repertoire, who inspired the hobo ballad, *The Big Rock Candy Mountains* (see p. 518).

43. THE FOGGY DEW—I
(East Anglian version)

CARL SANDBURG found this song in the Middle West, published a somewhat censored form of it in *The American Songbag*, and from this source it has spread, through the singing of Burl Ives and Josh White, across America and back to England, its country of origin. Here I give it the way it was sung to me in East Anglia, the English region where it has been most often recorded. Of course, we shall never know precisely how *The Foggy Dew* got from East Anglia to the Middle West; but the likelihood is that this rather bawdy ditty was not carried by prudish New Englanders, but by English settlers who came to America during the Ohio land boom.

Just the sort of person who would have enjoyed the song was the celebrated Anne Bailey who emigrated to the colonies from Liverpool at the age of forty-six. When the Indians killed her husband in 1774, Anne swore revenge, donned the buckskin costume of a scout, and spent sixteen years in Western Pennsylvania hunting Indians and bears. Mad Anne, as she was called, drank, chewed tobacco, and swore like a man. Riding her black horse, named Liverpool, skilled in the use of her heavy smooth-bore rifle, she was the equal of any man in the woods, while at the campfire she held audiences spellbound with her yarns of Queen Anne's London.

When Anne's second husband was murdered, she moved on to Ohio and built herself a log cabin on the river, sleeping on the floor and living off fish and game. From time to time she appeared in Gallipolis wearing her greasy petticoat and buckskin jacket, carrying her rifle and shot-bag over her shoulder, to swap yarns for drinks of whisky in the taverns. When one November morning in 1825 a hunter found old Anne dead in her cabin, they reckoned she had lived to be a hundred and twenty-five years old.

SOURCE FOR STORY: *Wilderness for Sale*, Walter Havighurst (Hastings House, N.Y., 1956), p. 239.

44. THE FOGGY DEW—II
(The Midwestern Sandburg version)

THE SPIRIT of the Middlewesterners, who kept the story of the irresistible weaver alive in the American wilderness, is reflected in this frontier wedding, where a pioneer Justice of the Peace joined the happy couple in terms more suitable to a land sale than a marriage ceremony.

Faller citizens, this here man and this here woman want to get hitched in the legal bond of wedlock. If any galoot knows anything to block the game let him toot his bazoo or else keep his jaw shet now and forevermore. Grab yer fins. You, John, do you solemnly swear to the best of yer knowledge that you take this woman to have and hold for yerself, yer heirs, executors and assignees for your and their use and benefits forever?

That fixes yer end. You, Maudy, will ye swear ye'll hang on to John for all comin' time and make him a good, true, honest up-an'-up wife under the penalties prescribed by law fer such cases in an' fer this territory? That you are lawfully seized in fee simple and free from all incumbrances and you have good right so to bargain and convey to said guarantee, yourself, your heirs? Then by the power invested in me I announce ye man and wife, and legalize ye to remain as such for ever, and ye stand committed till the fees and costs in the case be paid in full and may God have mercy on yer souls.

QUOTE: *North Star Country*, Meridel le Sueur (Duell, Sloan & Pearce, N.Y., 1945), p. 120.

45. IN THE WILDERNESS
46. THE PAW-PAW PATCH

> Here stands a loving couple, joined heart and hand,
> One of them wants a wife and the other wants a man.
> They will soon get married, if they can agree,
> So then it's all march down the river to hog and hominy.

IN SPITE OF CHURCHLY proscriptions, the lusty young people of the Midwest couldn't keep from dancing. In most communities, square-dancing to fiddle music was left to the riff-raff and the foreign element; so that in this region, too, the old custom of dancing and playing to vocal music was revived. Yet, even at the play-parties, the violent emotions which the church so feared occasionally broke through the surface. Hamlin Garland gives a vivid account of such an incident on the Nebraska frontier . . .

The dance was *Weevily Wheat* and Ed Blackler was her partner. Against the wall stood Marsh Belford, a tall, crude, fierce, young savage, with eyes fixed on Agnes. He was one of her suitors and mad with jealousy of Blackler to whom she was said to be engaged. He could not dance, and for that reason keenly resented Ed's supple grace and easy manners with the girls.

As soon as the song ceased and the dancers paused, Marsh, white with resolution, went up to Agnes and said something to her. She smiled, but shook her head and turned away. With deadly slowness of action Marsh sauntered up to Blackler and said something in a low voice.

'You're a liar,' retorted Edwin sharply.

Belford struck out with a swing of his open hand, and a moment later they were rolling on the floor in a deadly grapple. The girls screamed and fled, but the boys formed a joyous ring round the contestants and cheered them on to keener strife.

Agnes forced her way through the crowd . . . Her dignity, her beauty, her air of command awed the bully and silenced every voice in the room. She was our hostess and, as such, assumed the right to enforce decorum. Fixing her glance upon Joe whom she recognized as the chief disturber, she said, ' You'd better go home. This is no place for either you or Marsh.'

Sobered, shamefaced, the Belfords fell back and slipped out while Agnes turned to Edwin and wiped the blood from his face with self-contained tenderness.

QUOTE: *A Son of the Middle Border*, Hamlin Garland, p. 183. Copyright 1917, 1923, by Hamlin Garland. Used by permission of the Macmillan Company, New York.

47. THE LONE GREEN VALLEY

HAMLIN GARLAND comments on the attitude of Middlewestern men towards women . . .

They had the most appalling, yet darkly romantic conception of women. A ' girl ' was the most desired thing in the world, a prize to be worked for, sought for and enjoyed without remorse. She had no soul. The maid who yielded to temptation deserved no pity, no consideration, no aid. Her sufferings were amusing, her diseases a joke, her future of no account . . .

He might have added (and this is what the folk ballads tell us) that a ' bad girl ' was only pitied after she was dead, especially if she had been murdered. Even then, the sympathies of the singer and audience were clearly divided. Vance Randolph recalls one Ozark minstrel who paused as he was singing one of the murder ballads ' and with a gasping sob burst out in a paroxysm of rage. " Oh God!" he shrilled. " The son of a bitch! God rot such a critter! " ' Yet an evident relish stirs the singers when ballad heroines are beheaded, beaten to death with fence stakes, smothered, strangled, drowned, poisoned, shot, and stabbed.

79

For their masculine composers, these songs provided fantasy revenge upon the whole unsatisfactory, demanding feminine sex. The singers (who at least in my days of collecting were predominantly respectable farm women) certainly rejoiced in the demise of their less virtuous sisters, and wagged their heads devoutly over the warning prohibitions these ballads prescribed to their sex. I suspect, too, that they relished these scandalous carryings-on and, deep down somewhere, they shuddered with delight over the violent handling of the sinful heroines.

One has constantly to remind oneself of the extremes of repressiveness of the age that revelled in these bloody songs—an epoch when a leg was called a limb, even by country people—an age when women were bundled up in forty petticoats and shielded by bustles —a time when no respectable woman could speak to a stranger in the street without a breath of scandal falling upon her—a century when there were only two paths open to women, one leading to the red lights, the other towards the altar. For the people of this period, the folk ballads had a special significance; they stood for pleasure and for excitement, which the age had subordinated to work and to respectability. This is what Burl Ives, who grew up in southern Illinois, has to say about his grandmother's ballads.

Sometimes she would sing for hours. She would sing *Barbara Allen*, *Pearl Bryan*, *Jesse James*, *Lord Thomas* and many other ballads in an easy, flowing style. All these ballads would be sung while Grandfather was in the fields because he forbade her to sing them. He said they were sinful songs about killing and about unfaithful love. He said that man should use his voice only to sing in praise of God. To me, her ballads brought a world shining with excitement and color.

QUOTES: (a) *A Son of the Middle Border*, Hamlin Garland, p. 174.   (b) *Wayfaring Stranger*, Burl Ives (Holland Street Press, 1952).

48. YOUNG CHARLOTTE

ONE BALLAD almost certain to be encountered by the collector in any part of the country a few years ago was this tale of the girl who froze to death on a sleigh-ride because of her desire to go out as décolleté as possible. The story, with its slight touch of sex hovering round Charlotte's bare-shouldered and unchaperoned evening drive, reaches an enjoyably morbid conclusion as her escort embraces Charlotte's frozen corpse. (Poe was amusing the literate audience with similar and only slightly more sophisticated stories in the same epoch.) The moral was sledge-hammered home, so that even devout Baptists could sing this ' ballet ' without criticism. It spread in many versions across America, west and south, into country where a drop of snow was as rare as in Hell itself, reminding Americans of the pleasant winter sports of genteel New England.

In winter we had three or four months of sleighing. Then the whole country was a railroad, and gay times we had. O those beautiful winters, which would drive me shivering to the fireside now; what vivid delight have I had in your slidings and skatings, your sleddings and sleighings! One thing strikes me now with wonder, and that is the general indifference in those days to the intensity of winter. No doubt, as I have said before, the climate was then more severe; but be that as it may, people seemed to suffer less from it than at the present day. Nobody thought of staying at home from Church because of the extremity of the weather. We had no thermometers, it is true, to frighten us with the revelation that it was twenty-five degrees below zero.

The exhaustive researches of Phillips Barry into the history of *Young Charlotte* establishes several points: (1) it is based on a newspaper story about how a young lady froze to death on her way to a ball on January 1, 1840; (2) shortly thereafter, Seba Smith, a New England humorist, wrote and published a mock-tragedy ballad about the incident; (3) a blind Mormon versifier and singer, William L. Carter, spread his version of the Smith ballad through the Midwest; (4) it was then taken into oral circulation, and has been found in many forms across the United States.

QUOTE: *Recollections of a Lifetime*, Samuel Griswold Goodrich (N.Y., 1856). Note material from Barry, JAFL XXV, 156-168

49. TURKEY IN THE STRAW

THE BEST-LOVED SONGS of the Midwest and western frontier, indeed, of all America during the expansive nineteenth century, came out of the ' nigger-minstrel ' show. In these ' coon ' songs, America made her first innovations in the ' pop ' field, and, as in most of those that were to follow, Negro folk singers were the innovators.

The first scene in this drama of the crossing of culture, or, as the cynic might put it, the theft of black magic by whites, was played in 1828 in Pittsburgh. The old vaudevillian, Daddy Rice, was weary of the Irish-American songs in his act, and he could see his audience was bored with them as well. One day down by the Ohio River front, he saw a ragged Negro roustabout amusing himself by dancing, soft-shoe style, to his own song . . .

> Turn about and wheel about and do just so,
> And everytime I wheel about I jump Jim Crow . . .

Arms outstretched and dipping to mime the crow's flight, the Negro was, I suspect, performing the sort of African folk dance which one can still see in the Georgia sea islands. At any rate, the whole thing struck Rice as good material. He bribed the poor roustabout to come to the theatre, to teach him his dance, and to lend him his tattered costume. When the time came for his act, Rice appeared in blackface and mimicked the roustabout's song and dance. ' Such a thunder of applause as was never heard before broke out in the old theatre.' The uproar increased with each couplet, and Rice continued to improvise verses. When the half-naked black man appeared on the stage, wailing ' Massa Rice, give me nigger's hat—nigger's shoes—nigger's t'ings, the steamboat's comin',' the management had to shut the theatre in order to halt the laughter.

Next day, everyone in Pittsburgh was humming *Jim Crow*. Within a few months the blackface minstrel was established as the favourite American entertainer, a position he held for almost seventy years. Old Cuff, in a figurative sense, never did get back his clothes—or his music—and from that date American popular music has continued to grow steadily more African in character. Rice became one of the best-paid entertainers of his day, and had many talented imitators—Emmett, Christy, and later Foster, Bland, Work, and a host of others. Their next innovation was to introduce the Negro plantation orchestra to the stage (*see* p. 493).

For at least two generations the Negro slaves had been dancing to the music of small orchestras composed of banjos, bones, tambourines, triangles, fiddle, and simple rhythmic instruments. In 1840 Whitlock and Dick Meyers, later the key figures in the famous Virginia Minstrels, ' played the fiddle and banjo together for the first time ' in a theatre and, because of the public's reaction, ' retained *this novel idea* in memory for future reference '. At about the same time Dan Emmett, who had a blackface act in a circus, began singing to bones and banjo accompaniment.

During the theatrical slump of 1842 in New York, the managers ' were all at sea for a new idea ' which would be both distinctive and inexpensive. At this point the principal banker for the southern cotton interests in the city agreed to finance the production of the first minstrel show. This man was one of the chief opponents of abolition, and a prime mover in the plan to send the Negroes back to Africa. In the minstrel show he saw a way of convincing Northerners that the Negro slaves were a happy, carefree lot, and at the same time of providing a cheap, escapist form of entertainment for the workers, restless under the prevailing low standards of living. He backed the rehearsals of the enlarged Virginia Minstrels, which included banjoists, fiddlers, bone-players, singers, and comedians.

His experiment in launching this troupe succeeded beyond anyone's expectations. The predominantly Irish audience roared with relieved laughter when Gumbo and Cuff, presenting a distorted caricature of Negro behaviour, took their places as the butts for public merriment. The gay, slightly sexy music, with its unfamiliar, but easy syncopations, delighted everyone. In the little string and rhythm minstrel bands, Uncle Sam had an orchestrated music to match those of the Tyrolese and Alpine groups which had registered such a success in America. Triumphant tours of the Virginia minstrels, and their many imitators, followed; they took Europe by storm, and established their pseudo-Negro song-style as the most popular American form of entertainment.

The zany blackface songs kept the pioneers jigging and laughing for decades. They gave America the key to the ' front ' of the Negro mind—to the region of wit, of easy compliant laughter, of bubbling abandoned rhythm. That was enough for this generation of do-ers and Indian fighters. The ' coon ' songs lightened their load of trouble and guilt. Occupied with the extermination of one race, they felt relief in laughing, patronizingly and somewhat cruelly, at the foibles of another. With these songs, the Americans of the nineteenth century could escape their own preoccupation with death, for the music of the blackface minstrels had great vitality. It was a new style of mouth-music, boiling with tangy, lilting word-rhythms, and seething with unconventional images, quips, rhymes, and catch-phrases. In an innocent vein, these songs laughed at solemnity, and made the chaotic, changeful life of the booming nation seem as mad and funny as it really was.

50. LINCOLN AND LIBERTY

A WISCONSIN NEWSPAPER clipping gives the temper of the summer of 1860 when Abe Lincoln defeated Stephen Douglas for president and the country headed for war . . .

There won't be a damn thing this summer but politics. I tell you I can't meet anybody but what they're puttin' into me 'bout the Little Giant, Southern Negroes, Old Brown, the Constitution, the Spread Eagle, the Rail Splitter, and a thundering lot of other names.

Consarn it, why, the bullfrogs in the pond back of our barn are all on the titter, bellowing out:

> Ole Abe—Ole Abe—Ole Abe,
> Illinois—Illinois—Illinois,
> Put him through! Put him through!
> Put him through! Chug, chug!

It was a hard-fought election, a campaign enlivened by huge public rallies, mud-slinging, violent political debate, torch-light processions, and, above all, partisan songs. The managers of both candidates aimed at the grass roots; both stirred up the electorate and kept them loyal with parodies of popular and folk tunes.

The choice of *Rosin the Beau* as the tune of Lincoln's official campaign song could not have been improved upon. It was the drinking song of the western frontier; a favourite with the Irish, and it reminded frontier Republicans that their man liked a dram, a tune, and a rakish yarn.

QUOTE: *North Star Country*, Meridel le Sueur. Copyright 1945 by Meridel le Sueur. Used by permission of Duell, Sloan and Pearce, Inc.

51. WHEN JOHNNY COMES MARCHING HOME

WHEN THE IRISH BANDSMAN, Patrick Gilmore, arranged this best of all American marches in the early days of the Civil War, he made use of an Anglo-Irish folk tune already firmly established in the States. The shape of the air indicates that it belongs to the Captain Kidd family, whose lineage (*see* pp. 7-8) has been traced back at least as far as the sixteenth century, but *Johnny*'s immediate ancestor is probably the Irish anti-war song which runs . . .

> With yer guns and drums and drums and guns,
> Hurroo, hurroo . . .

In his *Irish Minstrelsy*, Spurling suggests that this song of soldier's protest dates back to 1802, when Irish regiments were recruited for a campaign in Ceylon. Perhaps the old railroad worker's ballad, widespread in both America and Great Britain, is an intermediate form . . .

> In eighteen hundred and forty-one
> I put me corduroy breeches on,
> I put me corduroy breeches on
> To work upon the railway . . .

The word ' skiball ' or ' skuball ' (meaning a brown and white horse) that occurs in the folk forms of *Johnny* may refer to the race-horse of the popular Anglo-Irish broadside, *The Noble Skuball*, thus recalling the fine job of running the Yankees did at Bull Run. At any rate, Gilmore seems to have simply respectablized a folk song already known to thousands of Irishmen who fought for the North and the South.

52. VIRGINIA'S BLOODY SOIL

. . . If it hadn't-a been for Irishmen, what would our Union done?   OLD BALLAD.

THE IRISH AGAIN. In Ireland, American agents of the federal government informed them that England favoured the southern cause. As they poured off the immigrant boats at Castle Garden, they herded into recruiting tents, drank whisky, and listened while politicians with Irish accents thundered, ' You have fought nobly for the Harp and the Shamrock. Fight now for the Stars and Stripes. Your adopted country wants you!' Thus, though the Irish were not specially abolitionist in sympathy, they became passionately pro-Union and raised scores of regiments to fight for Uncle Abe.

The 9th and 28th Massachusetts carried green flags, one bearing a harp and an inscription in Gaelic that meant ' clean the road '. Their regimental motto was—' As aliens and strangers, thou did befriend us '. Behind these Irish outfits marched the 15th of Maine, the 10th of New Hampshire, the fighting 69th of New York, the Connaught Rangers (many of whom were veterans of India and the Crimea), the 24th and the 116th of Pennsylvania, the 10th Ohio, the 71st of Indiana, the 11th and 17th of Wisconsin, and many more. Mister Dooley's remarks about his Uncle Mike applied to them all . . .

Me Uncle Mike was wanst told he's be sint to hell f'r his manny sins an' he deserved it, for, lavin' out the wan sin iv rinnin' away fr'm annywan, he was booked for ivrything from murdher to missin' mass. ' Well,' says me Uncle Mike, ' any place I can get into,' he says, ' I can get out iv,' he says, ' my bet on that,' he says.

39. THE LOVELY OHIO

As sung by Ed McCurdy, Tradition Record, 1003.

GUITAR– 2B
BANJO– 4A

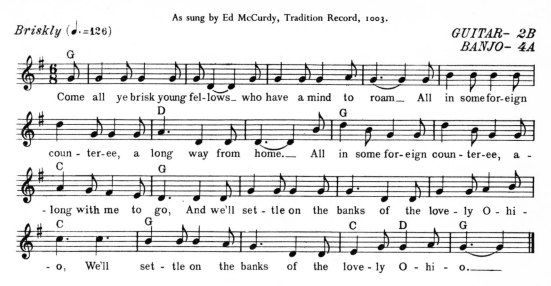

1 Come all ye brisk young fellows who have a mind to roam,
   All in some foreign counteree, a long way from home.
   All in some foreign counteree along with me to go,
   And we'll settle on the banks of the lovely Ohio,
   We'll settle on the banks of the lovely Ohio.

2 Come all you pretty fair maids, spin us some yarn
   To make us some nice clothing to keep ourselves warm.
   For you can knit and sew, my loves, while we do reap and mow,
   When we settle on the banks of the lovely Ohio . . .

3 There are fishes in the river, just fitted for our use.
   There's tall and lofty sugar cane that will give to us its juice,
   There's every kind of game, my boys, also the buck and doe,
   When we settle on the banks of the lovely Ohio . . .

40. HUDSON RIVER STEAMBOAT

FROM: p. 3, Vol. 5, No. 3, *Sing Out* (People's Songs, N.Y., 1955). As sung by
John and Lucy Allison.

GUITAR– 2 or 4
BANJO– 1 or 5

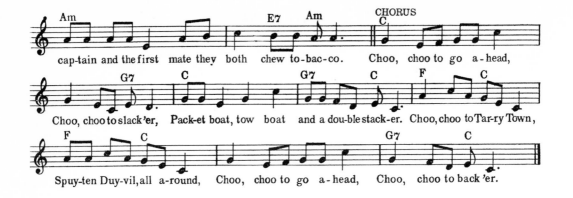

cap-tain and the first mate they both chew to-bac-co. Choo, choo to go a - head,

Choo, choo to slack 'er, Pack-et boat, tow boat and a dou-ble stack-er. Choo, choo to Tar-ry Town,

Spuy-ten Duy-vil, all a-round, Choo, choo to go a - head, Choo, choo to back 'er.

1 Hudson River steamboat, steaming up and down,
New York to Albany or any river town,
Choo, choo to go ahead,
Choo, choo to slack 'er,
The captain and the first mate they both chew tobacco.
CHORUS:
Choo, choo to go ahead,
Choo, choo to slack 'er,
Packet boat, tow boat and a double stacker.
Choo, choo to Tarrytown,
Spuyten Duyvil all around,
Choo, choo to go ahead,
Choo, choo to back 'er.

2 Shad boat, pickle boat, lying side by side,
Fisherfolk and sailormen, waiting for the tide,
Rain cloud, storm cloud over yonder hill,
Thunder on the Dunderberg, rumbles in the kill.   (CHO.)

3 The *Sedgewick* was racing and she lost all hope,
Used up her steam on the big calliope,
But she hopped right along, she was hopping quick,
All the way from Stony Point up to Pappaloppen Crick.
CHORUS:
Choo, choo to go ahead,
Choo, choo to slack 'er,
Packet boat, tow boat and a double stacker.
New York to Albany, Rondout and Tivoli,
Choo, choo to go ahead,
And choo, choo to back 'er.

41. EL-A-NOY

FROM: p. 162 of *The American Songbag*, Carl Sandburg (Harcourt, Brace & Co., N.Y., 1927). Used by permission. Common Irish ballad tune with its basis in the Gaelic song, *The Bog Deal Board.*
Piano arrangement by MATYAS SEIBER

1 Way down upon the Wabash sich land was never known,
If Adam had passed over it, the soil he'd surely own.
He'd think it was the Garden he'd played in when a boy,
And straight pronounce it Eden in the state of El-a-noy.
CHORUS:
Then move your family westward,
Good health you will enjoy,
And rise to wealth and honour
In the state of El-a-noy.

2 'Twas there the Queen of Sheba came with Solomon of old,
With an ass load of spices, pomegranates, and fine gold,
And when she saw this lovely land, her heart was filled with joy,
Straightaway she said, ' I'd like to be a queen in El-a-noy.' (CHO.)

3 She's bounded by the Wabash, the Ohio, and the Lakes,
She's crawfish in the swampy lands, the milksick and the shakes,
But these are slight divairsions and take not from the joy
Of living in this garden land, the state of El-a-noy. (CHO.)

4 Away upon the northward, right on the border line,
A great commercial city, Chicago you will find,
Her men are all like Abelard, her women like Heloise,
All honest virtuous people, for they live in El-a-noy.
FINAL CHORUS:
Then move your family westward,
Bring all your girls and boys,
And cross at Shawnee Ferry
To the state of El-a-noy.

42. OLEANA

Lyrics by Pete Seeger and Alan Lomax, tune from p.187 of Theodore C. Blegen
and Martin B. Ruud's *Norwegian Emigrant Songs and Ballads* (University of Minn.
Press, Minneapolis, 1936). Used by permission.

1 O to be in Oleana,
That's where I'd like to be,
Than be bound in Norway
And drag the chains of slavery.
CHORUS:
Ole, Oleana,
Ole-Oleana,
Ole-Ole-Ole-Ole,
Ole-Oleana.

2 In Oleana land is free,
The wheat and corn just plant themselves,
Then they grow four feet a day,
While on the bed you rest yourselves. (CHO.)

3 The little pigs, they roast themselves
And trot about this lovely land,
With knives and forks stuck in their backs
Inquiring if you'd like some ham. (CHO.)

4 The cows and calves do all the work,
  They milk and churn till the dairy's full,
  While the bull keeps herd production high
  And sends reports to Ole Bull.   (CHO.)

5 The sun keeps shining day and night,
  Till the moon politely asks a turn,
  As the harvest here is once a month,
  We've time to waste and money to burn.   (CHO.)

6 They pay you here for getting drunk,
  The more you drink, the more they pay,
  So the rich man is the lazy man,
  Who drinks all night and sleeps all day.   (CHO.)

7 So if you'd like a happy life,
  To Oleana you must go,
  The poorest man from the old country
  Becomes a king in a year or so.   (CHO.)

43. THE FOGGY DEW—I

Collected by Alan Lomax from singing of Harry Cox, Norfolk, England. SEE: Index
and Guide; Reeves 45, 111; melody a variant of *Bonnie Doone*.
Piano arrangement by MATYAS SEIBER

89

1 As I was an old bachelor,
I followed a rovin' trade,
And all the harm that ever I done,
I courted a servant maid.
I courted her one summer season
And part of the winter, too,
And many a time I rolled my love
All over the foggy dew.

2 One night as I laid in my bed,
A-takin' my balmy sleep,
This pretty fair maid come up to me
And how bitterly she did weep.
She wept, she mourned, she tore her hair,
'Alas, what shall I do?
This night I resolved to sleep with you
For fear of the foggy dew.'

3 Now all the first part of the night
How we did sport and play,
And all the latter part of the night
She in my arms did lay.
And when broad daylight did appear,
She cried, ' I am undone.'
' O hold your tongue, you silly young girl,
For the foggy dew is gone.'

4 I loved that girl with all my heart,
Loved her as I loved my life.
And in the early part of that year
I made her my lawful wife.
I never told her of her faults,
And never intend to do,
Yet many a time as she winks and smiles,
I think of the foggy dew.

44. THE FOGGY DEW–II

FROM: p. 14 of *The American Songbag*, Carl Sandburg (Harcourt, Brace & Co., N.Y., 1927). Used by permission. SEE: Randolph I, 394; Sharp II, 174.

Freely and smoothly ♩ = 100

GUITAR– *1 or 2 or 6A*
BANJO– *1 or 4B*

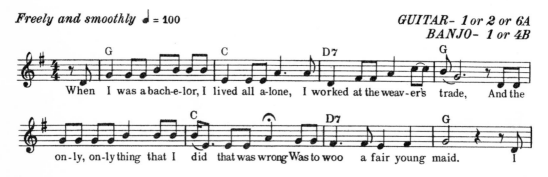

When I was a bach-e-lor, I lived all a-lone, I worked at the weav-er's trade, And the
on-ly, on-ly thing that I did that was wrong Was to woo a fair young maid.

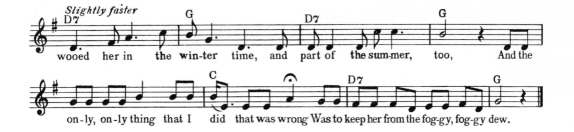

wooed her in the win-ter time, and part of the sum-mer, too, And the
on-ly, on-ly thing that I did that was wrong Was to keep her from the fog-gy, fog-gy dew.

1 When I was a bachelor, I lived all alone,
 I worked at the weaver's trade,
 And the only, only thing that I did that was wrong
 Was to woo a fair young maid.
   I wooed her in the winter time,
   And part of the summer, too,
   And the only, only thing that I did that was
                                        wrong
 Was to keep her from the foggy, foggy dew.

2 One night she came to my bedside,
 When I was fast asleep,
 She flung her arms around my neck
 And then began to weep.
   She wept, she cried, she tore her hair,
   Ah me, what could I do?
   So all night long I held her in my arms,
   Just to keep her from the foggy, foggy dew.

3 Still I am a bachelor, I live with my son,
 We work at the weaver's trade.
 And every time I look into his eyes
 He reminds me of that fair young maid.
   He reminds me of the winter time,
   And part of the summer, too,
   And of the many, many times I held her in
                                        my arms,
 Just to keep her from the foggy, foggy dew.

45. IN THE WILDERNESS

FROM: *American Play Party Songs*, B. A. Botkin (University of Nebraska Press, Lincoln, Nebraska, 1937).

First lit-tle la-dy in the wil-der-ness, In the wil-der-ness,
in the wil-der-ness, First lit-tle la-dy in the wil-der-ness On to Ga-li-lee.

CHORUS
Hands up, round the la-dy, Round the la-dy, round the la-dy, On to Ga-li-lee.

1 First little lady in the wilderness,
In the wilderness, in the wilderness,
First little lady in the wilderness
On to Galilee.
CHORUS:
Hands up, round the lady,
Round the lady, round the lady,
Hands up, round the lady,
On to Galilee.

2 Swing that lady out of the wilderness, *etc.*

3 Next old married lady go down the wilderness,
etc.

4 Next old maid go down the wilderness, *etc.*

5 Swing all the ladies out of the wilderness, *etc.*

6 First old hobo in the wilderness, *etc.*

7 First old soapstick in the wilderness, *etc.*
(toothpick, slopbucket, gentleman.)

46. THE PAW–PAW PATCH

SEE: Botkin I, 289; Randolph III, 364.

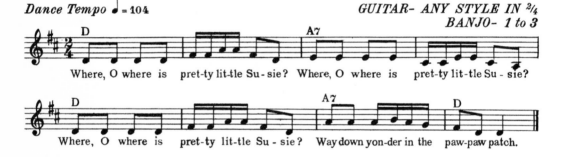

Dance Tempo ♩ = 104

GUITAR– ANY STYLE IN ²⁄₄
BANJO– 1 to 3

Where, O where is pret-ty lit-tle Su-sie? Where, O where is pret-ty lit-tle Su-sie?

Where, O where is pret-ty lit-tle Su-sie? Way down yon-der in the paw-paw patch.

CHORUS:
Where, O where is pretty little Susie?
Where, O where is pretty little Susie?
Where, O where is pretty little Susie?
Way down yonder in the paw-paw patch.

Pickin' up paw-paws, puttin' um in her pockets, *etc.*
(CHO.)

Come on, boys, let's go find her, *etc.* (CHO.)

47. THE LONE GREEN VALLEY

From the singing of R. L. Lunsford. SEE: Belden, 325; Laws, 184; Mackenzie, 365; Randolph II. Randolph says: song is related to *Murder of Betsy Smith*, an early 19th century British broadside. A woman in Mississippi in 1929 confessed to a murder by mailing the Governor of the State an adaptation of this song. Found in Maritime Canada, New England, South, Midwest.

Piano arrangement by MATYAS SEIBER

1 Way down in a lone green valley
  Down where the roses bloom and fade,
  There was a jealous lover
  In love with a beautiful maid.

2 One night the moon shone brightly,
  The stars were shining, too,
  And to this maiden's cottage
  The jealous lover drew.

3 'Come, love, and we will wander,
  Where the woods are gay,
  While strolling, we will ponder
  Upon our wedding day.'

4 So on and on they wandered,
  The night bird sang above,
  The jealous lover grew angry
  With the beautiful girl he loved.

5 Down on her knees before him
  She pleaded for her life;
  But deep into her bosom
  He plunged the fatal knife.

6 'O Willie, won't you tell me
  Why have you taken my life?
  You know I've always loved you,
  And wanted to be your wife.

7 'I never have deceived you,
  But with my dying breath,
  I will forgive you, Willie,
  And close my eyes in death.'

48. YOUNG CHARLOTTE

Words and music arranged by Alan Lomax. SEE: Belden, 309; Brown II, 492;
Flanders I, 111; Laws, 214; Randolph I, 105.
Piano arrangement by MATYAS SEIBER

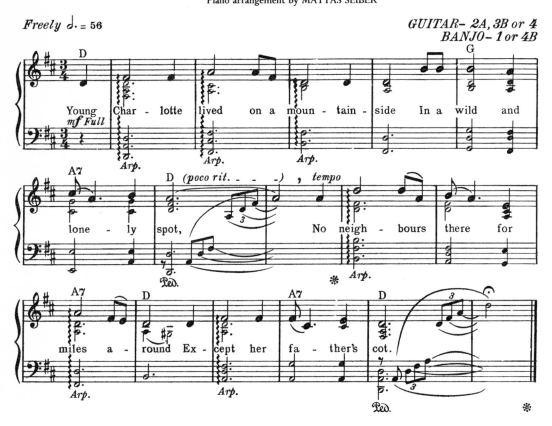

1 Young Charlotte lived on a mountainside
In a wild and lonely spot,
No neighbours there for miles around
Except her father's cot.

2 And yet on many-a winter's night
Young swains would gather there;
For her father kept a social board
And she was very fair.

3 It was New Year's Eve. The sun had set.
Why looks her anxious eye
So long from the frosty windows forth
As the merry sleighs go by?

4 At the village inn fifteén miles off
There's a merry ball tonight.
But the piercing air is cold as death,
Tho' hearts are warm and light.

5 But while she looks with longing eyes,
A well-known voice she hears,
And dashing up to the cottage door
Young Charlie's sleigh appears.

6 ' O daughter dear,' her mother says,
' This blanket round you fold,
For it's a dreadful night outside,
And you'll catch your death of cold.'

7 ' No, mama, no,' young Charlotte cried,
And she laughed like a gypsum queen,
' For to ride in the blankets muffled up
I never can be seen.'

94

8 'My silken coat is quite enough,
   It's lined all through, you know,
   Besides I have a silken scarf,
   Which round my neck I'll throw.'

9 With muffled face and silently,
   The long, cold miles were passed,
   When Charlie, with these frozen words
   The silence broke at last.

10 'O such a night I never saw,
   My reins I can scarcely hold.'
   And Lottie said in a trembling voice,
   'I am exceeding cold.'

11 He cracked his whip, urged on the team,
   More swiftly than before,
   Until another five long miles
   In silence they passed o'er.

12 'How fast,' said Charles, 'the frozen ice
   Is gathering on my brow.'
   Said Charlotte in a weaker voice,
   'I'm growing warmer now.'

13 'Why sit you like a monument
   That has no power to stir?'
   He asked her once, he asked her twice,
   But she answered not a word.

14 Then quickly to the lighted hall
   Her lifeless form he bore.
   Fair Charlotte was a frozen corpse
   That never could speak more.

15 He twined his arms around her neck,
   He kissed her marble brow,
   And his thoughts went back to where she
   'I'm growing warmer now.'   [said,

49. TURKEY IN THE STRAW

SEE: Brown III, 130; Sears. The melody is a common Irish piper's reel.

Rollicking ♩=116   GUITAR— ANY ²⁄₄ STYLE
BANJO— 1 to 3

As I was a-gwine on down the road, With a ti-red team and a heav-y load, I cracked my whip and the lead-er sprung, I says day-day to the wa-gon tongue.

CHORUS
Tur-key in the straw, haw, haw, haw, Tur-key in the hay, hay, hay, hay, Roll 'em up and twist 'em up a high tuck a-haw, And hit 'em up a tune called *Tur-key in the Straw.*

1 As I was a-gwine on down the road,
   With a tired team and a heavy load,
   I cracked my whip and the leader sprung,
   I says day-day to the wagon tongue.

CHORUS:
Turkey in the straw, haw, haw, haw,
Turkey in the hay, hay, hay, hay,
Roll 'em up and twist 'em up—a high tuck a-haw,
And hit 'em up a tune called *Turkey in the Straw.*

2 Then I come to a river and I couldn't get across,
 Jumped on a ' nigger ' and I thought he was a hoss,
 He rared and he pitched and he pawed and he squealed
 Till I drawed my gun and shot him in the heel.   (CHO.)

3 So I went a rackin' on down the road,
 I met Miss Terrapin and Mister Toad,
 And every time that toad would jump,
 Miss Terrapin hide behind the stump.
                (or)
 Every time Mister Toad would sing
 Miss Terrapin cut that pigeon wing.   (CHO.)

4 I met an old catfish swimmin' in the stream,
 I axed that old catfish what do he mean,
 Grabbed that catfish right by the snout
 And turnt Mister Catfish wrongside out.   (CHO.)

5 I loves to go a-fishin' on a bright summer day,
 To see the perches and the catfish play,
 With their hands in their pockets and their pockets in their pants
 Would you like to see the ladies do the kootchie-kootchie dance?   (CHO.)

Scholars believe that ' Turkey in the Straw ' is a folk remake of the early minstrel song, ' Old Zip Coon ', to which a number of minstrel composers laid claim: ' Zip Coon ' is also closely related to a jig tune, popular among Mississippi river boatmen, called ' Natchez under the Hill '. Introduced in the Bowery Theatre in 1834, it has innumerable zany stanzas.

1 O there once was a man with a double chin
 Who performed with skill on the violin.
 Well, he played in time and he played in tune,
 But he wouldn't play anything but *Old Zip Coon*.
 CHORUS:
 Old Zip Coon he played all night
 Till the owls and the bats took flight,
 He fiddled and he sawed by the light of the moon,
 But he wouldn't play anything but *Old Zip Coon*.

2 Now little Sukie Blue-Skin fell deep in love with me,
 She ax me to her house for to have a cup of tea,
 And what do you think she serve me for my supper?
 Pig's foot, cornbread, apple sauce and butter.   (CHO.)

3 Have you ever saw the wild geese flyin' crost the ocean?
 Now the wild goose motion is a very pretty motion,
 He gives a little wiggle when he commence for to swaller
 Then the wild goose holler—' Google-google-google-goller.'
 CHORUS:
 Old Zip Coon is a very learned scholar,
 He fiddles and he plays to earn a half a dollar.
 Old Zip Coon is a very learned scholar,
 And the tune for his banjo is *Coony in the Holler*.

50. LINCOLN AND LIBERTY

Words by F. A. Simkins. Tune: *Rosin the Beau*—a favourite tune for parodies in mid-19th century America—called in Ireland *Yougal Harbour* and much used for political songs. SEE: Randolph II, 371; Sandburg, 167; Sears Supplement; and *Treasury of American Songs*, Siegmeister.

1 Hurrah for the choice of the nation,
Our chieftain so brave and so true!
We'll go for the great reformation,
For Lincoln and Liberty, too.
We'll go for the son of Kentucky,
The hero of Hoosierdom through,
The pride of the Suckers, so lucky,
For Lincoln and Liberty, too.

2 They'll find what by felling and mauling,
Our rail-maker statesman can do;
For the people are everywhere calling
For Lincoln and Liberty, too.
Then up with the banner so glorious,
The star-spangled red, white and blue,
We'll fight 'til our banner's victorious
For Lincoln and Liberty, too.

3 Our David's good sling is unerring,
The Slavocrat's giant he slew,
Then shout for the freedom preferring
For Lincoln and Liberty, too.
We'll go for the son of Kentucky,
The hero of Hoosierdom through;
The pride of the Suckers, so lucky,
For Lincoln and Liberty, too.

51. WHEN JOHNNY COMES MARCHING HOME

SEE: Randolph II, 284 (he mentions sea chantey version *Johnny, Fill Up the Bowl*);
Sears. Seamus Ennis points similarity to Irish *Pretty Girl Milking a Cow*.

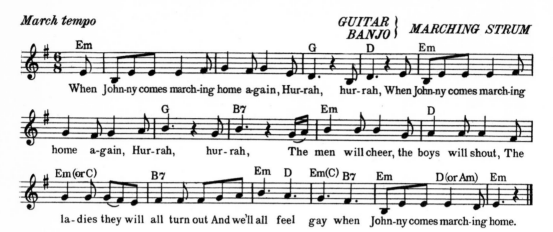

March tempo

GUITAR } MARCHING STRUM
BANJO }

When John-ny comes march-ing home a-gain, Hur-rah, hur-rah, When John-ny comes march-ing home a-gain, Hur-rah, hur-rah, The men will cheer, the boys will shout, The la-dies they will all turn out And we'll all feel gay when John-ny comes march-ing home.

The Southern Rebels sang . . .

1 In eighteen hundred and sixty-one, Skiball, says I, (2)
In eighteen hundred and sixty-one
We licked the Yankees at Bull Run,
  And we'll all drink stone blind,
  Johnny fill up the bowl.

2 In eighteen hundred and sixty-two, Skiball, says I, (2)
In eighteen hundred and sixty-two
The rebels put the Yankees through, *etc.*

3 In eighteen hundred and sixty-five,
We all thanked God we were alive, *etc.*

And they were answered from the Union lines with stanzas like . . .

1 In eighteen hundred and sixty-one,
The cruel rebellion had just begun, *etc.*

2 Through a mistake we lost Bull Run,
And we all skedaddled for Washington, *etc.*

3 In eighteen hundred and sixty-three,
Abe Lincoln set the Negroes free, *etc.*

4 In eighteen hundred and sixty-four,·
Abe called for a hundred thousand more, *etc.*

52. VIRGINIA'S BLOODY SOIL

From singing of Yankee John Galusha, as recorded by Frank Warner. Used by permission. Elektra—ELK 13. Irish come-all-ye tune.

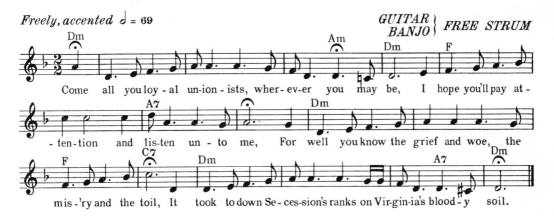

1 Come all you loyal unionists, wherever you may be,
I hope you'll pay attention and listen unto me,
For well you know the grief and woe, the mis'ry and the toil,
It took to down Secession's ranks on Virginia's bloody soil.

2 When our good old flag, the Stars and Stripes, on Sumpter's walls was hurled,
And high o'erhead on the forrardest walls the Rebels their flags unfurled,
It aroused each loyal Unionist and caused his blood to boil,
For to see that flag—Secession's rag—float o'er Virginia's soil.

3 And thousands left their native homes, some never to return,
And many's the wife and family dear were left behind to mourn,
There was one who went among them, who from danger would ne'er recoil,
Now his bones lie bleaching on the fields of Virginia's bloody soil.

4 When on the field of battle, he never was afraid,
Where cannons loud would rattle, he stood there undismayed,
When bullets rained about him he stood there with a smile,
Saying ' We'll conquer, boys, or leave our bones on Virginia's bloody soil (sile).'

5 In the first great fight of the Wilderness where many a brave man fell,
Our captain led his comrades on through Rebel shot and shell,
The wounded round they strewed the ground, the dead lay heaped in piles,
Their comrades weltered in their blood on Virginia's bloody soil.

6 The Rebels fought like fury or tigers drove to bay,
They knew full well of the truth they'd tell, they would not win the day,
It was hand to hand they fought 'em, the struggle was fierce and wild,
Till a bullet pierced our captain's brain on Virginia's bloody soil.

7 And now our hero's sleeping, with thousands of the brave,
No marble slab does mark the place that shows where he was laid.
He died to save our Union, he's free from care or toil.
Thank God! The Stars and Stripes still wave above Virginia's soil.

99

TIMBER TIGERS

53. THE FARMER AND THE SHANTY BOY

IN THE EYES of a boy in rural Maine in the 1820's the free-spending lumberjack who swaggered through town in the spring, dressed in his gaudy clothes, turning the air blue with his language, tearing bits out of the board side-walk with his caulked boots, was just the sort of independent, cocky, and uninhibited fellow he would admire to be. There were plenty of jobs and an endless demand for lumber, as Britain and America raced to build huge fleets of wooden ships and thousands of new wooden towns were thrown up on the frontier. Maine never saw such a boom. Thoreau writes that in 1837

. . . there were 250 saw mills on the Penobscot and its tributaries above Bangor, the greater part of them in this immediate neighborhood, and they sawed 200 million board feet annually. To this is to be added the lumber of the Kennebec, the Androscoggin, the Saco and the Passamaquoddy. No wonder that we hear so often of vessels which are becalmed off our coast, being surrounded for a week at a time by floating lumber from the Maine woods. The mission of the men there seems to be like so many forest demons, to drive the forest all out of the country, from every solitary beaver-swamp and forest and mountainside, as soon as possible . . .

By the 1850's the most accessible forests had been chopped down and sawn up, and a New England commentator was writing . . .

It would be a match for Dame Nature to locate a handsome pine tree beyond the grasp of a logman. Where the Eastern hunter pursues the mountain goat, the logger pursues the pine.

Maine no longer offered a suitable habitat for the timber tiger; but beyond Lake Erie, through the Lake States, lay an endless dark blanket of pine that was to keep the woodsman busy for two generations. The Maine story repeated itself, but on a vaster scale—the story of tremendous tracts of timber sold for a pittance, despoiled and left a waste of stumps in a few brief years—the story of a monster industry clawing down millions of acres of evergreens in an effort to keep up with the growth of a new nation. In 1882 the mills of little Saginaw, Michigan, sawed a billion board feet of lumber and boasted a hundred and twelve millionaires. Farther west, over a hundred million dollars of lumber was taken out of Minnesota forests by lumberjacks whose earnings averaged thirty dollars a month. On the Pacific Coast the statistics matched the trees, and these grew so thick and tall that the Lake State lumberjack swore that Paul Bunyan must have planted them.

The real hero of this sage was the daring and feckless lumberjack. Sometimes he paused in the midst of his Homeric labours, or at the end of a stupendous drinking bout, to reflect . . .

'Tis true, my boys, I've made lots of money,
But the curse of all bushmen it soon lays me low,
For the money it flies like the snow does in June, lads,
And back to the woods every Fall I must go . . .

For the ageing jack, whose joints were stiffening, he had an ironic remedy . . .

Take a little mosquito milk, put it on a cat's horn, and stir it with the crotch of a duck. That will cure your rheumatism sure as the freeze will come in the winter . . .

When the woodsman sang craft songs like this one, a note of envy and worry sounded beneath his confident pride in his craft and his contempt for the mossback. Most shanty boys had no home and wondered if they would ever have one. They all dreamed of retiring to a little farm some day, but few ever quit the woods. There was always more timber over the next rise.

54. THE LITTLE BROWN BULLS

> I am a jolly shanty boy, as you will soon discover,
> To all the dodges I am fly, a hustling pinewoods rover.
> A peavey hook it is my pride, an axe I well can handle,
> To fell a tree or punch a bull, get rattling Johnny Randle!
> Bung yer eye! Bung yer eye!

THIS RHYME of the woods defines the main tasks of the lumberjack and reflects the pride he took in his work. It was a proud thing for a man to be called the No. 1 jack in camp. Such a man could do any job in the woods but, in fact, he hired on to do just one. The choppers brought down the trees; the sawyers sawed them up and trimmed them into logs; the swampers cleared rough skidways; and the skidders hauled the towering loads of logs to the river's edge on their low, ox-drawn sledges.

A good axeman could fell a tree so accurately that it would drive a stake deep in the ground. One man bet he could chop a cord of wood in an hour and won his wager. Such men kept their axes sharp enough to shave with them, and often did.

The skidder or teamster, however, had the most highly skilled as well as the most dangerous job. Every night his road-monkey sprinkled the narrow skidways, and by morning they would be frozen as hard and slick as glass. Taking a ten-ton load of logs over such a road, up hill and down dale, was a perilous business. One Vermont teamster lost his nerve, when his sled seemed to be going out of control, and jumped off to save himself. The logs spilled off and killed the horses. His comrades, who felt he could have saved his team, spoke to him no more that winter.

Most teamsters loved the animals they drove, and in western camps they tell about a skidder whose team liked plug tobacco; he bought them so much ' chewing ' from the commissary that when pay day rolled around he was in debt to the company.

This thundering old woods' ballad, composed in Mart Douglas's camp, Northern Wisconsin, in 1872 or '73, records an epic contest between two ox-drivers, a Canadian-Scot and an American Yankee—the champion's belt, naturally, going to the American.

55. THE PINERY BOY

THERE IS AN old Minnesota woods saying that the lumbering industry in that state killed a Swede a day. In the East it was a Brunswicker or a Mainite a day. Death walked on quiet snowshoes in the winter woods and rode the jams with the river drivers. Its warning banshee cry could not be heard over the scream of the saws in the primitive mills. The Bangor or Saginaw girl who kissed her timber tiger goodbye in the fall could never be sure she'd see him again when the spring drive roared through town. A score of ballads tell the story—of Harry Dunn, killed by a so-called ' widder-maker ', the dead limb on the tree he was chopping:

> They worked along till ten o'clock
> All on that fatal day,
> Till a falling limb came down on him
> And crushed him to the clay.

—of Les Shrader who made the wrong move when the logs began to slide:

> So Les stepped in between the skids
> ' Look,' was all he said,
> And just as he glanced up and smiled
> The big log struck him dead.

—of Johnny Stiles, ground to death under a log jam on the wild Mustard River:

> He was ground from his heels to his shoulder,
> And rolled out as flat as your hand,
> And when we laid his poor corpse out
> He did not look like a man.
> Every bone in his body was broken,
> His flesh hung in tatters and strings;
> We buried him there by the river
> Where the lark and the whippoorwill sing.

—of Harry Bail, the sawyer, thrown against a moving saw blade:

> He went to work as usual,
> No danger did he fear,
> Till the lowering of the feed bar
> Which cut him most severe.
> It cut him round the shoulder blade,
> And half way down the back,
> It threw him down upon the floor
> When the carriage came running back . . .

To some readers, these verses may seem crude, distasteful, and unpleasantly sentimental, yet, when they are sung, their simplicity of language and their unconcealed emotion lends them a nobility that belongs not to art, but to reality itself. They are as solidly and uncompromisingly there as so many granite boulders in a river. Just as the boulders stand as remnants of mountains that have crumbled or great glaciers that have passed that way, so these shanty-boy tragedies are solid reminders of a tribe of giants who once trod our northern woods—illiterate, foul-mouthed, savage, drunken, many of them, but hardy, patient, work-proud, and gallantly brave.

56. THE RIVER IN THE PINES

WHEN SPRING LOOSED the frozen rivers of Maine or Wisconsin, they carried a huge load of logs on their backs to the mills at the river mouths. On top of the drive rode the rivermen, prodding on the mass of logs like so many cowboys with a herd of cattle—sleeping in snatches—living for days on end as wet as muskrats—shouting blasphemies in the joy of their spring-released muscles—and dreaming, as death followed every footstep, of the drinks and girls who waited for them at the end of the drive. They were the boys who feared no noise, they were the kings of the river.

All this was movement and glory. The moment of drama came when a huge log swung crossways in the narrows and stuck fast, and others packed behind it until thousands upon thousands of logs quickly formed a huge breastwork across the rushing stream. Then, as the drive groaned to a halt and the river piled up behind the jam, silence fell in the woods.

Below the jam the Connecticut was a mere trickle. They'd have to work fast, we knew, or soon the water would be backing up into the village. And they *were* working. We watched breathlessly as they danced like puppets to and fro across the barrier, looking for the key log, the king log, the single log that must be moved before the jam could be broken. Over all was the ominous feeling of impending danger. You couldn't shake it off, so you spoke in whispers.

There came a cry of warning. Slim Pete Hurd, one of our rivermen heroes, had ' got holt on ' the king log. We could see him twist it from its grudging fellows and roll it down. Then there came a quaking and a shifting of the huge mass as the drivers ran for shore, balancing themselves with their peaveys on the struggling logs. The jam ' hauled ' with a rush of tossing logs, and some of the men had tried to ride her out, Death riding everywhere among them.

Through the thunder of the mad logs we heard a cry, ' Pete's gone!' and, looking downstream where the crest of the floor was rolling, we saw a slim body thrown high in the air to fall again into the white water and among those grinding logs . . .

QUOTE: *Holy Old Mackinaw,* Stuart Holbrook, p. 88 (Macmillan, 1938). Used by permission of the Macmillan Company, New York.

57. CANADA-I-O

The lumberman's life is a wearisome one.
Some say it's free from all care,
With the ringing of an axe from morning till night,
In the middle of some forest so drear . . . OLD WOODS SONG

A camp boss recalls . . . ' A blankety-blank lumberjack said to me once, ' I want to take Saturday afternoon off.' I asked him why. ' Are you going to town?' ' No. I want to see what this place looks like in daytime.'

' Working on the drive, and sleeping out of doors, my clothes used to get full of lice. I'd pick the lice off my suspenders. I used to wear heavy woollen underwear, thick as leather, so I turned it inside out, and it'd take them two weeks to walk back through to me. When we was laid off, only the fittest lice survived. The rest died from famine by the million.'

ONLY ' if your heart was made of iron and your soul was cased in steel ' and your skin was impervious to bedbug bites—only if you could work up to your waist in snow for a whole winter for starvation wages and then blow the winter's work in a week's boozing

—only if you could ' eat hay with a dash of whiskey on it '—were you fit to be a lumberjack.

The vast pineries demanded endless supplies of such men; they kept coming into the woods every spring—Scots, Swedes, Irish, Yankees—and, although many of their songs register complaints, these hardships endured together gave them a feeling of triumphant manhood.

So from the Scots deportation song, *Caledon-i-o* grew *Canada-i-o*, the song of the Mainites who passed a dreadful winter at Three Rivers. The boys moved on into Pennsylvania where they sang about the cold and the bad food on *Cooley's Run-i-o*. When the Yankees made the big skip to the virgin forests round the Great Lakes, they had only to change one word to have a topical ballad about the brutalities of life in *Michigan-i-o*. And the same ballad later served the buffalo skinners and the Texas cowboys as *Trail to Mexico* (*see* Song 196).

Every winter they suffered and complained; every spring they blew their money in fabulous, free-handed binges, lined the pockets of the pimps and the barkeeps and then swore to reform. But the springtime lure of red lights and swinging doors proved too strong for most woodsmen.

Poverty and wanderlust impelled them to follow the pineries west. As they pulled their harsh bunkhouse blankets up to their chins, somewhere on the cold trail to Portland, they muttered the woodsman's ironic prayer . . .

> Now I lay me down to sleep
> Where the lice and bedbugs sleep.
> If I should die before I wake,
> Who in Hell will blow my stake?

QUOTES: *Bloodstoppers and Bearwalkers*, Richard Dorson (Harvard U.P., 1952).

58. MOOSEHEAD LAKE

Our cook was so bad that when he cooked for fifty men it took a hundred to eat it . . .

AUTHORITY IN THE LUMBERWOODS was split three ways—between the champion fighter of the outfit, the bull of the woods (the camp boss), and the bull (or head) cook; but the cook was the ' king bee '. A boss once stuck his head into the cook shack, and the cook roared at him, ' By God, I'll run this cookroom, sir, or on my breadboard die! ' Any jack who talked or ' mumbled ' over his vittles was liable to be slapped right off his seat by the outraged artist of the kitchen.

In the early days of lumbering in Maine, the men cooked for themselves over an open fire between the bunks. Their diet consisted of slabs of salt pork, mounds of baked beans, bread and black strap molasses, and tea so strong it would float a peavey (a lumberman's cant hook with a spike at the end). But camp fare improved as the industry moved west. Along the upper Mississippi cooks served plenty of fresh meat, mashed potatoes, rice, mounds of pancakes, prunes, puddings, and individual apple pies.

> Supper being over, we to our shanty go,
> And all smoke up our pipes till everything looks blue . . .

Blue and steamy, the song should have said, for wet socks and trousers and mackinaws steamed in the drying racks around the fire. A row of communal cribs or bunks (in Maine lined with spruce boughs, and further west with straw mattresses) ran down each side of the shed-like building, and below these was a low wooden bench (the deacon seat) where the jacks sat in their sock feet, smoking and chatting, swapping stories and songs. If there was a greenhorn in camp the older men would tell him one of the mossy old woods lies about ' the gilly grouse up Onion River who lays square eggs '—or the ' terrible tote-road shagimaw that prowls the woods and eats your mackinaw '. Of a singer, no more was required than that he have a good, clear voice and a good memory, and ' speak his words out plain '. Out west some bosses realized the importance of ballads to camp morale, for they often hired a man because he was a good singer.

This was the hour when the camp fiddler or dulcimer player might bring out his instrument and play a tune while two jacks (one with a bandana tied round his arm to show he was the female of the couple) did a squaw dance, or the camp step-dancer clogged and jigged in his caulked boots.

On weekdays the woods tigers turned in around 9 p.m. and without ceremony. A man simply removed his boots, crawled into the bunk, and pulled the communal blanket up to his chin. If the long, heavy horse-blanket that covered the men all down one side of the room was filthy and crawling with lice, so much the worse; the lumberjack was not finicky. Immediately he slept the sleep of the just and the weary.

At the first peep o' day the cook would be bawling *Day———light in the swa———mp*! If that savage cry did not rouse the sleepers, the shivering cookie beat out a rousing, clanging crescendo of dreadful iron notes on a great triangle of iron called the ' gut hammer '.

59. BOLD JACK DONAHUE

How many songs did these singers know? A hundred was not a great number to hold in mind. David S. Libbey could count up to very nearly three hundred, and two hundred was not unusual. Mr. William Tibbetts said that one night he and another man wanted to see which could sing the most songs, and they sang all night; he sang a hundred and twenty-five songs. One man wrote that he knew five hundred and fifteen songs— but many of them had no words. He was an old-time fiddler, and counted in his dance tunes.

' I was never much of a singer,' said one. ' But I could make some sort of noise, and I used to lie on my back and keep it up all night. But after I got married I forgot all that.' And this is the common explanation for having forgotten songs, that the better the wife, the more likely one is to forget a great part of what was once known; they take to hymns and Sunday-School melodies when there is a woman to play the organ on evenings at home.

' One night,' said another, ' a fellow in camp bet me a new red jersey that I couldn't sing fifty songs running and all on 'em different. I tell you, I kept it up all night, and never any part of the same one over again. And I could ha' sung some more, too, only he said he was satisfied that I'd earned that jersey good and fair, an' if it was just the same to me, he'd like to ketch a wink of sleep before breakfast.'

THE TUNES came from all over the English-speaking world—from Scotland, Ireland, England, Australia, and Canada. The lumberjacks sang many of the medieval ballads and lyrics; they sang minstrel pieces and sea chanteys; but the songs they liked best were the come-all-ye's, which recounted in plain language the tragedies and adventures of working stiffs, like themselves. A man was not considered a true woods singer unless he could get through the forty stanzas of *The Flying Cloud* and could thunder out the stirring Australian bandit ballad, *Bold Jack Donahue*.

The Donahue story began in 1823 in Dublin, when Bold Jack was sentenced to be transported to Australia for life for 'intent to commit a felony'. Brought to Australia in chains, Jack soon bunked out of his convict stockade and turned bushranger. His mates acted as his spies and in return Donahue kept them supplied with rum and tobacco and wrought instant retribution on any planter who oppressed his convicts. The whole colony was kept in an uproar by Donahue's daring robberies until 1830, when the bush police at last surrounded him and shot him down.

His ballad spread like wildfire through the colony—such a focus for popular discontent that soon it became a civil offence to sing it in any public place. Several variant songs thereupon appeared, with precisely the same content but different names for their heroes. One of these ballads, *The Wild Colonial Boy*, can be heard today in Irish pubs right round the world. The original ballad, meanwhile, took refuge in America, where fishermen, lumberjacks, and cowboys kept the bold bushranger's memory green.

QUOTE: *The Minstrelsy of Maine*, Eckstorm and Smyth, p. 304.

60. SILVER JACK

When O'Connor drew his pay, though he
                              drew it miles away,
The people of the city felt the shock of it,
                              they say.
When O'Connor reached the city, he reached it
                              with a jar,
He had all the cushions burning in the middle
                              of the car.
When at last they got him cornered, they had
                              rung in three alarms,
It took the whole department to tie his legs and
                              arms . . .

WHEN THE JACK hit town he hollered for drinks, and he was ready to buy them for himself and his comrades until his last dollar was gone. Richard Dorson tells of one Joe Donor who took such a load that he had to crawl down Main Street on his hands and knees in front of the whole town.

A passer-by said, 'Can I give you a lift? You've got more than you can carry.'

'By God,' says Joe, 'If I can't carry her, I can drag her.' He crawled back to his shack and lay outside in the snow all night. When Joe woke in the morning, he was frozen in and scared to death. He hollered like hell, and they had to chop him out of the snow.

Every lumbering town from Bangor to Portland had a reception committee of complaisant ladies waiting to take their share of the lumberjack's pay.

> I boldly walked in and stepped up to the bar,
> When a saucy young damsel said, ' Have a cigar.'
> A cigar I did take, in a chair I sat down,
> When this saucy young damsel come trippling round.

> She boldly came over, sit down on my knee,
> Saying, ' Jack, you're a woodsman I plainilye see.'
> Saying, ' Jack, you're a woodsman and that we all know,
> For your muscle is hard from your head to your toe ' . . .

Brawling was the third and absolutely essential item on the jack's programme of entertainment. The lumberman at play fought for the sheer joy of it. He seldom used guns or knives, preferring the rough-and-tumble of fisticuffs, wrestling, and ear-chawing. When he got his opponent down, he jumped on him with both feet and marked his chest and face with his caulked boots. Veteran lumberjacks carried the scars of these battles to their graves.

The king of Michigan lumberwoods fighters was Jack Driscoll, known as Silver Jack because of his prematurely white hair. ' No law touched him—not even smallpox caught him. He feared neither man, beast, nor the Devil.' Silver Jack could fell an ox with one blow of his giant fist and tie bowknots in iron horse-shoes. The redoubtable French-Canadian, Joe Fournier, who used to butt holes in mahogany bars for a pastime, once challenged Silver Jack, and Jack folded the Canuck with one pile-driving blow to the solar plexus. Between his fights and his river-driving, Jack Driscoll served two terms for armed robbery in the state penitentiary at Jackson, Michigan.

Like most of the old-timers of the woods, he lived hard and died a bachelor at the age of fifty with just enough money under his pillow to pay for a pauper's funeral. They buried him in an unmarked grave in L'Anse, Wisconsin, in 1895, but his name lives on in two wood poems. My father found this bunkhouse rhyme in western cowcamps, and I have set it to an original tune in lumberjack style, since it seemed a pity that such a memorial to such a man should not be sung.

QUOTES: (a) Holbrook, p. 114. (b) *Bloodstoppers and Bearwalkers*, Dorson.

61. THE FROZEN LOGGER

When I got back in the woods this mornin', chips was still fallin' from the day before . . .

THE PRINCE of the timber tigers was legendary Paul Bunyan . . .

> Paul Bunyan. You have heard of Paul,
> He was the kingpin of them all,
> The greatest logger in the land,
> He had a kick in either hand.
> And licked more men and drove more miles
> And got more drunk in more new styles
> Than any other peavy prince
> Before or then or ever since.

When a man faced the hardships and the terrors of the dark forests of the wintry North, it was nice to have Paul Bunyan in mind. Joking about what old Paul had done made a big job seem easier, and this motivation certainly lies behind the Paul Bunyan legends, indeed, behind all our tall tales. As for Paul's origins, no one can be quite sure of them. The stories about him combine folk memories of Gargantua, Finn McCool, and Munchausen. Nearer to home, scholars have pointed out the connexions of Paul with the Yankee liar, with Davy Crockett, and with Mike Fink. Historically, there was a red-headed woodsman of giant stature who figured in the Papineau rebellion in Canada in 1837 and later became a lumbercamp boss. Oldtime Canadian lumberjacks tell yarns about Paul Bonhomme of the Two Mountain country and about the trickster *Bon Jean*, which French Canadians pronounce *bongyenne*. Other students have pointed out the similarity of the Bunyan tales to certain Scandinavian and Red Indian myths. Probably traces of all these legends now rest on Paul Bunyan's giant shoulders. The Bunyan stories were published in an embellished form in 1914, and have been rewritten since by half a dozen authors, and thus fragments of myth from literary sources have been introduced, even into the oral tales.

He was quite a feller. Once he swum the Manistee River with a ton of loose hay on his back and carried eight quarts of loose blackberries in each hand. Those were some berries, too. We had to squeeze the juice out of them to make pies. We tried it without squeezing 'em and them pies just run over, and when we opened the kitchen door, they just floated right away on their own juice . . .

Out west the timber grew taller and so did the stories about Paul Bunyan . . .

He didn't stop to build skidways and the likes of that—he just hitched on a quarter section of the land and hauled it up the river and sifted the logs out of it, and put 'em into the river and hitched old Babe, the big blue ox, on the rubbish and hauled it back to where it come from.

Old Paul had three different voices he used. The one fer speakin' inside an ordinary room rushed at you like a twenty mile gale of wind—Paul could control that one. The second one he used to give orders in the woods sounded like a Siberian thunderstorm. The third one, for when he got to cussin' and swearin', sometimes set the woods on fire. I remember one time it took five hundred men a week to put out the fire he set off that way . . .

The hotel he built, too, was so high that the last seven stories had to be put on hinges so they could swing back to let the moon go by . . .

Now there was always more weather wherever Paul was. Take the winter of the Blue Snow. That was the coldest winter anybody ever saw. The thermometer dropped to 73½ degrees below zero and every degree was a foot long. It got so cold, the flames froze in the lamps and we couldn't blow them out—had to break them off and throw them out of the windows. Cook used to grind them up and use them for red pepper. In the spring thaw, they started a fire in the woods that lasted all summer. That was some winter, though. It got so cold it took me three days and thirty-nine minutes to light a match on a steam grindstone . . .

QUOTES: Corn, hotel stories from p. 85, Daniel Hoffman, *Paul Bunyan* (University of Pa. Press, 1952).

53. THE FARMER AND THE SHANTY BOY

FROM: p. 443 of *Ballads and Songs of Missouri*, Belden (University of Mo. Press, 1940). Used by permission. SEE: Flanders I, 166; Rickaby, 48. This version from a Wisconsin singer. Song found between Maine and Minnesota. Brought from New Brunswick to Maine before 1850. A type of song common in Great Britain which resembles the medieval Latin debate *De Phillide et Flora*. Tune related to: *The Trees are Growing Green*, *Black Water Side*, and other Anglo-Irish airs.

Piano arrangement by MATYAS SEIBER

Smoothly ♩· = 69

GUITAR- 2B & 6B
BANJO- 4A

As I strolled out one ev-e-ning Just as the sun went down, So care-less-ly I wan-dered, Till I came to Tren-ton town. I heard two maids con-vers-ing, As I slow-ly passed them by, One said she loved a far-mer's son, And the o-ther a shan-ty boy.

1 As I strolled out one evening
  Just as the sun went down,
  So carelessly I wandered,
  Till I came to Trenton town.
  I heard two maids conversing,
  As I slowly passed them by,
  One said she loved a farmer's son,
  And the other a shanty boy.

2 'O how I love my shanty boy
  Who goes off in the fall!
  He is both stout and healthy
  And fit to stand a squall.
  With pleasure I'll receive him
  In the spring when he comes down,
  For his money with me he'll share quite free,
  While your mossback he has none.'

3 'O how you praise your shanty boy
  Who goes off in the fall!
  He's ordered out before daylight
  To stand the storms and squalls;
  While happy and contented
  My farmer's son will stay,
  And tell to me some tales of love
  While raging storms go by.'

4 'O I could not listen to the silly stuff
  Your mossback has to say,
  For some of them are green enough
  That cows might eat for hay.
  How easy it is to tell them
  When they come into town,
  For the little kids run after them
  Saying, " Mossy, how are you down?*" '

5 'O what I have said of your shanty boy
  I pray you'll excuse me,
  And from this silly mossback
  I hope I may get free.
  If ever I get free from him
  With a shanty boy I'll go,
  And leave him broken-hearted
  His field to plough and sow.'

* doing

54. THE LITTLE BROWN BULLS

Collected and arranged by Alan Lomax from singing of a Michigan lumberjack.
SEE: Beck; Laws, 152; Lomax IV, 224; Rickaby, 65. The air occurs in Britain
in many forms, e.g., *Green Bushes*.

Free ballad style ♩=126

GUITAR-⎫
BANJO-⎬ *FREE STRUM*

Not a thing on the ri-ver__ Mc-Clusk-y__ did fear, As he swung his gored
stick o'er his big spot-ted steers; They were round, plump and hand-some, girt-in'
eight foot__ and three, __ Said Mc-Clusk-y, the Scots-man, 'They're the lad-dies__ for me'.

1 Not a thing on the river McClusky did fear,
  As he swung his gored* stick o'er his big spotted steers;
  They were round, plump and handsome, girtin' eight foot and three,
  Said McClusky, the Scotsman, ' They're the laddies for me.'

2 Then along came Bold Gordon, whose skidding was full,†
  As he hollered, ' Whoa hush,' to his little brown bulls,
  Short-legged and shaggy, girtin' eight foot and nine,
  ' Too light,' said McClusky, ' to handle our pine.'

3 The day was appointed and soon did draw nigh,
  For twenty-five dollars their fortune to try,
  Both eager and anxious next morning was found,
  The judge and the scaler appeared on the ground.

4 Along came Bold Gordon, his pipe in his jaw,
  To his little brown bulls he hollers, ' Whoa, haw!'
  He says, ' Chew your cuds, boys, you need never fear,
  For we easily can beat them, the big spotted steers.'

5 Says McClusky to Sandy, ' We'll take off their skins,
  We'll dig them a hole and we'll tumble them in,
  We'll mix up a dish and we'll feed it to them hot,
  We'll learn them damn Yankees to face the bold Scot.'

6 After supper was over, McClusky appeared
  With belt ready-made for his big spotted steers,
  To make it he tore up his best mackinaw,
  He was bound to conduct it according to law.

7 Then up stepped the scaler, saying, ' Hold on you awhile,
  Your big spotted steers are behind just one mile,
  You skidded one hundred and ten and no more,
  Whilst Bold Gordon has beat you by ten and a score.'

8 The boys then all laughed and McClusky did swear
  As he tore out by handfuls his long yellow hair,
  So it's fill up your glasses and fill them up full
  And we'll drink to the health of the little brown bulls.

* goad   † expert

55. THE PINERY BOY

FROM: p. 85 of *Ballads and Songs of the Shanty Boy*, F. Rickaby (Harvard U.P., 1926).
Used by permission. SEE: Belden, 186; Guide (*Sweet William*); Randolph I, 300;
Sharp II, 86. *The Sailor Boy* is known in print and tradition in all Britain, Maritime
Canada, Southern Mountains and Midwest. See also note on *Black is the Colour*.
Seamus Ennis notes tune common in S.E. Ireland.

Flowing ♩=112

GUITAR— ANY 2/4 STYLE
BANJO— 1, 2 & 4B

O, a rafts-man's life is a wear-i-some one, It caus-es man-y fair maids to weep and mourn, It
caus-es them to weep and mourn For the loss of a true love that nev-er can re-turn.

1 O a raftsman's life is a wearisome one,
It causes many fair maids to weep and mourn,
It causes them to weep and mourn
For the loss of a true love that never can return.

2 ' O father, O father build me a boat
That down the Wisconsin I may float,
And every raft that I pass by,
There I will enquire for my sweet Pinery Boy.'

3 As she was rowing down the stream
She saw three rafts all in a string,
She hailed the pilot as they drew nigh,
And there she did enquire for her sweet Pinery Boy.

4 ' O pilot, O pilot, tell me true,
Is my sweet Willie among your crew?
O tell me quick and give me joy,
For none other will I have but my sweet Pinery
[Boy.

5 ' O auburn was the colour of his hair,
His eyes were blue and his cheeks were fair,
His lips were of ruby so fine,
Ten thousand times they've met with mine.'

6 ' O honoured lady, he is not here,
He's drowned in the Dells, I fear;
'Twas at Lone Rock as we passed by,
O there is where we left your sweet Pinery Boy.'

7 ' Dig me a grave both long and deep,
Place a marble slab at my head and feet,
And on my breast a turtle dove
To let the world know that I died for love,
And at my feet a spreading oak,
To let the world know that my heart was broke.'*

*The last couplet runs to the tune of the final two lines of
the melody.

56. THE RIVER IN THE PINES

FROM: p. 119 of *Ballads and Songs of the Shanty Boy*, F. Rickaby (Harvard U.P., 1926).
Used by permission. As sung by William Bartlett, Eau Claire, Wisconsin. Tune
said to be Swedish in origin, although Peter Kennedy finds many similar Irish
airs—*Hot Asphalt, The Lament of William Riley*, etc.
Piano arrangement by MATYAS SEIBER

1 O Mary was a maiden when the birds began to sing,
  She was fairer than the blooming rose so early in the spring,
  Her thoughts were gay and happy and the morning gay and fine,
  For her lover was a river-boy from the River in the Pines.

2 Now Charlie he got married to his Mary in the spring,
  When the trees were budding early and the birds began to sing.
  ' But early in the autumn when the fruit is in the wine,
  I'll return to you, my darling, from the River in the Pines.'

3 'Twas early in the morning in Wisconsin's dreary clime,
  When he rode the fatal rapids for that last and fatal time.
  They found his body lying on the rocky shore below
  Where the silent water ripples and the whispering cedars blow.

4 Now every raft of lumber that comes down the Chippeway,
  There's a lonely grave that's visited by drivers on their way.
  They plant wild flowers upon it in the morning fair and fine,
  'Tis the grave of two young lovers from the River in the Pines.

57. CANADA-I-O

FROM: *Maine Woods Songster*, Phillips Barry (Powell, Cambridge, Mass., 1939). As sung by Mrs. Annie Marston, Charleston, Maine. Words attributed to Ephraim Braley, same place, 1854. SEE: Beck, 16; Gray, 37; Laws, 152; Rickaby, 41; see Freedman, 415 for notes. Root song probably Scots *Caledoni-o*. Next stage, English broadside, *Canada-i-o*.

Piano arrangement by MATYAS SEIBER

1 Come all ye jolly lumbermen and listen to my song,
But do not get discouraged, the length it is not long,
Concerning of some lumbermen who did agree to go,
To spend one pleasant winter up in Canada-i-o.

2 It happened late one season in the fall of '53
A preacher of the gospel one morning came to me,
Said he, ' My jolly fellow, how would you like to go
To spend one pleasant winter up in Canada-i-o?'

3 To him I quickly made reply and unto him did say
' In going out to Canada depends upon the pay.
If you will pay good wages, my passage to and fro,
I think I'll go along with you to Canada-i-o.'

4 ' Yes, we will pay good wages and will pay your passage out,
Provided you sign papers that you will stay the route.
But if you do get homesick and swear that home you'll go,
We never can your passage pay from Canada-i-o.'

5 It was by his gift of flattery he enlisted quite a train,
Some twenty-five or thirty, both well and able men.
We had a pleasant journey, o'er the road we had to go,
Till we landed at Three Rivers up in Canada-i-o.

6 After we had suffered there some eight or ten long weeks,
We arrived at headquarters up among the lakes,
We thought we'd found a paradise, at least they told us so,
God grant there may be no worse hell than Canada-i-o.

7 To describe what we have suffered is past the art of man,
But to give a fair description, I will do the best I can.
Our food, the dogs would snarl at it, our beds were on the snow,
We suffered worse than murderers up in Canada-i-o.

8 Our hearts were made of iron and our souls were cased in steel,
The hardships of that winter could never make us yield,
Field, Philips, and Norcross, they found their match, I know,
Among the boys that went from Maine to Canada-i-o.

9 But now our lumbering is over and we are returning home,
To greet our wives and sweethearts and never more to roam,
To greet our wives and sweethearts and never more to go
Unto the God-forsaken place, called Canada-i-o.

58. MOOSEHEAD LAKE

FROM: p. 226 of *Our Singing Country*, John and Alan Lomax (Macmillan, N.Y., 1937). From singing of Elmer George, Calais, Vt. SEE: Flanders I, 174; Gray, 60; Laws, 154; see also Beck and Rickaby for similar songs to *Derry Down* tune.
Piano arrangement by MATYAS SEIBER

Rowdy ♩ = 200

GUITAR- 4
BANJO- 1 (WALTZ TIME)

1 In eighteen hundred and ninety-two
Bant Breau and George Elliot they started a crew,
They were jolly good fellows as ever you saw,
And they landed us safely upon Moosehead Lake.
CHORUS:
Lovely fa-de-little-aro, sing too-ral-all-day.

2 Upon the Northwest carry we met with the boss,
And then we got on a spree,
We built him a storehouse and likewise a camp,
Lo   one of our bold woodsmen all on that wild tramp.   (CHO.)

3 About five in the morning the cook would sing out,
' Come bullies, come bullies, come bullies turn out.'
And some would not mind him, but back they would lay,
And it's ' Jesus H. Christ, will you lay there all day?'   (CHO.)

4 Bill Mitchell, you know, kept our shanty,
And as mean a damn man as you ever did see.
He'd lay around the shanty from morning till night,
And if a man said a word he was ready to fight. (CHO.)

5 One morning 'fore daylight, Jim Lou he got mad,
Whipped hell out of Mitchell, and the boys was all glad,
And Bill's wife she stood there, the truth I will tell,
She was tickled to death to see Mitchell catch hell. (CHO.)

6 Old Griffin he stood there, the grizzly old drake,
A hand in the racket we feared he would take.
Some of the boys, they pulled him away,
He says, ' Fight and be damned, I've nothing to say.' (CHO.)

7 And then on a Sunday, the boss he would say,
' Your axes go grind, for there's no time to play.
For next Monday morning to the woods you must go,
And forty-five spruce every day you must throw.' (CHO.)

8 About six in the evenings to the camps we'd all steer,
' Side board the grindstone ' was all you could hear.
' Side board the grindstone ' for the turns they'd all fight,
And keep the damned old grindstone a-furling all night. (CHO.)

59. BOLD JACK DONAHUE

FROM: p. 306 of *Ballads and Sea Songs of Nova Scotia*, W. Roy Mackenzie (Harvard U.P., 1928). Used by permission. Sung by Dick Hines, River John, N.S. SEE: Lomax I, 209. Relative of *Van Diemen's Land*. Both songs of Irish and Australian origin.

Piano arrangement by MATYAS SEIBER

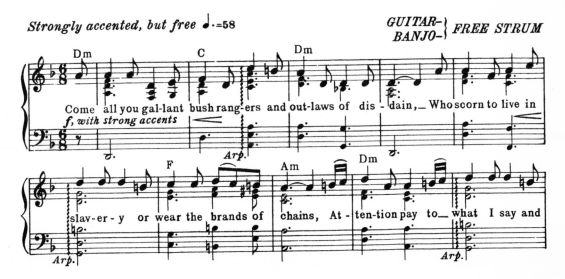

val-ue it if you do,___ I will re-late the match-less fate of bold Jack Don-a-hue.

Arp.

NB. This song can be also accompanied rhythmically, *i.e.* $\frac{6}{8}$ ⏀⏀ etc.

1 Come all you gallant bushrangers and outlaws of disdain,
Who scorn to live in slavery or wear the brands of chains,
Attention pay to what I say and value it if you do,
I will relate the matchless fate of bold Jack Donahue.

2 This bold undaunted highwayman, as you shall understand,
He was banished for his natural life from Erin's happy land,
In Dublin City of renown his first breath ever he drew,
And his deeds of valour entitled him of bold Jack Donahue.

3 He scarcely there had reached his fate on the Australian shore,
When he took to the highway as he had done before,
And every day the newspapers would publish something new
Concerning of that highwayman they called Jack Donahue.

4 As Donahue and his companions walked out one afternoon,
Little thinking of the brands of death that would afflict them soon,
To their surprise the horse-police well armed came in view,
And in quick time they did advance to take bold Jack Donahue.

5 'O no,' said cowardly Wangelo, 'such things can never be.
Don't you see there's eight or ten of them? It's time for us to flee.
And if we wait, we'll be too late, and the battle we'll surely rue.'
'Then begone from me, you cowardly dogs!' cried bold Jack Donahue.

6 The sergeant said to Donahue, 'Discharge your carabine!
Or do you intend to fight with us or unto us resign?'
'To surrender to such cowardly dogs I never intend to do,
This day I'll fight for liberty,' cried bold Jack Donahue.

7 'Now if they had been true to me I would recall their fame,
But people will look on them with scorn and great disdain.
I'd rather range the wild woods round like a wolf or kangaroo
Than I'd work one hour for the government!' cried bold Jack Donahue.

8 The sergeant and the corporal they did their men divide,
Some men fired behind him and others at his side,
The sergeant and the corporal they fired at him, too,
Till at length a ball it pierced the heart of bold Jack Donahue.

9 Nine rounds he fired, shot five police before the fatal ball
That pierced the heart of Donahue and caused him for to fall.
And as he closed his struggling eyes he bade the world adieu,
Kind Christians all, pray for the soul of Bold Jack Donahue.

60. SILVER JACK

Words: Lomax, *Cowboy Songs* (Macmillan, N.Y., 1938), 234; tune by Alan Lomax.
SEE: Laws, 157; Rickaby, 125.

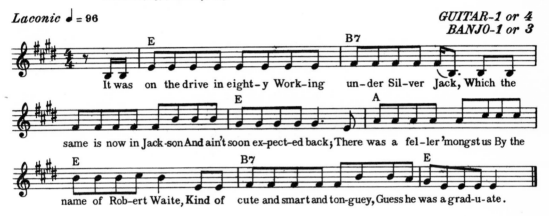

1 It was on the drive in eighty
Working under Silver Jack,
Which the same is now in Jackson
And ain't soon expected back;
There was a fellow 'mongst us
By the name of Robert Waite,
Kind of cute and smart and tonguey,
Guess he was a graduate.

2 He could talk on any subject,
From the Bible down to Hoyle,
And his words flowed out so easy,
Just as smooth and slick as oil.
He was what they call a sceptic,
And he loved to sit and weave
Hifalutin' words together,
Tellin' what he didn't believe.

3 Now back in camp one Sunday
We was all just settin' around,
Smokin' niggerhead tobacco
And hearin' Bob expound—
' Hell,' he said, ' was all a humbug—'
And he made it plain as day
That the Bible was a fable
And we 'lowed it looked that way.

119

4 These miracles and suchlike
Were too rank for him to stand,
' And as for Him they called the Saviour,
He was just a common man.'
' You're a liar,' someone shouted,
' And you've got to take it back,'
Then everybody started—
'Twas the words of Silver Jack.

5 And he cracked his fists together
He stacked his duds and cried,
' It was in that there religion
That my mother lived and died;
And though I haven't always
Used the Lord exactly right,
When I hear a chump abuse Him,
He's got to eat his words or fight.

6 Now this Bob, he weren't no coward,
And he answered bold and free,
' Stack your duds and cut your capers
For there ain't no flies on me.'
And they fit for forty minutes,
And the crowd would whoop and cheer
When Jack spit up a tooth or two
Or Bobby lost an ear.

7 But at last Jack got him under
And he slugged him onct or twict,
And straightway Bob admitted
The divinity of Christ;
But Jack kept reasoning with him
Till the poor cuss gave a yell
And 'lowed he'd been mistaken
In his views concernin' Hell.

8 Then the fierce encounter ended
And they riz up from the ground,
And someone brought a bottle out
And kindly passed it round.
And we drank to Bob's religion
In a cheerful sort o' way,
But the spread of infidelity
Was checked in camp that day.

61. THE FROZEN LOGGER

Composed by James Stephens, various printings and recordings.

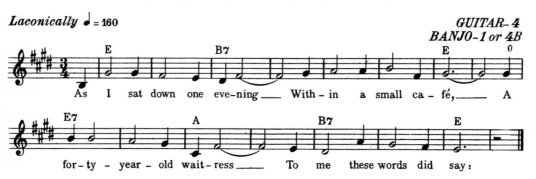

1 As I sat down one evening
Within a small café,
A forty-year-old waitress
To me these words did say:

2 ' I see you are a logger
And not a common bum,
For no one but a logger
Stirs his coffee with his thumb.

3 ' My lover was a logger,
There's none like him today;
If you poured whisky on it,
He'd eat a bale of hay.

4 ' He never shaved the whiskers
From off his horny hide,
But he drove them in with a hammer
And bit 'em off inside.

5 ' My logger came to see me
  On one freezing day,
  He held me in a fond embrace
  That broke three vertebrae.

6 ' He kissed me when we parted,
  So hard he broke my jaw;
  I could not speak to tell him
  He'd forgot his mackinaw.

7 ' I saw my logger lover
  Sauntering through the snow,
  A-going gaily homeward
  At forty-eight below.

8 ' The weather tried to freeze him,
  It tried its level best.
  At one hundred degrees below zero
  He buttoned up his vest.

9 ' It froze clean through to China,
  It froze to the stars above,
  At one thousand degrees below zero
  It froze my logger love.

10 ' They tried in vain to thaw him,
  And if you'll believe me, sir,
  They made him into axe-blades
  To chop the Douglas fir.

11 ' And so I lost my lover,
  And to this café I come,
  And here I wait till someone
  Stirs his coffee with his thumb.'

WORKERS AND FARMERS

62. THE JULIE PLANTE

THE DEEPWATER SAILORS from New England who shipped out on the Great Lakes expecting to find a soft berth and easy voyages received a rude surprise. The runs between ports were brief, but this only meant more work for the crews in loading and unloading the grain, the lumber, and the iron ore. Whipped by continental winds and tempests of polar origin, the lakes churned up tremendous seas, and in these narrow waters there was little room for a vessel to run before a storm . . . Someone has said that if the Lakes were drained, the bottom would be found covered with skeletons of hundreds of vessels and thousands of men lost there since navigation began in the early eighteenth century.

Apart from the sea chanteys, which were sung on the Lakes in the days of sail, shipwreck songs form the largest section of the folklore of the Great Windy Lakes. This ballad comes from the pen of W. H. Drummond (1865-1907), famous for his poetry in *habitat*, or French-Canadian English, but it appealed so much to the Lake sailors that, long before it was published, it was a favourite in bar-rooms all round the Lakes.

63. RED IRON ORE

A MINING ENGINEER, named George Sturz, who was a dreamer and a stubborn man, came into the low-lying hills west of Lake Superior with the conviction that he would discover valuable mineral deposits there. He and his Negro servant, Bonga, fought through the tamarack, endured the attack of hordes of mosquitoes during long summer months, until Sturz found the iron deposits he was looking for. In 1884 he watched the first schooner laden with almost pure iron ore put out from a Minnesota port bound for the iron foundries of the East. Other iron pits opened back of Duluth and, before Sturz died, he saw on the Lakes a fleet of vessels of larger tonnage than the combined Pacific and Atlantic maritime fleets of the U.S.A., carrying the iron for the sinews of the nation east along the Lakes.

This ballad, set to the ever-fresh Irish derry-down tune, stems from the days of sailing ships and shovel loading. Today the leading docks of Duluth can pour twelve thousand tons of iron into the hold of an ore-carrying steamer in a quarter of an hour. Then with her decks nearly awash, the great vessel surges out into the wicked chop of Lake Superior to race her sister ships for the ports along Lake Erie's shore.

SOURCE: *North Star Country*, Meridel le Sueur.

64. THE AVONDALE MINE DISASTER

GEORGE KORSON in his *Minstrels of the Mine Patch* tells the terrible story that lies back of this ballad of the first great anthracite mine disaster. Early in the morning of September 6,

1869, a fire started in the shaft of the mine at Avondale. No alternative escape route or source of air supply had been provided for this primitive death-trap, and when the flames roared up the shaft and set the breaker at the mouth on fire, the men below were doomed. While rescuers at the surface battled with the fire, the men underground frantically threw up a barricade of boxes and barrels, stuffing the cracks with bits of their clothing to keep out the dreaded black damp. A rescue party at last groped their way through the dark alleys of the mine and found the bodies of sixty-seven miners, horribly bloated and deformed by the poisonous gases, behind an ineffective shelter. The final toll of the dead in this Pennsylvanian Black Hole came to one hundred and ten men and boys.

No one knows who composed the ballad. It appeared soon after the victims of the disaster were buried, printed on penny broadsides and attributed to various miner authors. Hundreds of copies were sold. Everyone in the coalfields sang it. Versions have been picked up as far away as Newfoundland.

Such ballads continue to be sung because the disaster at Avondale was not the last or even the most frightful of the accidents that have killed so many miners.

The practice of composing mine disaster ballads has by no means died out. George Korson has collected two fat books of American miners' songs, and when I visited the Durham coalfields in England in 1952, I was handed a sheaf of broadsides which had been published in this century. The proceeds from their sale are customarily given to the families of men killed in mine disasters.

65. MY SWEETHEART'S A MULE

MINING MULES were almost as tough as the miners themselves. Horses usually proved too nervous for underground work, but a mining mule, with a leather guard to protect his head from the roof, and a flickering lamp set between his ears, could surefootedly pick his way along the dark passages, pulling several times his own weight in coal. A mule became so accustomed to life underground that, when he was put out to pasture in the sunlight, he would refuse to eat grass until he had watched his companions for several days. Despite their stubbornness, they proved to be tough, unexcitable, loyal members of the underground team. The men grew deeply attached to their four-footed comrades, and sometimes went on strike when the management transferred a mule from one mine to another.

66. THE FARMER IS THE MAN

AFTER THE CIVIL WAR the railroads fingered out across the Middle West, financed by huge grants of government land. Railroad agents in Europe and the East spread the news about the wonderlands of the West, and the country filled up with new farmers. The freshly turned sod produced bumper crops and the Middle West became the breadbasket of the world. Then the railroads raised their freight and storage rates and when the price of corn and wheat tumbled, the railroads and banks began to foreclose mortgages on the newly developed farmlands. They told the farmers that they had overproduced.

' They tell us about over-production,' cracked one hayseed. ' It's like my old man. His whiskers hang down in front like a mattress and on top he's as bald as a billiard table. Over-production on the chin and bad distribution upstairs. Hell, he ain't got time to shave. At night he just takes off his britches and throws them under the bed, rolls over and meets them on the other side and then hollers at me to go and feed the stock. We came out here and worked ourselves to death to make good homes for our families, and all we got to show for it is mortgages! What we have to do from now on is raise less corn and more hell!'

The people banded together for political action in the grange, the Farmers' Alliance, the Greenback-Labor Party, and the Populist Party. The paper, *The Great West*, distributed at the first convention of the Populists, said:

Men of the West, the party of the common people is come and it is a giant at birth. Its sledge hammer swings with the muscles of the toiling army. Its songs will come out of the oppressed.'

It was a singing convention. Under placards that read ' WE DO NOT ASK FOR SYMPATHY OR PITY. WE ASK FOR JUSTICE ' the new songs spread like prairie-fire through the hall.

QUOTE: *North Star Country*, Meridel le Sueur.

67. THE HOUSEWIFE'S LAMENT

' You had to be a stout body to be a woman way up west in the Ohio wilderness,' said one old lady, who had raised a big crop of children and grandchildren. ' There wasn't no time to get outside the clearin'. Squash, pumpkins, potatoes, beans, beets, turnips and the rest of the garden truck to be planted, hoed and gathered. Made our own candles and spun our own flax and wool. The man of the house would go off hunting and git a deer or two, and then laze around between crops. But we never got away from the spinning wheel, the cooking fire and the baby's cradle. I remember a neighbor lady who picked up her knitting and knitted a few rounds at her own husband's funeral, she was so used to keeping busy the whole time.'

An epitaph on a Midwestern tombstone read . . .

> Thirteen years I was a virgin,
> Two years I was a wife,
> One year I was a mother,
> The next year took my life . . .

Hamlin Garland sensitively describes what the harsh life on a prairie farm did to the women . . .

I now began to perceive dimly that my mother was not well. Although large and seemingly strong, her increasing weight made her long days of housework a torture. She grew very tired and her sweet face was often knitted with physical pain.

She still made most of our garments as well as her own, she tailored father's shirts and underclothing, sewed carpet rags, pieced quilts and made butter for market—and yet, in the midst of it all, found time to put covers on our baseball, and to do up all our burns and bruises.

Being a farmer's wife in those days meant laboring outside any regulations of the hours of toil. I recall hearing one of the tired housewives say, ' Seems like I never get a day off, not even on Sunday,' a protest which my mother thoroughly understood and sympathized with.

MRS. SARA A. PRICE of Ottawa, Illinois, who lost sons in the Civil War, recorded this song of feminine protest in her diary.

QUOTES: (a) *Wilderness For Sale*, Havighurst. (b) *A Son of the Middle Border*, Hamlin Garland, p. 139.

68. ME FATHER'S A LAWYER IN ENGLAND

THE ANCESTOR of this world-travelling working-class ditty is the bawdy Aberdonian rhyme that begins . . .

> My father was hung for sheep-stealing,
> My mother was burnt for a witch,
> My sister's a bawdy-hoos keeper,
> And I am a son-of-a-bitch . . .

This song and the spirit that produced it did not die when the hard-boiled Celtic labourers, who hacked down the forests and laid the rails, became city workers. They kept on singing and they kept on telling big lies that nerved them for their new jobs on skyscrapers, subways, and miles of paved streets. Jack Conroy found this story in Chicago . . .

A man that sets bricks in a pavement only needs to have a weak mind, a strong back and a great big hand with long fingers that will stretch and won't strain easy. It ain't no job for a violin player, you can bet your sweet life.

The Wild Man from Williamson County blew into town, ridin' a panther broke to saddle and usin' a rattlesnake sportin' seventeen rattles and a button for a whip, asked for a job on the paving gang and the boss was glad enough to give it to him. It was sizzlin' hot in July and you could fry a steak to a cinder anywheres on the sidewalk. 'I'm a man is work-brickle,' said the Wild Man. 'I'm a man as can't say quit. When I lay a-holt I'm like a turtle, and I don't let loose till it thunders.' 'Brother,' said the foreman, 'if it's labor your heart craves for, you got it right here on the premises. Just lay your lily whites on some of them bricks, slap 'em down on that there sand, and show me you know how to back up your mouth.'

Well, sir, when that Wild Man started in, he jumped up ten feet in the air, and the first brick he nailed a-holt of was smashed into a red powder. The way he dropped them bricks sounded like a hailstorm on a tar roof. The carriers done their best to slow him down, because these pavin' jobs, they don't last none too long, nohow. They slammed bricks on his heels and they bounced 'em off his fingers, but he never paid 'em the least bit of mind. Fourteen men was huffin' and puffin' on the sand drag, clippin' along fifteen miles an hour, and then he had to wait for 'em lots of times. While he was waitin', he packed two hundred bricks under each arm back and forth across the street just to keep limbered up. Or sometimes he lay on the flat of his back and juggled ten bricks at once with his feet. He was the doin'est man that ever hit this burg, and that ain't no lie nor whore's dream.

I tell you, good people, if you want to work on ary paving gang, be sure to ask and enquire if they's a man from Williamson County on the job, or if one has been seen in them parts lately. If there is, or if he has, don't never bother to start.

QUOTE: Botkin II, 531 (by Jack Conroy—from Chicago Industrial Folklore—MS. of Federal Writers' Project of Illinois).

69. THE HORSE NAMED BILL

AFTER THE GREAT ADVENTURES were over, after the bad men and the Indians had departed and the land was tamed, the people settled down to peaceful lives and quiet folklore. The tall tales of the frontier were replaced by jokes told round the cracker barrels in the country stores. The fellows who inherited the Yankee predilection for stretching the truth just to hear it pop joined liars' clubs and competed in national contests. Their favourite subject—the only aspect of Middlewestern life that could not be civilized—was the weather.

From a Wisconsin liars' club comes this tale of a horse and a man out in a prairie blizzard.

Tom saw a bad storm coming and went on his pony down to the coulee before the blizzard broke to get to the animals. Before darkness fell, his horse stepped into a badger hole and broke its leg and he had to shoot the animal. It was doubtful if a human could live through the night in the snow and the wind. He slit the belly of the horse open, ripped out its entrails, crawled inside the carcass, pulling the ribs together. Against his will he drifted into sleep. Daylight awakened him and he peeped through the jagged ribs to see the sun shining through Arctic cold on hard-packed snow.

When he tried to pry the ribs apart he found the carcass had frozen solid and himself imprisoned inside, able only to get his hands and wrists through the narrow slit which he had not been able quite to close. As he pondered his imminent death from cold and starvation, he heard a couple of coyotes sniffing about the carcass. That gave him an idea. He waited till the coyotes were close to the narrow slit in the carcass, then thrust his hands out like lightning and grabbed the tail of each.

The frightened animals took flight, pulling the carcass across the snow with Tom inside holding tight to their tails; he got his bearings and learned to guide them by pulling the tail of one or the other. Within ten minutes they were hauling his odd carriage up the long slope to his farm. As the carcass came abreast of his front door he let go of the tails of the coyotes, who vanished over the top of the hill, and as his craft skidded to a halt he shouted to his wife, who got an axe and chopped him out. After he'd had a cup of coffee, he went and did the chores.

QUOTE: *North Star Country*, Meridel le Sueur.

70. LOVE IS PLEASIN'

THE TIDE keeps running west across the ocean, bringing new singers and new songs; but the songs that are picked up and passed on by American singers are usually variations on themes that have always been popular. Thus in the 1940's Jean Ritchie, the Kentucky folk singer, met an Irish kitchen-maid just come over to New York City, who had this lovely Irish variant of the *Turtle Dove—Waly, Waly—Tender Ladies* family (*see* song 99). Jean learned the song almost without thinking, and the rest of us, also without reflection, accepted it as one of our own.

62. THE JULIE PLANTE

FROM: the Ivan Walton Collection (University of Mich.). Used by permission.
Words by William Drummond. SEE: Rickaby, 93. Seamus Ennis points out
melody like Irish *As I Roved Out* and Scots *Trooper and the Maid*—basically old Irish
jig tune.

Piano arrangement by MATYAS SEIBER

1. On wan dark night on de Lake St. Clair
   De win' she blow, blow, blow,
   An' de crew of de wood scow *Julie Plante*
   Got scar' an' run below.
   For de win' she blow like hurricane,
   By'n by she blow some more,
   An' de scow bus' up jus' off Grosse Pointe
   Ten acres from de shore.

2. De captain walk on de fron' deck,
   He walk on de hin' deck, too;
   He call de crew from up de hol'
   An' he call de cook also.
   De cook she's name was Rosie,
   She com' from Montreal
   Was chamber-maid on lumber barge
   On de beeg Lachine Canaal.

3 De night was dark like wan black cat,
   De wave run high an' fas',
   W'en de captain take hees poor Rosie
   An' lash her to de mas'.
   An' den he take de life preserve
   An' jump off in de lake,
   Say'n, ' Au revoir, ma Rosie dear,
   I go drown for your sake.'

4 Nex' mornin' veree earlee,
   'Bout half pas' two-t'ree-four,
   De captain, scow, an' poor Rosie
   Was corpses on de shore.
   For de win' she blow like hurricane,
   An' den she blow some more,
   An' de scow bus' up jus' off Grosse Pointe,
   Ten acres from de shore.

5 Now, all good wood scow sailormen,
   Take warnin' by dat storm,
   An' go marree some nice French girl,
   An' leev on wan beeg farm.
   De win' may blow like hurricane
   An' s'pose she blow some more,
   You can't get drown on Lake St. Clair
   So long you stay on shore.

63. RED IRON ORE

FROM: p. 164 of *Ballads and Songs of the Shanty Boy*, F. Rickaby (Harvard U.P., 1926). Used by permission. As sung by M. C. Dean, Virginia, Minnesota.
SEE: Lomax II, 477. The Irish *Derry Down* tune, which occurs in many songs of the North—see *Moosehead Lake*. Related to *The Dreadnought* and *Little Brown Bulls*.

Ballad style ♪ = 152

GUITAR-4 (WALTZ TIME)
BANJO-1 (WALTZ TIME)

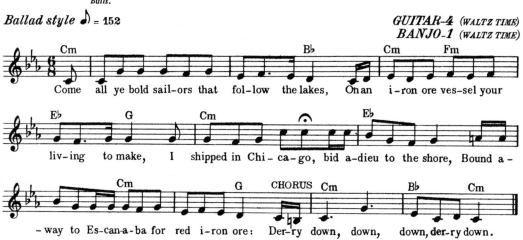

Come all ye bold sail-ors that fol-low the lakes, On an i-ron ore ves-sel your liv-ing to make, I shipped in Chi-ca-go, bid a-dieu to the shore, Bound a-way to Es-can-a-ba for red i-ron ore: Der-ry down, down, down, der-ry down.

1 Come all ye bold sailors that follow the lakes,
   On an iron ore vessel your living to make,
   I shipped in Chicago, bid adieu to the shore,
   Bound away to Escanaba for red iron ore:
   CHORUS:
   Derry down, down, down, derry down.

2 Next morning we hove up along the *Exile*,
  And soon was made fast to an iron ore pile,
  They lowered their chutes and like thunder did roar,
  They spouted into us that red iron ore. (CHO.)

3 Some sailors took shovels, while others got spades,
  And some took wheelbarrows—each man to his trade,
  We looked like red devils, our fingers got sore,
  We cursed Escanaba and that damned iron ore. (CHO.)

4 The tug *Escanaba* towed us out of the Minch,
  The *Roberts*, she thought she'd left us in a pinch,
  And as she passed by us, she bid us goodbye,
  Saying, ' We'll meet you in Cleveland next 4th of July.' (CHO.)

5 Through Old Louise Island it blew a fresh breeze,
  We made the Foxes, the Beavers, the Skilligalees,
  We flew by the Minch for to show her the way,
  And she never hove in sight till we were off Thunder Bay. (CHO.)

6 Across Saginaw Bay the *Roberts* did ride,
  With dark and deep water rolling over her side,
  We went through North Passage—O Lord, how it blew,
  And all round the Dummy the fleet followed, too. (CHO.)

7 Now the *Roberts*'s in Cleveland, made fast stem and stern,
  And over the bottle we'll spin a big yarn,
  But Captain Harvey Shannon had ought to stand treat,
  For getting to Cleveland ahead of the fleet. (CHO.)

64. THE AVONDALE MINE DISASTER

FROM: *Minstrels of the Mine Patch*, G. G. Korson (Grafton Press, 1927). Used by permission. Words from James Fox, Scranton; tune from David Rodden, Nanticoke. SEE: Greenleaf, 123; Laws, 208; AAFS—76B, album 16.

Smoothly and steadily ♩. = 92

GUITAR- 2A, 2B, 6B
BANJO- 4A

Good Christians all, both great and small, I pray ye lend an ear, And listen with at-ten-tion while the truth I will de-clare; When you hear this la-men-ta-tion, it will cause ye to weep and wail, A-bout the suf-fo-ca-tion in the mines of A-von-dale.

1 Good Christians all, both great and small, I pray ye lend an ear,
And listen with attention while the truth I will declare;
When you hear this lamentation it will cause ye to weep and wail,
About the suffocation in the mines of Avondale.

2 On the sixth day of September, eighteen hundred and sixty-nine,
Those miners all then got a call to go work in the mine;
But little did they think that death would gloom the vale
Before they would return again from the mines of Avondale.

3 The women and the children, their hearts were filled with joy,
To see the men go work again, and likewise every boy;
But a dismal sight in broad daylight soon made them all turn pale,
When they saw the breaker burning o'er the mines of Avondale.

4 From here and there and everywhere they gathered in a crowd,
Some tearing off their clothes and hair and crying out aloud,
'Get out our husbands and our sons, Death he's going to steal
Their lives away without delay, in the mines of Avondale.'

5 But all in vain, there was no hope one single soul to save,
For there is no second outlet from the subterranean cave.
No pen can write the awful fright and horror that did prevail
Among those dying victims in the mines of Avondale.

6 A consultation then was held, 'twas asked who'd volunteer
For to go down this dismal shaft, to seek their comrades dear;
Two Welshmen brave, without dismay, and courage without fail,
Went down the shaft, without delay, in the mines of Avondale.

7 When at the bottom they arrived and thought to make their way,
One of them died for want of air, while the other in great dismay,
He gave a sign to hoist him up, to tell the dreadful tale,
That all were lost forever in the mines of Avondale.

8 Sixty-seven was the number that in a heap were found,
It seemed they were bewailing their fate in underground;
They found the father with his son clasped in his arms so pale.
It was a heart-rending scene in the mines of Avondale.

9 Now to conclude and make an end, their number I'll pen down;
One hundred and ten of brave stout men were smothered underground;
They're in their graves till the last day, their widows may bewail
And the orphans' cries, they rend the skies, all round through Avondale.

65. MY SWEETHEART'S A MULE

FROM: *Minstrels of the Mine Patch*, G. G. Korson (Grafton Press, 1927). Used by
permission.

Piano arrangement by MATYAS SEIBER

My sweetheart's a mule in the mines,
I drive her without any lines,
On the bumpers I sit and tobacco I spit
All over my sweetheart's behind.

131

66. THE FARMER IS THE MAN

FROM: *Resettlement Song Sheets*, edited Charles Seeger (Washington, 1936).
SEE: Greenway.

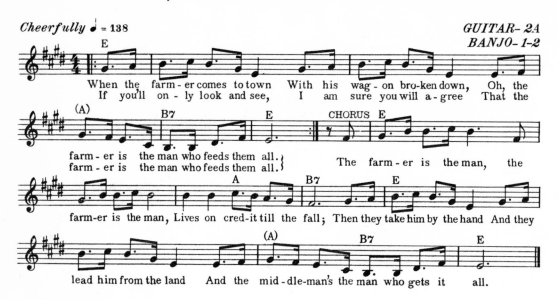

1 When the farmer comes to town
With his wagon broken down,
Oh, the farmer is the man who feeds them all.
If you'll only look and see,
I am sure you will agree
That the farmer is the man who feeds them all.
CHORUS:
The farmer is the man, (2)
Lives on credit till the fall;
Then they take him by the hand
And they lead him from the land
And the middleman's the man who gets it all.

2 When the lawyer hangs around,
While the butcher cuts a pound,
Oh, the farmer is the man who feeds them all.
And the preacher and the cook
Go a-strolling by the brook,
Oh, the farmer is the man who feeds them all.

CHORUS:
The farmer is the man, (2)
Lives on credit till the fall
With the interest rate so high
It's a wonder he don't die,
For the mortgage man's the man who gets it all.

3 When the banker says he's broke,
And the merchant's up in smoke,
They forget that it's the farmer feeds them all.
It would put them to the test
If the farmer took a rest,
They'd know that it's the farmer feeds them all.
CHORUS:
The farmer is the man, (2)
Lives on credit till the fall;
And his pants are wearing thin,
His condition, it's a sin,
He's forgot that he's the man who feeds them all.

67. THE HOUSEWIFE'S LAMENT

FROM: p. 28, vol. 6, of *Sing Out* (People's Songs, N.Y., 1956). Used by permission. Related to *The Old Man's Lament*—see No. 192.

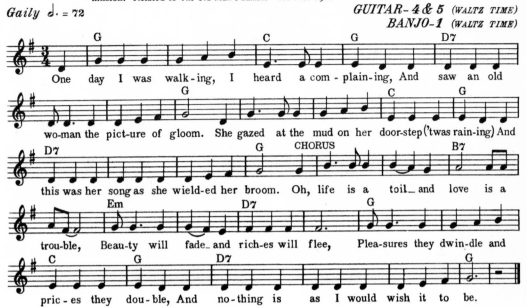

1. One day I was walking, I heard a complaining,
   And saw an old woman the picture of gloom.
   She gazed at the mud on her doorstep ('twas raining)
   And this was her song as she wielded her broom.
   CHORUS:
   Oh, life is a toil and love is a trouble,
   Beauty will fade and riches will flee,
   Pleasures they dwindle and prices they double,
   And nothing is as I would wish it to be.

2. There's too much of worriment goes to a bonnet,
   There's too much of ironing goes to a shirt,
   There's nothing that pays for the time you waste on it,
   There's nothing that lasts us but trouble and dirt.   (CHO.)

3. In March it is mud, it is slush in December,
   The midsummer breezes are loaded with dust,
   In fall the leaves litter, in muddy September
   The wallpaper rots and the candlesticks rust.   (CHO.)

4. There are worms on the cherries and slugs on the roses,
   And ants in the sugar and mice in the pies,
   The rubbish of spiders no mortal supposes
   And ravaging roaches and damaging flies.   (CHO.)

5. With grease and with grime from corner to centre,
   Forever at war and forever alert,
   No rest for a day lest the enemy enter,
   I spend my whole life in a struggle with dirt.   (CHO.)

6 Last night in my dreams I was stationed forever
On a far little rock in the midst of the sea,
My one chance of life was a ceaseless endeavour
To sweep off the waves as they swept over me.   (CHO.)

7 Alas! 'Twas no dream; ahead I behold it,
I see I am helpless my fate to avert.—
She lay down her broom, her apron she folded,
She lay down and died and was buried in dirt.   (CHO.)

68. ME FATHER'S A LAWYER IN ENGLAND

FROM: p. 935 of *Songs and Ballads of Southern Michigan*, Gardner and Chickering (University of Mich. Press, 1939). Used by permission. As sung by B. A. Chickering, Belding, Michigan, 1931. SEE: JAFL XXIX, 187. This song in its Irish and Scots form is violent and bawdy, indicating a provenance among soldiers, tinkers, and criminals. It has a very wide urban currency. See *Wanderin'*, *Ridin' Ol' Paint*, Sandburg, etc. Common Irish jig tune.

1 Me father's a lawyer in England,
Me mother's a justice of peace,
Me sister's a Shaker and an apple-pie baker,
She makes them of taller* and grease.
CHORUS:
To-me-fang, to-me-fang, fang-o-leary.
To-me-fang, to-me-fang, fang-o-lay,
To-me-hoot-te-toot, too-te-toot, larry,
To-me-whack, fal-dee-diddle al-a-day.
To-me-whack, fal-dee-diddle al-de-day.
* tallow

2 Me father is a hedger and ditcher,
Me mother does nothing but spin;
Me sister is a Shaker and an apple-pie maker.
O how the money comes in.

3 Me wife she is dirty, she's nasty;
She is lousy and itchy and black,
She is a divil for fighting and scolding;
Her tongue goes clickety-clack.

4 Me sister she works in a laundry,
   Me father, he fiddles for gin,
   Me mother, she takes in washing,
   Me God, how the money rolls in.

This same ditty is popular at Australian singsongs.

1 My father's an apple-pie baker,
   My mother makes synthetic gin,
   My sister sells sin to the sailors,
   My God, how the money rolls in.

2 My brother's a street missionary,
   He saves little girlies from sin,
   He'll save you a blonde for a dollar,
   My God, how the money rolls in.

69. THE HORSE NAMED BILL

FROM: p. 340 of *The American Songbag*, Carl Sandburg (Harcourt, Brace & Co., N.Y., 1927). Used by permission. As sung by Red Lewis, Sauk Center, Minnesota.
SEE: Randolph III, 203.

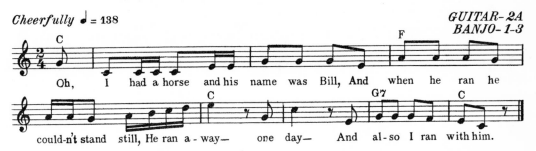

Cheerfully ♩ = 138   GUITAR– 2A / BANJO– 1-3

Oh, I had a horse and his name was Bill, And when he ran he could-n't stand still, He ran a-way— one day— And al-so I ran with him.

1 Oh, I had a horse and his name was Bill,
   And when he ran he couldn't stand still,
   He ran away—one day—
   And also I ran with him.

2 He ran so fast he could not stop.
   He ran into a barber shop,
   And fell exhaustionized—with his eye-teeth—
   In the barber's left shoulder.

3 I had a gal and her name was Daisy
   And when she sang the cat went crazy
   With deliriums—St. Vituses—
   And all kinds of cataleptics.

4 One day she sang a song about
   A man who turned himself inside out
   And jumped—into the river—
   He was so very sleepy.

5 I'm going out in the woods next year
   And shoot for beer—and not for deer—
   I am—I ain't—
   I'm a great sharpshootress.

6 At shooting birds I am a beaut.
   There is no bird I cannot shoot
   In the eye, in the ear, in the teeth,
   In the fingers.

7 Oh, I went up in a balloon so big,
   The people on the earth they looked like a pig,
   Like a mice—like a katydid—like flieses
   And like fleasens.

8 The balloon turned up with its bottom side higher,
   It fell on the wife of a country squire,
   She made a noise like a doghound, like a steam
   And also like dynamite.   [whistle,

9 Oh, what could you do in a case like that?
   Oh what could you do but stamp on your hat,
   On your mother, and your toothbrush—and everything—
   That's helpless.

70. LOVE IS PLEASIN'

From singing of an Irish servant girl, recorded by Jean Ritchie, N.Y., 1940's.
SEE notes on *Fair and Tender Ladies*, *Winter's Night*, and *Waly, Waly* in Index and
Guide. Seamus Ennis says: one of the oldest west of Ireland tunes.
Piano arrangement by MATYAS SEIBER

1 O love is pleasin' and love is teasin'
And love's a pleasure when first it is new;
But as love grows older, at length grows colder,
And fades away like the morning dew.

2 I left my mother, I left my father,
I left my brother and my sisters, too,
I left my home and my kind relations,
I left them all for the love of you.

3 If I'd a-knowed before I courted,
That love had a-been such a killin' crime,
I'd a-locked my heart in a box of gold,
And tied it up with a silver twine.

4 O love is pleasin' and love is teasin',
And love's a pleasure when first it is new,
But as love grows older, at length grows colder,
And fades away like the mornin' dew.

THE MARITIME PROVINCES

71. THREE YOUNG LADIES

WHILE THE SINGING of folk songs has recently become the passion of a generation of young people in northern cities, the old pioneer folk-song tradition has virtually disappeared from the North, except in one area, the Maritime Provinces of Canada. There, collectors have been reaping a harvest of ancient songs comparable to that of the Appalachians; there new folk songs have been growing out of the humus of the old.

In Maine, Phillips Barry tells us that he collected the great majority of his songs from recent Irish immigrants who were keeping alive the traditional songs set aside by the established England and Scots families for whom they worked. Thus the newcomers Americanized themselves, and the ballads survived by retreating down the social scale. Mackenzie gives the same report from Nova Scotia. His best informants were descendants of a group of recently arrived French Huguenot refugees, who had so thoroughly adopted the ballad viewpoint of their Canadian hosts that their preferred songs were jingoist British pieces against the French! Fresh arrivals from Ireland and Scotland kept the fire burning, and the isolation and enforced cultural self-dependence of the coastal villages gave shelter to the old songs.

It seems likely that this area was the principal point of distribution for the journalistic ballad about work, which became the rage of the West. The east coast area was most receptive to this come-all-ye style, and to the creation of new factual ballads, indeed, many important lumberjack ballads seem to have been composed by Maritime singers. Thus, the Maritimes may be termed the heartland of the northern folk-song region, exhibiting its characteristics in the most pronounced fashion. Voices are more open; the lustier songs of Britain are more frequently sung; there are, as might be expected, more songs of sea life. Otherwise, the Maritime folk-song pattern is virtually identical with that of New England, and may be regarded as indicative of what the folk music of the north-east area was like in colonial times.

It is significant that the violent old ballads are still of such importance to these modern North-easterners. Among others they treasure this ancient incestuous story of the robber who had lived so long in the wilds that he failed to recognize his own sisters, and killed them when they refused to yield to him. This is a ballad theme widespread in Scandinavia, among the Scots tinkers, and on the rugged North Atlantic coast—that is, among people accustomed to long separation from their loved ones. Kenneth Peacock recorded this version from the singing of Mrs. Ken Monk, of King's Cove, Newfoundland.

72. THE KANGARO

THIS FAVOURITE Anglo-American song for children was already old in the time of King Charles I. After its first publication in a joke book in the year 1627, it became a part of the print-transmitted English nursery song tradition, and has appeared in most Mother Goose collections since this vogue began about two hundred years ago. That folk are still altering the song in their own way, however, shows up in their substitution of 'kangaro' for 'carrion crow' in this lively version from Chezzetook, Nova Scotia. Walter Roast, the singer who gave it to Helen Creighton, apparently did not know the fine concluding stanza:

'Zooks,' quoth the tailor, 'I care not a louse,
For we shall have puddings, chitterlings and souse . . .'

73. THE MAID ON THE SHORE

THE SONGS OF MERMAIDS and sirens echo faintly in this rare and lovely ballad which has been recorded once in England, once in Ireland, once each in Maine, Missouri, California, and Oregon, but several times in the Maritime Provinces. Clearly it belongs to the more permissive northern tradition, for the South has two completely innocent songs about mermaids. Its most important connexions are with a type of pastoral ballad (especially popular in France, but known also in Britain), in which a clever maiden outwits her lover and keeps her virginity in spite of very risky circumstances. *The Ballad of Broomfield Hill*, for instance, tells of a girl who wagers her knight that she can meet him in a lonely meadow and yet return home a maid. She then causes him to fall into a magical sleep, leaves sure signs of her visit, and scampers home in safety. Risqué ballads of this type are fairly common in the Northeast, particularly in the Maritime Provinces, but rare in the South.

It is quite possible, in fact, that this ballad originated somewhere along the north-east coast and that its composer was an English-speaking Frenchman, as were so many of the best Nova Scotia singers. There is an occasional ineptness of phrasing which hints that *Maid on the Shore* may have been translated from another language, or at least thought out in one. Further, the song is characterized by a certain vagueness and a sort of cloying sweetness, which one seldom encounters in the Anglo-American tradition, but often in the French pastoral ballad.

74. THE MARY L. MACKAY

THE GREAT TRADITION of Anglo-American sea ballads has never died out among the fishermen and sealers of the Maritime Provinces of Canada. This salty verse, born on heaving, spray-swept decks, has its own way of being sung . . .

His attitude was characteristic—left hand deep in his waistband pocket and right hand gripping his glass; one shoulder as if to windward, and feet well apart to meet the heave of the deck, evidently, eyes bent on the lookout at the forem'st head, and a voice pitched to reach that same forem'st head with certainty, against a fresh and rising breeze—standing so, as if he were to the wheel, Wesley sang the ballad. Omitting not a single course of that lively vessel nor a single order, he sailed her from the dock, out of the harbor, down the coast, off to the Bank, westerly again, across the Bay of Fundy and into the harbor of Gloucester and rounded her off to the owner's dock. Wesley's fellow skippers entered heartily into the chorus. With feet well braced and bodies swaying, the skippers roared the toast after a fashion that must have carried every syllable of it to every awakening sleeper in the block.

That is the way fishermen sing. And when you have heard a great song sung that way, sung as Captain Archie sings, you remember that you have heard something as much a part of out-of-doors as the great winds of heaven—and yet it is art.

QUOTE: *Minstrelsy of Maine*, Eckstorm and Smyth (Houghton Mifflin, 1927).

75. MARY ANN

A CENTURY AGO, Edouard Hovington, a singing French voyageur and trapper, who cruised the North Canadian woods for the Hudson Bay Company, learned a fragment of this song from an Irish sailor. The song became his companion at lonely camp fires in the wilderness of the North; it changed as he set his traps along the blue rivers and cold, pale lakes. At last, in the 1920's, he taught it to Marius Barbeau, the dean of Canadian folklore, who kindly permitted it to be published in this volume. The song is a lusty Canadian cousin of the Scots *Waly, Waly*, and the English *Turtle Dove*.

76. WHEN A MAN'S IN LOVE

. . . A SONG which hints at the survival of Irish country courting customs, such as bundling, in the Maritime Provinces . . . Irish immigrants flocked into the United States and Canada all during the first part of the nineteenth century, bringing folk song from western counties, where traditional music was still a part of everyday life, into a land where it was a dying art. They filled the vacuum, and while the established settlers of Scots and English origin listened in the silence of their new-found respectability, the Irish took over their ballad tradition and added to it new songs about their adventures in the woods and upon the waters of their new home. Mrs. Greenleaf, in her work on Newfoundland folk songs, describes the Irish manner of singing that became typical not only of Newfoundland, but of the whole of the North. The singer, after protesting modestly . . .

that he ' has the cold ' and ' never could sing anyway ', he gives judicious attention to the little movable spit-box filled with sawdust and conveniently placed under the sofa. Then, fixing his eyes on vacancy, he begins his song. He sings with unchanged volume of tone, without effort at impersonation. The chief characteristic of his singing is the embellishment of the basic melody with the greatest possible variety of turns, slurs, grace-notes, quavers, unexpected accents and subtle syncopations. As the story develops, emotion is roused. When he comes to about the middle of the last line he stops singing, and mumbles the rest in his speaking voice, thus indicating the conclusion of the song and his descent to earth from the heights of Parnassus. Although a perfectly familiar convention to a Newfoundland audience,* this conclusion is so surprising to Americans that they invariably laugh, however tragic the song.

QUOTE: Greenleaf, p. xxxviii.

* And in Ireland, as well as among American lumberjacks—*Author*.

77. A GREAT BIG SEA
78. I'ZE THE BYE
(from Newfoundland)

EVERYWHERE in the Celtic world—in Spanish Galicia, Brittany, Scotland, Wales, Ireland, and the West of England—one finds the practice of singing dance tunes, when no instrument is present to supply the music. The Newfoundlanders call it ' chin-music ' . . .

. . . The singer thinks of the rhythm required for the first figure and commences to tap it out with the heels and toes of both rubber-booted feet. Many people say that if you tied a singer's feet down he could not sing at all. A suitable tune soon comes to mind, and he begins it, sometimes singing words, but more often vocables to carry the tune and mark the rhythm. The tunes are complicated with syncopations, rapid notes, slides and turns, and the singer takes breath when he can. Their effect is mesmeric and of all the dance tunes I heard, I was able to record but one correctly. The pitch is always true, and the masters of the dance-song can sing for every other dance all the evening, and conclude by favoring the company with a long ballad, and show no signs of hoarseness at the finish.

QUOTE: Greenleaf, p. xxxii.

71. THREE YOUNG LADIES

As sung by Mr. and Mrs. Ken Monk, King's Cove, Newfoundland, collected by
Ken Peacock. SEE: Brown II, 44; Child, No. 14; Coffin, 46; Flanders II, 61;
Greenleaf, 10; Greig, 15. Found frequently Maritime Canada; occasionally
North-East—rarely South.

1 Three young ladies went out for a walk,
    All-a-lee and a-lone-ee-o,
  They met a robber on the way,
    On the bonny, bonny banks of the Vergie-o.

2 He took the first one by the hand,
  He whipped her round till he made her stand.

3 Saying, ' Will you be a robber's wife,
  Or will you die by my pen-knife?'

4 ' I will not be a robber's wife.
  I'd rather die by your pen-knife.'

5 He took in his hands his own pen-knife
  And then he took her own sweet life.

6 He took the second by the hand . . .

*Verses 7-11 repeat the drama with the same lines for the
two other young ladies till the third says:*

12 ' I will not be a robber's wife,
   Nor will I die by your pen-knife.

13 ' If my brothers were here tonight,
   You would not have killed my sisters bright '

14 ' Where are your brothers, I pray you tell?'
   ' One of them is a minister.'

15 ' What's the other, I pray you tell?'
   ' He's out a-robbing, just like yourself.'

16 ' The Lord have mercy! Look what I've done!
   I've killed my sisters all but one.'

17 He then picked up his own pen-knife,
   And there he took his own sweet life.

72. THE KANGARO

As sung by Aubrey Murphy, Mosherville, N.S., Canada, Columbia Record ML4948. SEE: Belden, 270; Creighton II, 244; Guide; Mackenzie, 376; Opie, 111; Sharp II, 324.

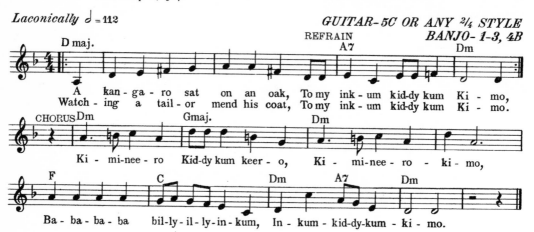

1 A kangaro sat on an oak,
      To my inkum kiddy kum ki-mo,
   Watching a tailor mend his coat,
      To my inkum kiddy kum ki-mo.

   CHORUS:

   Ki-mi-nee-ro
   Kiddy kum keer-o,
   Ki-mi-nee-ro-ki-mo,
   Ba-ba-ba-ba billy-illy-inkum,
   Inkum-kiddy-kum ki-mo.

   * molasses

2 Bring me my arrow and my bow,
      Till I go shoot that kangaro. (CHO.)

3 The old man fired, he missed his mark,
      He shot the old sow through the heart. (CHO.)

4 Bring me some 'lasses* in a spoon,
      Till I go heal that old sow's wound. (CHO.)

5 O now the old sow's dead and gone,
      Her little ones go waddling on. (CHO.)

73. THE MAID ON THE SHORE

FROM: p. 63 of *Ballads and Sea Songs of Newfoundland*, Elizabeth Greenleaf (Harvard U.P., 1933). Used by permission. As sung by Mrs. Annie Walters, Rocky Harbor, 1929. SEE: Belden, 107; Creighton II, 64; Mackenzie, 74. Melody related to the Irish *Cutting Down Broom*.

roam all a-lone on the shore, shore, shore, But to roam all a-lone on the shore.

1 'Twas of a young maiden who lived all alone,
  She lived all alone on the shore-o;
  There was nothing she could find to comfort her mind,
  But to roam all alone on the shore, shore, shore,
  But to roam all alone on the shore.

2 'Twas of a young captain who sailed the salt sea,
  Let the wind blow high or low-o.
  ' I will die, I will die,' the young captain did cry,
  ' If I don't get that maid on the shore, shore, shore . . .

3 ' I have lots of silver, I have lots of gold.
  I have lots of costly wear-o.
  I'll divide, I'll divide with my jolly ship's crew,
  If they'll row me that maid from the shore, shore, shore . . .'

4 After long persuadence they got her on board,
  Let the wind blow high or low-o,
  Where he placed her on a chair in his cabin below,
  ' Here's adieu to all sorrows and care, care, care . . .'

5 Where he placed her on a chair in his cabin below,
  Let the winds blow high or low-o,
  She sung charming and sweet, she sung neat and complete,
  She sung captain and sailors to sleep, sleep, sleep . . .

6 She robbed him of silver, she robbed him of gold,
  She robbed him of costly wear-o,
  And she stole his broadsword, instead of an oar,
  And she paddled her way to the shore, shore, shore . . .

7 ' My men must be crazy, my men must be mad,
  My men must be deep in despair-o,
  To let her go 'way, with her beauty so gay,
  And paddle her way to the shore, shore, shore . . .'

8 ' Your men was not crazy, your men was not mad,
  Your men was not deep in despair-o,
  I deluded the sailors as well as yourself,
  I'm a maiden again on the shore, shore, shore . . .'

74. THE MARY L. MACKAY

FROM: p. 24 of *Songs and Ballads from Nova Scotia*, Helen Creighton (Dent & Sons, Toronto, 1933). Used by permission. As sung by Edmund Henneberry, Devils Island, N.S. Words composed by Frederick W. Wallace. Published in *Canadian Fishermen*, 1914.

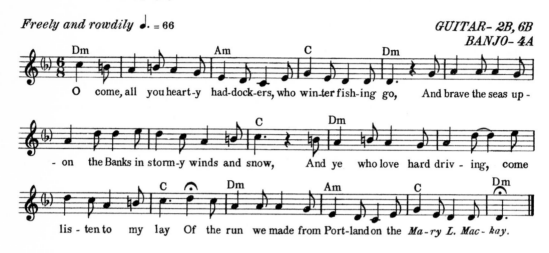

1 O come, all you hearty haddockers, who winter fishing go,
   And brave the seas upon the Banks in stormy winds and snow,
   And ye who love hard driving, come listen to my lay
   Of the run we made from Portland on the *Mary L. Mackay*.

2 We hung the muslin on her, the wind began to hum,
   Twenty hardy Nova Scotia men chock full of Portland rum,
   Mainsail, foresail, jib and jumbo, on that wild December day,
   As we passed Cape Elizabeth and slugged for Fundy Bay.

3 We slammed her by Monhegan as the gale began to scream,
   Our vessel took to dancing in a way that was no dream,
   A howler o'er the toprail we steered sou'west away,
   O she was a hound for running, was the *Mary L. Mackay*.

4 ' Storm along and drive along, punch her through the ribs,
   Don't mind your boarding combers as the solid green she dips.
   Just mind your eye and watch the wheel,' our skipper he did say.
   ' Clear decks we'll sport tomorrow on the *Mary L. Mackay*.'

5 We slammed her to Matinicus, the skipper hauled the log,
   ' Sixteen knots! Lord Harry, ain't she just the gal to jog?'
   The half-canned wheelsman shouted, as he swung her on her way,
   ' Just watch me tear the mainsail off the *Mary L. Mackay*.'

6 The rum was passing merrily and the gang was feeling grand,
   Long necks dancing in her wake from where we left the land,
   Our skipper he kept sober, for he knew how things would lay,
   And he made us furl the mainsail on the *Mary L. Mackay*.

7 We laced our wheelsman to the box as he steered her through the gloom.
A big sea hove his dory-mate right over the main-boom.
It tore the oil pants off his legs and you could hear him say,
' There's a power of water flying o'er the *Mary L. Mackay*.'

8 Our skipper didn't care to make his wife a widow yet,
He swung her off to Yarmouth Cape with just her foresail set.
And passed Fourchu next morning and shut in at break of day,
And soon in sheltering harbour lay the *Mary L. Mackay*.

9 From Portland, Maine, to Yarmouth Sound two-twenty miles we ran,
In eighteen hours, my bully boys, now beat that if you can.
The gang said 'twas seamanship, the skipper he kept dumb,
But the force that drove our vessel was the power of Portland rum.

75. MARY ANN

FROM: *Come a-Singing*, Ed. Marius Barbeau for the National Museum of Canada.
Used by special permission. SEE: Guide and Index (*Turtle Dove, Waly, Waly*).
Also notes on *Fair and Tender Ladies* and *Winter's Night*.
Piano arrangement by MATYAS SEIBER

And I am bound a-way for the sea, Ma-ry Ann.

O fare thee well, my own true love,
O fare thee well, my dear,
For the ship is a-waiting, the wind blows high,
And I am bound away for the sea, Mary Ann. (2)

2 O—yonder don't you see the dove
A-sitting on the stile?
She is mourning for the loss of her own true love,
As I do now, for you, my dear Mary Ann. (2)

3 A lobster boiling in the pot,
A blue-fish on the hook,
They are suffering long, but it's nothing like
The ache I bear for you, Mary Ann. (2)

4 O had I but a flask of gin
With sugar here for two,
And a great big bowl for to mix it in,
I'd pour a drink for you, Mary Ann. (2)

76. WHEN A MAN'S IN LOVE

FROM: p. 214 of *Traditional Songs of Nova Scotia*, Helen Creighton and Doreen Senior (Ryerson Press, Toronto, 1950). Used by permission. To the tune of *The Star of the County Down*, known throughout Ireland. Probably composed by Irish bard in the 18th century, S.W. Ireland.
Piano arrangement by MATYAS SEIBER

snow. The moon had gent-ly— shone her light O'er the dark and lone-some way, When I ar-rived at her sweet cot Where all my—trea-sure lay.

1 When a man's in love, sure he fears no cold,
Like I not long ago,
Like a hero bold for to seek my love,
I set out through frost and snow.
The moon had gently shone her light
O'er the dark and lonesome way,
When I arrived at her sweet cot
Where all my treasure lay.

2 I gently rapped at my love's door
And softly she arose.
'O let me in, my own dear love,
And soft the door unclose.
Now let me to your chamber, love,
O let me to your bed,
O let me to your chamber, love,
For I am wet and ill.'

3 'To let you to my chamber, love,
My parents would ne'er allow,
Come sit you down by a good fireside,
And I'll sit there with you.'
Her hands were soft and her breath was sweet,
And her tongue it did slowly glide,
I stole a kiss from her ruby lips
And all her colour fades.

4 'It's many's the night and many's the day
I came for to visit you
And tossed about with cold winds and storms
And wet with the morning dew;
It's many's the night I have courted you
Against your parent's will,
I never forced you to be my bride,
So now, my love, sit still.

5 'For tomorrow I am going away
To old Columbia's shore,
And never more will you behold
Your lover any more.'
'Don't talk of going away, my love,
For those words do break my heart.
Come let us go and get married,
Before you and I do part.'

6 'Perhaps your parents will forget,
Perhaps they will forgive,
For I resolve this very night
Along with you to live.'
And with a kiss the bargain was made
And the wedding soon went on,
And now they are free from all courting cares
Since they unite in one.

77. A GREAT BIG SEA

FROM: *Old Time Songs of Newfoundland* (Gerald S. Doyle, St. John's, Newfoundland, 1955). Used by permission. Melody from Scots *Gaberlunzie Man*.

Lively ♪ = 208   *GUITAR – ANY 2/4 STYLE*
BANJO – 1-3

A great big sea hove in Long Beach, Right-fol-lar-fa-did-dle-did-dle-di-do. A great big sea hove in Long Beach And Gran-ny Snooks, she lost her speech, To-me-right-fol-did-dle-fol-dee.

1 A great big sea hove in Long Beach,
   Right-fol-lar-fa-diddle-diddle-di-do,
   A great big sea hove in Long Beach
   And Granny Snooks, she lost her speech,
   To-me-right-fol-diddle-fol-dee.

2 A great big sea hove in the harbour, (2)
   And hove right up in Kio's parlour.

3 O dear mother, I wants a sack, (2)
   With beads and buttons all down the back.

4 Me boot is broke, me frock is tore. (2)
   And Georgie Snooks I do adore.

5 O fish is low and flour is high, (2)
   So Georgie Snooks he can't have I.

6 But he will have me in the fall,
   And if he won't I'll h'ist my sail
   And say goodbye to old Canaille.

78. I'ZE THE BYE

FROM: *Old Time Songs of Newfoundland* (Gerald S. Doyle, St. John's, Newfoundland, 1955). Used by permission. Seamus Ennis says melody from Irish, *Follow Me up to Carlow*.

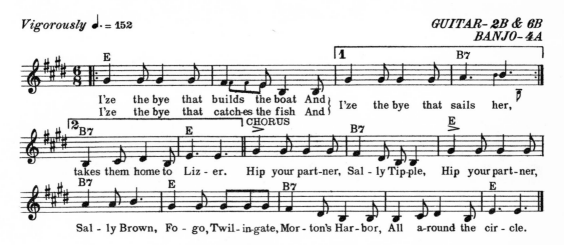

1 I'ze the bye that builds the boat
And I'ze the bye that sails her,
I'ze the bye that catches the fish
And takes them home to Lizer.
CHORUS:
Hip your partner, Sally Tipple,
Hip your partner, Sally Brown,
Fogo, Twilingate, Morton's Harbor,
All a-round the circle.

2 I took Lizer to a dance,
And faith and she could travel,
And every step that she would take
Was up to her knees in gravel. (CHO.)

3 Salts and rinds to cover your flake,
Cake and tea for supper.
Codfish in the spring of the year,
Fried in maggoty butter. (CHO.)

4 Susan White, she's out of sight,
Her petticoat wants a border,
Old Sam Oliver in the dark,
He kissed her in the corner. (CHO.)

PART II. THE SOUTHERN MOUNTAINS AND BACKWOODS

THE SOUTHERN MOUNTAINS
AND BACKWOODS

. . . includes most of the areas of marginal land and centres of ' poor white ' population in the Southern states as far as East Texas, the Southern Appalachians being the spine of the region. Although the cultural gap between the planter whites and the mountaineers was considerable, the lowland poor whites shared the song preferences of their mountaineer cousins. The Northern border was of mixed song culture: (1) In Southern New Jersey along the Pennsylvania border and the Ohio Valley, Northern and Southern white song cultures have interpenetrated. (2) The Ozarks, Texas, and Oklahoma, though strongly Southern in many respects, produced a new batch of folk songs from a mixture of Northern and Southern traits, and are thus considered in Part III, the West.

Southern backwoods singing was mostly unaccompanied, rubato, highly ornamented and solo; the voice ' oriental ', high-pitched and nasal, produced out of a tense body and throat. Accompaniments on stringed instruments have been introduced within the last century, altering the scales and the rhythms, but hardly affecting the singing style. The singers tend to be withdrawn and impersonal in their delivery, but intensely emotional at the same time, the male singers, as in many eastern countries, using such a high, thin tone as to sound quite womanish. Unison singing is rare and poorly blended. Prior to the urban hillbilly style, harmony was seldom used except by the trained choruses of the singing schools.

This is an antique tradition with traits from many parts of Britain, moulded into a distinctive regional style by a common pattern of life. The area is strongly Protestant. The Non-Conformist revival exacerbated the moral and emotional conflicts of this Calvinist and patriarchal folk and touched all their music with melancholy, while their free-and-easy life as log-cabin dwellers and marginal farmers gave their songs a tang of wildness and abandon unknown in Britain and the North. Poverty and isolation permitted this backwoods music to develop on its own for more than a century. Thus it grew strong enough to absorb urban influences and produce a regional style (hillbilly) which has attracted a vast city audience.

ACROSS THE BLUE RIDGE

79. JOHN RILEY

   . . . My folks come over with Christopher Columbus on an old sail ship. But when they got up hyur, they got kindly wild and tuk to follerin' game, a-wanderin' to and fro, till the generations, they all evaporated and the only ones of um war left war them with strength enough to climb up into the hills.

NO WONDER this Southern mountaineer was a bit vague about his antecedents. Until quite lately, we have known very little about the origins of the mountain folk. Theirs was the unremarked passage of the poor across the Atlantic and through the wilderness. The wide and almost impenetrable ranges of the Appalachians, into which they plunged, isolated them from the main currents of American life for more than a century. The lowland South shunned them because they remained loyal to the Federal Government during the Civil War. Thus, until fifty years ago less was known about the lives of these descendants of Daniel Boone and Davy Crockett than about most American Indian tribes. As one old Kentuckian put it, ' All we folks knew up in the hills was we war a-livin'.'

It appears now that the Appalachian mountaineers came from two main stocks. First there were the poor whites from coastal Virginia and the Carolinas, descendants of manumitted white slaves, indentured servants or impecunious later immigrants. These folk, predominantly English in descent, grew weary of living on the fringes of the planter society along the coast and gradually drifted west into the hills. Towards the end of the eighteenth century these hill farmers and pioneers encountered a tide of Scots, Irish, and German settlers, who had reached the limits of the best lands in Pennsylvania and turned south-west down the soft valley of the Shenandoah, looking for homes in the wilderness. The Scots-Irish formed the vanguard of this latter group, and as their singing style eventually came uppermost in the mountains, a word about their history is pertinent here.

Early in the seventeenth century James I broke the back of the Irish rebellion by driving the Ulster Irish off their lands and replacing them with a colony of sixty thousand lowland Presbyterian Scots. This hard-working, abstemious, ballad-singing folk so throve in their new homes as farmers and silk-weavers, that within a century their exports were threatening English manufactures and agriculture. Thereupon the Crown crushed their silk industry with an embargo and imposed a programme of ruinous taxation and expropriation on the farmers. By 1729 these so-called Scots-Irish folk were emigrating to ' wild Americkay ' at the rate of six thousand per year and this current soon doubled. Like John Riley of this ballad, most of them ' sailed over to Pennsylvany ' where William Penn's Quaker government had promised them freedom of worship and free land in the west.

' Being by habit a border people, they pushed to the western fringe of settlement in Pennsylvania, where they at once engaged in sanguinary wars with the Indians.' The good land being soon taken up, the overflow of these radical, small farmers turned south, sticking to the uplands and shunning the slave-owning, Episcopalian, Tory society of the lowlands, which they mistrusted. When Thomas Walker and Daniel Boone brought news of rich land over the mountains to the west, this hardy, hot-headed, dissenting folk swarmed across the Blue Ridge and disappeared in the green tangle of the Appalachians.

A typical pioneer family travelled afoot, carrying their household goods on a couple of packhorses. Along with axe and hunting rifle, they could take little that reminded them as vividly of their homes across the sea as the old ballads with their beloved Celtic tunes. Some of these folk kept travelling west, as the Indians were pressed back towards the Mississippi. Having gained a taste for a free-and-easy backwoods life, they avoided the lowlands, where the southern planter society established itself, and founded their settlements in the marginal lands of the South where they could live as they pleased. Today we find their descendants, singing the same basic stock of songs in the same vocal style, scattered across the whole upland South as far west as Texas and Oklahoma.

Many of the pioneers who passed through the Appalachian gaps lingered on in the vast jungle of green mountains that spread across seventy thousand square miles of the Virginias, Eastern Kentucky and Tennessee, Western North Carolina and Northern Georgia. They became woodsmen, their lives confined to the territory over which they could range on foot. They built their cabins in valleys ' so narrow you had to pry um open to pour in the daylight ', and they farmed hillside patches ' so steep a man had to tie hissef to a tree to keep from fallin' out of his own cornfield '. What roads there were ran among the boulders in the beds of the mountain torrents. As the nineteenth century rolled on, the big world that lay ' way over yonder acrost the mountains ' grew dim and far away. Cut off from the towns and stores, the hill folk learned to ' make do or do without', building their own houses, weaving their own garments, gathering their own medicines in the woods and distilling their music, like their whisky, in a ' mountainy ' way.

Various students have remarked that the isolation of mountain life permitted the preservation of many old songs and tunes which did not survive in Great Britain. This observation is true, but, it seems to me, misses the main point. In the quiet of the hills the varied currents of song, which still follow their separate courses to this very day in the British Isles, came together to form the wild river that we know as mountain music. Looked at in one way, this Southern mountain folk-music is more British than anything one can find in Great Britain; it is truly Scots-Irish-English. Looked at in another, this Appalachian tradition, the product of a century and a half of frontier living, gives us a magnificent view of the cultural life processes of the early American frontier. For the isolation of the mountains did not halt its growth. On the contrary, the mountains provided a shelter in which the pioneer folkways of the late eighteenth century could continue to evolve undisturbed for almost a century longer than anywhere else in the United States. Thus in the Appalachians we find examples of the oldest British ballads and tunes performed in a style that probably dates from the Middle Ages, alongside of a vigorous modern regional music. Happily for the historian of popular culture, there is also material from the intermediate stages of development.

The majority of the songs in this section were actually recorded in the mountains, yet they represent, at least in a general way, the musical culture of the entire backwoods South, settled by folk like John Riley. All these poor whites shared the same ballad tradition. They disappeared into the Southern wilderness to hunt bears, fight Indians, plant corn, still moonshine, attend brush arbour meetings, and, finally, mix their musical heritage with that of the

American Negro. The ballad of the Scots-Irish immigrant John Riley, which is still beloved by Southern mountain singers, tells of the first part of their adventures.

QUOTE: Alberta Pierson Hammun's article 'The Mountain People' in *The Great Smokies and the Blue Ridge,* edited by Roderick Peattie. Copyright, 1943, by Vanguard Press, Inc. Reprinted by permission of the publishers, Vanguard Press, Inc.

80. CUMBERLAND GAP

AMONG the folk who pioneered south from Pennsylvania into the Appalachians were the ancestors of Abraham Lincoln, Stonewall Jackson, Davy Crockett, and Sam Houston, the father of Texas. Daniel Boone, one of that company, settled for a time on the Yadkin in Virginia, but after several years of struggle with debt and taxes, he shoved for the west on the trail of Thomas Walker, who had found the Cumberland Gap in 1750. Boone followed Walker's trace along the blue Holston, the Clinch, and the Powell rivers, turned north through the gap in the Cumberland Mountains, and then pushed on into the fat blue-grass country of central Kentucky. Years later, after his explorations has taken him to the Mississippi Valley, Boone said, ' I have never found but one Kentucky—a spot on earth where nature seems to have concentrated all her bounties . . .'

According to Boone, Kentucky lay on the happiest lines of longitude and latitude that girdled the globe. Acting against the express orders of the government, he was soon leading parties of settlers into the region, and in 1775, just a year before the Revolution, he and his wild companions brought about the purchase of the Kentucky territory from the Cherokees for £10,000. Cumberland Gap became the most important mountain gateway in the tide of Western settlement.

When Boone and the poor folks from the crowded eastern states looked down upon the fair lands of ' old Kaintuck ', they must have felt like celebrating. In this virgin wilderness a hunter could scarce travel a few rods without starting a bear or a fat buck. The sweet rivers ran silver with fish. The corn grew so fast in the fertile soil that ' a man had to step up out of the way to keep from being carried up over the tree tops'.

Cumberland Gap, one may imagine, witnessed some of the wildest jubilations that ever took place on the continent. No frontiersman ever travelled without his horn or, if he could manage it, his keg of strong, Monongahela whisky. Whisky was his remedy against snake-bite, chills and fever, fatigue, and loneliness, and his partner at any kind of jollification. Many a horn passed from hand to hand in the Cumberland Gap and many a wild jig was danced there.

We do not know if fiddlers played at these Cumberland Gap dances. Although the fiddle was the most common musical instrument in the saddle-bags of the pioneers, even it was rare in those far-off and dangerous years. Yet if fiddles were lacking, the settlers still were masters of the Celtic art of mouth music, those rhymed verses which precisely match the dance tunes and guide the feet of the dancers. At home in Scotland Burns and his friends were dancing to braw songs, such as

Tail toddle, tail toddle,
Tommy gars my tail toddle,
But an' ben wi' diddle doddle,
Tommy gars my tail toddle . . .

On the Southern frontier, Americanized Scots continued to rhyme in the same vein . . .

> Buckskin mocassin, towheaded Bill,
> Once went a-courtin' up Jingleberry Hill,
> The first one courted was a pretty gal to see,
> They set right down to Jingleberry tea.
> Possum sop and polecat jelly,
> I ate so much I burst my belly,
> Me an' my gal and her granpap
> All raised the devil in Cumberland Gap . . .

These so-called fiddle-sings were the favourite songs of the men and probably the earliest of native pioneer songs. They were, indeed, one way of taming this new land, for when the unfamiliar landmarks and its animals were named and sung about, they became familiar and friendly. Thus in their rhyming jingles the backwoodsmen covered up the Indian sign and set their Scots-Irish stamp upon the wilderness.

Tax-gatherers, lawyers, old ladies and parsons were far behind over the mountains. In ' old Kaintuck ' a man had elbow-room. For a time these ' Kentucky screamers ', these ' ring-tailed roarers', who felt themselves to be ' half-man, half-horse and half-alligator ', behaved as they ' bodaciously ' and ' teetotaciously ' pleased!

81. THE DEER CHASE

Now I knowed it were the time of year for old bucks to be hardening their horns, so I took the sunny side of the Sugar Loaf. I kept my eyes skinned all the way up, but never seen anything till I got nairly to the top, when up jumped one of the poxtakedest biggest old bucks you ever seen. He dashed round the mounting faster nur a shootin' star of lightnin'. Howsomever I blazed away at him, but he were goin' so fast round the Loaf, and the bullet goin' straight forrud, I missed him.

I felt that my credit as a marksman and of old Bucksmasher was gittin' mighty under repair. I didn't like to be out-generaled in any such a way by such a critter.

Next mornin' I went right smack into my blacksmith's shop, took my hammer and bent old Bucksmasher just to suit the mounting, so that when the pesky old buck started round the mounting, the bullet might take the twist with him, and thus have a fair shake in the race.

I loadened up and moseyed off to try the experiment. I arrove at the spot and up he jumped, hoisted his tail like a kite, kicked up his heels in a banterin' manner, for he'd outdone me so often, he'd got real sassy. I lammed away at him, and away he went round the mounting and the bullet after him—so good a man and so good a boy. I stood chock still. Presently round they come like a streak of sunshine, both buck and bullet, bullet singin' out, ' Where is it? Where is it?' ' Go to it, my fellers,' says I, and away they went round the Loaf like a Blue Ridge storm. Afore you could crack your finger, they was around again, bucklety-whet. Just as they got near me, the bullet throwed him down.

I throwed down old Bucksmasher, out with my butcher knife, jerked off my shot bag and hung it on the horn of one of the prettiest things you ever seen. I thought I'd look at it better when I struck my buck. I knifed him monstrous quick and turned round to look at the curious thing I'd hung my shot bag on, and it were gone most out'n sight. I soon see it were the moon passin' along, and I'd hung my shot bag on the corner of it. I hated mightily to lose it, for it had all my ammernition in it, and 'bout a pound of Thompson's powder . . .

QUOTE: *Fishers River, N.C.*, by ' Skitt ' (H. E. Taliaferro) (Harper, N.Y., 1859).

82. LILY MUNROE

AN OLD mountaineer, when asked if his folks had fought in the Revolutionary war, looked puzzled. 'You mean that old war . . . that big old war when we freed the Yankees?' A Smokey Mountain woman said, 'The first of my folks to come, come over to fight for the King. But when they got hyur, they saw how the colonists were being imposed on, so they swapped sides and started fightin' for America. And that contrary streak still kindly runs in my family . . .'

A 'contrary streak still kindly ran' in a majority of the families that poured over the mountains from Virginia in 1763, after the territory had been ceded by the French. From the beginning they rebelled against the authority of the King's governors, and in 1772, under the leadership of Nolichucky Jack Sevier, they set up the republic of Franklin in the state of Tennessee—'the first men of American birth to establish a free and independent community on the continent.' In 1775, one year before the Revolutionary war began in New England, they signed a militant declaration of independence. During the first months of the Revolution they fought battles against the British troops and their Indian allies deep in the wilderness. And, at a time when Washington's army was in difficulties in the North, the buckskinclad troops from the Republic of Franklin routed the army of Cornwallis at the battle of King's Mountain, North Carolina. A story from that battle establishes an American background for the ballad that is to follow.

Benny Wise's wife couldn't rest easy in her mind and had followed the army to King's Mountain. The days went by and every time one of the big guns went BOOM! she would say, 'O God! Did that one git Benny?'

The last fighting was the worst. Then the mountain men came thundering down off the hill, shouting and putting forth some of the best cussing it's ever been permitted a woman to hear. But Benny Wise's wife wasn't interested, because Benny wasn't one of those who came down off the hill in the flare of Ferguson's burning wagons.

'Hasn't anybody seen Benny Wise?' she kept asking.

At last a smoke-grimed somebody from home came past. 'Yes, I seen him. He's hit, but he's all right.'

'O thank God!'

'And ain't you heard? We won!'

Benny Wise's wife did not know it was news that would thrill the whole country, shock it out of the darkest period of discouragement it had yet known, and give it heart again. All she knew was that the mountain men had won . . . and that Benny was all right.

To a mountain singer's fancy, this British ballad might conjure up any war in history that had been important in her life, from the American Revolution to World War II.

QUOTES: Peattie.

83. RATTLESNAKE

THE CHEROKEE, who claimed Kentucky and Tennessee, were an intelligent, well-organized, and fearless people. Defeated by the whites in 1759, they attacked the frontier settlements as soon as the Revolutionary war broke out in 1776, a move they soon regretted. Seven thousand frontiersmen, led by renowned Indian fighters like Boone, counter-attacked, burnt the Indian corn, cut down their peach trees, levelled their villages, killed and scalped every adult they caught, and, swaggering amid the ruins of the Indian villages, sold the children into slavery. Twenty years after these massacres, the sight of a white man was sufficient to send an Indian child screaming into the forests. The war of extermination continued, in spite of every attempt of the Indians to live peacefully with the whites, until most of the Indians were dead or driven out of the Central South.

The veteran of these Indian wars was as savage a fighter as ever walked the earth— a dead shot, equally skilful with a knife—a man who bragged about the number of ears he had bitten off and eyes he had gouged out in rough-and-tumble fights. His folk heroes were men like Davy Crockett and Mike Fink, who, before they waded into a victim, used language to gather into themselves the strength of all the animals they had conquered in the woods.

I'm shaggy as a bear, wolfish about the head, active as a cougar and can grin like a hyena till the bark will curl off a gum log. There's a sprinkling of all sorts in me, from the lion down to the cougar; and before our war is over, you will pronounce me an entire zoological institute . . .

84. SINGLE GIRL

Come all you Virginia girls and listen to my noise,
Don't go with them Tennessee boys,
For if you do, your fortune will be
Hoecake and hominy and sassafras tea.

THUS the old pioneer song warned the lowland girls to steer clear of the tall young hunters who came down from the Tennessee Gap telling stories of Indian fights and bear hunts across the mountains to the west. These men were hunters and fighters. They left the rest of the work to the women, who chopped wood, carried water and did the ploughing and planting with a rifle handy in case of Indian attacks. Babies came every year. In the family of Jean Ritchie, a fine mountain ballad singer, her great-great-grandmother gave birth to eleven children that lived—her great-grandmother, ten,—her grandmother, ten—and her own mother, fourteen. My own grandmother bore fourteen babies of her own and raised the eight children of her predecessor, who had died in childbirth.

After years of isolation in the hills, far from stores, the people learned to do without shoes, and often went barefoot even when the snow lay deep in the laurel thickets. Men dressed in buckskin and women in homespun, and the log cabins, built of unfinished green logs, were unchinked. A man that would bother to seal up his cabin against the weather would be laughed at for ' fussin' around like some ol' granny-woman '. The hand-hewed shingles curled after a season or so, so that the roofs leaked. The wind blew in through the cracks in the floor in the winter, and the dirt and mud sifted in everywhere, no matter what efforts the housewife made with her little broom of sedge grass.

In time of illness you took strong home remedies and kept your mouth shut about your pain. When babies came, an old midwife might attend who believed that ' it would ease your pain, honey, if you lay on your side and hollered '. No wonder a leathern-faced old mountain woman warned her granddaughter against marriage. ' Don't do hit, honey, don't do hit '. She was thinking of the ways of the mountain men.

SOURCE: Kephart.

159

85. GENTLE FAIR JENNY

The Taming of the Shrew theme occurs in several British ballads common in America. The American background for these songs is suggested in this account of Kentucky mountain family life at the beginning of this century.

. . . the way of the mountains is a patriarchal existence. The man of the house is Lord. He takes no orders from anybody at home or abroad. Whether he shall work or visit or roam the woods with dog and gun is nobody's affair but his own. About family matters he consults with his wife, but in the end his word is law. If Madame be a bit shrewish, he is likely to tolerate it as natural to the weaker vessel; but if she should go too far he checks her with a curt ' Shet up!' and the incident is closed.

The mountain farmer's wife is not only a household drudge but a field hand as well. She helps to plant, hoes corn, gathers fodder, sometimes even plows or splits rails. It is the commonest of sights for a woman to be awkwardly hacking up firewood with a dull axe. When her man leaves home on a journey, he is not likely to have laid in wood for the stove or hearth; so she and the children must drag from the hillside whatever dead timber they can find.

And yet it is seldom that a highland woman complains of her lot. She knows no other. From aboriginal times the men of her race have been warriors, hunters, herdsmen, clearers of forests and the women have toiled in the fields. Indeed, she would scarce respect her husband if he did not lord it over her and cast upon her the menial tasks. It is ' manners ' for a woman to drudge and obey. All respectable wives do that. And they stay at home where they belong, never visiting or going anywhere without first asking their husband's consent.

One old lady summed up her content with her husband by saying, ' He was a good man. If me or any of the children ever done anything wrong, he'd whip us.'

QUOTE: *Our Southern Highlanders*, Horace Kephart, p. 260 (Macmillan, N.Y., 1922). Reprinted by permission of the Macmillan Company, New York.

79. JOHN RILEY

As sung by Peggy Seeger. SEE: Brown II, 305; Guide and Index (*John Reilly*); Randolph I, 262; Sharp II, 22 (*George Reilly*). Found U.S. in N.C., Ky., Tenn., Va., recently in North Ireland and Norfolk, England.
Piano arrangement by MATYAS SEIBER

1 As I walked out one morning early
   To breathe the sweet and pleasant air,
   Who should I spy but a fair young maiden,
   Whose cheeks were like the lily fair?

2 I stepped up to her and kindly asked her
   If she would be a sailor's wife.
   ' O no, kind sir, I'd rather tarry
   And remain single for all my life.'

3 ' What makes you so far from all human nature?
   What makes you so far from all human kind?
   You are young, you are youthful, fair and
                                   handsome,
   You can marry me if you're so inclined.'

4 ' The truth, kind sir, I'll plainly tell you,
   I could have married three years ago
   To one John Riley who left this country,
   Who has been the cause of my grief and woe.'

5 'Come along with me, don't think of Riley.
    Come go with me to a distant shore.
    We will set sail for Pennsylvany,
    Adieu to England for evermore.'

6 'I'll not go with you to Pennsylvany,
    I'll not go with you to a distant shore;
    For my heart is with Riley and I can't forget him,
    Although I may never see him no more.'

7 Now when he saw that she loved him truly,
    He gave her kisses one, two, three,
    Saying, 'I am Riley, your long-lost lover,
    Who has been the cause of your misery.'

8 'If you be he and your name be Riley,
    I will go with you to that distant shore,
    We will set sail for Pennsylvany,
    Adieu to England for evermore.'

9 They locked their hands and their hearts together
    And to the church house they did go,
    And they got married to one another,
    They're living together, doing well.

80. CUMBERLAND GAP

As sung by Peggy Seeger. SEE: Brown III, 381; Lomax II, 274; Randolph III, 264.
Related to *Sugar in the Gourd*.

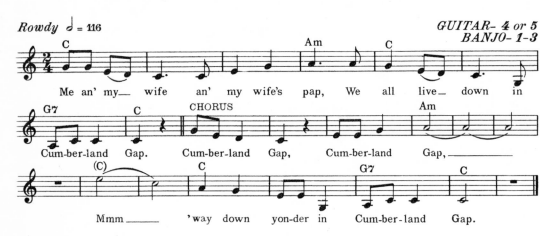

1 Me an' my wife an' my wife's pap,
    We all live down in Cumberland Gap.
    CHORUS:
    Cumberland Gap, Cumberland Gap,
    Mmm* . . .'way down yonder in Cumberland Gap.

2 Cumberland Gap is a noted place,
    Three kinds of water to wash your face. (CHO.)

3 The first white man in Cumberland Gap
    Was Doctor Walker, an English chap. (CHO.)

4 Daniel Boone on Pinnacle Rock,
    He killed Injuns with his old flintlock. (CHO.)

5 Lay down, boys, and take a little nap,
    Fo'teen miles to the Cumberland Gap. (CHO.)

* *A hum that turns into a yell.*

162

6 Old Aunt Dinah, if you don't keer,
   Leave my little jug a-settin' right hyer.   (CHO.)

7 Old Aunt Dinah tuck a little spell,
   Broke my little jug all to hell.   (CHO.)

8 I've got a woman in Cumberland Gap,
   She's got a boy that calls me ' pap '.   (CHO.)

9 Me an' my wife an' my wife's pap,
   All raise hell in Cumberland Gap.   (CHO.)

81. THE DEER CHASE

As sung by Uncle Dave Macon and arranged by Alan Lomax. SEE: Brown III, 250.
Peter Kennedy finds this melody common in England as dance tune (*The Big Ship Sails*).

CHORUS:
Away and away, we're bound for the mountain,
Bound for the mountain, bound for the mountain,
Over the mountains, the hills and the fountains,
Away to the chase, away, away.

1 We heed not the tempest, the toil nor the danger,
As over the mountain away goes Ranger,
All night long, till the break of dawn,
Merrily the chase goes on;
   Over the mountains, the hills and the fountains,
   Away to the chase, away, away.   (CHO.)

163

2 Now we're set just right for the race,
  The old hound dogs are ready for the chase,
  The deer is a-bounding and the hounds are
                                    a-sounding,
  Right on the trail that leads o'er the mountain.
    Over the mountains, *etc.* (CHO.)

3 Listen to the hound bells, sweetly ringing,
  Over the mountain the wild deer's springing,
  All night long till the break of dawn,
  Merrily the chase goes on.
    Over the mountains, *etc.* (CHO.)

4 See there the wild deer, trembling, panting,*
  Trembling, panting, trembling, panting,
  Only for a moment for hunger standing,
  Then away on the chase away, away.
    Over the mountains, *etc.* (CHO.)

* *Tempo for this stanza* ♪ = 144, *slower.*

82. LILY MUNROE

As collected and arranged by Alan Lomax. SEE: Belden, 171; Brown II, 314;
Guide (*Polly Oliver*); JEFSS IV, 84, VIII, 9; Ord, 233; Randolph I, 215. This song
appears in broadsides in Britain and probably America, but in its present form is
widely current in U.S. but not found in England, although related to *William
Taylor, Polly Oliver*, etc.
Piano arrangement by MATYAS SEIBER

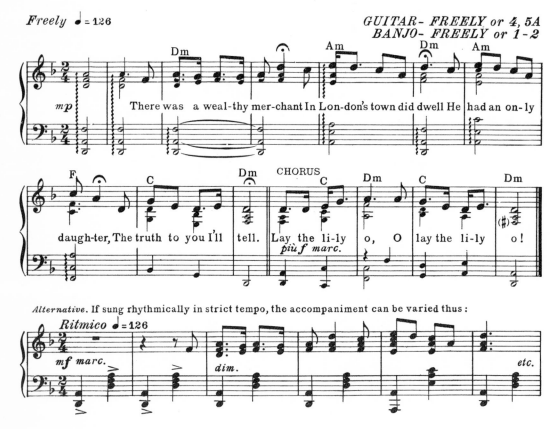

1 There was a wealthy merchant
In London's town did dwell;
He had an only daughter,
The truth to you I'll tell.

CHORUS:
Lay the lily O, O lay the lily o!

2 Her sweetheart went a-sailin'
With trouble on his mind,
A-leavin' of his country
And his darlin' love behind.   (CHO.)

3 His sweetheart dressed herself all up
In a man's array,
And to the war department
She then did march away.   (CHO.)

4 'Before you come on board, sir,
Your name we'd like to know!'
A smile played over her countenance,
'They call me Lily Munroe.'   (CHO.)

5 'Your waist is slim and slender,
Your fingers they are small,
Your cheeks too red and rosy
To face a cannon ball.'   (CHO.)

6 'My waist, I know, is slender,
My fingers they are small,
But it would not make me tremble
To see ten thousand fall.'   (CHO.)

7 The drum began to beat,
The fife began to play,
Straightway to the field of battle
They all did march away.   (CHO.)

8 And when the war was ended,
This girl, she searched the ground,
Among the dead and wounded,
Until her love she found.   (CHO.)

9 This couple they got married,
So well they did agree;
This couple they got married,
And why not you and me?   (CHO.)

83. RATTLESNAKE

From singing of Aunt Molly Jackson, Clay County, Ky., collected and arranged
by Alan Lomax.

Freely ♩ = 92   GUITAR—FREE STRUM, THEN 2A (OR ANY ²⁄₄ STYLE)
BANJO—FREE STRUM, THEN 1-3
accelerato (♩ = 126)

Rat-tle-snake___ O rat-tle-snake, What makes your teeth so white? I've been in the bot-tom
all my life, An' I ain't done no-thin' but bite, bite, Ain't done no-thin' but bite.

1 Rattlesnake, O rattlesnake,
What makes your teeth so white?
I've been in the bottom all my life,
An' I ain't done nothin' but bite, bite,
Ain't done nothin' but bite.

2 Muskrat, O muskrat,
What makes you smell so bad?
I've been in the bottom all of my life
Till I'm mortified in my head, head, *etc.*

3 Groundhog, groundhog,
  What makes your back so brown?
  It's a wonder I don't smotherfy,
  Livin' down in the ground, ground, *etc.*

4 Rooster, O rooster,
  What makes your claws so hard?
  Been scratchin' this gravel all my days,
  It's a wonder I ain't tired, *etc.*

5 Jaybird, O jaybird,
  What makes you fly so high?
  Been robbin' your cornpatch all my life,
  It's a wonder I don't die, die, *etc.*

84. SINGLE GIRL

Collected, adapted, and arranged by Alan Lomax. SEE: Belden, 437; Brown III, 54; JEFSS VIII, 145; Randolph III, 69; Sharp II, 32. Widely known England and America, not North-East. This song is related to *Still I Love Him*, see *Skiffle Album*, Lomax (Robbins, 1957).

With drive ♩ = 100

GUITAR- ANY ²/₄ STYLE
BANJO- 1-3

When I was sin-gle, I went dressed so fine, Now I am mar-ried, go

rag-ged all the time. Lord,___ I wish I was a sin-gle girl a-gain.

1 When I was single, I went dressed so fine,
  Now I am married, go ragged all the time.
  CHORUS:
  Lord, I wish I was a single girl again. (2)

2 Dishes to wash and spring to go to,
  Now I am married, I've everything to do. (CHO.)

3 When I was single, eat biscuits and pie
  Now I am married, eat cornbread or die. (CHO.)

4 When I was single, my shoes they did screak,
  Now I am married, my shoes they do leak. (CHO.)

5 Two little children, lyin' in the bed,
  Both of them so hungry, Lord, they can't hold up their heads. (CHO.)

6 Wash um and dress um and send um to school,
  Long comes that drunkard and calls them a fool. (CHO.)

7 When I was single, marryin' was my crave,
  Now I am married, I'm troubled to my grave. (CHO.)

85. GENTLE FAIR JENNY

As sung by Jean Ritchie, Viper, Ky. SEE: Belden, 92; Brown II, 185; Child, No. 277; Coffin, 146; Creighton II, 94; Freedman, 450; Grieg, 218; Guide (*Robin a-thrush*); Index (*Wee Cooper of Fife*); Randolph I, 187; Sharp I, 271; Wells, 121.
Piano arrangement by MATYAS SEIBER

1 Sweet William married him a wife,
  Gentle fair Jenny, come rosemary,
To be the comfort of his life,
  The dew flies over the green valley.

2 He married his wife and took her home,
But I think her married a little too soon.

3 His wife would neither card nor spin,
For fear of spoiling her delicate skin.

4 His wife would neither bake nor brew
For fear of spoiling her high-heeled shoe.

5 Sweet William come in from a-jogging the plough,
It's 'O my sweet wife, is the food ready now?'

6 'There's cheese and johnny-cake on the shelf,
If you want any more you can get it yourself.'

7 Sweet William has gone out to his barn,
And there he's taken his sheepskin down.

8 He laid the sheepskin over her back,
And with two little willows went whickety-whack.

9 'I'll tell my family and all my kin,
How you this quarrel did begin.'

10 'Go tell your family and all your kin,
That I was tanning my old sheepskin,'

11 Now he comes in from a-jogging the plough,
It's ' Sit you down, sir, the meal's ready now.'

12 Now they live free from care and strife,
And she makes William a very good wife.

THE OLD BALLADS

86. THE DEVIL'S NINE QUESTIONS

EARLY America saw the Devil as a real and living personage. Rocks in New England were scarred by his hoofprints, as he carried off maidens, screaming and howling, over the hills, or came after the men who had sold their souls to him in return for money or success. In one tale he appeared as a snake among the red-hot coals. This serpent coiled up on the dying man's pillow, and when his subject gave the death rattle, the snake flew up the chimney with something looking like a dried apple in its mouth.

A mountain woman tells of the last moments of her mean old husband . . . ' I knowed he war goin', because all the dogs from fur and nigh come around and howled. Hit wur a dark night. But plain as day, comin' down yon side the mountain, through the bresh so thickety a butcher knife couldn't cut hit, I seen the Devil a-comin'. He war ridin' a coal-black cart, drivin' a coal-black oxen. The cart come down to the door and stopped. When it come, it come empty. But when it went away, hit had a big black ball in hit that war Arzy's soul.'

In the recurring dream of one of the best mountain ballad singers she ran through the woods towards her home, pursued by the Devil, tall and black. When she fell exhausted, heard him approach, felt his hot breath, she looked up to see her father leaning over her. This mountain girl remembers that the children in her family so feared their quiet, over-worked, and, normally, gentle father that they would grow tongue-tied in his presence. The one time she, herself, defied him, he whipped her mercilessly with a thorny branch from a rosebush . . . Davy Crockett left home for good at the age of twelve because he could not face another whipping by his father.

Stroppings, canings, paddlings, lashings, cuffings, switchings, and many more torments were, until recently, considered the normal accompaniment of growing up in both America and Britain. The Puritans at one time passed a law which solemnly condemned to death a child that dared to raise his hand against his parents. Dickens, Dostoyevsky, and other humanistic writers of the nineteenth century have described at length the degraded position of children in Western European society; their real terrors certainly explain the hold that stories and ballads about bogeymen, devils, and witches have exercised over the imaginations of our people, particularly the women, who were taught never to fight back. In the folk-lore of the Devil or the bogeyman we can feel the bottomless fear aroused by ruthless, authoritarian father figures who have held women and children in thrall for centuries.

SOURCES: (a) Peattie. (b) Ritchie.

87. COCK ROBIN

OF THE two best-loved children's ballads in English, the first is the story of an animal wedding in which all the animal guests are killed and eaten, the second begins at an inquest and goes on to a funeral; nor is this strange when one considers the blood-stained stanzas of the

Anglo-American ballads beloved of adults. In our culture, children, like their parents, have a passionate relish for violence—in nursery rhymes, cowboy pictures, comic books, murder mysteries, etc. Oppressed, humiliated, denied, bullied, and talked down to by a race of strong giants, their fancies have naturally run to violence and death. In their dreams they have revenged themselves and in their nightmares they have been punished for their guilty thoughts.

The roots of Cock Robin probably go back to Nordic myths about the ritual murder of the bringer of fire and the spring; for the robin or the wren was often sacrificed in European renewal-of-the-year ceremonies. The ballad itself, which has parallels in several European languages, first appeared in print in 1744 when Robert Walpole fell from power. But there can be little doubt that the song antedates this event and was merely revived at that time for the purposes of political satire. Since the eighteenth century, there have been innumerable reprints and parodies, the most notable being Byron's savage and melancholy lines on the death of John Keats in 1821.

> Who killed John Keats?
> I, said the *Quarterly*,
> So savage and Tartarly,
> It was one of my feats . . .

88. THE HOUSE CARPENTER

FOR SOME considerable time, and especially in America, the ballads have been women's songs, attached to the household and the fireside. The men, left to themselves, sang humorous or bawdy songs which satirized love (see *Cumberland Gap,* etc.,) or composed songs about work or deeds of violence (to which whole sections of this volume are devoted). If the men sang the old ballads, this was in the presence of women and was a recognition of feminine interests.

Some writers have explained the feminine attachment to these old, bloody ballads as a result of the natural conservatism of women, whose horizon was limited to their fireside and garden. This explanation merely begs the question. The popularity of a body of songs in a given area or within a given group represents a pattern of preference that corresponds to patterns of conduct and feeling. In my opinion the British folk songs most popular in the backwoods were not merely survivals from a body of lore handed on indiscriminately from overseas sources, but a selection from that lore of vehicles for fantasies, wishes, and norms of behaviour which corresponded (with considerable precision, I believe) to the emotional needs of pioneer women in America. In fact, the universally popular ballads represented the deepest emotional preoccupations of women who lived within the patriarchal family system sketched in the previous pages.

The present ballad, one of the favourite folk songs of early America, but an especial favourite in the South, characterizes man as a tempting demon and romantic love as a temptation that destroys women. In the British original the returned lover, James Harris, is actually a demon from Hell (in some versions the Devil himself).

> They had not sailed a league, a league,
> A league, but barely three,
> Until she espied his cloven foot
> And she wept right bitterly.

The girl asks:

> ' O what is yonder mountain,' she said,
> ' All so dreary with frost and snow?'
> ' O yonder is the mountain of Hell,' he cried,
> ' Where you and I must go.'

The Devil disappeared from most American versions, but the man stands out, as all the more demonic, as Death himself. The woman, believing her first lover is dead, marries and has a secure home with children. The old lover returns and offers her an escape. In the first moments of her romantic adventure, she is splendid—' she glittered and glistened and proudly she walked '—till she is ' taken to be some queen '. But this escape from domestic sordidness lasts scarcely a month. She begins to weep—not for her house or her husband, whom she despises, but for her children. Then, as a punishment for her guilt, she and her lover sink in the sea to rise no more.

This song was sung by women who had come with their men to Pennsylvania and the lowlands—by their daughters who lived and died hard in mountain log cabins—in turn, by their daughters sinking deeper in the squalor of backwoods life. For them, the easiest path out of a bad marriage was to run off with another man. Yet that way, the road of adventure, they would lose what they had and die in guilt, far from their children.

The House Carpenter ballad, in this view, represents the longings of pioneer women for love or for an escape from their log cabin life—both sinful wishes to the Calvinist. The ballad heroine has one moment of romantic splendour. Then she is harshly punished. No fantasy could have been better calculated to reinforce the Calvinist sexual morality of our ancestors. It counselled them to stick to what they had. Indeed, no women have ever been more long-suffering, or more hard-working helpmates, yet they did enjoy songs about women who rebelled, especially if the rebels were punished in the last stanza.

89. BARBARA ALLEN

AT THE TIME of its origin (probably early in the seventeenth century) this plaintive Scots song was only one among hundreds of such folk ballads, yet from the first it made a special impact. On January 2, 1666, Samuel Pepys wrote in his diary . . . ' In perfect pleasure I was to hear her (Mrs. Knipps, the actress) sing, and especially her little Scots song *Barbary Allen* . . .' A century later Oliver Goldsmith registered an even stronger reaction . . . ' The music of the finest singer is dissonance to what I felt when our dairymaid sung me into tears with *Johnny Armstrong's Last Goodnight*, or *The Cruelty of Barbara Allen*.' In 1942, a gnarled old Georgia farmer, who had been my guide through the mountains, said, ' Just do me one favour now, before we say goodbye. Just sing me that old song about Bob'ry Allen one time. My old mammy used to sing it to me, and it looks like ever' time I hear it, it just makes the ha'r rise straight up on my head.' This ballad, if no other, travelled west with every wagon. As someone remarked, they sang *Barbara Allen* in Texas ' before the pale faces were thick enough to make the Indians consider a massacre worth while '. What, then, is the content of the story which so consistently drew tears from the English, and raised the hackles of the pioneers?

In the normal ballad there is almost no incident. A girl refuses a man who says he is dying for love of her. He expires when she turns from him; then she, too, dies of remorse. In fact the song dwells largely upon the sickbed scene and upon Willie's feeling of weakness, his pallor and his helplessness in the face of the proud and angry maid. Barbara is glad to see her Willie dying because of a small misunderstanding which could have been cleared up in a moment. Her remorselessness and Willie's extraordinary demise are not really explained, but represent an undercurrent of powerful feelings which it is assumed the audience understands. In fact, the song is the vehicle for the aggressive fantasies of women and the frustrations of men, of which both the ballad singers and their listeners are unconsciously aware. They apparently believe that men can actually die of love.

One is reminded at once of poor Jude, whose love for the capricious Sue Bridehead brought him to a tragic end. More vividly, one thinks of the sensations of the unsatisfied lover or husband whose choking, burning, aching passion causes him to swear, ' I will die if I cannot have you,'—who, when he is denied, often ' turns to the wall and bust out a-cryin',' just as Willie did.

Rocky Scots mountaineers, phlegmatic British Empire builders, and poker-faced westerners were not prone to such emotional outbursts—in public and in the day-time. Only in the privacy of their nuptial chambers may these stern heroes have wept. There the women, resentful of domestic slavery, rebelling against the painful duties of marriage, longing for tenderness, carrying their culture's conviction that love-making was a loathsome and unhappy duty, could take their revenge. In other words, Barbara Allen, when viewed in this light, is frigid western woman humbling and destroying the man whom she sees as her enemy and antagonist. That she dies at once of remorse, immediately frees her and her sisters of the guilt of hard-heartedness.

No other supposition can, I feel, explain the unique position that this ballad occupies in our tradition. Literary scholars have said, ' The popularity of this song is undoubtedly due to its inclusion in ten or more nineteenth century songbooks and on innumerable broadsides.' Certainly these printings helped to spread the song, but why so many printings? Were the printers free from the emotional problems that have tormented the people of America and Britain for several centuries and which psycho-analysts have recently described?

The restrictive sexual mores of the western world set their hot brand upon the flesh of presidents, of poets, of cowboys, of captains, of men and of women of every class and every religion. Revolt there was, exceptions by the score can be discovered, but the bent of the age did turn women cold, virtuous, and vengeful. The literature of the nineteenth century is full of such characters. Barbara Allen takes revenge for all of them, especially, of course, for the mountain girls, victims of the Calvinist code, who came to the conviction that falling in love was like falling in love with death, but who, because love was the only road open towards personal realization, expected, even yearned, to suffer. In many, many American versions the singers show their unconscious wish to punish the true villain of the whole history, the girl's mother, by gratuitously causing her to die as well . . .

> Sweet William died on a Saturday night,
> Barbara died on Sunday,
> Her mother died for the love of both
> And was buried on Easter Monday.

90. THE TWO SISTERS

THE ROOTS of this ballad go far back into pre-Christian Scandinavia, when the folk believed in magical retribution—in the bones of the dead rising to accuse their murderer. In its primitive form the ballad tells of a girl murdered out of spite by her jealous elder sister; a musical instrument is contrived out of her bones, her golden hair strung to the frame; by chance, this human harp or fiddle is played at the wedding feast of the murderess and the dead girl's betrothed. There the strings of the instrument begin to sing, and sing on and on about the crime of the jealous sister until she is seized by her father, put to the torture and executed.

This tale may be viewed as a fantasy arising from sibling rivalry in our precariously balanced family system. Sisters, competing for the attention of their parents and of available young men, but not permitted by family loyalty to exhibit their jealousy openly, have such dreams or day-dreams of violence. The younger and weaker and favoured child, afraid of her dominant older sister, may fantasy her own murder and the sure punishment of the criminal older sister.* The older sister, who in moments of anger relishes the idea of killing her favoured younger sister, expiates her crime and rids herself of guilt by imagining, dreaming, singing of the sure retribution meted out to her in the ballad.

Folk tales of this content have been found throughout the western world, and the northern ballad form spread early to all Scandinavia, to Iceland, to the Faroes, to the British Isles and the United States. In recent versions the magical singing bones disappear, and the guilty are discovered in normal ways. Yet the story did not lose its appeal. Professor Child points out that *The Twa Sisters* was one of the few ancient ballads still commonly sung in Britain in the early part of the twentieth century, although the edge of the fantasy had been further concealed by turning the ballad into a comic tabloid piece.

> The sister was sent beyond the seas
> And there was devoured by black savagees . . .

North, south and west this cruel story travelled to every part of the United States, and its disturbing character has driven the folk to revise it in a number of ways. The human harp appears in only two or three of these, but the miller who discovers the drowned girl is usually a partner in the crime. Occasionally the ballad has a happy ending, but generally the sister and her accomplice (father) both receive capital punishment. This accords with the American idealization of women, as beings generally incapable of violence. Men can kill, not women, unless some man ' does them wrong ' or, in this case, collaborates with them. In one West Virginia version the miller is the father, and he drowns his own daughter, thus bringing almost to the surface the incestuous aspect of this old story.

Of course, for generations of American pioneer women who loved *The Two Sisters* this dark content has remained at the unconscious level. For them singing it over in the evening with their friends, it has always been an ' old love song ', the ever-recurring refrain repeating again and again the pleasure-filled lines:

> I'll be true to my true love,
> If my love will be true to me.

or in a beautiful chorus from the North Carolina hills:

> Prove true, true to my love, prove true to me.

* Fairy tales such as *Cinderella* and *The House in the Wood* are examples of the many folk stories dealing with sister rivalry.

91. LADY GAY

THE DEATH-WISH of mothers against children is another of the old British ballad themes which has especially attracted American singers, and infanticide is the motif of several frontier ballads, notably *The Cruel Mother* and *Lady Gay*. The former is widespread in the North, the latter, in which the death-wish is masked, one of the commonest southern ballads. Its popularity was reinforced in the '20s by the excellent Victor recording of Buell Kazee, and this version, now general in the mountains, is printed here.

Full texts of *Lady Gay* contain another familiar antique trait—the excessive grief of the living troubling the dead—but this all but disappears in most American forms. There remains: (1) the mother's rejection of her children by sending them off to school; (2) their return and refusal to accept her love. Under its sorrowful religious masque, the ballad conceals hostility and guilt, and perhaps, too, a hint that the mother was a witch who wanted her children to study the black arts ('grammaree'—witchcraft in Scots). A pertinent story, testifying to the lively belief of the backwoodsmen in witchcraft, was collected by Vance Randolph in the Ozarks.

A young man wanted to marry the traditional farmer's daughter, but the match was opposed by his mother, who was able to 'do things'. He married the girl anyhow, and they had a baby. One day the young folks was picking blackberries and the baby was sleeping under a tree only a few yards away. The husband heard a noise and found that an old sow had mangled the infant so badly that it died. The boy looked at the sow and saw that it had eyes exactly like his mother's. He accused the old woman and threatened her life, but she denied everything. Their next baby was also attacked by a sow, but the father got there before it was hurt. He looked at the sow, and the animal trotted away. The boy went home, loaded a rifle with a silver ball and pointed it at his mother. She screamed and begged and confessed on her knees that she had killed his baby. Then in the presence of all the kinfolk she swore that she would not molest his family again, and he was persuaded by his sisters to spare her life. The old witch kept her promise, and the young couple raised their other children without any supernatural interference.

QUOTE: *Ozark Superstitions,* Vance Randolph (Columbia University Press, 1947). Reprinted by permission of author and publisher.

92. THE FARMER'S CURST WIFE

LUMBERJACKS, sailors, children, housewives, northerners, southerners, and westerners have all chuckled over this old Scots ballad; in fact, the story of the virago who was a terror to the very demons of Hell seems no less popular in the United States today than it has been for a thousand years in Europe and the Orient. Everyone realizes that 'Hell hath no fury like a woman', as this Ozark story points out . . .

In several widely separated localities I have heard the story of a savage, ill-tempered woman who was always fighting with her husband. She died suddenly, and some people thought the man must have poisoned her, but the doctors found no evidence of poison. After her death, the widower continued to live in the old house. Neighbors heard noises, as if he was still fighting with his wife. Dishes breaking, shouts and curses, furniture being thrown around, and so on. One neighbor rushed over there and found the man sitting quietly in front of the fire. All the racket seemed to be in the lean-to kitchen. The neighbor could plainly hear the woman cursing; he recognized her voice as well as certain unusual cuss words and obscene phrases to which she had been partial in life. ' Don't get excited,' said the widower quietly, ' she ain't mad at nobody but me.'

Of course, every ballad, like every good story, has many meanings. Upon some superstitious old shrews, this tale acted as a quietus, when the patience-tried old man would sing it out behind the barn—or so I have been told. The ladies hushed because they half-believed that the Devil might come and carry them off, as he had the farmer's curst wife. Yet here again, one encounters the assumption that men have an absolute and limitless power over their women.

In the original medieval story we find an impoverished farmer desperately trying to till his land with swine hitched to the plough. He cannot spare his son's labour, but gladly gives his shrewish wife to the Devil. She thereupon turns Hell upside down, and, in many American versions, returns to earth to paddle her old man's head with the butter-stick, to bully-rag him and, in some versions, to march away over the hill, cheerfully whistling her devil's ditty. American Calvinist men, whose feminine house-slaves had been robbed of their sensuality, unconsciously recognized the extent of their tyranny, and were afraid. In the Ozarks, if a man divorces his first wife, and marries again unhappily, they say, ' e's swapped a witch for the Devil.'

QUOTE: Randolph V.

93. DEVILISH MARY

THE MOUNTAIN people still have many yarns about witches, and one of the best tells about the time Jack hired out as miller in a mill where no one had ever survived a night . . .

' Bedads, I'll get along all right,' says Jack. So Jack baked him some bread un made him some coffee un fried him some meat. All at once, the little cabin got dark as midnight. Jack got up and stirred his fire, and when he looked round, every crack in the house was full of cats—jest as thick as they could stick—with their eyes jest shining.

That sort of scared Jack, and he jest set down and commenced to eatin'. All of a sudden one big old black cat hollered, ' Sop, doll, sop.' Then all the cats sat down on the floor. She walked up and popped her paw in his meat sop and licked hit and hollered, ' Sop doll, sop.' Jack said, ' Stick your old paw in here again and I'll whack it off.'

She did hit again and he hacked it off. When he hacked it off, it fell into the fryin' pan—hit was a woman's hand, with a ring on the finger, and she hollered ' Whar-a-a,' and all them cats went out through the cracks and the moon shined back in as bright as day. So he tuk that hand and he wrops hit up in some tissue paper and drops hit down in his coat pocket.

Next morning he wuz up bright and early and had his breakfast over and was grinding and whistling when the miller comes down. Said, ' Why, hello, Jack, I see you're still alive.'

' Yes bedads, I'm still alive,' says Jack. And he told all about the cats, and pulled this hand out of his pocket and handed it to the man.

He says, ' Hit's my wife's hand.'

Jack says, ' O surely not.'

He says, ' Yes, hit is.'

174

Jack says, ' Well, she was a big black cat when I hacked it off.'

' Well, hit is,' says the Miller, ' fer this is a ring I put on her hand yesterday.' So he tuk the hand and went up to the house. Says, ' Nancy, let's see your right hand.'

She poked out her left. Says, ' Nancy, hit's yer right hand I want.'

She begin cryin' and said, ' I haven't any.'

So he says, ' Now tell me all about this, Nancy, and I won't have you burned.'

' Well I didn't want you to have a miller. I wanted you to keep the mill yourself. So I got all my friends, and witched 'em into cats, and we put pizen into the millers' sop. And when I went to put pizen into this man's sop, he hacked off my hand.'

So the miller gathered up all the other witches and had 'em burned, and that made the other husbands mad, and they had his wife hung. He wouldn't let 'em burn her, 'cause he had said she shouldn't be. So Jack made an end of a good many witches.

QUOTE: JAFL XXXVIII, 1925 (Isabel Gordon Carter), p. 354.

175

94. ROBIN HOOD AND ARTHUR O'BLAND

ONE SIGN of the antiquity of the American ballad tradition is the discovery of a number of Robin Hood ballads in the United States.

From Wise County, Virginia, near where this ballad was collected, comes the following Robin Hood tale, found by Richard Chase, and reprinted in part, with his permission, from *American Folk Tales and Songs*, Signet Books, 1956.

Robin Hood was a very poor boy. He was like myself, I reckon; he just had the one father and mother.

The King shot his father and killed him—in the Shirewood forest, for killin' the one deer. Anyhow, he had him put to death for that—for killin' one deer.

Robin was quite a kid at that time. His mother was a school-teacher, and she took so much composure from teachin' school, and a-walkin' backwards and forwards so far, that she took pneumonia and died, at the time Robert was eleven years old. So, Robert's uncle taken him, to raise him and keep him.

Robert's father had learned him to be a great shot with the bow and ar-row durin' his days before he died.

The King had put up a bull's-eye and the best shot at that would take a great crown from there that day. Robert entered that at eleven years old. The King and three more of his—I don't know what you might call it— his priest-es or everwhat they might have been—were takin' the air under a big tree. They laughed at little Robert as he come along and asked him where he was goin'.

Robert said, ' I've started to shoot at that bull's-eye.'

They laughed and made po-light of him.

Kings says, ' Huh! ' Said, ' You couldn't hit my hat—ten steps.' Said, ' You see those three deer over yonder a-grazin '? '

Robert looked. He said, ' Yes.'

' Shoot at the lead one.'

He drawed his bow and ar-row, and at the time his bow and ar-row landed, the lead deer fell dead.

' All right, son. I have *you* for a death punishment.' And he invited his men to take him under arrest. Robert pulled his bow and ar-row and he killed all three of 'em, and started on his way back to the Shirewood Forest. He didn't go on to accept the bull's-eye for a target. Well, they appointed another King at that time.

Robin had went back in the Shirewood Forest, and they heard so much about him there was fellows come and begin to join him until he had quite a band of men . . .

QUOTE: *American Folk Tales and Songs*, compiled by Richard Chase. © 1956 by Richard Chase. Published in a Signet Key edition by the New American Library of World Literature, Inc.

95. THE GOLDEN VANITY

Sir Walter Rawleigh has built a ship,
In the Neatherlands,
Sir Walter Rawleigh has built a ship,
In the Neatherlands,
And it is called the Sweet Trinity,
And was taken by the false gallaly
Sailing in the Low-Lands.

So begins the broadside of 1682, collected by that worldly antiquarian, Samuel Pepys. Raleigh plays the villain's role in this original version of the ballad of the first frogman.

The story is the same as in my copy, except at the end Raleigh offers a compromise—his gold, but not his daughter's hand in marriage. The honest skin-diver replies:

> ' Then fare you well, you cozening lord,
> Seeing you are not so good as your word . . .'

. . . but, as it is not clear whether he then swims back to Dover or drowns, the Pepys version seems to be more of a slap at the upper classes than a tragedy.

Popular fantasy, which cherished this ballad, also improved it. The Scots bring the story to a happy ending; the lad threatens to sink his master's ship, whereupon his mates haul him on board and ' prove to him far better than their word '. In most English and American versions, however, the lad dies of exhaustion and is buried at sea, or else he chooses death in the lonesome sea rather than drown all his shipmates. The Scots' conclusion is found more frequently in the North, the latter more often in the South; but more significant is the ballad's astonishing popularity all over America. It has been recorded in every part of the country, sung by both men and women, by traditional singers and hillbilly harmonizers, by sailors and lumberjacks, by dwellers on the coast and by people who never saw a piece of water wider than a water trough.

The story of the courage, skill and humane morality of the little cabin-boy appeals strongly to democratic sentiment; our sympathies are always with the underdog, the little fellow. The affection of American folk singers for this Jack tale, this primitive Horatio Alger yarn, shows in a variety of charming names with which they have christened Raleigh's galleon—*The Gold China Tree, The Golden Vallady, The Merry Golden Tree, The Golden Merrilee, The Golden Willow Tree, The Yellow Golden Tree, The Turkey Shivaree*, etc.

96. THE RAMBLIN' BOY

. . . A frontier is often the retreat of loose individuals, who, if not familiar with crime, have very blunt perceptions of virtue. The genuine woodsman, the real pioneer, are independent, brave and upright. But, as the jackal pursues the lion to devour his leavings, the footsteps of the sturdy hunter are closely pursued by miscreants destitute of his nobler qualities . . .

Such men were Micajah Harpe and his brother, Little Willie, who killed for pleasure, Jim Girty, the bully of Natchez, and John Murrell, the ' speculator ', who, on his own confession, had robbed and killed so many men up and down the South that ' it would take me a week to tell you about them all '. Here, Murrell gives his own account of the beginning of his bloody career.

By the time I was twenty, I began to acquire considerable character as a villain, and I concluded to go off and do my speculation where I was not known, and go on a larger scale. I had been acquainted with some old hands for a long time, who had gave me the names of some royal fellows between Nashville and Tuscaloosa, and between Nashville and Savannah, in the State of Georgia, and many other places.

Myself and a fellow by the name of Crenshaw gathered four good horses, and started for Georgia. We got in company with a young South Carolinian just before we got to Cumberland mountain. We concluded he was a prize. Crenshaw winked at me, I understood his idea. We had traveled several miles on the mountain, when we passed near a great precipice; just before we passed it, Crenshaw asked me for my whip, which had a pound of lead in the butt, I handed it to him and he rode up by the side of the South Carolinian and gave him a blow on the side of the head and tumbled him from his horse; we lit from our horses and fingered his pockets; we got twelve hundred and sixty-two dollars. Crenshaw said he knew of a place to hide him, and gathered him under the arms and me by his feet, and conveyed him to a deep crevice in the brow of the precipice, and tumbled him into it, he went out of sight; we then tumbled in his saddle, and took his horse with us, which was worth two hundred dollars. We turned our course for South Alabama, and sold our horses for a good price. We frolicked for a week or more, and was the highest larks you ever saw. We commenced sporting and gambling, and lost every damned cent of our money . . .

The right ballad for such men—and there have been many among the feudists, the moonshiners and the bandits of the old South—was this old highwayman's goodnight, known as *The Flash Lad* and *In Newry Town*—common in southern England, in the southern mountains and in the West. A variant chorus I collected in Kentucky runs:

> I'll ramble and rove and call for my board,
> Let the world do what it will,
> For I have jined this roving gang,
> And no one cares for me.

QUOTE: Botkin IV, 221. *A History of the Life of John Murell*, A. Q. Walton (Athens, Tenn., 1835).

97. THE BAD GIRL

FOR THE HISTORY of this ballad see pp. 363-4. The singer, Mrs. Texas Gladden, our finest traditional ballad singer, is a member of the most remarkable of America's folk-singing families, the James Smiths of Virginia. As folk songs are so often transmitted in a family tradition, the musical genealogy of the Smiths can tell much about our folk-song history. This is how Hobe Smith, Mrs. Gladden's brother, and a wizard on fiddle and banjo, explained it to me.

Well, I'll tell ye. All the ginerations of us Smiths kindly tuck to music. Always picking on some insterment or singing some ditty—that was the Smith way. An' if we managed to marry somebody who didn't keer for it, why purty soon they'd give up and git a divorce and leave, and then we'd marry somebody that *did* love music. That way it just kep' a-runnin' through the family. My brother, now, I just wish he was here. He's a Holiness preacher and won't play none of these worldly tunes, but, Lord have mercy, he can sing a hymn till it would just make old Satan go to shoutin' glory! This Arthur Smith feller, the fiddler on the radio who's noted out to be the fastest fiddler in the South, well, he's a cousin. And you can foller the Smiths all over the United States and you'll find music going on. I hear there's some of us out west in Kansas that are the best musicianers in the state.

They tell me it began when old Jeems Smith, the head of the whole family and a fiddler, crossed over the great waters from Ireland to the Virginia colony. He come back up here in these hills and found this salt-lick, where the deer were right numerous, built him a homestead and settled down. A feller come along one day with a rifle and a saddle hoss old Jeems fancied, and Jeems sold him the salt-lick and that's the reason the Smith family don't own the big alkali plant where we all work now. We Smiths always liked a big family and a good tune more than money.

Now that there Smith family tree you've drawed—you take all them first ginerations, the men was all fiddlers and the girls all good singers. Drop on down and you begin to get a banjo picker or two in the crowd. Then they was mostly banjo pickers, like my daddy, King Smith, who learnt me to play. I took to it so natural that when I come to the house, Mama would tell Old King to put his banjo by and let somebody handle it who could. Then one day I met a colored feller who come in here to work on the railroad, who could make a guitar talk just like it was a banjo. And I put by the banjo and tuck up the guitar. Now these younger generations mostly play guitars and you won't hardly find a real good old banjer picker in the whole bag.

178

Hobe went out on the front porch for a moment and one of his daughters whispered, ' If you think Dad can play, I wish you could hear our brother, Jimmy. He's the one works up in the nylon mill in Delaware. Papa's ashamed to touch a guitar when Jimmy's home!'

98. A FAIR BEAUTY BRIDE

SOUTHERN folk singers generally made no distinction between the traditional ballads and the love songs. Both conveyed the same melancholy, nostalgic feeling, and both were termed ' old-time love songs '. Thus, as the old British stories gradually lost their significance in the New World, the ballads were often turned, bit by bit, into lyric songs. The present song is an example of a British come-all-ye in the early stages of becoming a lyric piece.

86. THE DEVIL'S NINE QUESTIONS

Collected by Alan Lomax from Texas Gladden. AAFS-4 AI. SEE: Botkin IV, 717;
Child, No. 1 (*Riddles Wisely Expounded*); Coffin, 29; Freedman, 3; Wells, 169.
Oldest version—15th century MS. in Oxford.

A quiet ballad ♩ = 138   *GUITAR– ANY ²⁄₄ STYLE*
BANJO– 4B

'O you must answer my ques-tions nine, Sing nine-ty-nine and nine-ty, Or you're not God's, you're one of mine, And you are the weav-er's bon-ny.'

1 ' O you must answer my questions nine,
   Sing ninety-nine and ninety,
   Or you're not God's, you're one of mine,
   And you are the weaver's bonny.'

2 ' What is whiter than the milk?
   And what is softer than the silk?'

3 ' Snow is whiter than the milk,
   And down is softer than the silk.'

4 ' O what is higher than a tree?
   And what is deeper than the sea?'

5 ' Heaven's higher than a tree,
   And Hell is deeper than the sea.'

6 ' What is louder than a horn?
   And what is sharper than a thorn?'

7 ' Thunder's louder than a horn,
   And death is sharper than a thorn.'

8 ' What's more innocent than a lamb?
   And what is meaner than womankind?'

9 ' A babe's more innocent than a lamb,
   And the devil is meaner than womankind.'

10 ' You have answered my questions nine,
   And you are God's, you're none of mine.'

87. COCK ROBIN

SEE: Opie, 130; Sharp II, 299. In Verse 5, if *shovel* is pronounced *showl*, as it was in the 14th century, there is a rhyme—another indication of the song's antiquity.

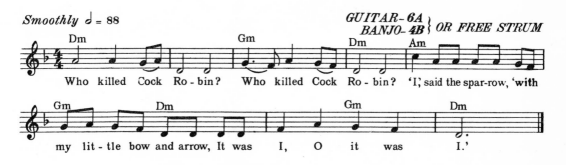

1 Who killed Cock Robin?
   Who killed Cock Robin?
   ' I,' said the sparrow, ' with my little bow and arrow,
   It was I, O it was I.'

2 Who caught his blood-o?   (2)
   ' I, 'said the fish, ' with my little silver dish, *etc.*

3 Who sewed his shroud-o?   (2)
   ' I,' said the eagle, ' with my little thread and needle,' *etc.*

4 Who made the coffin?   (2)
   ' I,' said the snipe, ' with my little pocket knife,' *etc.*

5 Who dug his grave-o?   (2)
   ' I,' said the owl, ' with my little wooden shovel,' *etc.*

6 Who lowered him down-o?   (2)
   ' I,' said the crane, ' with my little golden chain,' *etc.*

7 Who sang the preachment?   (2)
   ' I,' said the rook, ' with my little holy book,' *etc.*

88. THE HOUSE CARPENTER

Collected by Alan Lomax from Texas Gladden, Salem, Va., 1941. AAFS-1A,
L.C.11. SEE: Barry, 304; Belden, 79; Brown II, 171; Child, No. 243; Coffin,
138; Flanders I, 95; Guide (*James Harris*); JEFSS III, 84; Randolph I, 166; Sharp
I, 244.

Piano Arrangement by MATYAS SEIBER

1 'Well met, well met, you old true love.'
   'Well met, well met,' said she.
   'I have just returned from the sea-shore sea,
   From the land where the grass grows green.

2 'Well, I could have married a king's daughter there,
   And she would have married me,
   But I refused the golden crown
   And all for the sake of thee.'

3 'If you could have married a king's daughter there,
   I'm sure you are to blame;
   For I am married to a house carpenter
   And I think he's a nice young man.'

4 'If you'll forsake your house carpenter
   And come and go with me,
   I'll take you where the grass grows green,
   To the lands on the banks of the sea.'

5 She went an' picked up her sweet little babe,
   And kissed it, one, two, three,
   Sayin', 'Stay at home with your father dear
   And keep him good company.'

6 She went and dressed in her very best,
   As everyone could see;
   She glittered and glistened and proudly she walked
   The streets on the banks of the sea.

7 They hadn't been sailing but about three weeks,
   I'm sure it was not four,
   Till this young lady began to weep,
   And her weeping never ceased any more.

8 'Are you mourning for your house carpenter?
   Are you mournin' for your store?'
   'No, I am mournin' for my sweet little babe
   That I never will see any more.'

9 They hadn't been sailing but about four weeks,
   An' sure it was not more,
   Till the ship sprang a leak from the bottom of the sea
   And it sank to rise no more.

89. BARBARA ALLEN

Adapted and arranged by Alan Lomax. SEE: Belden, 60; Brown II, 111; Coffin,
87; Child, No. 84; Creighton II, 49; Guide and Index; Randolph I, 126; Sharp I,
183; Wells, 113.

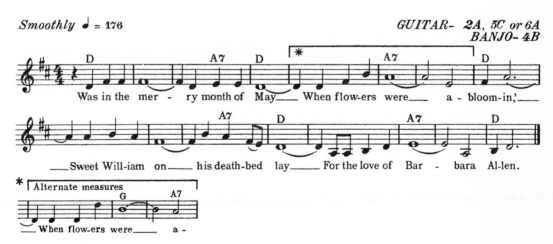

Smoothly ♩ = 176

GUITAR- 2A, 5C or 6A
BANJO- 4B

1 Was in the merry month of May
   When flowers were a-bloomin',
   Sweet William on his deathbed lay
   For the love of Barbara Allen.

2 Slowly, slowly she got up,
   And slowly she went nigh him,
   And all she said when she got there,
   'Young man, I think you're dying.'

3 'O yes I'm sick and very low,
   And death is on me dwellin',
   No better shall I ever be
   If I don't get Barbara Allen.'

4 'Don't you remember the other day
   When you were in the tavern,
   You toasted all the ladies there
   And slighted Barbara Allen?'

5 'O yes, I remember the other day
   When we were in the tavern,
   I toasted all the ladies there,
   Gave my love to Barbara Allen.'

6 He turned his pale face to the wall,
   And death was on him dwellin'.
   'Adieu, adieu, my kind friends all,
   Be kind to Barbara Allen.'

7 As she was walkin' through the fields,
   She heard the deathbells knelling,
   And every toll they seemed to say,
   'Hardhearted Barbara Allen.'

8 She looked east, she looked west,
   She saw his corpse a-comin'.
   'Lay down, lay down the corpse,' she said,
   'And let me gaze upon him.'

9 'O mother, mother, make my bed,
   O make it long and narrow,
   Sweet William died for me today,
   I'll die for him tomorrow.'

10 Sweet William died on a Saturday night,
   And Barbara died on Sunday,
   Her mother died for the love of both,
   And was buried on Easter Monday.

11 They buried Willie in the old churchyard,
   And Barbara there anigh him,
   And out of his grave grew a red, red rose,
   And out of hers a briar.

12 They grew and grew in the old churchyard
   Till they couldn't grow no higher,
   They lapped and tied in a true love's knot.
   The rose ran around the briar.

90. THE TWO SISTERS

Recorded by Herbert Halpert from Horton Barker, Chilhowie, Va., 1939.
L.C. 33 A. SEE: Belden, 16; Brown II, 32; Coffin, 38; Flanders I, 3; Freedman,
161; Guide and Index; Randolph I, 50; Sharp I, 26; Wells, 149. Reported as a
play-party song from Nebraska, Ky., Miss.

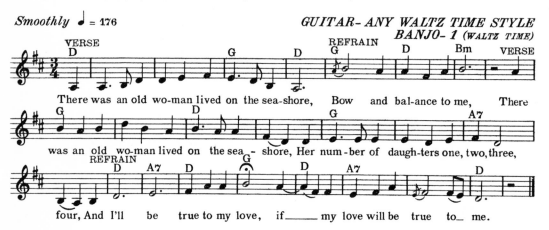

1 There was an old woman lived on the seashore,
      Bow and balance to me,
   There was an old woman lived on the seashore,
   Her number of daughters one, two, three, four,
      And I'll be true to my love, if my love will be true to me.

184

2 There was a young man came courtin' them then, (2)
And the oldest one got struck on him.

3 He bought the youngest a beaver hat, (2)
And the oldest one thought hard of that.

4 'O sister, O sister, let's walk the seashore, (2)
And see the ships as they sail o'er.'

5 While these two sisters were walking the shore, (2)
The oldest pushed the youngest o'er.

6 'O sister, O sister, please lend me your hand, (2)
And you may have Willie and all of his land.'

7 'I never, I never will lend you my hand, (2)
But I'll have Willie and all of his land.'

8 Sometimes she sank and sometimes she swam, (2)
Until she came to the old mill dam.

9 The miller, he got his fishing hook (2)
And fished the maiden out of the brook.

10 'O miller, O miller, here's five gold rings, (2)
To push the maiden in again.'

11 The miller received those five gold rings (2)
And pushed the maiden in again.

12 The sister was hung on the gallows high, (2)
And the miller was burned at the stake nearby.

91. LADY GAY

As sung by Buell Kazee, Eastern Ky., *Listen to Our Story*, Brunswick 80089.
SEE: Brown II, 95; Child No. 79; Coffin, 83; Flanders, II, 64; Randolph I, 122;
Reeves, 225; Sharp, I, 150. Not current in Britain in modern times.

Piano arrangement by MATYAS SEIBER

1 There was a lady and a lady gay,
  Of children she had three.
  She sent them away to the North counteree
  For to learn their grammaree.

2 They had not been there very long,
  Scarcely six months and a day,
  Till death, cold death, come hasting along,
  And stole those babes away.

3 It was just about old Christmas time,
  The nights being cold and clear,
  She looked and she saw her three little babes
  Come running home to her.

4 She set a table both long and wide,
  And on it, she put bread and wine.
  ' Come eat, come drink, my three little babes,
  Come eat, come drink of mine.'

5 ' We want none of your bread, mother,
  Neither do we want your wine;
  For yonder stands our Saviour dear,
  And to him we must resign.

6 ' Green grass grows over our heads, mother,
  Cold clay is under our feet,
  And every tear you shed for us,
  It wets our winding sheet.'

92. THE FARMER'S CURST WIFE

Collected by John A. Lomax. SEE: Belden, 94; Brown II, 188; Freedman, 452;
Child No. 278; Grieg, 220; Guide and Index; Randolph I, 191; Creighton II, 95.

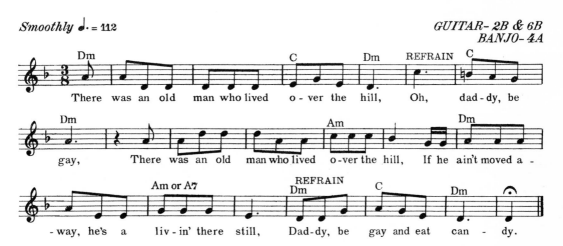

Smoothly ♩. = 112

GUITAR- 2B & 6B
BANJO- 4A

1 There was an old man who lived over the hill,
   Oh, daddy, be gay,
   There was an old man who lived over the hill,
   If he ain't moved away, he's a-livin' there still,
   Daddy, be gay and eat candy.

2 The Devil, he come to his field one day,   (2)
   Says, ' Your old wife I'm gonna take away.'

3 ' O take, O take her with all of my heart,   (2)
   And I hope to my soul that you'll never part.'

4 So he took the old lady all up in a sack,   (2)
   And off to Hell he went clickety-clack.

5 When he got her down 'bout half of the road, (2)
   He says, ' Old lady, you're a devil of a load.'

6 And when he got her to the gates of Hell,   (2)
   Says, ' Punch up the fire, I'm gonna scorch her well.'

7 Nine little devils come a-draggin' a chain,   (2)
   She took it away and she knocked out their brains.

8 Ten little devils went a-climbin' the wall,   (2)
   Says, ' Take her back, daddy, she's a-murdrin' us all.'

9 She found the old man lyin' late in his bed,   (2)
   She picked up the butter-stick and paddled his head.

10 Away she went whistelin' over the hill,   (2)
   ' If the devil won't have me, I wonder who will?'

11 That goes to show what a woman can do,   (2)
   She's worse than the Devil and she's worse than you.

93. DEVILISH MARY

FROM: p. 136 of *Our Singing Country*, John and Alan Lomax (Macmillan, N.Y., 1941). As sung by Jesse Stafford, Crowley, La., 1934. SEE: Randolph, 186; Sharp II, 200. Peter Kennedy has found similar tunes in Ireland—*The Wearing of the Breeches*.

Piano arrangement by MATYAS SEIBER

1 I went up to London town
To court a fair young lady,
I inquired about her name,
And they called her Devilish Mary.
CHORUS:
Come-a-fa-la-ling, come-a-ling, come-a-ling,
Come-a-fa-la-ling, come-a-derry.

2 We sat down to courtin',
  She got up in a hurry.
  Made it all up into her mind
  To marry the very next Thursday.   (CHO.)

3 Well, she filled my heart with sadness,
  She sewed my side with stitches,
  She jumped and kicked and popped her heels
  And swore she'd wear my britches.   (CHO.)

4 One day I said to Mary,
  We'd better be parted;
  No sooner had I said the word,
  Than she bundled up her clothes and started.(CHO.)

5 If ever I marry in this wide world,
  It'll be for love, not riches,
  Marry a little girl about four feet high
  So she can't wear my britches.   (CHO.)

94. ROBIN HOOD AND ARTHUR O'BLAND

FROM: *Traditional Ballads of Virginia*, Arthur K. Davis (Harvard U.P., 1929).
Used by permission. SEE: Child, No. 126; Coffin, 106; Wells, 35. Alluded to in
Piers Plowman of 1377, and in 15th-century chronicles. Few Robin Hood songs
found in Britain recently.
Piano arrangement by MATYAS SEIBER

189

1 When Phœbus had melted the shackles of ice,
  And likewise the mountains of snow,
  Bold Robin Hood, that archer so good,
  Went frolicking abroad with his bow.

2 He left his merry men all behind,
  As through the green woods he passed.
  There did he behold a forester bold,
  Who cried, ' Friend, whither so fast?'

3 ' I'm going,' said Robin, ' to kill a fat buck
  For me and my merry men all,
  And likewise a doe before that I go,
  Or else it will cost me a fall.'

4 ' You'd best have a care,' the forester said,
  ' For these are His Majesty's deer.
  Before that you shoot, that thing I'll dispute,
  For I am head forester here.'

5 ' Let's measure our weapons,' said Bold
                                    Robin Hood,
  ' Before we begin this affray;
  I wouldn't have mine any longer than thine,
  For that would be counted false play.'

6 ' I pass not for length,' the stranger replied,
  ' For mine is of oak so free;
  Six foot and a half will knock down a calf,
  I'm sure it will knock down thee.'

7 About and about they lustily dealt
  For almost two hours and more;
  At ev-e-ry bang, the woods, they rang,
  They plied their work so sore.

8 And Robin he raged like a wild boar,
  As soon as he saw his own blood.
  Bland was in haste and laid on so fast,
  As if he was cleaving of wood.

9 ' Hold your hand,' said jolly Robin,
  ' And let our quarrel fall.
  Here we might thrash our bones to smash
  And get no money at all.'

10 ' Tell me, tell me, where is Little John?
   Of him I fain would hear,
   For we are related by the mother's side,
   And he is my kinsman near.'

11 Then Robin he put his horn to his mouth
   And blew both loud and shrill.
   And quickly and soon appeared Little John
   Come tripping over the hill.

12 ' What's the matter?' then said Little John,
   ' O master, I pray me tell?
   Why do you stand with your staff in your hand?
   I fear that all isn't well.'

13 ' O man, I stand, and he makes me to stand,
   The tanner who stands by my side;
   He is a bold blade and master of his trade,
   And sorely he's tanning my hide.'

14 ' He's to be commended,' said Little John,
   ' If such a thing he can do;
   If he is so stout, then we must have a bout,
   And he shall tan my hide, too.'

15 ' Hold your hand,' said jolly Robin;
   ' As I do understand,
   He's a yeoman good and of your own blood,
   His name is Arthur O'Bland.'

16 Then Little John flung his staff away
   As far as he could fling,
   Then out of hand to Arthur O'Bland,
   And about his neck he did cling.

17 For love and respect there was no neglect,
   They neither were nice nor coy;
   Each other did face with a comely grace,
   And both did weep for joy.

18 Then Robin he took them both by the hand
   And danced all around an oak tree;
   Said, ' Three merry men and three merry men,
   And three merry men are we.'

19 'And ever hereafter, as long as we live,
We three shall be as one;
The woods they will ring and the old wives sing
Of Robin Hood, Arthur, and John.'

95. THE GOLDEN VANITY

As sung by the Carter Family, arranged by Alan Lomax. SEE: Belden, 97; Brown
II, 191; Child, No. 286; Coffin, 153; Colcord, 154; Creighton I, 20; Index and
Guide; Randolph I, 195; Sharp I, 282; Wells, 53.

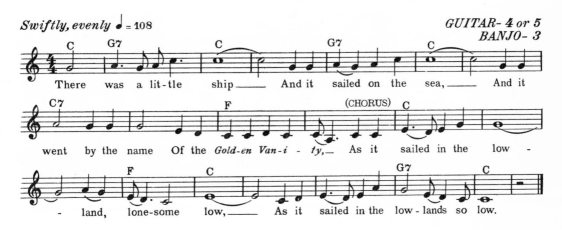

Swiftly, evenly ♩ = 108   GUITAR– *4 or 5*
                                                            BANJO– *3*

There was a lit-tle ship___ And it sailed on the sea,___ And it
went by the name Of the *Gold-en Van-i-ty,*___ As it sailed in the low-
-land, lone-some low,___ As it sailed in the low-lands so low.

1 There was a little ship
  And it sailed on the sea,
  And it went by the name
  Of the *Golden Vanity*,
    As it sailed in the lowland, lonesome low
    As it sailed in the lowlands so low.

2 There was another ship
  That sailed upon the sea,
  And the name that they called her
  Was the *Turkey Roveree*,
    As she sailed, *etc.*

3 'Captain, O Captain,
  Now what will you give me,
  If I will sink
  That *Turkey Roveree*?
    As she sails,' *etc.*

4 'O I will give you gold
  And I will give you fee,
  And my fairest daughter
  Will be wed to thee,
    If you sink her in the' *etc.*

5 So he bowed his breast
  And away swum he,
  And he swum till he come
  To the *Turkey Roveree*,
    As she rolled in the, *etc.*

6 Some was playin' cards
  And some was playin' dice,
  And some was takin'
  Their best friends' advice,
    As she rolled in the, *etc.*

191

7 He had a little instrument
Just fitted for his use,
And he bored nine holes
And he bored them all at once,
    And he sank her in the, *etc.*

8 Some threw their hats
And some threw their caps,
They all tried to stop
Them awful water gaps,
    As she sunk in the, *etc.*

9 Well, he bowed to his breast
And back swum he,
He swum till he come
To the *Golden Vanity*,
    As she rolled in the, *etc.*

10 ' Captain, O Captain,
Take me on board,
And do unto me
As good as your word,
    For I'm drowning in the, *etc.*

11 But he hoisted his sails
And away sailed he,
And he left that poor sailorboy
To drown in the sea,
    To drown in the lowland, lonesome low,
    To drown in the lonesome sea.

96. THE RAMBLIN' BOY

Collected and arranged by Alan Lomax from Justus Begley, Hazard, Ky. L.C.
31 B 2. SEE: Belden, 136; Brown II, 355; Guide and Index (*The Robber*); Randolph II, 83-5. Found in southern and western England. In States, south as far as
Miss. A ' goodnight '; there is also a white spiritual variant.

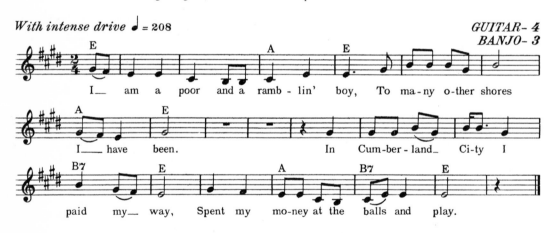

With intense drive ♩ = 208   GUITAR- 4
                                                                 BANJO- 3

I am a poor and a ramb-lin' boy, To ma-ny o-ther shores
I have been. In Cum-ber-land Ci-ty I
paid my way, Spent my mo-ney at the balls and play.

1 I am a poor and a ramblin' boy,
To many other shores I have been.
In Cumberland City I paid my way,
Spent my money at the balls and play.

2 In Cumberland City I married me a wife,
I loved her as I love my life,
She treated me kind both night and day,
And caused me to rob on the broad highway.

3 O my pretty little miss, sixteen years old,
Her hair just as yellow as the shining gold,
The prettiest face, O the sweetest hands,
Bless the ground on where she stands.

4 So, my pretty little miss, now fare you well,
I love you so well no tongue can tell,
If pleasure no more on earth I feel,
I wouldn't serve you as you served me.

5 Now my mother sits and weeps and moans,
   My sister says she's left alone,
   My true love cries in deep despair,
   With her dark brown eyes and her long curly hair.

6 So I'll get me some paper and it's I'll sit down,
   Drop a few lines to my Governor Brown,
   And every word shall be the truth,
   O pray for the governor to turn me loose.

7 I'll buy me a ticket in Greenville town,
   Get on a train and it's I'll sit down,
   O the wheels will roll and the whistle will blow,
   And it'll take me six months to get back home.

8 Come, young and old, and stand around,
   To see me laid in this cold ground,
   I'm not ashamed or afraid to die,
   But I hope to meet you bye and bye.

97. THE BAD GIRL

Collected by Alan Lomax from Texas Gladden, Salem, Va., 1941. SEE: Belden,
393; Brown II, 614; Freedman, 424; Index (*St. James Hospital*); JEFSS, 129-30;
Mackenzie, 301; Randolph I, 179; Sharp II, 164; also note on *The Sailor Cut Down
in His Prime*.

Piano arrangement by MATYAS SEIBER

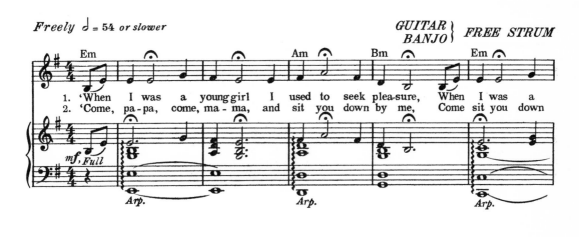

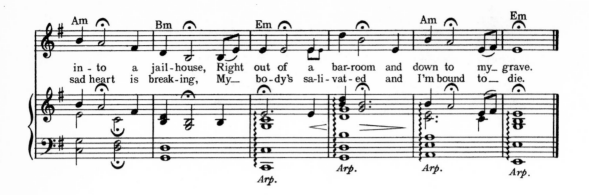

in - to   a   jail-house, Right out of   a   bar-room and down to   my grave.

sad heart   is   break-ing, My bo-dy's sa-li-vat-ed   and   I'm bound to die.

1 ' When I was a young girl I used to seek pleasure,
    When I was a young girl I used to drink ale;
    Out of an alehouse and into a jailhouse,
    Right out of a bar-room and down to my grave.

2 ' Come, papa, come, mama, and sit you down by me,
    Come sit you down by me and pity my case;
    My poor head is aching, my sad heart is breaking,
    My body's salivated and I'm bound to die.

3 ' Oh, send for the preacher to come and pray for me,
    And send for the doctor to heal up my wounds;
    My poor head is aching, my sad heart is breaking,
    My body's salivated and I'm bound to die.

4 ' I want three young ladies to bear up my coffin,
    I want four young ladies to carry me on;
    And each of them carry a bunch of wild roses
    To lay on my coffin as they pass along.'

5 One morning, one morning, one morning in May,*
    I spied this young lady all wrapped in white linen,
    All wrapped in white linen and cold as the clay.

  *This stanza consists of three lines of text, and the singer
    performs it by skipping the first 4½ bars of music and
    beginning his melody in the midst of the 5th bar — or with
    the tune for the second line of the ballad.

194

98. A FAIR BEAUTY BRIDE

Collected and arranged by Alan Lomax from singing of Aunt Molly Jackson,
Eastern Ky. SEE: Belden, 164; Brown II, 293; JEFSS II, 81; Randolph I, 348;
Sharp II, 105. Better known in America than England.

Note: If possible, disregard the bar lines and sing with complete freedom, dwelling on important words and pausing at
the end of each line.

1 Once I courted a fair beauty bride,*
  I courted her by day and I courted her by night,
  Her parents found out I was courting her for love,
  They locked her in her sitting-room and threw the keys away.

2 I rapped on her window just to let her know,
  I rapped on her window as hard as I could go,
  I rapped on her window, she answered me and cried,
  ' I'll ne'er forget you, Johnny, until the day I die.'

3 Then the thought struck me then to the army I would go,
  To see if my true love would forsake me or no,
  But when I got there, the army shined so bright,
  It put me in remembrance of my own heart's true delight.

4 Six long years before I returned
  Back to my own, my native home again,
  Her parents saw me coming, they wrang their hands and cried,
  ' Our daughter loved you dearly and for your sake she died.'

5 There I stood like a man a-going deranged,
  And the tears run down my cheeks like small showers of rain,
  Crying, ' Lord, have mercy on me, and tell me what to do,
  My true love's sleeping in her grave, and I want to go there, too.'

* bright

LONESOME LOVE SONGS
99. FAIR AND TENDER LADIES

THE TRADITION of modern European lyric poetry began in Spain, Provence, and Sicily, inspired by contact with the Arab world, where women were veiled and sequestered behind walls by their jealous fathers and husbands. Provençal court poets suffered, like so many saintly Arabs, from a self-imposed code which demanded eternal, platonic adoration of their *donnai*. This note of romantic torment sounds in the lyric poetry of Southern Spain and Italy, whose women still live in almost Oriental seclusion. In northern lands, however, where women had greater independence and contact between the sexes was freer, love songs took on a heartier, lustier, franker tone. Thus, although one can find songs of despairing lovers in the British Isles, they occur alongside of ditties which speak of the pleasures of courtship and the fleshly delights of love. Songs such as this common Somerset piece are conspicuous by their rarity in American collections . . .

‘ O where are you going, my pretty milking maid,
With your red rosy cheeks and your coal-black hair?’
‘ I’m going a-milking, kind sir, ’ she answered me,
‘ For it’s rolling in the dew makes the milkmaids fair.’

‘ O may I go with you, my pretty milking maid,
With your red rosy cheeks and your coal-black hair?’
‘ O yes, you may go with me, kind sir,’ she answered me,
‘ For it’s rolling in the dew makes the milkmaids fair.’

By contrast the lyric songs and ballads of the Southern mountains rival Spanish ‘ cante hondo ’ in their melancholy. These ‘ old-time mountain love songs ’ gather together the sorrowful themes from England, Scotland, and Ireland, with little of their gaiety and sensuality. Southern backwoods folk, tormented by a conviction of sin, sang like so many dolorous knights and ladies. In a great flowering of lyric song snatches of old British songs were given new American verses. These were constantly reworked by mountain banjo-pickers and the romantic women they courted, and stanzas of rare beauty were created.

When your heart was mine, true love,
And your head lay on my breast,
You could make me believe by the falling of your arm
That the sun rose up in the west . . .

There’s many a star shall jingle in the west,
There’s many a leaf below,
There many a damn will light upon a man
For treatin’ a poor girl so . . .

100. BLACK IS THE COLOUR

ITS OPENING stanza comes from *The Sailor Boy*, the lament of a young maiden for her drowned sailor sweetheart, long popular on both sides of the Atlantic (see p. 112).

Black is the colour of my true love's hair,
His cheeks are red as roses fair,
If he would return, it would give me joy,
For none will I have but my sweet
sailor boy . . .

The tune belongs to the same family as *Fair and Tender Ladies, Poor Way-faring Stranger, Green-back Dollar* and others. Yet, although these elements can be traced to other songs, the mountain people have here woven a lovely new song out of old materials, touching it with the same passionate lyricism that produced this Georgian portrait of a young lady :

. . . her skin was as white as the inside of a frogstool, and her cheeks and lips as rosy as a perch's gills in dogwood blossom time—and such a smile. Why, when it struck you fair and square it felt just like a big horn of unrectified old Monangaheley, after you'd been sober for a month, attending a ten-horse prayer meeting twice a day and most of the night . . .

101. AUNT SAL'S SONG

WOMEN were a scarce commodity on the frontier, and a young fellow with no particular prospects might well despair of finding himself a pretty girl for a wife. The spirited young girls, ready to marry by thirteen or fourteen, demurely tormented their awkward lovers and then laughed behind their backs. This Kentucky mountain song gives the picture of a frontier courtship from the feminine point of view.

102. I'M TROUBLED

DAVY CROCKETT, the Tennessee bear-hunter and politician, tells how it felt to be a young man in love in those days. The year was 1803 and Davy had just turned seventeen.

. . . I have heard people talk of hard loving, yet I reckon no poor devil in the world was ever cursed with such hard love as mine has always been, when it came on me. I soon found myself head over heels with this girl, and I thought that if all the world were chink, and all belonged to me, I would give it all away if I could just talk to her as I wanted to: but I was afraid to begin, for when I would think of saying anything to her, my heart would begin to flutter like a duck in a puddle; and if I tried to outdo it and speak, it would get right smack up in my throat and choke me like a cold potato. It bore on my mind in this way, till at last I concluded I must die if I didn't broach the subject; after several trials, I could say a little. I told her how well I loved her; that she was the darling object of my soul and body; and I must have her, or else I should pine down to nothing, and just die away with the consumption.

I found my talk was not disagreeable to her, but she was an honest girl and she told me that she was engaged to her cousin. The news was worse to me than war, pestilence or famine; but I still knowed I could not help myself. I saw quick enough my cake was dough, and I tried to cool off as fast as possible; but I had hardly safety pipes enough, as my love was so hot as mighty nigh to burst my boilers . . .

QUOTE: *The Life of Davy Crockett Written by Himself*, Signet Books, 1955 (Copyright 1955 by the New American Library of World Literature Inc., 501 Madison Ave., N.Y., 22).

103. LOVIN' HANNAH

SOON Davy found a pretty Quaker girl . . .

I would have agreed to fight a whole regiment of wild-cats if she would only have me. I gave her mighty little peace, till she told me at last she would have me. We fixed the time to be married; and I thought if that day come, I should be the happiest man in the created world or the moon or anywhere else . . .

The girl, however, jilted Davy. When he heard the news from her sister, it was

. . . as sudden to me as a clap of thunder on a sunshiny day. It struck me perfectly speechless for some time, and made me feel so weak that I thought I should sink down. My heart was bruised and my spirits were broken down. I now began to think that, in making me, it was entirely forgotten to make my mate; that I was born odd, and should always remain so and that nobody would have me.

My appetite failed me, and I grew daily worse and worse. They all thought I was sick; and so I was. And it was the worst kind of sickness—a sickness of the heart, and all the tender parts, produced by disappointed love . . .

QUOTE: ibid.

104. THE GAMBLING SUITOR
105. CHICKENS THEY ARE CROWIN'

STILL broken-hearted, Davy hears about a country frolic where he can meet with a charming, unmarried girl. He goes hunting a wife and meets the girl's mother.

Her mother was in no way bashful. She came up to me and praised my red cheeks, and said she had a sweetheart for me. I had no doubt that she had been told what I come for. I was introduced to her daughter, and I must confess I was plaguey well pleased with her from the word go. She had a good countenance and was very pretty, and I was full bent on making up an acquaintance with her.

It was not long before the dancing commenced, and I asked her to join me in a reel. She very readily consented to do so; and after we had finished our dance, I took a seat alongside of her, and entered into a talk, making as good use of my time as I could. We continued our frolic till near day, when we joined in some plays, calculated to amuse the youngsters. I had not often spent a more agreeable night. In the morning, however, we all had to part; and I found my mind had become much better reconciled than it had been for a long time . . .

These country ' plays, calculated to amuse youngsters ', which Davy Crockett speaks of, certainly included old English ring games, like *Three Dukes a-Riding*, kissing games, dialogue songs, such as *The Gambling Suitor* in which a young couple acts out a comic courtship, and play party songs like *Chickens They Are Crowin'*.

QUOTE: ibid.

106. HOW OLD ARE YOU, MY PRETTY LITTLE MISS?

DAVY CROCKETT continues his Tennessee wilderness courtship . . .

It was about two weeks after this that I was sent for to engage in a wolf hunt. I went as large as life, but I had to hunt in strange woods, and in a little while I didn't know where home was or anything about it. Night was coming on fast. At this distressing time I saw a little woman streaking it along like all wrath, and so I cut on too. I run on till she saw me and she stopped; for she was lost as well as me. When I came up to her, who should she be but my little girl, that I had been paying respects to. She had been out hunting her father's horses and had missed her way. She had been traveling all day and was mighty tired, and I would have taken her up and toated her, if it hadn't been that I wanted her just where I could see her all the time, for I thought she looked sweeter than sugar; and by this time I loved her almost well enough to eat her.

At last I came to a path, that I knowed must go somewhere, and so we followed it, till we came to a house at about dark. Here we sat up all night courting, and in the morning we parted. She went to her home, from which we were distant about seven miles, and I to mine, which was ten miles off . . .

QUOTE: ibid.

107. WHISTLE, DAUGHTER, WHISTLE

PERHAPS this song reflects the old belief that one could summon magical aid, in this case a witch, by whistling . . . Davy Crockett tells how he married his pretty Tennessee sweetheart in spite of difficulties . . .

At our next meeting we set the day of our wedding; and I went to my father's to make arrangements for an infair, and returned to ask her parents for her. When I got there, the old lady looked at me as savage as a meat axe. I hadn't been there long before she as good as ordered me out of her house. I told the girl that I could come the next Thursday and bring a horse for her and she must be ready to go. Her mother declared I shouldn't have her; but I knowed I should, if somebody else didn't get her before Thursday.

When Thursday came I cut out to her father's house to get her. I rode up to the door and asked the girl if she was ready, and she said she was. I then told her to light on the horse I was leading, and she did so.

Her father, though, had commenced persuading me to stay and marry there; he said his wife, like many women, had entirely too much tongue. I told him that if she would ask me to stay and marry at her house, I would do so. With that he sent for her, and she asked my pardon for what she had said, and invited me to stay. She said it was the first child she ever had to marry, and she couldn't bear to see her go off in that way; that if I would light, she would do the best she could for us. I sent off then for the parson and got married in a short time, for I was afraid to wait long, for fear of another defeat.

The next day we cut out for my father's, where we met a large company of people that had been waiting a day and a half for our arrival. We passed the time quite merrily, until the company broke up; and, having gotten my wife, I thought I was completely made up, and needed nothing more in the whole world . . .

QUOTE: ibid.

108. WINTER'S NIGHT

STABLE married love was often a luxury in pioneer families whose menfolk were hunters, explorers, and Indian fighters. Wild animals, Indian arrows, bad men, the western trail took a heavy toll of lives. Bored husbands and skittish lovers often just skedaddled west and disappeared. There is a famous western yarn of a Kentuckian who went out to get wood for breakfast and came back seven years later and filled the woodbox. His wife looked up and said, ' Thanks, honey, I'm just about to set breakfast on the table.'

Songs of parting or of parted lovers form the largest single group of southern lyric songs. The lovers swear to be faithful. They look forward to the pains of loneliness and anxiety they will suffer, almost it seems, with relish. The same motifs occur again and again in the many songs of parting. Stanzas drift from song to song with comparative freedom, yet they occur sufficiently often in the familiar clusters to enable one to identify certain songs from region to region. *Winter's Night* (which generally includes the ' shoe-my-feet ' stanzas, the ' turtle dove ' theme, the oaths of fidelity and the ' cold-night-sweet-wine ' opener) has been found from North Carolina to Texas.

109. WHO'S GONNA SHOE YOUR PRETTY LITTLE FEET ?

. . . IS THE modern hillbilly member of the family of songs linked by the ' shoe-your-feet ' motif. This theme song for a restless, travelling people will be found again in this volume as the root material out of which *John Henry* grew. It occurs in many ballads, minstrel pieces, work songs—indeed it was by far the most persistent lyric note in southern folk song until the blues appeared.

In origin, these verses form a part of the Scots *Lass of Roch Royal*, a ballad which has rarely been found in the United States in a complete form. The faithful Lady Margaret with her illegitimate son in her arms, goes to Lord Gregory's castle. He is asleep, and his mother feigns his voice from behind the closed castle door and drives poor Margaret away. In despair she embarks in a small boat, a storm comes up and Lord Gregory wakes to see his mistress and son drowned before his eyes. He dies of heartbreak. The tragic mood of the ballad, which persists in these favourite frontier stanzas, would certainly have caught the morbid fancy of pioneer singers, but the portrait of the wicked mother-in-law and the theme of the bastard baby offended our grandmothers. I have recently, however, heard the whole song sung in all its detail by a charming and refined old Irish countrywoman of more than eighty.

110. THE CUCKOO

NO CREATURE is more common in southern English love songs than the cuckoo, the herald of spring and bearer of good omens to lovers. From ancient times the bird has been a sexual symbol and, because it leaves its eggs in the nests of other birds for them to hatch, has acquired the reputation of an adulterer; thus, men with unfaithful wives were called *cuckolds*. The many American songs mentioning the cuckoo suggest the importance of this 'messenger of spring' in the lore of the West.

111. THE FOURTH DAY OF JULY

. . . A LATER FIVE-STRING banjo variant of *The Cuckoo*. The majority of the songs on preceding pages of this volume were sung by the pioneers with little or no accompaniment. The fiddle* was king on the frontier, but it could only accompany the voice in unison, and play variations on the tune between stanzas. There were also two so-called dulcimers—one a zither played with beaters, on which the lumberjacks sometimes made dance music; the other a three-stringed affair (a type of psaltery) on which the Southern mountaineer musician picked the tune, while the other two strings produced a faint, sweet drone. Thus, when the five-string banjo was introduced into the mountains after the Civil War and for the first time provided a true accompanying style for the ancient solo-song tradition, a musical revolution was set in motion.

No complete history of this remarkable instrument has yet been written. Its direct ancestor is the West African *bania*, an offspring of the dojigger said to have been invented by Ham to keep himself amused on the Ark. Both *bania* and banjo belong to an old family of Near-Eastern chordophones, which for uncounted centuries had accompanied long, highly decorated modal solo songs of the sort one can loosely term Arabic or Oriental. As these tunes belong to the same stylistic family as many medieval airs, the banjo was a happy, though fortuitous choice for southern mountain tunes. Negro slaves early brought the *bania* into the United States, and Jefferson notes the popularity of their primitive three- or four-stringed *banjar* in the Negro country-dance orchestras of Virginia. Thus, even

* Even it was rare (*see* page 226).

before 1800 it had probably been used to accompany all manner of jigs and reels. When the black-face minstrels began to imitate Negro songs and dances and adopted the banjo, they also acquired a stock of ready-made and lively Afro-American accompanying styles and country dance tunes. The minstrel songs became America's first popular music, and with frets and a fifth (drone) string added, the standard five-string banjo was widely manufactured and sold both in America and Great Britain. Banjo virtuosos, like those who toured with the old-time minstrels, can still be encountered in New York and, especially, London.

Very likely the banjo and its raggy music hastened the decay of older folk-song traditions in the northern and western parts of the United States. However, the instrument came into the mountains so late and so gradually that mountain musicians had time to make an adjustment between their old, modal songs and this new-fangled (but actually old Oriental) instrument. (A player in north-east Kentucky told me that he saw his first banjo in the 1870's.)

Since the Negroes had already discovered how to use the banjo to play country-dance tunes, mountain fiddlers found it a natural accompanying instrument. It sang a silvery, ringing, rhythmic counterpoint to their wailing melodies. To compose banjo settings for their melancholy love songs, which were such close kin to their fiddle airs, was an easy step. Subsequently, these untaught musicians developed their own tunings, their own ' licks ' (*see* banjo appendix) and their own ways of playing tunes which left the ancient modal melodies practically undisturbed. The banjo accompaniment did not force changes upon the old, slow songs except that the *fermatas* and rests were given a definite time value within the framework of steady, pulsating banjo rhythms. The tunes were not speeded up; they still could wander in their old leisurely way while the banjo maintained an even, bright tempo, reminding one of much near-Eastern music.

Presently there sprang up a family of new songs called ' banjer pieces '—songs broken up into brief phrases which allowed the banjo to make comments on the melody. These later ' banjer pieces ' show even stronger Negro influence—in blued notes or, as in the present instance, in adopting the solo-chorus form. This tune is very similar to that of the Negro work-song *Stewball*. (*See* record appendix.)

112. THE WAGONER'S LAD
113. OLD SMOKEY

O the boys of Virginia are brave roaring blades,
Deceiving young maidens is part of their trade,
They'll kiss them and coax them and spend their money free,
Then they're off to the next with a fiddle-dee-dee.

PROMINENT among the roaring blades of the frontier were the wagoners who, before the days of railroads, transported a great part of the freight of the growing country. Davy Crockett, when he ran away from home, cruised round the country for several years, working on the wagons that plied between his native Tennessee and Eastern cities. As free-lance entrepreneurs, sophisticated travellers and men with the smell of money and far places about them, the wagoners cut a wide swathe among the ladies. This song of the girl seduced and deserted by a dashing wagoner comes from England but became a universal favourite in the mountains and the South, turning up in all sorts of combinations. A slow banjo piece, it seems to be the ancestor of the western *Jack of Diamonds* or *Rye Whisky*. Robert Gordon thus describes the setting for these lonesome tunes.

The best introduction to banjo songs is to be found at night in some tiny cabin far up the rocky branch. Supper is over, and the whole family is gathered in the big room at the front of the house.

In response to a low call without, the oldest boy slips quietly through the door and returns with a guest, a tall smiling youth of about eighteen, carrying a banjo, its head covered by his coat to protect it from the night air. He claims to have dropped in just accidentally, but the obvious care with which he is dressed, and the self-conscious look on the face of the oldest girl of the family proclaim this to be merely a polite fiction. She does not speak to him, however, or he to her.

He will not play until he is asked, and then only after the proper amount of urging. He is likely to begin with one of the more characteristic banjo songs, slower in rhythm and more lyrical than those of the fiddler. There will be more sentiment and less humor. If it is a love song it will probably be in the form of a long, rambling dialogue or monologue.

He sings as he picks—not loudly, almost crooning—his mouth barely open, his head thrown back, perhaps his eyes partly closed. The music will be plaintive, with none of the quick snap of the fiddle song. Certain lines will be drawn out into almost a wail. ' Lonesome tunes ', the mountaineer calls such songs. His hearers will not contribute any verses, though from time to time one of them may join in softly . . .

QUOTE: Gordon, p. 79 (Banjo Songs).

114. I NEVER WILL MARRY

It is too often supposed that when songs are handed on over a long period by word of mouth, they merely decay and that, when changes are made in text and tune, these changes merely represent degenerations. Academic critics who know the printed ballad, but have seldom heard it alive, have pointed *ad nauseam* to the superiority of the full texts of the old Scots versions over the briefer, sometimes garbled American texts. They have not realized that the American people often operated upon the tradition received from Great Britain like a board of talented and tactful editors.

I Never Will Marry, as it appeared in an 18th century broadside, ran to hard-to-sing stanzas like the following . . .

> One morning I walked by myself on the shore
> The tempest did sing and the waves they did roar,
> Yet the noise of the winds and the waters was drowned
> By the pittiful cry and the sorrowful sound . . .

. . . so on for thirteen verses, including:

> My love lies in his watery grave,
> And hath nothing to show for his tomb but a wave.
> I'll kiss his dear lips than the coral more red
> That grows where he lies in his watery bed.

During the three centuries that the song has passed through the hands of folk singers, the pretentious sentimentality of the original has been rubbed away, and the text and tune have been polished into shining simplicity. This is a version I heard one night in 1940 booming out of a Washington juke-box, sung by a team of North Carolina hillbillies.

115. JOHNSON BOYS

Sum tell it out—jest like a song,
I'll gin it to you, sweet and strong.

The only objection ever made to me in this arr county was made by the wimin 'cause I war a bachelor. I never told you before why I remained in the state of number one. No fellar stays single pre-meditated, and a hansum fellar like me, who all the gals declar' to be as enticin' as a jay bird, warn't goin' to stay alone ef he could help it.

I did see a creatur once named Sofy Mason, up the Cumberland, nigh onto Nashville, Tennessee, that I tuk an orful hankerin' arter; and I sot in to lookin' anxious for matrimony and gin to go reglar to meetin', and tuk to dressin' tremengeous finified, jest to see ef I could win her good opinion. She did git to lookin' at me, kind of shy, jest as a hoss does at suthin he's scart at, when I sidled up to her and blarted out a few words about the sarmin—she said ' yes ', but, cuss me ef I know whether that were the right answer or not, and I'm a thinkin' she didn't know nuther. Well, we larfed and talked a leetle all the way along to her daddy's, and thar I gin her the best bend I had in me, and raised my bran new hat as peert and perlite as a minister, lookin' all the time so enticin' that I sot the gal tremblin' . . .

One Sunday morning I wur a leetle mite late to meetin' and when I got thar the furst thing I seed war Jake Simons, sittin' bang up agin Sofy in the same pew with her daddy. Thar they war, singing hymns out of the same book. I biled a spell with wrath and then turned so sour I could taste myself.

After meetin' out they walked, linked arms, a-smilin and lookin' as pleased as a young couple at their furst christening, and Sofy turned her cold shoulder at me so orful pinted that I wilted down. I'd a shot Jake, but I thort it war a free country, and the gal had a right to her choice without bein' made a widder, so I jest sold out and traveled. I've allays thort since then, boys, that wimin wur a good deal like licker, ef you lov em too hard they're sure to throw you some way.

Then here's to wimin, then to licker,
Thar's nuthin' swimmin' can be slicker.

QUOTE: Blair, p. 353.

99. FAIR AND TENDER LADIES

Collected and adapted by Alan and Elizabeth Lomax. SEE: Belden, 477 (who says this is an American compound of old lyric elements); Brown III, 290; Randolph I, 315; Sharp II, 128. Sometimes called *Little Sparrow*.

Smoothly or freely ♩ = 108

GUITAR- 5C or 6A
BANJO- 4B

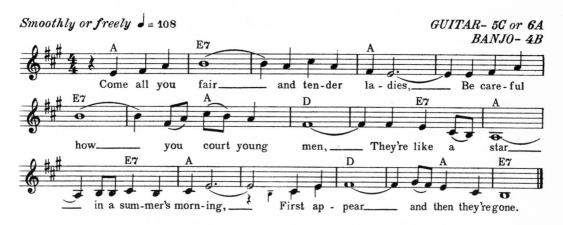

Come all you fair_____ and ten-der la-dies,___ Be care-ful how___ you court young men,___ They're like a star___ in a sum-mer's morn-ing,__ First ap-pear___ and then they're gone.

1 Come all you fair and tender ladies,
   Be careful how you court young men,
   They're like a star in a summer's morning,
   First appear and then they're gone.

2 They'll tell to you some loving story,
   They'll tell to you some far-flung lie,
   And then they'll go and court another,
   And for that other one pass you by.

3 If I'd a-knowed before I courted
   That love, it was such a killin' crime,
   I'd a-locked my heart in a box of golden
   And tied it up with a silver line.

4 I wish I was some little sparrow
   That I had wings could fly so high,
   I'd fly away to my false true lover
   And when he's talkin' I'd be by.

5 But as I am no little sparrow
   And have no wings so I can't fly,
   I'll go away to some lonesome valley
   And weep and pass my troubles by.

100. BLACK IS THE COLOUR

FROM: p. 31 of *English Folk Songs of the Southern Appalachians*, Cecil Sharp (Oxford U.P., 1932). Used by permission of Novello & Co. Ltd. SEE: Brown III, 306; Randolph, 296; Sharp II, 31, 84, 388 (for full English note). Randolph shows connexions with English broadsides—*Down by the River, The Lost Lover*—see *Pinery Boy*. Tune similar to *Fair and Tender Ladies*.

Piano arrangement by MATYAS SEIBER

GUITAR- 6A or 5C
BANJO- 4B

Softly and smoothly ♩ = 48

But black is the col-our____ of my true love's hair,
Her cheeks are like____ some ro-sy fair,____
____ The pret-ti-est eyes____ and the neat-est hands,
I love the ground where-on she stands.

1 But black is the colour of my true love's hair,
  Her cheeks are like some rosy fair,
  The prettiest eyes and the neatest hands,
  I love the ground whereon she stands.

2 I love my love and well she knows,
  I love the ground whereon she goes,
  If you no more on earth I see,
  I won't serve you as you have me.

206

3 The winter's passed and the leaves are green,
The time is passed that we have seen,
But still I hope the time will come
When you and I shall be as one.

4 I go to the Clyde for to mourn and weep,
But satisfied I never could sleep,
I'll write you a letter in a few short lines,
I'll suffer death ten thousand times.

5 So fare you well, my own true love,
The time has passed, but I wish you well,
But still I hope the time will come
When you and I will be as one.

6 I love my love and well she knows,
I love the ground whereon she goes,
The prettiest face and the neatest hands,
I love the ground whereon she stands.

101. AUNT SAL'S SONG

FROM: The Settlement School, Pine Mt., Ky. SEE: Belden, 426; Brown III, 27;
Sharp II, 6. Is also a Negro song. This version is known as *Aunt Sal's Song* because
Aunt Sal often sang at Pine Mountain, Ky. See also—*Quaker's Courtship.*
Piano arrangement by MATYAS SEIBER

1 A gentleman came to our house,
He would not tell his name,
I knew he came a-courtin',
Although he were ashamed,
O, although he were ashamed.

2 He moved his chair up to my side,
His fancy pleased me well,
I thought the spirit moved him
Some handsome tale to tell, *etc.*

3 O there he sat the livelong night
   And never a word did say,
   With many a sigh and bitter groan
   He oftimes wished for day, *etc.*

4 The chickens they begun to crow
   And daylight did appear,
   ' How d'ye do, good morning, sir
   I'm glad to see you here, '*etc.*

5 He was weary of the livelong night,
   He was weary of his life,
   ' If this is what you call courting, boys,
   I'll never take a wife,' *etc.*

6 And when he goes in company,
   The girls all laugh for sport,
   Saying, ' Yonder goes that ding-dang fool,
   He don't know how to court,' *etc.*

102. I'M TROUBLED

Adapted and arranged by Alan Lomax. SEE: Brown III, 344; Greenleaf, 121.
Song connected with *The Cuckoo, On Top of Old Smokey,* etc.
Piano arrangement by MATYAS SEIBER

1 I'm troubled, I'm troubled,
   I'm troubled in my mind,
   If trouble don't kill me,
   I'll live a long time.

2 My cheeks was as red,
   As the red, red rose,
   But now they're as pale as
   The lily that blows.

3 I'll build me a cabin
   On the mountain so high,
   Where the wild birds can't see me
   Or hear my sad cry.

4 I'm sad and I'm lonely,
   My heart it will break,
   My true love loves another,
   Lord, I wisht I was dead.

103. LOVIN' HANNAH

From singing of Jean Ritchie. SEE: Belden, 292; Brown II, 367; Creighton I, 175; JEFSS I, 25; Joyce, 190; Randolph IV, 232; Sharp II, 254 (*The Irish Girl*). Peter Kennedy has recently found variants in Northern Ireland: (a) *Charming Molly*, (b) *Going to Church Last Sunday*, (c) *Farewell Ballymonny*.

Piano arrangement by MATYAS SEIBER

1. I rode to church last Sunday,
   My true love passed me by.
   I knew her love was changin'
   By the rovin' of her eye.

   By the rovin' of her eye,
   By the rovin' of her eye,
   I knew her love was changin'
   By the rovin' of her eye.

2. My love is fair and proper
   Her hands are neat and small.
   And she is quite good lookin'
   And that's the best of all, *etc.*

3. O Hannah, lovin' Hannah,
   Come, give to me your hand,
   You said if you ever married,
   That I should be the man, *etc.*

4. I'll go down by the waters
   When everyone's asleep,
   I'll think on lovin' Hannah,
   And then set down an' weep, *etc.*

104. THE GAMBLING SUITOR

From singing of Jean Ritchie and Paul Clayton, as published in *American Folk Tales and Folk Songs*, compiled by Richard Chase (Signet Key edition by The New American Library of World Literature, Inc.) © 1956 by Richard Chase. SEE: Brown III, 10; Randolph III, 361; Sharp II, 249. Found in Miss., Ind., and Mich.

Woman:
O Sir, I see you coming again.
Pray tell me what it's for?
When I left you in Barbourville
I told you to come no more, no more,
I told you to come no more.

Man:
O miss, I have a very fine house
It's newly built with pine,
And you may have it at your command
If you will be my bride, *etc.*

Woman:
O Sir, I know it's a very fine house,
Also a very fine yard,
But who will stay at home with me
When you're out playing cards? *etc.*

Man:
I never played a card in all my life,
I never thought it right,
If you will consent to be my bride
I'll stay 'way nary a night, *etc.*

Woman:
Now miss, I have a very fine farm,
It's sixty acres wide,
And you shall have it at your command
If you will be my bride, *etc.*

Woman:
Sir, I know it's a very fine farm,
Full of very fine fruit,
As you come in, I'll drive you out
For you know a hog must root, *etc.*

Man:
O Miss, I have a very fine horse,
It paces like the tide,
And you may have him at your command
Whenever you want to ride, *etc.*

Woman:
Sir, I know it's a very fine horse,
Also a very fine barn,
But his master drinks and gambles
I'm afraid his horse'll learn, *etc.*

Man:
Well, Madam, you don't like me at all,
It's very plain to tell,
I'll go marry whom I please
You can go do as well, *etc.*

105. CHICKENS THEY ARE CROWIN'

FROM: p. 378, *English Folk Songs of the Southern Appalachians*, Cecil Sharp (Oxford U.P., 1932). Used by permission of Maud Karpeles and the O.U.P. As sung by Ben Finlay, Little Goose Creek, Clay Co., Ky., as a play-party song. SEE: JAFL XXIV, 274; Sandburg, 125.

Smoothly ♩ = 72

GUITAR– FREE STRUM *or 5C or 6A*
BANJO– 4B

The chick-ens they are crow - in', a - crow - in', a - crow-in', The
chick-ens they are crow - in', for it is al-most day - light.

1 The chickens they are crowin', a-crowin', a-crowin',
The chickens they are crowin', for it is almost daylight.

2 My mother she will scold me, will scold me, will scold me,
My mother she will scold me for stayin' away all night.

3 My father he'll uphold me, uphold me, uphold me,
My father he'll uphold me and say I done just right.

4 I won't go home till mornin', till mornin', till mornin',
I won't go home till mornin', and I'll stay with the girls all night.

5 The chickens they are crowin', a-crowin', a-crowin',
The chickens they are crowin', for it is almost daylight.

106. HOW OLD ARE YOU, MY PRETTY LITTLE MISS?

As sung by Peggy Seeger. SEE: Brown III, 21; Guide and Index (*Seventeen Come Sunday*); JEFSS II, 9-10 (lyric seems to be derived from Child, 29); Randolph I, 330; Reeves, 126; Sharp II, 156. Peter Kennedy finds frequently in Northern Ireland, southern England. Song is common in America. See Brown II, 49; Grieg, 246. Is the favourite song of old singer on Sugar Loaf Mountain. He says, 'Seventeen is the right age to catch a girl. If she's older than that she's apt to be getting uneasy, and it comes too easy.'

1 ' How old are you, my pretty little miss?
  How old are you, my honey?'
  ' If I don't die of a broken heart,
  I'll be sixteen next Sunday.'
  CHORUS:
  Rink to my dink to my diddle diddle dum, ⎫ (2)
  Rink to my dink to my doodle. ⎭

2 ' Can you court, my pretty little miss?
  Can you court, my flower?'
  ' I can court more in a minute and a half,
  Than you can in an hour.' (CHO.)

3 ' Will you marry me, my pretty little miss?
  Will you marry me, good looking?'
  ' I'll marry you, but I won't do
  Your washing or your cooking.' (CHO.)

107. WHISTLE, DAUGHTER, WHISTLE

SEE: Brown II, 457; Guide; Newell, 96; Randolph I, 410; Reeves, 223; Sharp II, 169.

Quietly ♩ = 100

GUITAR- ANY 2/4 STYLE
BANJO- 4B or 1-3

'Mo-ther, I would mar-ry and I would be a bride, And I would have a young man for-ev-er at my side, For if I had a young man, O how hap-py I would be, For I am tired and O so wea-ry of my vir-gin-i-ty.'

1 'Mother, I would marry and I would be a bride,
   And I would have a young man forever at my side.
   For if I had a young man, O how happy I would be,
   For I am tired and O so weary of my virginity.'

2 'Whistle, daughter, whistle, and you shall have a cow.'
   'I cannot whistle, mother, I guess I don't know how.
   For if I had a young man, O how happy I would be,
   For I am tired and O so weary of my propriety.'

3 'Whistle, daughter, whistle, and you shall have a sheep.'
   'I cannot whistle, mother, I can only weep.
   For if I had a young man, O how happy I would be,
   For I am tired and so weary of my singularity.'

4 'Whistle, daughter, whistle, and you shall have a man.'
   'I can whistle . . . ' (*She whistles the rest of the line.*)
   'You impudent little daughter, and what makes you whistle now?'
   'I'd rather whistle for a man than for a sheep or cow.'

108. WINTER'S NIGHT

FROM: p. 14 of *Folk Songs of Alabama*, Byron Arnold (University of Alabama Press, 1950). Used by permission. SEE: Belden, 480; Brown III, 299; Child, No. 76; Coffin, 79; Guide and Index (*Turtle Dove*); Reeves, 38, 213, 218; Sharp II, 114; Wells, 119.

Piano arrangement by MATYAS SEIBER

1 As I rode out last winter's night,
  A-drinkin' of sweet wine,
  Conversin' with that pretty little girl
  That stole this heart of mine.
  CHORUS:
  So fare you well, my own true love,
  So fare you well for a while.
  I'm goin' away, but I'm comin' back,
  If I go ten thousand miles.

2 She is like some pink or rose
  That blooms in the month of June,
  Or like some musical instrument
  Just lately put in tune.   (CHO.)

3 'O who will shoe your feet, my love,
  And who will glove your hands,
  And who will kiss your red, rosy cheeks,
  While I'm gone to the foreign land?'

4 'My father will shoe my feet, my love,
  My mother will glove my hand,
  And you may kiss my red, rosy cheeks
  When you come from the foreign land.' (CHO.)

5 'O don't you see that lonesome dove
  A-flyin' from vine to vine,
  A-mournin' for the loss of a mate,
  And why not me for mine?'

6 'Ten thousand miles away, my love,
  You know that never can be,
  For the parting of our old true love
  Would be the death of me.'

7 'If I prove false to you, my love,
  The rocks shall melt in the sun,
  The fire shall freeze till evermore be,
  And the raging seas shall burn.'   (CHO.)

8 'The blackest crow that ever flew
Will surely turn snow white,
If ever I prove false to you, my love,
Bright day will turn to night.

9 'Bright day will turn to night, my dear,
And the roaring billows burn,
If ever I prove false to the girl I love,
Or I a traitor turn.' (CHO.)

10 'If I am taken sick, my love,
Whilst I am so far from home,
I hope that God will ease my pain
And listen to my moan.'

11 'I wish to God I'd never been born,
Or had died when I was young,
I never would have mourned for the loss of a
Nor love no other one.' (CHO.)   [mate

109. WHO'S GONNA SHOE YOUR PRETTY LITTLE FEET?

Adapted and arranged by Alan Lomax. SEE: Brown III, 303, and notes on previous song.

Smoothly ♩ = 144

GUITAR– ANY WALTZ TIME STYLE
BANJO– 1 (WALTZ TIME)

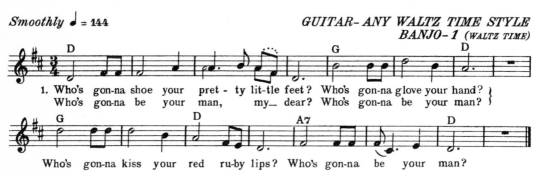

1. Who's gon-na shoe your pret-ty lit-tle feet? Who's gon-na glove your hand?
Who's gon-na be your man, my dear? Who's gon-na be your man?
Who's gon-na kiss your red ru-by lips? Who's gon-na be your man?

1 Who's gonna shoe your pretty little feet?
Who's gonna glove your hand?
Who's gonna kiss your red ruby lips?
  Who's gonna be your man?
  Who's gonna be your man, my dear?
  Who's gonna be your man?
  Who's gonna kiss your red ruby lips?
  Who's gonna be your man?

2 Mama's gonna shoe my pretty little feet,
Papa's gonna glove my hand,
Sister's gonna kiss my red ruby lips,
And I don't need no man,
  And I don't need no man, my love,
  And I don't need no man.
  Sister's gonna kiss **my** red ruby lips,
  And I don't need no man.

3 The longest train I ever saw
Was a hundred coaches long,
The only woman I ever did love
Was on that train and gone,
  On that train and gone, my love,
  On that train and gone,
  Only woman I ever did love
  Was on that train and gone.

4 I wisht to the Lord I'd never been born
Or died when I was young,
I'd never have seen her rosy cheeks
Nor heard her lyin' tongue,
  Nor heard her lyin' tongue, babe,
  Nor heard her lyin' tongue,
  I'd never have seen her rosy cheeks
  Nor heard her lyin' tongue.

110. THE CUCKOO

As sung by Jean Ritchie. SEE: Belden, 473; Brown III, 271; Creighton II, 143;
Guide and Index; Herd, *Ancient and Modern Scots Songs*, II, 180; JAFL XXX, 346,
Randolph I, 271; Reeves, 97; Sharp II, 177 and 392 for English notes.
Piano arrangement by MATYAS SEIBER

1 The cuckoo, she's a pretty bird.
  She sings as she flies,
  She brings us glad tidings,
  And she tells us no lies.

2 She sucks all the pretty flowers
  To make her voice clear,
  And she never sings 'cuckoo'
  Till the spring of the year.

3 Come all you young women,
  Take warning by me,
  Never place your affections
  On the love of a man.

4 For the roots they will wither
  The branches decay.
  He'll turn his back on you
  And walk square away.

5 A meeting, it's a pleasure,
  And a parting is a grief,
  But an inconstant lover
  Is worse than a thief.

6 A thief he'll but rob you
  And take what you have,
  While an inconstant lover
  Will lead you to your grave.

7 The grave will decay you
  And turn you to dust,
  Not a man in ten thousand
  That a poor girl can trust.

8 He'll hug you and kiss you
  And call you his own,
  Perhaps his other darlin'
  Is a-waitin' at home.

9 *Repeat stanza one.*

III. THE FOURTH DAY OF JULY

As sung by Clarence Ashley, Folkways 57 FP 253, adapted and arranged by Alan
Lomax. SEE: Brown III, 80; Flanders I, 172 (*Skewball*); JAFL XXX, 349, and
XXXIX, 149; JEFSS III, 90; Lomax II, 68 (*Stewball*); Scarborough, 279.
Piano arrangement by DON BANKS

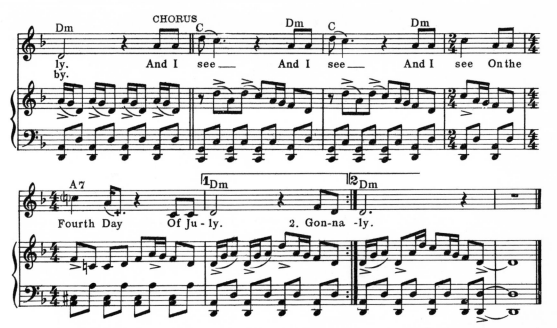

Note: This setting is a transcription for piano of what the banjo-picker does; at first it will require as much practice as boogie-woogie but will be just as rewarding in the end. Can be applied to many songs.

1 O the cuckoo
Is a pretty bird,
She wabbles
As she flies.
She never
Hollers ' cuckoo '
Till the Fourth Day
Of July.

CHORUS:

And I see—
And I see—
And I see
On the Fourth Day
Of July.

2 Gonna build me
A castle
On the mountains
So high,
So I can
See Willie
As he goes
On by.   (CHO.)

3 I often
Have wondered
What makes women
Love men.
Then I've looked back
And wondered
What makes men
Love them.   (CHO.)

4 Jack o' Diamonds,
Jack o' Diamonds,
I know you
Of old.
You robbed my
Poor pockets
Of silver
And gold.   (CHO.)

112. THE WAGONER'S LAD

As sung by Buell Kazee, Eastern Ky., Folkways 7, 251. SEE: Belden, 473; Brown III, 275; JAFL XX, 268, XXVIII, 159; Randolph IV, 216; Sharp II, 123. Known in many variants U.S. and Britain—(see *The Cuckoo*).

Long and lonesome ♩ = 138   GUITAR- *1 OR FREE STRUM*
BANJO- *3* (FAST)

The heart is the for-tune of all wo-man-kind, They're al-ways con-trolled, they're al-ways con-fined, Con-trolled by their fami-ly un-til they are wives, Then slaves to their hus-bands the rest of their lives.

1 The heart is the fortune of all womankind,
They're always controlled, they're always confined,
Controlled by their family until they are wives,
Then slaves to their husbands the rest of their lives.

2 I've been a poor girl, my fortune is bad,
I've always been courted by the wagoner's lad,
He courted me daily by night and by day,
And now he is loaded and going away.

3 ' Your parents don't like me because I am poor,
They say I'm not worthy of entering your door;
I work for my living, my money's my own,
And if they don't like me, they can leave me alone.'

4 ' Your horses are hungry, go feed them on hay,
Come sit down here by me as long as you stay.'
' My horses ain't hungry, they won't eat your hay,
So fare you well, darling, I'll feed on the way.'

5 ' Your wagon needs greasing, your whip is to mend,
Come sit down here by me as long as you can.'
' My wagon is greasy, my whip's in my hand,
So fare you well, darling, no longer to stand.'

113. OLD SMOKEY

As arranged by Alan Lomax. FROM: JAFL XLV, 105; *Folksongs from the Southern Highlands*, M. Henry (J. J. Augustin, N.Y., 1937), p. 80. SEE: Brown III, 287; Sharp II, 123.

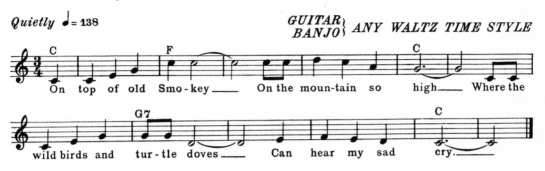

1 On top of old Smokey
On the mountain so high
Where the wild birds and turtle doves
Can hear my sad cry.

2 Sparking is a pleasure
Parting is a grief,
But a falsehearted lover
Is wuss nor a thief.

3 They'll tell you they love you
To give your heart ease,
And as soon as your back's turned
They'll love who they please.

4 I wrote him a letter
In red rosy lines.
He sent it back to me
All twisted in twine.

5 He says ' Keep your love letters
And I'll keep mine.
You write to your true love
And I'll write to mine.

6 ' Your parents is against me
And mine is the same.
If I'm down on your book, love,
Please blot out my name.

7 ' I can love little
And I can love long.
I can love an old sweetheart
Till a new one comes along.

8 ' I can hug them and kiss them
And prove to them kind.
I can turn my back on them
And alter my mind.'

9 ' My horses ain't hungry,
They won't eat your hay.
So farewell, my darlin',
I'll feed on the way.

10 ' I'll drive on to Georgia,
And write you my mind.
My mind is to marry
And leave you behind.'

11 I'll go on old Smokey
On the mountain so high,
Where the wild birds and turtle doves
Can hear my sad cry.

12 As sure as the dewdrops
Fall on the green corn,
Last night I were with him,
Tonight he is gone.

114. I NEVER WILL MARRY

Arranged by Alan Lomax from the singing of the Carter Family. SEE: Belden, 167; Randolph I, 341. Said to be derived from the broadside ballad ' The Sorrowful Ladie's Complaint.' *Roxburghe Ballads*, IV, 397.

Long and lonesome ♩=138

GUITAR— 4 or 6A
BANJO— 1 or 4B

One morn-ing I ram-bled___ Down by the sea - shore,___ ___ The wind it did whis-tle___ And the wa-ters did roar.

1 One morning I rambled
Down by the seashore,
The wind it did whistle
And the waters did roar.

2 I heard some fair maiden
Give a pitiful cry,
And it sounded so lonely
It swept off on high.
CHORUS: (*Sung to the verse melody*)
' I never will marry
Nor be no man's wife.
I intend to live single
All the days of my life.

3 ' The shells in the ocean
Shall be my death bed,
While the fish in deep water
Swim over my head.'   (CHO.)

4 She cast her fair body
In the water so deep,
And she closed her pretty blue eyes,
Forever to sleep.   (CHO.)

115. JOHNSON BOYS

As sung by Lily Mae Ledford and arranged by Alan Lomax. SEE: Brown III, 394.

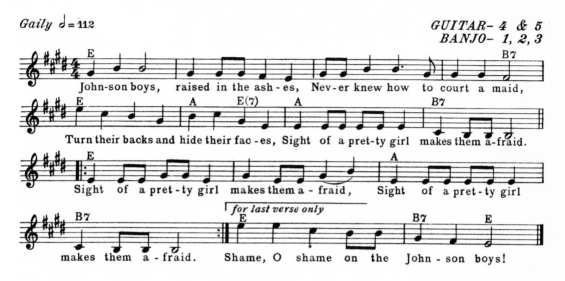

1 Johnson boys, raised in the ashes,
  Never knew how to court a maid,
  Turn their backs and hide their faces,
  Sight of a pretty girl makes them afraid. (3)

2 Johnson boys went a-courtin',
  The Coon Creek girls so pretty and sweet,
  They couldn't make no conversation,
  They didn't know where to put their feet. (3)

3 The Johnson boys, they went a-huntin',
  Took two dogs and went astray,
  Tore their clothes and scratched their faces,
  They didn't get home till the break of day. (3)

4 The Johnson boys went to the city,
  Ridin' in a Chevrolet,
  They came home broke and a-walkin',
  They had no money for to pay their way, (3)
    Shame, O shame on the Johnson boys.

FROLIC TUNES

116. UNCLE JOE

IN GEORGE PORTER's fabulous description of a country frolic that took place on the ' Knobs '
near Knoxville, Tennessee, we hear the fiddle as it sounded to pioneer ears, and feel the
excitement of the dance as Davy Crockett's people felt it.

You may talk of your bar hunts and your deer hunts, and knottin' tigers' tails through the bung holes of
barrels, and cock fitin and all that, but if a regular-bilt frolick in the North of ' Old Knox ' don't beat em all
blind for fun, then I'm no judge of fun, that's all! I said fun, and I say it agin, from a kiss that cracks like a
wagin-whip up to a fite that rouses up all outdoors, and as to laughin, why they invented laughin, and the last
laugh will be hearn at a Knob dance about three in the mornin! I'm jest getting so I can ride arter the motions
I made at one at Jo Spraggins's a few days ago.

I'll try and tell you who Jo Spraggins is. He's a fiddler, a judge of a hoss, and a hoss himself! He can
make more spinnin wheels, kiss more spinners, thrash more wheat and more men than any one-eyed man I
know on. He loves a woman, old sledge* and sin in eny shape. He lives in a log house about ten yards squar;
it has two rooms, one at the bottom an one at the top of the ladder—has all out of doors fur a yard, and all the
South fur its occupants at times. He gives a frolick onst in three weeks in plowing time and one every Saturday
night the balance of the year, and only axes a 'fip ' for a reel, and two bits fur what corn-juice you suck; he
throws the gals in, and a bed, too, in the hay, if you git too hot to locomote. The supper is made up by the
fellers; everyone fetches sumthin; some a lick of meal; some a middlin of bacon; some a hen; some a
possum; some a punkin; some a grab of taters or a pocket full of peas, or dried apples, and some only fetches a
good appetite and a skin chock full of pertickler deviltry. Jo then mounts Punkinslinger bar-backed, about
three hours afore the sun goes down and gives all the gals item. He does this a leetle of the slickest—just rides
past in a peart rack, singin' . . .

> Hop up, my ladies, three in a row,
> Don't mind the weather if the wind don't blow . . .

QUOTE: Blair, p. 363.

*A card game

117. SALLY ANNE

An owl couldn't have cotch a rat before I was in site of Jo's with my gal, Jule Sawyers, up behind me. She
hugged me mitey tite because she was ' feered of fallin' off that dratted poney '. She said she didn't mind a fall,
but it might break her leg and then goodbye frolicks—she'd be fit fur nothing but to nuss brats ollers arter-
wards. I now hearn the fiddle ting-tong-ding-domb. I gave Julie a kiss to sorter molify my natur and put her
in heart like, an' in we walked. ' Hey, here ain't Dick and Julie.' Jist like we hadn't been rite thar only last
Saturday nite. ' Well, I know, we'll have a reel now. Hurrah!'

' Go to it while you're young.'

' Hurrah for the brimstone kiln—every man praise his country.'

' Clar the ring!'

' Misses Spraggins, drive out these dratted tow-headed brats of your'n—give room!'

224

Come here, Suze Thompson, and let me pin your dress behind. Your back looks edzactly like a blaze on a white oak.'

'Hello thar. Gin us *Forked Deer*, old fiddle teaser, or I'll give you forked lightning.'

'Whoop! Hurraw! Gather your gals for the breakdown!'

'Give us *Forked Deer*.'

'No, give us *Natchez Under the Hill*.'

'O, shucks, give us *Rocky Mountain* or *Misses McLoud*.'

'*Misses McLoud* be darned—and *Rocky Mountain*, too. Jist give us *She Wouldn't and She Couldn't and She Didn't Come at All*!' 'Give him a horn, and every time he stops repeat the dose and nary another string'll break tonite. Tink-tong! Ting-tong! All rite. Now go it!' . . . and if I know what goin' it is, we did go it.

QUOTE: Blair, p. 363.

118. CRIPPLE CREEK

. . . About midnite, Misses Spraggins sung out, ' Stop that ar dancin and come and get your supper!'

Jo sung out, ' Knives is scase, so give what thar is to the gals and let the balance use their paws—they was invented afore knives eney how. Now, gents, jist walk into the fat of this land. I'm sorter feerd the honey won' last till daybreak, but the liquor will, I think, so you men when you drink you'n, run an kiss the gals fur sweetnin —let them have the honey, it belongs to them naturally.'

Well, we danced and hurrawed without anything of very pertickler interest to happen, till about three o'clock, when the darndest muss was kicked up you ever did see. Jim Smith sot down on the bed alongside of Bet Holden, and just fell to huggin of her bar fashion. She tuck it very kind till she seed Sam Henry a-lookin on from behind about a dozen galls, then she fell to kickin an a hollerin an a screechin like all wrath. Sam, he come up and told Jim to let Bet go. Jim told him to go to a far-off countree whar they give away brimstone and throw in the fire to burn it. Sam hit him strate atween the eyes an, after a few licks, the fightin started.

O hush! It makes my mouth water now to think what a beautiful row we had. One feller from Cady's Grove knocked a hole in the bottom of a fryin-pan over Dan Turner's head, and left it a hangin round his neck, the handle flyin about like a long cue, and thar it hung till Jabe Thurman cut it off with a cold chisel the next day! That was his share fur that nite, sure. Another feller got knocked into a meat barrel: he was as mealy as an Irish tater and as hot as hoss-radish; when he bursted the hoops and cum out he rared a few. Two fellers fit out of the door, down the hill and into the creek and thar ended it, in a quiet way all alone.

Arter we made friends all round (except the fiddler—he's hot yet), and danced and liquored at the tail of every reel till sun up, when them that was sober enuff went home, and them that was wounded staid whar they fell. Dick and Julie had to ride ' Shank's mare '. She was weak in two of her legs, but t'other two—O my stars and possum dogs!—they make a man swaller tobacker jist to look at 'em, and feel sorta like a June bug was crawling up his trowsers and the waistband was too tight for it to git out. I'm a-goin' to marry Jule, I swar I am, and sich a cross! Think of a locomotive and a cotton gin! Whoo! Whoopee!

QUOTE: Blair, p. 363.

119. CINDY

To BE a master fiddler, some believed, you had to meet the Devil at midnight at the cross-roads or in the graveyard and enter into a contract with him. A Negro fiddler remembers his own midnight visit to the churchyard . . .

I goes thar and sets myself down and chuned up my fiddle. Then I struck into *Ol' Dan Tucker*—that's the Devil's chune, you know, and it's the first thing the Devil will learn you to play. Well, sir, I set thar and learned to play that real good.

Afterwards I tried *Dixie* and kep' at it till I could play that tolerable good, too, but pretty soon I heard something over back of the church, *bangity-bang*! I was listening with both ears and still a-playin' my fiddle when some hot steam come about me, and that steam was so warm and fainty it almost made me sick. I thought, ' This ain't natural. Thar mus' be ghos'es hyar somewhar.'

The mo' I studied 'bout it, the mo' skeered I was. I put my hand up to see whether my hat was on my head, and I found my hair was standin' straight up and had carried my hat with it. Jus' then some steam came aroun' me so hot it scorched my face, and I throwed my fiddle down and ran. If any ghos'es wanted it, they could have it and practise on it all they wanted. But if I could have stood it to play in the churchyard an hour or two longer, I could have played anything.

For the story of such part-minstrel songs as *Cindy see* p. 493.

QUOTE: *Battleground Adventures*, Clifton Johnson (Houghton Mifflin, 1915).

120. SHADY GROVE

Dad remembered for us the first day he ever heard the fiddle played. He was a little slip of a boy, he said, about nine years old, and he was going to school to old man Nick Gerhart. (About 1870.) He'd been off somewheres courting in Virginny and he had brought a feller home with him to the schoolhouse to visit. That stranger had a fiddle in his hand, first one any of us had ever seen, and pretty soon he propped it in the cradle of his arm here and begun to play that thing. Lordie! I thought that was the prettiest sweepingest music. I hadn't heard a sound like that in my life before, and it seemed like the only thing I'd been a-waitin' for all this time. I wanted to holler and jump up and down. I just mortally couldn't stand to sit still on that log bench and that tune snakin' around so. Finally I let out a yell and leapt off'n that bench and commenced to dance and clog around. Everybody hollered out a-laughing, and some of the other boys jumped up, too. Every time he'd touch that bow to them strings, hell would tear loose in that schoolhouse.

After a while, that feller left, and our teacher tried to settle us, put us back to our books, but I couldn't even see the print in that speller. I kept seeing that old fiddle bow race around on *Shady Grove*. We around there had always sung that tune middling fast, hopped around to it a little bit, but that fiddle had tuck out with that'n like the Devil was atter her. I was so tickled about that I kept laughing and wriggling round in my seat and saying the words to *Shady Grove* out loud instead of my lesson.

QUOTE: *Singing Family of the Cumberlands*, Jean Ritchie (Oxford University Press, New York, 1955). Reprinted by permission of the publishers.

121. SALLY GOODIN

Cedarhead was a stern and righteous man and a preacher, and it was his everlasting grief and shame that his young boys . . . loved fiddling mighty near better than they loved eating. Cedarhead saw this and at last put it against the law for them to play a fiddle any more, and he broke up every one the boys had made. Well, the boys didn't do a thing but make more instruments, and they hid them in holler logs in the woods. Then they'd slip off and fiddle away and sing.

Once, Cedarhead and his boys were clearing some new ground, and they got to rolling logs. The old man noticed that they kept surrounding a main big old one. ' Boys,' he thundered out, ' what you a-savin' this big one for last?' The boys, they looked at one another and came up kind of slow and timid to help prize, and that big log went leaping down the mountain side.

Purty soon the fiddles began to fly ever which way. Strings a-poppin', gourds a-bustin', must of been eight or ten of the instruments hid away in there. 'Cording to Cedarhead, he personally tore up Hell in the new ground that day!

QUOTE: ibid.

122. JUBILEE

THERE WERE always those white mountain families who would not permit their young people to attend country frolics like the Knob Dance, but where dancing was forbidden, singing games were not, and the ancient children's amusements were acted out by grown-ups. Late in the evening, the more daring couples would begin to swing and change partners in square-dance style, yet, because conventions had been honoured, the old folks did not call them dances. They permitted songs like *Jubilee* to be sung, although it was a Devil's ditty in everything but name. Jean Ritchie recorded this song for me in 1949.

116. UNCLE JOE

From p. 58 *Our Singing Country,* John and Alan Lomax (Macmillan, N.Y., 1941).
As sung by Uncle Eck Dunford, Galax, Va.   SEE: Brown III, 119; Lomax IV, 58,
Randolph II, 323, who shows its links with *Jump Jim Crow,* first published N.Y.,
1829, which became popular around the world. Heard among Hindu minstrels in
Delhi! The tune is *Miss McCloud's Reel.*
Piano arrangement by DON BANKS

Rollicking ♩ = 208   GUITAR– *4 or 5*
                                                           BANJO– *1-3*

1. Did you ev-er go to meet-in', Un-cle Joe, Un-cle Joe? Did you
2. Will your horse car-ry dou-ble, Un-cle Joe, Un-cle Joe? Will your
3. Is your horse a sin-gle foot-er, Un-cle Joe, Un-cle Joe? Is your

ev-er go to meet-in', Un-cle Joe? Did you ev-er go to meet-in', Un-cle
horse car-ry dou-ble, Un-cle Joe? Will your horse car-ry dou-ble, Un-cle
horse a sin-gle foot-er, Un-cle Joe? Is your horse a sin-gle foot-er, Un-cle

Joe, Un-cle Joe? Don't mind the wea-ther when the wind don't blow.
Joe, Un-cle Joe? Don't mind the wea-ther when the wind don't blow.
Joe, Un-cle Joe? Don't mind the wea-ther when the wind don't blow.

1 Did you ever go to meetin', Uncle Joe, Uncle Joe?
Did you ever go to meetin', Uncle Joe?
Did you ever go to meetin', Uncle Joe, Uncle Joe?
Don't mind the weather when the wind don't blow.
CHORUS:
Hop up, my ladies, three in a row,   (3)
Don't mind the weather when the wind don't blow.

2 Will your horse carry double, Uncle Joe, Uncle Joe? *etc.*

3 Is your horse a single-footer, Uncle Joe, Uncle Joe? *etc.*

4 Would you rather ride a pacer, Uncle Joe, Uncle Joe? *etc.*

117. SALLY ANNE

As collected and arranged by Alan Lomax. SEE: Botkin I, 302; Sharp II, 351.
Is same air as *Sandy Land*, fiddle tune common as far west as Texas. Also related to
Sally Goodin.

Piano arrangement by DON BANKS

Ev-er see a musk-rat, Sal-ly Anne?
Shake that lit-tle foot, Sal-ly Anne.

2. Sift—

1 Did you ever see a muskrat, Sally Anne,
   Draggin' his slick tail through the sand,
   Pickin' his banjo an' raisin' sand,
   Did you ever see a muskrat, Sally Anne?
   CHORUS:
   Ever see a muskrat, Sally, Sally,
   Ever see a muskrat, Sally Anne?

2 Sift that meal and save the bran,
   Gwine to the weddin' with Sally Anne,
   Shake that little foot, Sally Anne,
   You're a pretty good dancer, Sally Anne.
   CHORUS:
   Shake that little foot, Sally, Sally,
   Shake that little foot, Sally Anne.

3 Make my livin' in the sandy land,
   Raise big 'taters in the sandy land,
   Big mushmelons in the sandy land,
   Sandy bottom, sandy land.
   CHORUS:
   I'm gonna marry you, Sally, Sally,
   I'm gonna marry you, Sally Anne.

4 Sal's got a meatskin* laid away,
   To grease that wooden leg, so they say,
   Dinah's got a wooden leg, so they say,
   Shake that wooden leg, Dinah-o.
   CHORUS:
   Shake that wooden leg, Dinah, Dinah,
   Shake that wooden leg, Dinah-o.

* piece of bacon rind

118. CRIPPLE CREEK

Collected and arranged by Alan Lomax. SEE: Brown III, 354; Sharp II, 352, 358.
Common in South and West as banjo and fiddle tune.

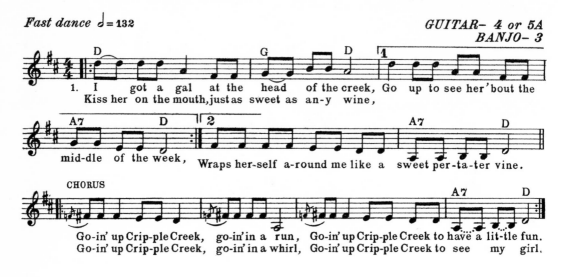

Fast dance ♩ = 132

GUITAR— 4 or 5A
BANJO— 3

1. I got a gal at the head of the creek, Go up to see her 'bout the
Kiss her on the mouth, just as sweet as an-y wine,

mid-dle of the week, Wraps her-self a-round me like a sweet per-ta-ter vine.

CHORUS

Go-in' up Crip-ple Creek, go-in' in a run, Go-in' up Crip-ple Creek to have a lit-tle fun.
Go-in' up Crip-ple Creek, go-in' in a whirl, Go-in' up Crip-ple Creek to see my girl.

1 I got a gal at the head of the creek,
   Go up to see her 'bout the middle of the week,
   Kiss her on the mouth, just as sweet as any wine,
   Wraps herself around like a sweet pertater vine.
   CHORUS:
   Goin' up Cripple Creek, goin' in a run,
   Goin' up Cripple Creek to have a little fun.
   Goin' up Cripple Creek goin' in a whirl,
   Goin' up Cripple Creek to see my girl.

2 Girls on the Cripple Creek 'bout half grown,
   Jump on a boy like a dog on a bone.
   Roll my britches up to my knees,
   I'll wade old Cripple Creek when I please.

3 Cripple Creek's wide and Cripple Creek's deep,
   I'll wade old Cripple Creek afore I sleep,
   Roads are rocky and the hillside's muddy
   And I'm so drunk that I can't stand study.*

* steady

232

119. CINDY

Collected and arranged by Alan Lomax. SEE: Brown III, 482; Randolph III, 376; Scarborough, 67; White, 161 (where he shows connexion with an ante-bellum stage minstrel song); Verse 4 is from Randolph, III, 376. Widely popular square dance and banjo tune.

Fast dance ♩ = 112

GUITAR– 4
BANJO– 3

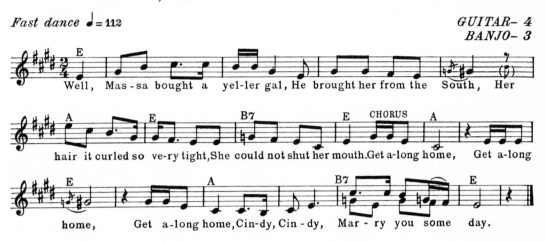

1 Well Massa bought a yaller gal,
   He brought her from the South,
   Her hair it curled so very tight,
   She could not shut her mouth.
   CHORUS:
   Get along home,
   Get along home,
   Get along home, Cindy, Cindy,
   Marry you some day.

2 He took her to the blacksmith shop
   To have her mouth made small,
   She backed her ears and gapped her mouth
   And swallowed shop and all. (CHO.)

3 Cindy is a pretty gal,
   She comes from the South,
   She's so sweet the honey-bees
   Swarm all round her mouth. (CHO.)

4 I been to the East and to the West
   I been to the jaybird's altar,
   But the prettiest gal I ever seen
   Was Jimmie Shirland's daughter. (CHO.)

5 She hugged me and she kissed me,
   She wrang her hands and sighed,
   She swore I was the prettiest man
   That ever lived or died. (CHO.)

6 Apples in the summertime
   Peaches in the fall,
   If I can't have my Cindy gal
   I won't take none at all. (CHO.)

7 Finger-rings, finger-rings,
   Shine like glittering gold,
   How I love that pretty little girl,
   It never can be told. (CHO.)

233

120. SHADY GROVE

Tune from singing of Jean Ritchie, lyrics from JAFL XXVIII, p. 182. SEE: Brown
III, 552.

Piano arrangement by DON BANKS

CHORUS
Sha - dy grove, my true love,

VERSE
Peach - es in the sum-mer-time,

Sha - dy grove I know, Sha - dy grove, my true love, I'm bound for the sha-dy grove.
Ap - ples in the fall, If I can't get the girl I love Won't have none at all.

*Note: Alternate verses may be played an octave higher
† Optional chords in parentheses

CHORUS:
Shady grove, my true love,
Shady grove, I know,
Shady grove, my true love,
I'm bound for the shady grove.

1 Peaches in the summertime,
   Apples in the fall,
   If I can't get the girl I love,
   Won't have none at all.   (CHO.)

2 Once I was a little boy,
   Playin' in the sand,
   Now I am great big boy,
   I think myself a man.   (CHO.)

3 When I wus a little boy,
   I wanted a whittlin' knife;
   Now I am a great big boy
   An' I want a little wife.   (CHO.)

4 Wish I had a banjo string,
   Made of golden twine,
   And every tune I'd pick on it—
   Is ' I wish that girl were mine.'   (CHO.)

5 Some come here to fiddle en dance,
   Some come here to tarry,
   Some come here to fiddle en dance,
   I come here to marry.   (CHO.)

6 Ev'ry night when I go home,
   My wife, I try to please her,
   The more I try, the worse she gets,
   Damned if I don't leave her.
   CHORUS:
   Shady grove, my little love,
   Shady grove, my darlin',
   Shady grove, my little love
   Goin' back to Harlan.

7 Fly around, my blue-eyed girl,
   Fly around, my daisy,
   Fly around, my blue-eyed girl,
   Nearly drive me crazy.   (CHO.)

8 The very next time I go that road
   And it don't look so dark and grazy,
   The very next time I come that road
   I'll stop and see my daisy.   (CHO.)

9 I once had a mulie cow,
   Mulie when she's born,
   Took a jay-bird forty year
   To fly from horn to horn.   (CHO.)

121. SALLY GOODIN

Collected and arranged by Alan Lomax. SEE: Brown III, 126; JAFL, XXVIII, p. 178; Randolph II, 350. Known from Carolinas to Texas.

Square Dance Tempo ♩ = 160

GUITAR— *4 or 5A*
BANJO— *1, 2 or 3*

Had a piece of pie an' I had a piece of pud-din', An' I gave it all a-way just to see my Sal-ly Good-in. Well, I looked down the road an' I seen my Sal-ly com-in', An' I thought to my soul that I'd kill my-self a-run-nin'.

1 Had a piece of pie an' I had a piece of puddin',
An' I give it all away just to see my Sally Goodin. } (2)
Well, I looked down the road an' I seen my Sally comin',
An' I thought to my soul that I'd kill myself a-runnin'. } (2)

2 Love a 'tater pie an' I love an apple puddin'
An' I love a little gal that they call Sally Goodin. } (2)
An I dropped the 'tater pie an' I left the apple puddin'
But' I went across the mountain to see my Sally Goodin. } (2)

3 Sally is my doozy an' Sally is my daisy,
When Sally says she hates me I think I'm goin' crazy. } (2)
Little dog'll bark an' the big dog'll bite you,
Little gal'll co'te you an' big gal'll fight you. } (2)

4 Rainin' an' a-pourin' an' the creek's runnin' muddy,
An' I'm so drunk, Lord, I can't stand studdy, } (2)
I'm goin' up the mountain an' marry little Sally,
Raise corn on the hillside an' the devil in the valley. } (2)

122. JUBILEE

Recorded by Alan Lomax from singing of Jean Ritchie in 1949. A composite of stanzas from many play-party and square-dance songs. Last two verses added from the record *Southern Singing Games*, Elektra EKLP 2.

Square Dance Tempo ♩ = 116

GUITAR- ANY ¾ STYLE
BANJO- 1, 2 or 3

It's all out on the old rail-road, It's all out on the sea,
All out on the old rail-road, Far as I can see.

CHORUS

Swing and turn, Ju-bi-lee, Live and learn, Ju-bi-lee.

1 It's all out on the old railroad,
It's all out on the sea,
All out on the old railroad,
Far as I can see.
CHORUS:
Swing and turn, Jubilee,
Live and learn, Jubilee.

2 Hardest work I ever done,
Workin' on the farm,
Easiest work I ever done,
Swingin' my true love's arm.   (CHO.)

3 If I had a needle and thread,
As fine as I could sew,
I'd sew my true love to my side
And down this creek I'd go.   (CHO.)

4 If I had no horse to ride,
I'd be found a-crawlin'
Up and down this rocky road
Lookin' for my darlin'.   (CHO.)

5 Some will come on Saturday night,
Some will come on Sunday,
If you give 'em half a chance,
They'll be back on Monday.   (CHO.)

6 I won't have no widder man,
Neither will my cousin,
You can get such stuff as that
For fifteen cents a dozen.   (CHO.)

7 Coffee grows on a white oak tree,
Sugar runs in brandy,
Girls are sweet as a lump of gold,
Boys as sweet as candy.   (CHO.)

8 All I want's a big fat horse,
Corn to feed it on,
Pretty little girl to stay at home,
And feed it when I'm gone.   (CHO.)

WHITE SPIRITUALS

123. THE SEVEN BLESSINGS OF MARY

THE PURITANS looked upon the old English Christmas customs as Popish or pagan. The Puritan Parliament wiped the holiday off the calendar, and Roundhead soldiers clapped carol singers into prison. Thus, during the early years of the English colonization of America, carol-singing was in public disrepute; it continued only in remote country districts in England, and not until the time of Dickens was it rediscovered by antiquarians and revived in English cities. The Lowland Scots and the Scots-Irish Calvinists had already abandoned Christmas.

Perhaps this explains why so few of the English carols, and none of the ritual dances and ceremonies survived in American folk tradition. Most of Niles' carols seem to come from English collections. Aside from the ballad of *Joseph and Mary and the Cherry Tree*, the *Number Song* is the most common folk carol in the United States. Various forms of the *Songs of the Twelve* (*see* No. 254) have been collected everywhere in the United States, and *The Seven Pleasures of Mary*, first printed in the fifteenth century, has been found in the Blue Ridge and Smokey Mountains.

124. THE TWELVE DAYS OF CHRISTMAS

IN OLD ENGLAND this song was sung on Twelfth Night as a Christmas game of forfeits. The players sat in a row, the first one singing the first round of the tune, the second the second, the third the third, and so on, until one made a mistake or named the gift wrongly. This player paid a forfeit. The song went on and on and the game continued until a number of forfeits had been accumulated. The forfeits were then counted and each owner had to redeem his fault by performing some task. Several versions of this game have been noted in the mountains of East Tennessee, but it normally occurs as a song. (*See also* No. 254.)

125. AM I BORN TO DIE ?

THE MAJORITY of the settlers who followed Daniel Boone's Wilderness Road into Kentucky before the Revolution turned into shouting Baptists and Methodists during the Great Revival that flamed up west of the mountains in 1800 and, for a generation, roared through the South-east like a forest fire. American folk religion and folk spirituals took their shape at the great ' camp meetings ' and ' brush-arbour ' meetings that were held during these years.

Weather was warm and dry; there was a break in the farm tasks, wheat already harvested and corn not yet ripe for husking. Along roads, signs pointed the way to the assembly and listed the camp meeting rules. As they approached the meeting ground, the road was worn deep with travel and the weeds hung white with dust. Then through the woods, still miles away, came a sound like a great wind rising and falling. The fervor reached out to the newcomers. They whipped up the tired horses, anxious now to be swept out of themselves, to be seized and shaken by the Pentecostal power.

Soon they found a thinned-out forest and hundreds of horses tethered among the trees. Amid acres of wagons, carts, traps, buckboards, they pulled the sweated harness off the team. They hurried on, the great sound enveloping them now, past rows of tents, smoldering fires, signs and numbers posted on the trees. They pushed through the restless fringes of the crowds and saw, over a multitude of heads, the preacher swaying on the raised platform. Already their voices were joining the great chorus, Glory! Glory! Glory! that answered the preacher's cry.

The nasal voices of these folk, who by habit were solo singers, rang like steel on a whetstone. ' Their singing " burst all bonds of guidance " ': in one meeting ' six different hymns were sung at one time, and very loud with violent motions of the body '. This anarchy of camp-meeting music was resolved in three different ways: (1) by the intervention of the shape-note singing schools (*see* notes on *Captain Kidd* and *Weeping Mary*), (2) by a gradual singing-to-pieces of the formal hymns and the creation of songs which were largely chorus and in which the whole group could unite, and (3) by a revival of the old style of lining out the hymns, such as this one.

The latter style—in which the deacon intones a verse, then leads his congregation through it—was one way the Puritans sang their psalms. The practice still lives among the old order Amish, the Wee Free Kirk Presbyterians on the west coast of Scotland, and in many Southern Hard-Shell Baptist churches. When the Negroes sing their ' old Dr. Watts songs', they blend their voices in perfect and spontaneous harmony, so that the effect is like a mighty organ playing in the darkness of the South. Among the white Baptists, every singer sticks to his own pitch and his version of the tune, and there is no harmony, but a thrilling reedy unison.

Yet even though the ragged unison of these white Baptists is sometimes painful listening, the folklorist can only feel grateful for their rugged Scots-Irish individualism. Their non-conformity, their refusal to give in to majority rule in singing, their loyalty to the songs of their ancestors, have preserved for us hundreds of beautiful old tunes and variants of these tunes which would otherwise have disappeared. Once these old-time Baptists heard a song they liked, they would never knowingly change it. Thus, when an obscure revivalist in 1815 set these words by Charles Wesley to a variant of the *Lord Lovel* melody, achieving a well-nigh perfect song, he succeeded in pleasing six generations of backwoods white spiritual singers. This ' surge song ' has been reprinted in fourteen folk-hymn books and has been sung in this form by millions of Southerners . . . The four-part arrangement on page 246 came from the pen of the Kentucky Sacred Harper, Ananias Davidson, in 1817, and, with all its unconventional chords, is here published, as the country singing conventions have performed it for more than a century.

QUOTE: *Wilderness For Sale*, Walter Havighurst, p. 262.

126. ON MY JOURNEY HOME

MRS. FRANCES TROLLOPE, who described our domestic manners in the 1830's, writes of what she saw and heard at a frontier camp meeting where these spirituals took shape . . .

One of the preachers began in a low nasal tone, and like all other Methodist preachers assured us of the enormous depravity of man as he comes from the hands of his Maker, and of his perfect sanctification after he has wrestled sufficiently with the Lord to get hold of him, etc. As they sung, they kept turning themselves round to every part of the crowd, and, by degrees, the voices of the whole multitude joined in chorus. It is certain that the combined voices of such a multitude heard at dead of night from the depths of their eternal forests, the many fair young faces turned upward and looking paler and lovelier as they met the moonbeams, the dark figures of the officials in the middle of the circle, the lurid glare thrown by the altar fires on the woods beyond, did altogether produce a fine and solemn effect; but ere I had well enjoyed it, the scene changed and sublimity gave place to horror and disgust . . .

Above a hundred persons . . . came forward, uttering howlings and groans so terrible that I shall never cease to shudder when I recall them. They appeared to drag each other forward, and on the word being given ' Let us pray ', they all fell on their knees; but this posture was soon changed for others that permitted greater scope for the convulsive movements of their limbs; and they were soon all lying on the ground in an indescribable confusion of heads and legs. They threw about their limbs with such incessant and violent motion that I was every instant expecting some serious accident to occur . . . After the first wild burst that followed their prostration, the moanings, in many instances, became loudly articulate . . .

The stunning noise was sometimes varied by the preachers beginning to sing; but the convulsive movements of the poor maniacs only became more violent. At length the atrocious wickedness of this horrible scene increased to a degree of grossness that drove us from our station; we passed the remainder of the night in listening to the ever-increasing tumult in the pen. To sleep was impossible . . .

QUOTE: *Domestic Manners of America*, Mrs. Frances Trollope, 1830.

127. WAY OVER IN THE HEAVENS

THE TWO white spirituals we have just considered were folk songs only in so far as their tunes were concerned. The text of No. 125 was composed by Charles Wesley, one of the founders of Methodism; the text of No. 126 by Isaac Watts (1674-1748). These men wrote hundreds of hymns designed to bring their new dissenting doctrines to the masses.

As the camp-meeting movement gained ground and put its fiery, popular seal upon the religion of the South, the folk singers in the audience dismembered the formal literary poems of the hymn writers, literally singing them to pieces, until one line or phrase could serve for an entire song. As in the chanteys, the song leader had only to sing the first line and then the congregation could swing on through the remainder of the stanza and lift the chorus straight through the roof of the brush arbour.

' Sister, my soul's happy,' they sang, and happy they might well have been. Unlike their forbears, who had been confined in the slums of mill towns, trapped in the dwindling commons of stagnant English villages or driven into the rocky western wastes of Scotland and Ireland—they now had a green and virgin continent before them. For centuries their ancestors had fought for freedom of worship, for political liberty, for release from the tyranny of caste and class, and now they had won all these in a blow. They saw themselves as the free-est people who had ever been, living in an earthly paradise.

In liberty-loving old ' Kaintuck ', Negroes joined in their meetings, and led in the development of songs that grew steadily simpler and more repetitive. In a short time, the pioneer spirituals became true folk songs, communal both in form and origin.

128. WEEPING MARY

As THE making of the shape-note song-books fell into the hands of rural Southerners, more revival spirituals were recorded from tradition and published.

Weeping Mary, a white spiritual, sung in New York revivals in the 1820's, by Ranters in England in 1823, and by Negro slaves as well, was first recorded and arranged by Georgia farmer-composer John McCurry in his *Social Harp* in 1853. McCurry, who lived in a hill-county populated largely by people of Scots-Irish descent, packed his song-book with the lively five-toned airs that his neighbours liked.

The shape-note singing movement enjoyed a tremendous popularity in the rural South up until about 1870, and the oblong ' Sacred Harps ' ran into editions of hundreds of thousands. Great singing camp meetings took place, religious in tone, but social and musical in fact, where thousands of singers, some hardly literate, sang in four-part polyphony. The old shape-note songs lost their hold on the masses as the fires of the Great Revival flickered out, but one can still attend so-called ' Sacred Harp ' meetings in parts of East Texas and the middle South. They are affairs which no lover of folk song should miss.

The singers stand in a hollow square round the leader—the basses on his right, men and women trebles (tenors) on his left, a mixed choir of tenors (sopranos) in front and the women altos behind him. He calls out the number of the song. There is a rustling of pages, as his choir riffles through the leaves of their books to the chosen song. The leader keys the tunes, by singing the first phrase, then he sweeps his country choir through the whole song in sol-fa, cueing each part, and finally they sail through all the verses at a rattling pace. Children, greybeards, shy young girls—everyone takes his turn as conductor. The most skilled singers move round the square changing their part from bass to treble and from alto to tenor just for the fun of it, scarcely glancing at their books, seeming to know all the parts for five to six hundred hymns.

No one who knows the songs and who loves to sing is barred from these conventions, and no vocal snobs are present. If Sister So-and-So has a voice that shrills out over the ensemble like a snake-charmer's oboe, no one appears to notice. Here, music-making is the thing; democratic group song makes the old folks weep and shout with pleasure. A Texan opined, ' You'd have to put up a mighty high fence to keep me out of a Sacred Harp singing.' When I asked a Georgia farmer why he liked Sacred Harp songs, he smacked his oblong hymn-book with his great red farmer's hands, and rumbled, ' Because ever' word in that air book is *The Truth*!'

129. DEATH, AIN'T YOU GOT NO SHAME ?

DR. JACKSON found this superb folk spiritual among mountain whites in Tennessee, and, after pointing to its occurrence in collections of Negro spirituals, cites it as proof that they are derived from white sources. The evidence, it seems to me, points in another direction. White hymns normally look on death as a joyous release from sin and sorrow; only in Negro spirituals does death appear as an uncertain blessing or an enemy.

Indeed, I suspect that this song is one of the many contributions of Negroes to the white repertoire. At the folk level the Jim Crow line has never been of great effect, and much of southern folklore is an Afro-American hybrid. The people of the upland South, especially, never shared in the lowland pattern of prejudice. Many mountaineers fought on the Union side or stayed at home to bushwhack the Rebel troops, so that the mountain area formed a bulwark against southern invaders in the Civil War. Earlier, in the great revival, poor whites accepted Negroes as fellow brothers in Christ; in fact, the Negro Baptist church had its origins in the mountain country west of the Blue Ridge.

Though certainly Negroes learned their first hymns from white sources, it seems likely that the whites were assisted from the earliest times in making their revival spirituals by Negro singers. The Negroes had the secret of creating songs of great beauty within the fragmentary compass of the easy-to-sing, congregational, leader-chorus formula, and it was in this direction that the white folk spiritual has steadily developed, producing more and more songs in the simple and moving style of this white-Negro song about death.

SOURCE : Jackson I–IV.

130. O DAVID

LATE in the nineteenth century the camp-meeting and shape-note movements lost their hold on the ' solid and respectable ' whites of the South, leaving the poor of the rural and manufacturing slums in need of folk religious release. A new revival at once burst out— the so-called Holy Roller Church—one of the most radical forms of Protestant dissent that has ever existed. The trained minister is a figure of secondary importance in these Holiness churches. Insofar as they are led at all, it is by visionary singing leaders, frequently women. The service is largely given over to dancing and music-making. The music is fast, highly rhythmic, accompanied by drums, tambourines, guitars, banjos, horns, or whatever is handy, and many tunes are hot and blue and Negroid. The songs are prolonged, with a gradually accelerating beat, until dancers and singers ' get happy ' in the Negro sense, and ' shout all over the church '—rolling on the floor, screaming, dancing, but all in strict rhythm to the songs.

White Holiness churches, in the heart of the Jim Crow belt, invite Negroes to participate in their services. Negro churches have white members. Ministers and church officials move with remarkable freedom between Negro and white congregations. In the North and West, where this movement has taken a strong hold in city slums, Negroes and whites, possessed of the spirit, dance and roll on the floor together.

It is difficult to estimate how many Holiness people there are, for they have split into almost as many denominations as there are individual churches, but from the statistics that existed in the late forties, the movement apparently comprised a membership at least as large as any other Protestant denomination. . . In this people's revival, Negroes and their music were openly received into the white church. *O David*, a modern Holiness spiritual from Eastern Kentucky, has the shape of the most primitive type of Negro solo-chorus work song.

123. THE SEVEN BLESSINGS OF MARY

SEE: *The Folk Hymns of North America*, A. M. Buchanan (Schirmer) for full references. Also Creighton II, 275 for note on how it came to Canada from Herts.; Flanders I, 185, II, 211; Index. This is a 15th century carol recorded in the South.

Joyously ♩ = 96

GUITAR- 4
BANJO- 1 or 2

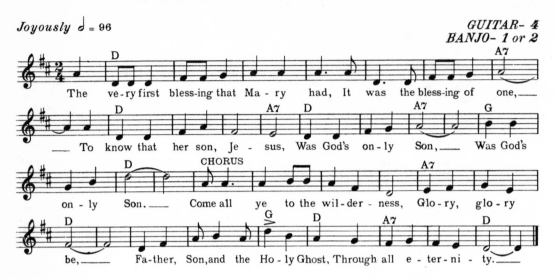

1 The very first blessing that Mary had,
It was the blessing of one,
To know that her son, Jesus,
Was God's only Son,
Was God's only Son.
CHORUS:
Come all ye to the wilderness,
Glory, glory be,
Father, Son and the Holy Ghost,
Through all eternity.

2 The second blessing that Mary had,
It was the blessing of two,
To know that her son, Jesus,
Could read the Bible through. (2) (CHO.)

3 The very next blessing that Mary had,
It was the blessing of three,
To know that her son, Jesus,
Could make the blind to see. (2) (CHO.)

4 The very next blessing that Mary had,
It was the blessing of four,
To know that her son, Jesus,
Would live to help the poor. (2) (CHO.)

5 The very next blessing that Mary had,
It was the blessing of five,
To know that her son, Jesus,
Could bring the dead alive. (2) (CHO.)

6 Mary counted her blessings,
She counted them one by one,
She found that her greatest blessing,
Was her Godly son. (2) (CHO.)

7 The very last blessing that Mary had,
It was the blessing of seven,
To know that her son, Jesus,
Was safe at last in Heaven. (2) (CHO.)

124. THE TWELVE DAYS OF CHRISTMAS

SEE: Flanders II, 213; Gomme II, 315; Guide and Index; Sears. For history of this type see *The Holy Baby*, p. 482.

Quickly ♩ = 144

GUITAR– *2A, 3, 4*
BANJO– *1 or 2 PLAYED FAST*

1. On the first day of Christ-mas my true love sent to me, A ① par - tridge
2. On the sec-ond day of Christ-mas my true love sent to me, (to ②)
3. On the third day of Christ-mas my true love sent to me, (to ③)
4. On the (fourth, fifth, etc.)

in a pear tree. (to ⊕) ② Two tur-tle doves, And a (to ①) ③ Three French hens, (to ②)
④ Four cal-ling birds, (to ③)

⑤ Five gold rings, four call-ing birds, three French hens, two tur-tle doves, And a

par - tridge in a pear tree. (to ⊕) ⑥ Six geese a - lay - ing, (to ⑤)
⑦ Sev-en swans a - swim-ming, (to ⑥)
⑧ Eight maids a - milk-ing, (to ⑦)
⑨ Nine pip - ers pip - ing, (to ⑧)
⑩ Ten drum-mers drum-ming, (to ⑨)
⑪ 'lev - en lords a - leap-ing, (to ⑩)
⑫ Twelve lad - ies danc-ing, (to ⑪)

On the first day of Christmas my true love sent to me
A partridge in a pear tree.
On the second day of Christmas my true love sent to me
Two turtle doves and a partridge in a pear tree.

On the third day . . .

Three french hens, *etc.* . . . .

On the fourth day . . .

Four calling birds, *etc.* . . . .

On the fifth day . . .

Five gold rings, *etc.* . . . .

Six geese a-laying . . .
Seven swans a-swimming . . .
Eight maids a-milking . . .
Nine pipers piping . . .
Ten drummers drumming . . .
'leven lords a-leaping . . .
Twelve ladies dancing . . .

125. AM I BORN TO DIE ?

Published: *Original Sacred Harp*, p. 47. Words by Charles Wesley. Tune claimed
by Ananias Davidson (Kentucky Harmony, 1815). SEE: Jackson II, 155 (resembles
Lord Lovel).

Fervently ♩ = 80   GUITAR- FREE STRUM

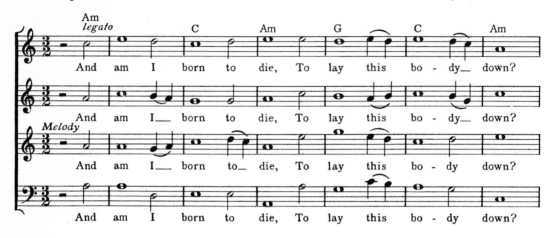

1 And am I born to die,
  To lay this body down?
  And must my trembling spirit fly ⎫
  Into a world unknown?   ⎬ (2)

2 Waked by the trumpet's sound,
  I from the grave shall rise
  To see the Judge with glory crowned ⎫
  And view the flaming skies.   ⎬ (2)

3 How shall I leave the tomb?
  With triumph or regret?
  A fearful or a joyful doom? ⎫
  A curse or blessing meet?   ⎬ (2)

4 I must from God be driv'n,
  Or with my Saviour dwell;
  Must come at his command to Heav'n, ⎫
  Or else depart—to Hell.   ⎬ (2)

246

126. ON MY JOURNEY HOME

FROM: p. 282 of *Spiritual Folk Songs of Early America*, G. P. Jackson (J. J. Augustin, N.Y., 1937). Used by permission. SEE: Jackson II, 227; *Original Sacred Harp*, p. 43. Other variants and printings: Jackson III, 279; *Social Harp*, 30. Taken down by Jackson at the United Sacred Harp Singing Convention in Atlanta, Georgia, 1938. Georgia tradition.

1   When I can read my title clear
    To mansions in the skies,
    I'll bid farewell to every fear
    And wipe my weeping eyes.
    CHORUS:
    I feel like, I feel like
    I'm on my journey home. } (2)

2   Should earth against my soul engage
    And hellish darts be hurled,
    Then I can smile at Satan's rage
    And face a frowning world.   (CHO.)

3   Let cares like a wild deluge come
    And storms of sorrow fall;
    May I but safely reach my home.
    My God, my heaven, my all.   (CHO.)

127. WAY OVER IN THE HEAVENS

FROM: p. 235 of *Down East Spirituals*, G. P. Jackson (J. J. Augustin, N.Y., 1943). Used by permission. Jackson noted it down from a singer in Tennessee who had heard it in camp meetings before the Civil War.

1. I wish't I had a-heard ye when ye called me,   (3)
   To sit on the seat by Jesus.
   CHORUS:
   Way over in the heavens,   (3)
   To sit on the seat by Jesus.

2. Sister, my soul's happy,   (3)
   When I sit on the seat by Jesus.   (CHO.)

3. I have a mother in the heavens,   (3)
   Sitting on a seat with Jesus.   (CHO.)

4. Won't you be glad when he calls you?   (3)
   Sitting on a seat with Jesus.   (CHO.)

128. WEEPING MARY

SEE: Jackson I, 255, II, 178. Attributed to John G. McCurry in *Sacred Harp*, 1852.
The text occurs in the *English Primitive Methodist Hymn Book*, 1823. Traditional in
New York State revivals 1820's.

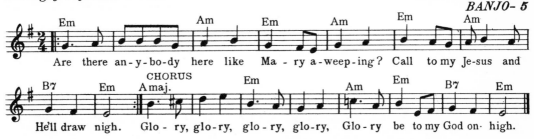

1 Are there anybody here like Mary a-weeping?
   Call to my Jesus and He'll draw nigh. } (2)

CHORUS:
Glory, glory, glory, glory,
Glory be to my God on high.

2 Are there anybody here like Peter a-sinking?
   Call to my Jesus and He'll draw nigh. (CHO.)

Other stanzas can be formed, such as:
   John a-riding,
   Paul a-preaching,
   Martha mourning, *etc.*

129. DEATH, AIN'T YOU GOT NO SHAME ?

FROM: p. 173 of *Spiritual Folk Songs of Early America*, G. P. Jackson (J. J. Augustin,
N.Y., 1937). Used by permission. Jackson collected it from a Nashville, Tenn.
informant, who told him that he heard it from 'barefoot whites' in the backwoods of Wayne Co., Tenn., 1936. Also a version from Negroes in Beaufort,
South Carolina.

1 Death, ain't you got no shame, shame?

   Death, ain't you got no shame, shame?

   Death, ain't you got no shame, shame?

   Death, ain't you got no shame?

2 Left his pappy to moan, moan, *etc.*

3 Left his widder a-lone, -lone, *etc.*

4 Left his mammy to weep, weep, *etc.*

130. O DAVID

Collected and arranged by Alan Lomax. SEE: Jackson IV, 226; for references to related folk songs see Brown III, 647-8. Song is akin to Negro *Little David Play on Your Harp.*

Fast and joyously ♪ = 184

GUITAR– 4, 7A or 7B
BANJO– 5

1. O David, Yes! Yes! My little David, Yes! Yes! And he killed Goliath, Yes! Yes! Yes, he killed Goliath, Yes! Yes!

2. My little David, Yes! Yes! My little David, Yes! Yes! Was a shepherd's boy, Yes! Yes! Was a shepherd's boy, Yes! Yes!

1 O David,
Yes! yes!
My little David,
Yes! yes!
And he killed Goliath,
Yes! yes!
Yes, he killed Goliath,
Yes! yes!

2 My little David,
Yes! yes!
My little David,
Yes! yes!
Was a shepherd's boy,
Yes! yes!
Was a shepherd's boy,
Yes! yes!

3 He killed Goliath,
Yes! yes!
He killed Goliath,
Yes! yes!
And he shouted for joy,
Yes! yes!
And he shouted for joy,
Yes! yes!

4 O David,
Yes! yes!
O David,
Yes! yes!
Play on, David,
Yes! yes!
Play on, David,
Yes! yes!

ROWDY WAYS

131. GROUNDHOG

PERHAPS the best of all banjo pieces is the comic mountain ballad of the groundhog hunt. The song has a swift pace and a ferocity which seems inappropriate to the chase of a small and innocent marmot like the groundhog or wood-chuck (*marmota monax*). Perhaps in Davy Crockett's time it may have been a bear-hunting epic . . .

> Blow your horn and come on hyar,
> We'll go to the backwoods and catch us a bar,
> The children screamed and the children cried,
> They love bar-meat cooked and fried . . . and so on . . .

for the bear, both in America and Europe, was once regarded as the animal prognosticator of spring, instead of the groundhog.

According to an ancient belief (still taken more or less seriously by many farmers), the weather on Candlemas (Groundhog) Day determines the good or ill luck that will attend spring sowing and planting, which should begin on that date. If the day is sunny and the groundhog (or bear) can see his shadow when he comes forth from his winter den, wintry weather will continue and blast tender crops. If the day is gloomy and bad, the animal will cast no shadow and the omens are for a good spring. The old folk calendar, however, was a notoriously vague affair, and, as opinions differed about the precise day for Candlemas, there has always been room for argument about the accuracy of the groundhog's prognostications. The Missouri Legislature sought to settle these discussions by fixing the date as February 2nd, but old-timers, in Arkansas especially, claim that Groundhog Day is February 14th. As the Supreme Court has not yet given its opinion, the matter can be regarded as still unsettled. Humanity likes to have considerable latitude in the matter of omens.

SOURCE: Leach.

132. SORGHUM SYRUP

WHATEVER the political and economic issues at stake, Johnny Reb went to war to defend the proposition that the South was in all respects superior to the North; that southern cooking was tastier, southern whisky smoother, southern horses faster, and southern women sweeter. This is the spirit of this rebel song from North Carolina (the state of the peanut or goober grabbler), learned from an ex-cowboy in Texas, with additional verses from Brown, Vol. III, page 460. (For more southern soldier songs see pp. 344-5.)

133. THE GOOD OLD REBEL

THE RESISTANCE of the South to change, after the Civil War, was compounded of equal parts of economic misery, race prejudice, sentimentality, and sheer stubbornness. During the reconstruction period, public wound-licking by southerner demagogues, who a few years earlier were cheerfully preparing to burn down Washington, became a favourite ritual. Self-pity and defence of southern shibboleths, such as the purity of southern womanhood, put a whole generation of grown men into white nightgowns, committing themselves, by secret ridiculous rites, into the hands of the mendacious and malicious leaders of the Ku Klux Klan. There were some Southerners, however, who still kept their heads and their sense of honour. Innes Randolph, of the Virginia Randolphs and an ex-officer of Jeb Stuart's cavalry, wrote the satire on the unreconstructable rebel, which was received with shouts of joyous, healing laughter at Confederate Army conventions.

134. MOONSHINER

THE AGE-OLD Celtic conflict with the excise-men flared up again in the American hills, for the American backwoods farmer, like his ancestors in Scotland and Ireland, was willing to fight for his right to still his own whisky. In 1780, Western Pennsylvania rose in the Whisky Rebellion which President George Washington had to put down by force of arms. All during the nineteenth century, the southern backwoodsman fought a guerilla war with government 'revenooers'—a conflict that still raises the annual toll of shooting scrapes and court cases throughout the South. For the poor farmer, the freedom to make his own liquor is not only a point of honour and a source of pleasure, but a matter of economics. His scanty grain crop brings more cash if he markets it in liquid form.

> One drop'll make a rabbit whup a fool dawg,
> And a taste will make a rat whip a wild hog,
> Hit'll make a mouse bite off a tom cat's tail,
> Make a tadpole have a fuss with a whale.

The moonshiner's song is a member of the *Waggoner's Lad* family, and kin to *Old Smokey*, *Rye Whisky*, and others.

SOURCE: Verse in note comes from Brown III, 73.

135. DIG A HOLE IN THE MEADOW

One day I asked a mountain man, ' How about the revenue officers? What sort of men are they?'
' Torn-down scoundrels, every one.'
' Oh, come now.'
' Yes, they are; plumb ornery—lock, stock, barrel and gunstick.'
' Consider what they have to go through. Their occupation is hard and dangerous. Here in the mountains, every man's hand is against them.'
' Why is it agin them? We ain't all blockaders; yet you can search these mountains through with a fine-tooth comb and you won't find ary critter as has a good word to say for the revenue. The reason is 't we know

them men from way back; we know whut they uster do afore they jined the sarvice, and why they did it. Most of them were blockaders their own selves, till they saw how they could make more money, turncoatin'.'

' It must be a ticklish business for an officer to prowl about the headwaters of these mountain streams looking for " sign ".'

' Hell's banjer! They don't go prodjeckin' around lookin' for stills. They set at home on their hunkers till some feller comes and informs.'

' What class of people does the informing?'

' Oh, sometimes hit's some pizen old bum who's been refused credit. Sometimes hit's the wife or mother of some feller who's drinkin' too much. Then, again, hit may be some rival blockader who aims to cut off the other feller's trade, and, same time, divert suspicion from his own self. But ginerally, hit's jest somebody who has a grudge agin the blockader fer family reasons, or business reasons, and turns informer to git even.'

QUOTE: Kephart, p. 169.

136. HURRAH, LIE!

And we're a' blind drunk, man,
An' I am jolly fu' . . .

THIS old Scots drinking song lived on in the mountains because it had all the elements of an American tall-tale.* No subject has stimulated our national bent for exaggeration more than the size, intelligence and ferocity of American insects. A Texan describes the Gulf Coast mosquito . . .

They tell me the Houston mosquito wears forty-five inch undershirts, and in Galveston they have to be included in the cow ordinance. But to tell the literal truth, the Texas mosquito is no bigger than the ordinary Texas mocking bird . . .

A soldier boy from Mississippi interrupts . . .

One time I was walkin' out through the country, and I got tired and couldn't get no rides. An' it begin to snow, so I stopped in an old country house to spend the night. Somethin' kept bitin' me, an' it was pretty hard to figure out what it was. So I had a large box of matches, an' I struck them till they was about all gone. An' I eventually discovered it was bed-bugs. So I took my bed and put it down on the floor. An' by that time my matches were all gone. I felt around then, and found a bucket of syrup, opened it up and poured the syrup all around my bed. Then I went back to sleep. I was dreamin' an' heard the prettiest music I ever heard in my life, an' it keeped on till I woke. Then I discovered what it was. All those bed-bugs had got together and got into the matchbox, was usin' them match stems for paddles, and was paddlin' crosst the syrup, singin' ' On Jordan's stormy banks I stand '. Anyone who knows the song would know the balance of it:

And cast a wishful eye
Over there across the pond
Where my possessions lie.

QUOTE: *Southern Folklore Quarterly*, VIII, 2, 1944. P. 103, Herbert Halpert.

* *See also* p. 5.

131. GROUNDHOG

FROM: JAFL XLV, 1932, p. 175; p. 154 of *Folk Songs from the Southern Highlands*, M. Henry. SEE: Brown III, 253; Randolph III, 150; Sharp II, 340.

Swift ♩ = 112

GUITAR- ANY ²⁄₄ STYLE
BANJO- 1, 2 and 3

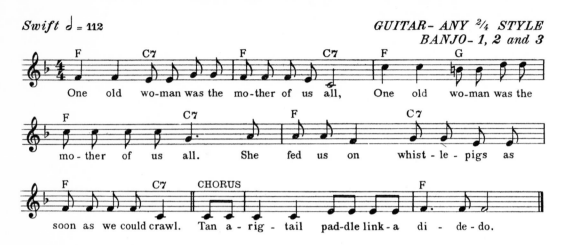

One old wo-man was the mo-ther of us all, One old wo-man was the mo-ther of us all. She fed us on whist-le-pigs as soon as we could crawl. Tan a - rig - tail pad-dle link-a di - de-do.

1 One old woman was the mother of us all,   (2)
She fed us on whistle-pigs as soon as we could crawl.
Tan-a-rig-tail, paddle link-a di-de-do.

2 Come on, boys, and let's go down,   (2)
Let's catch a whistle-pig in the groun'.

3 Up come Jonah from the plough,   (2)
Catch the whistle-pig, catch him now.

4 Blow your horn and call your dogs,   (2)
We'll go to the backwoods and catch a ground hog,
Come a ring-tail, paddle link-a di-de-oh.

5 Treed him in a rock, treed him in a log,   (2)
Dagone, boys, what a big groundhog!

6 Skin that whistle-pig, save that hide,   (2)
Makes the best shoe-strings I ever tied.

7 Take that groundhog, put him on to bile,   (2)
Bet, by jinks, you could smell him a mile.

8 Up come Grace with a snigger and a grin,   (2)
Groundhog gravy all over her chin.

9 Up come Cloe, happy as a crane,   (2)
Swan she'd eat them red-hot brains.

10 They eat whistle-pig, all they could hold,   (2)
Till there was none left in the bowl.

11 I set a steel trap up on the hill,   (2)
Now we'll have whistle-pig at our will.

132. SORGHUM SYRUP

Recorded and arranged by Alan Lomax from the singing of cowboy Alec Moore,
Austin, Texas. Other stanzas have been added from Brown III, 460.

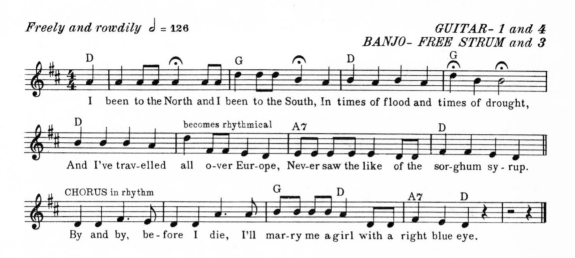

Freely and rowdily ♩ = 126

GUITAR– 1 and 4
BANJO– FREE STRUM and 3

I been to the North and I been to the South, In times of flood and times of drought,

And I've trav-elled all o-ver Eur-ope, Nev-er saw the like of the sor-ghum sy-rup.

CHORUS in rhythm

By and by, be-fore I die, I'll mar-ry me a girl with a right blue eye.

1 I been to the North and I been to the South,
   In times of flood and times of drought,
   And I've travelled all over Europe,
   Never saw the like of the sorghum syrup.
   CHORUS:
   By and by, before I die,
   I'll marry me a girl with a right blue eye.

2 A soldier was a-settin' by the road one day
   And he was lookin' very gay,
   By his side he had some meal,
   He'd just stolen from an old tar-heel.* (CHO.)

3 He made his fire to bake his bread,
   And when it was done he laughed and said,
   'In all the world, there's none surpasses
   Good cornbread and sorghum molasses.' (CHO.)

4 In a canteen by his side
   That he was tryin' hard to hide,
   From the eyes of those who were passin',
   Was a quart of sorghum molasses. (CHO.)

5 As I went up Atlanta street,
   A tar-heel girl I chanced for to meet.
   Says she to me, ' Are you a traveller?'
   ' Yes, by ginger, I'm a goober grabbler.'† (CHO.)

6 There's Alabama, thus you see,
   Tennessee or what you please,
   South Carolina, tar and rawsum,‡
   Good old Georgia, goobers and sorghum. (CHO.)

* a native of North Carolina   † a peanut farmer   ‡ resin

133. THE GOOD OLD REBEL

Recorded and arranged by John A. Lomax. FROM: p. 535 of *American Ballads and Folk Songs* (Macmillan, N.Y., 1934). SEE: Brown III, 464; Lomax II, 535; Randolph II, 291.

Freely ♩ = 44

GUITAR 1
BANJO- 1 and 2 ⎰ or FREE STRUM

O I'm a good old re-bel, Now that's just what I am; For this 'fair land of free-dom' I do not care a damn. I'm glad I fit a-gainst it, I on-ly wish we'd won, And I don't want an-y par-don For an-y-thing I done.

1 O I'm a good old rebel,
Now that's just what I am;
For this ' fair land of freedom '
I do not care a damn.
I'm glad I fit against it,
I only wish we'd won,
And I don't want any pardon
For anything I done.

2 I hates the Constitution,
This great republic, too.
I hates the Freedmen's Bureau
In uniforms of blue.
I hates the nasty eagle,
With all his brag and fuss,
But the lyin', thievin' Yankees,
I hates 'em wuss and wuss.

3 I hates the Yankee nation
And everything they do;
I hates the Declaration
Of Independence, too.
I hates the glorious Union,
'Tis dripping with our blood;
And I hates the stripéd banner
And I fit it all I could.

4 I followed Old Marse Robert
For four year, near about,
Got wounded in three places,
And starved at Point Lookout.
I cotch the rheumatism
A-campin' in the snow,
But I killed a chance of Yankees—
And I'd like to kill some mo'.

5 Three hundred thousand Yankees
Is stiff in Southern dust;
We got three hundred thousand
Befo' they conquered us;
They died of Southern fever,
And Southern steel and shot,
And I wish it was three million
Instead of what we got.

6 I can't take up my musket
And fight 'em now no mo';
But I ain't a-goin' to love 'em,
Now that is sartin sho;
And I don't want no pardon
For what I was and am,
And I won't be reconstructed,
And I do not give a damn.

134. MOONSHINER

Arranged by Alan Lomax. SEE: Lomax II, 170. This song is a composite of *The Wagoner* and *Rye Whisky* with the *I'm Troubled* type as in Brown III, 344. Peter Kennedy remarks similarity with British *Wild Rover* still common in Ireland, southern England.

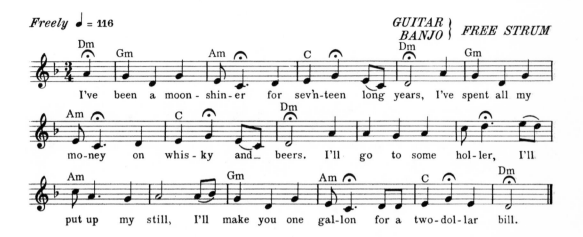

1 I've been a moonshiner for sev'nteen long years,
I've spent all my money on whisky and beers.
I'll go to some holler, I'll put up my still,
I'll make you one gallon for a two-dollar bill.

2 I'll go to some grocery and drink with my friends,
No women to follow to see what I spends.
God bless those pretty women, I wish they were mine,
Their breath smells as sweet as the dew on the vine.

3 I'll eat when I'm hungry and drink when I'm dry,
If moonshine don't kill me, I'll live till I die.
God bless those moonshiners, I wish they were mine,
Their breath smells as sweet as the good old moonshine.

135. DIG A HOLE IN THE MEADOW

Arranged by Alan Lomax. SEE: Lomax IV, 302; Sharp II, 204. This is a modernized hillbilly version of *Darlin' Corey*.
Piano arrangement by DON BANKS

lay lit - tle Lu - lie down.___   1. The

stock-in'_____ feet on the floor.

CHORUS:
Dig a hole, dig a hole in the meadow,
Dig a hole in the cold, cold ground,
Dig a hole, dig a hole in the meadow,
Just to lay little Lulie down.

1 The first time I saw little Lulie,
   She was standin' in the still-house door,
   Brogan shoes all in her hand
   An' her stockin' feet on the floor.   (CHO.)

2 Wake up, wake up, little Lulie,
   And go get me my gun,
   I ain't no man for trouble,
   But I'll die before I'll run.   (CHO.)

3 Last time I saw little Lulie,
   She was standin' on the banks of the sea,
   Two pistols strapped round her body,
   And a banjo on her knee.   (CHO.)

4 Wake up, wake up, little Lulie,
   What makes you sleep so sound?
   The highway robbers are comin',
   Gonna tear your playhouse down.   (CHO.)
                  or
   Them revenue officers are comin'
   To tear your still-house down.   (CHO.)

136. HURRAH, LIE!

FROM: p. 97 of *American Mountain Songs*, Ethel Park Richardson and Sigmund Spaeth (Greenberg, 1927). Used by permission. SEE: JAFL XXXIX, 1926, 165; full background JEFSS IV, 113; Randolph III, 200; Reeves, 220. A Scots drinking song *We're A' Fu'*. Earliest published example, *Martin and His Man*, 1609.

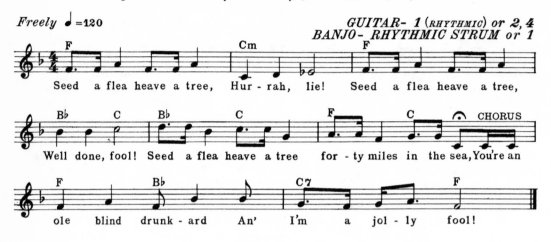

1 Seed a flea heave a tree,
   Hurrah, lie!
Seed a flea heave a tree,
   Well done, fool!
Seed a flea heave a tree forty miles in the sea,
   You're an ole blind drunkard,
   An' I'm a jolly fool!

2 Seed the wood cut the axe,   (2)
   Seed the wood cut the axe, seed the chickens chewin' **wax**.

3 Seed a eel eat a seal,   (2)
   Seed a eel eat a seal, seed a apple with nary peel.

4 Seed a hant climb the stairs,   (2)
   Seed a hant climb the stairs, seed the badman sayin' his prayers.

5 Seed a rat ketch a cat,   (2)
   Seed a rat ketch a cat—if you tell a yarn that's bigger'n that.

MURDER BALLADS

137. ROSE CONNELLY

WILFUL and cold-blooded murders such as this West Virginia ballad relates, came naturally to people whose ancestors were Indian fighters, bear hunters, moonshiners and feudists. The practice of violence, formed in necessity, degenerated into the habit of killing for its own sake. (*See also* p. 306.) The old Border ballad tradition, which linked love and death, fitted the code of the backwoods, where justice so often lay in the hands of the clan with the most political influence.

> *Boze :* Talkin' 'bout killin' people, there ain't nothin' to it. I don't see what a man worry his self bout a trial for. If I has enough 'gainst a man, I'd set on the roadside one night an' pick him off jes like I would a bird. There ain't nothin' to it. If they ketch you an' you use your head a little bit an' know what lawyer to git, you'll come clear.
>
> *Pede :* It seems to me you'd have to fret some about the trial.
>
> *Boze:* Well, there ought'n to be nothin' to it. If somebody do you dirt, there ain't no use to wait for the courts, cause they ain't goin' to do nothin'. The best way is to trust in God an' your gun . . .

QUOTE: *Carolina Wilderness*, E. C. L. Adams (Scribner Magazine, Vol. 89, 6, p. 615).

138. OMIE WISE

JONATHAN LEWIS was born in the late eighteenth century near Centre meeting house on Polecat Creek in Guilford County, North Carolina, and belonged to a proud and pugnacious tribe. He courted lovely Naomi Wise, an orphan who worked as a servant and field hand for Mr. Adams. Lewis compromised Naomi, then engaged to marry her; but when his ambitious mother found a better match for him, he resolved to do away with poor Naomi. She agreed to elope with him, and at the appointed hour took her water-pail to the trysting place at Adams' spring. This spring is said to be still flowing, but no one will drink the water and the ground around is hallowed. Old settlers once could point to the stump upon which Naomi stood to mount behind John Lewis that fatal evening.

The story runs that Naomi began to complain when she realized they were riding in the wrong direction, and then John Lewis told her his real intentions. He tied her dress above her head, rode into the middle of Deep River, and held Naomi under the water with his foot. When he heard someone coming, he spurred his horse for home. His mother asked him (just as in the English *The Ballad of the Bloody Miller* from which this ballad derives) why he was so wet and pale.

Next day, in order to throw off suspicion, he went courting a girl named Martha Huzza, and the officers found him on the front porch with Martha on his lap. Confronted with Naomi's corpse, Lewis calmly stroked the dead girl's hair and denied the crime. The following day, a vast company attended Naomi's funeral, and the mood of Guilford County was to lynch Jonathan Lewis. Eleven soldiers were sworn in by the local judge to guard the jail, but, although they protected Lewis from the mob, they did not prevent his escape. With the aid of friends, he broke out of the ' shackley jail ' and disappeared in the West.

These were the happenings of the year 1808. ' Time rolled on and Lewis would have been forgotten if it had not been for the ballad of *Omi Wise*, which was sung in every home.' News came that Lewis was living on the Ohio River, and a party of Guilford men rode off to capture him and brought him back for trial; but, as most of the witnesses to the crime were dead or gone west, he was acquitted. The folk of the North Carolina hills say that he confessed the crime on his death-bed. Meanwhile, the ballad spread to the West, and it is known to folk singers in every state between North Carolina and Texas.

SOURCE: Brown II, 690.

139. TOM DULA

THE STATESVILLE, North Carolina *American* of May, 1868, carried the following story:

Thomas C. Dula suffered the extreme penalty of the law by hanging, near this place, at 17 minutes past 2 o'clock p.m., on May 1st, having been a second time convicted of the murder of Laura Foster of Wilkes County, more than a year ago. Under the gallows he made a long address to several thousand persons who were present to witness his execution, and avowed his preparations to appear in another world. On the night previous to the execution, he made confession of his guilt, which we copy from his own hand.

' I declare that I am the only person that had a hand in the murder of Laura Foster, April 30th, 1868.'

Most of the folks who saw Tom Dula stretched must have doubted the truth of both his speech and his confession. The whole community felt sure that Tom was protecting ' the other woman in the case ', Ann Melton, and that she had a hand in the stabbing. The superstitious believed that Tom and Laura were already singeing in Hell, and that Ann Melton's name was an item in the Devil's black account book. Their story, bloody enough to inspire a Scots border balladist, is still told around firesides in the North Carolina mountains.

Dula, like many another wild young American of the time, enjoyed the Civil War and was sorry when it ended. Back home in Wilkes County, he acquired the reputation of a desperado, and cut a wide swathe among the ladies of the hills across the Yadkin, which a *Herald Tribune* reporter described as a territory in which ' free-lovism prevails, and it is a wise child that knows his own father '. He courted Laura Foster, blue-eyed, beautiful and ' wild as a buck ', but his fancy soon fixed upon Ann Melton, whom one old-timer recalled as ' the purtiest woman I ever looked in the face of '. This new affair, however, was soon blighted when Dula realized that he had caught a disease from Laura Foster. He swore that he would ' put her through ' for this misfortune, and apparently, he and Ann then conspired to murder Laura.

One Thursday night, Ann Melton and Tom Dula dug a grave on a lonely hillside. Next day, Tom lured Laura away from her father's house with a promise to marry her. They rode together to the vicinity of the grave, where Ann was hiding in the bushes with a knife in her hand. Tom took a drink, then wiped his mouth with his bandana and, tenderly offering to wipe Laura's mouth with the same handkerchief, stuffed it down her throat. Ann darted out of the bushes and stabbed Laura in the stomach. When the two had made sure that their

victim was dead, they buried her in a shallow grave on the mountainside and returned to their homes.

Even then their conduct excited suspicion, and, when Laura's body was discovered six weeks later, both were arrested. Dula's trial dragged on for nearly two years but, for reasons he kept to himself, he always denied that Ann Melton had anything to do with the crime. Even in the ballad, which he composed during his last days in jail, he did not mention her name. So it was that, when she finally came to trial, she got off with a short sentence. As one old-timer remarked, 'She'd-a been hung, but her neck was just too pretty to stretch hemp. She was guilty. I knowed it. Everybody knowed it, and Tom Dula could-a proved it, but he loved her, I reckon. Anyhow he shore died for her. But, ef they'd been ary women on the jury, she'd-a got first degree. The men couldn't look at that woman and keep their heads.'

The women had their revenge when Ann Melton died. They told how the Devil carried her off, while black cats ran squawling up the walls of her room, and the smell of frying meat filled the air. The story and the ballad still make folk shiver in the Carolina mountains—'Lawsee, we talked about it so much, seems as though I may dream that very murder tonight. I'm nearly scairt!'

SOURCE: Brown II, 703 *ff*.

263

140. WILD BILL JONES

A FIGHT between two mountain bravos, like the one in the present ballad, is the sort of incident that sparked the longest and bloodiest of mountain feuds.

Long ago in the mountains of Clay County, Kentucky, Dr. Abner Baker married a Miss White. Some time later, accusing her of adultery with one Daniel Bates, he separated from her and killed Bates. The White clan, rising in defence of their kinswoman's honour, prosecuted Baker for murder, but he was found ' not guilty '. Nevertheless, the Whites managed to have him tried a second time for the same crime, and Dr. Baker was convicted and hung, and the great Baker–White feud began. After one killing, the widow of the dead man told reporters: ' I have twelve sons. It will be the chief aim of my life to bring them up to avenge their father's death. Each day I shall show my boys the handkerchief stained with his blood, and tell them who murdered him.'

After a score of people had been bushwhacked, State troops and cannon finally pacified the Bakers and the Whites, but the feuding tradition lingered on. When I last visited Clay in 1933, my friends invited me to go along to their favourite dance-hall. They promised me a lively evening—' There's been a killin' at the place mighty nigh ev'y Sat'day this year.'

141. JOHN HARDY

ONE of the most rousing American ballads and the best of mountain banjer ' pieces ' is the story about the Negro murderer, John Hardy. Because he worked in the tunnels of the West Virginia mountains in the same epoch as John Henry, the two songs have sometimes been combined by folk singers, and the two characters confused by ballad collectors. The fate of steel-driving John Hardy, however, took him on another path than John Henry's. He shot and killed another Negro in a crap game at Shawnee Coal Company's Camp, a place now called Eckman, West Virginia. His white captors protected him from a lynch mob that came to take him out of jail and hang him. When the lynch fever subsided, Hardy was tried during the July term of the McDowell County Criminal Court, found guilty and sentenced to be hanged. While awaiting execution in jail, he is said to have composed this ballad, which he later sang on the scaffold. He also confessed his sins to a minister, became very religious, and advised all young men, as he stood beneath the gallows, to shun liquor, gambling, and bad company. The order for his execution shows that he was hanged near the courthouse of McDowell County, January 19, 1894. His ballad appears to have been based upon certain formulae stanzas from the Anglo-Scots ballad stock. (*See* stanzas, p. 317.)

142. CHARLES GUITEAU

OUT of thirty-four Presidents of the United States, six have died in office, three of these by assassination, with unsuccessful attempts on three other chief executives. Probably each one of these national dramas produced a crop of doggerel ballads, but only three or four of them have lasted. *Booth Killed Lincoln*, a poor piece in which the South shows its sympathy for the killer, was never widely popular in the mountains. In contrast, the murder of President James A. Garfield, an ex-union general and a Republican, by Charles Guiteau in Washington on July 2, 1881, gave rise to two good ballads.

Although Garfield lingered and suffered for seventy-nine days before he died, the sympathy of the ballad-maker runs strongly with his murderer. Guiteau was a pitiful nobody whom the state seized and executed, while Garfield was a powerful figure who had become the symbol of the rich man's party, too long in office; and at Guiteau's sensational trial, the scandal of the Republican pork-barrel was exposed, leading directly to reforms in the Civil Service system. Guiteau testified that he had been promised a diplomatic post as a reward for his work in Garfield's campaign, but that subsequently Garfield had refused to acknowledge the commitment. Although the man was unsuited for the post and was obviously a vengeful megalomaniac, people felt sorry for him, perhaps because he was such an absurd and hopeless sort of person. Then, ballad singers have always sided with a criminal, seized and executed by the mighty hand of the state. In the long tradition of ' criminal goodnights ' from the hanging of Jack Hall to the machine-gunning of Bonny Parker, the guilty party, no matter how hideous his crimes, has been presented in a sympathetic light.

Whether or not he has confessed at his trial, he often does so in his ballad, at the same time calling God to witness that he is sorry for his act. This formula, which at first glance may appear absurdly sentimental, is actually the key to the psychological function of these ballads. Such songs furnish the singers and their audience with outlets for strong aggressive emotions; in a word, they enable the folk to commit crimes in fantasy. Without the pious ending, a residue of guilty emotion would remain in the heart of the singer. Therefore a moralizing conclusion is essential to the ballad's effect within the framework of a culture where aggression and rebellion are considered wrong. The singer needs to reidentify himself with the ' good people '.

Neither the medieval ballad nor the American Negro murder ballads have such conclusions, for in these cultures individual acts of violence were simply a normal part of life. However, in the Anglo-American culture of the past three hundred years, where open aggression has been thoroughly repressed, the murder ballad had to assume the form of an apology for violence. These ballads, therefore, are confessions of these repressed feelings, common to a society, rather than of specific crimes committed by specific criminals. The formula represents a community fantasy and so outweighs the facts of any particular crime.

The present example is a case in point. The confession of Charles Guiteau is a very literal adaptation of an earlier broadside piece, the ballad of James A. Rogers, who was hanged for murder in New York City in 1858. His ballad begins:

> My name is James Rogers, the same I ne'er deny,
> Which leaves my aged parents in sorrow for to cry,
> It's little ever they thought, all in my youth and bloom,
> I came to New York for to meet my fatal doom . . .

The Guiteau ballad follows the Rogers story with a minimum of changes, adding scarcely any new material from the facts of the actual assassination in Washington. The small-time political hanger-on thus acquired the glamour of the young murderer. Of course, it is the habit of the come-all-ye maker to use an old ballad with as few alterations as possible and to fit an old set of verses to a new set of facts; but this is probably not due to an ineptness of these composers. The main function of their songs is to reflect inherited patterns of emotion and fantasy rather than to tell objective stories.

The Guiteau ballad shows several stylistic improvements over its model, and, while the latter song was quickly forgotten, the former spread through the South and Midwest as far as South Dakota. The present version comes from Victor record No. 20797B, sung by Kelley Harrel and issued in 1927. This record certainly reinforced the popularity of the song that kept the memory of Garfield and his murderer green.

143. MISTER MACKINLEY

Zolgotz, mean man,
He shot MacKinley with his handkerchief in his hand,
In Buffalo, in Buffalo . . .

ACTUALLY, Zolgotz was an idealistic young Polish anarchist with nihilist leanings. MacKinley, the popular leader in the successful war with Spain, was under attack from some quarters as an imperialist; he had come as principal guest to the first great Pan-American Exposition in Buffalo. There, at a great public reception, Zolgotz was able to approach him and fire at close range. One bullet pierced MacKinley's abdomen, and he died of this wound two weeks later. The assassin was tried, convicted and sent to the electric chair within a month.

I believe that nothing is known about the origin of this fine, ironic, bluesy ballad. Stylistically, it is akin to the Negro songs of that decade—*Frankie, Stagolee, Brady, The Boll Weevil* —but all extant versions have been collected from Southern whites, and it has been several times recorded by hillbilly singers. The first time I heard it was from Basil May in Clay County, Kentucky. He sang it like a fast hillbilly blues with a walking bass on his big guitar.

137. ROSE CONNELLY

Collected and arranged by Alan Lomax. FROM: *Folk Song: U.S.A.*, John and Alan Lomax (Duell, Sloan & Pearce, 1947), p. 302. SEE: Brown II, 248; Laws, 188. A rare American ballad—perhaps of West Virginian origin. Peter Kennedy notes that the tune is similar to *Rosin the Beau*.

1 Down in the willow garden
   Where me and my love did meet,
   There we sat a-courting,
   My love dropped off to sleep.
   I had a bottle of the Burglar's wine
   Which my true love did not know,
   And there I poisoned that dear little girl
   Down under the banks below.

2 I stabbed her with a dagger,
   Which was a bloody knife.
   I threw her in the river,
   Which was a dreadful sight.
   My father often told me
   That money would set me free,
   If I would murder that dear little girl,
   Whose name was Rose Connelly.

3 But now he sits in his own cottage door,
   A-wiping his weeping eye,
   A-waiting for his own dear son
   Upon the scaffold high.
   My race is run beneath the sun,
   Lo, Hell's now waiting for me,
   For I have murdered that girl I love,
   Whose name was Rose Connelly.

138. OMIE WISE

As sung by G. B. Grayson, Victor 31625 B, on American Folk Music Folkways
Disc, No. 13. SEE: Belden, 322; Brown II, 690; Laws, 186; Randolph II, 86;
Sharp II, 144. Widespread in the South. Derived from English stall ballad *The Oxford Girl*, or *The Bloody Miller*.

1 I'll tell you all a story about Omie Wise,
  And how she was deluded by John Lewis's lies.

2 He promised to marry her at Adamses' springs,
  He'd bring her some money and some other fine things.

3 He gave her no money, but flattered the case,
  Saying, ' We will get married, 'twill be no disgrace.'

4 She got up behind him, away they did go,
  They rode till they came where deep waters did flow.

5 ' Now Omie, poor Omie, I'll tell you my mind,
  My mind is to drown you and leave you behind.'

6 ' O pity your infant and spare me my life,
  And let me go rejected and not be your wife.'

7 But he kicked her and cuffed her, until she could not stand,
  And then he drowned little Omie below the mill dam.

8 Now Omie is missing, as we all do know,
  And down to the river a-hunting they go.

9 Two little boys were fishing just at the break of dawn,
  They spied poor Omie's body come floating along.

10 They found her a-floating on the water so deep,
  Which caused many people to sigh and to weep.

11 They arrested John Lewis, they arrested him today.
  They buried little Omie down in the cold clay.

12 ' My name is John Lewis, my name I'll not deny,
   I murdered my own true love, I'll never reach the sky.

13 ' Go hang me or kill me, for I am the man,
   Who murdered little Omie down by the mill dam.'

139. TOM DULA

From *Folk Song: U.S.A.*, copyright, 1947, by Frank Warner and J. and A. Lomax,
copyright, 1958, by Ludlow Music, with additional verses from Henry, *Folk Songs
from the Southern Highlands*, p. 325.

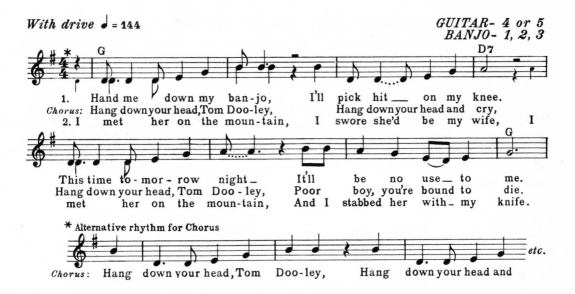

With drive ♩ = 144

GUITAR- 4 or 5
BANJO- 1, 2, 3

1. Hand me down my ban-jo, I'll pick hit __ on my knee.
Chorus: Hang down your head, Tom Doo-ley, Hang down your head and cry,
2. I met her on the moun-tain, I swore she'd be my wife, I

This time to-mor-row night __ It'll be no use __ to me.
Hang down your head, Tom Doo-ley, Poor boy, you're bound to die.
met her on the moun-tain, And I stabbed her with __ my knife.

* Alternative rhythm for Chorus

Chorus: Hang down your head, Tom Doo-ley, Hang down your head and etc.

1 Hand me down my banjo,
  I'll pick hit on my knee,
  This time tomorrow night
  It'll be no use to me.
  CHORUS:
  Hang down your head, Tom Dooley,
  Hang down your head and cry,
  Hang down your head, Tom Dooley,
  Poor boy, you're bound to die.

2 I met her on the mountain,
  I swore she'd be my wife,
  I met her on the mountain,
  And I stabbed her with my knife. (CHO.)

3 This time tomorrow,
  Reckon where I'll be,
  Down in some lonesome valley
  A-hangin' on a white-oak tree.

4 I had my trial at Wilksboro',
  And what d'you reckon they done?
  They bound me over to Statesville
  And that's where I'll be hung. (CHO.)

5 The limb a-bein' oak, boys,
  The rope a-bein' strong,
  Bow down your head, Tom Dooley,
  You know you're gonna be hung.

6 Mammy, O mammy,
   Don't you weep or cry,
   I've killed poor Laurie Foster
   And you know I'm bound to die. (CHO.)

7 Pappy, O pappy,
   What shall I do?
   I lost all my money
   And killed poor Laurie, too.

8 O what my mammy told me,
   Is about to come to pass,
   Red whisky and pretty women,
   Would be my ruin at last. (CHO.)

140. WILD BILL JONES

FROM: p. 36 of *American Mountain Songs*, Richardson and Spaeth (Greenberg, 1927).
Used by permission. SEE: Randolph II, 105-6; Sharp II, 74. Song occurs Miss.,
Ark., N.C., Tenn., Ky., (most frequently) Va., Calif.
Piano arrangement by DON BANKS

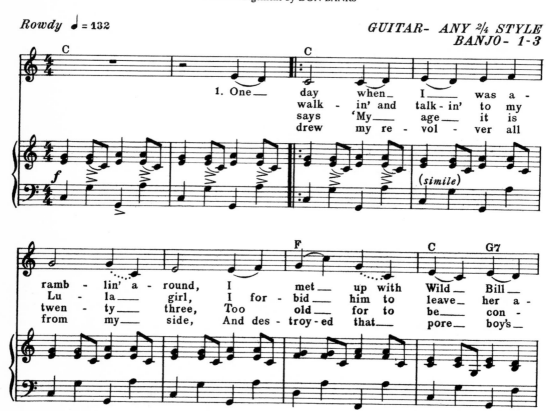

1 One day when I was a-ramblin' around,
  I met up with Wild Bill Jones,
  A-walkin' and talkin' to my Lula girl,
  I forbid him to leave her alone.

2 He says, ' My age it is twenty-three,
  Too old for to be controlled!'
  I drew my revolver all from my side
  And destroyed that pore boy's soul.

3 Well he rolled and he staggered and fell to the
  And he gave one dying groan,   [ground,
  And he placed his eyes on my Lula girl's face,
  Saying, ' Darlin', you're left all alone.'

4 Then they fastened on my wrists the handcuffs,
  And they marched me to Frankfort jail,   [boys,
  I had no friend or relations there,
  No one to sign my bail.

5 If I had the wings of an eagle, love,
  Far away to the heavens I would fly,
  I would take me a dose of old morphine,
  I would bid this ole world goodbye.

6 O pass yore jugs an' yore bottles around,
  Let's all git on a spree!
  Today was the last of Wild Bill Jones,
  And tomorrow'll be the last of me.

141. JOHN HARDY

Adapted and arranged by Alan Lomax. SEE: Brown II, 563; Randolph II,
144; Sharp II, 35. Versions from N.C., W.Va., Ark., Mo., Tenn., Calif.,
Fla. In Mississippi it is sung by whites only. This mountain ballad may well
have its roots in the stanza which occurs in *Little Matthy Groves* (and many other
Child ballads) of the runner who comes to a river bank where ' he bows to his breast
and he swum '.

land, Ought - a seen poor___ John --ny get-tin' a - way, Lord,

Lord, Ought - a seen John___ Har - dy get-tin' a - way.

1 John Hardy was a brave little man,
   He carried two guns ev'ry day,
   Killed him a man in the West Virginia land,
   Oughta seen poor Johnny gettin' away, Lord, Lord,
   Oughta seen John Hardy gettin' away.

2 John Hardy was standin' at the barroom door,
   He didn't have a hand in the game,
   Up stepped his woman and threw down fifty cents,
   Says, ' Deal my man in the game, Lord, Lord . . .'

3 John Hardy lost that fifty cents,
   It was all he had in the game,
   He drew the forty-four that he carried by his side
   Blowed out that poor Negro's brains, Lord, Lord . . .

4 John Hardy had ten miles to go,
   And half of that he run,
   He run till he come to the broad river bank,
   He fell to his breast and he swum, Lord, Lord . . .

5 He swum till he came to his mother's house,
   ' My boy, what have you done?'
   ' I've killed me a man in the West Virginia land,
   And I know that I have to be hung, Lord, Lord . . .'

6 He asked his mother for a fifty cent piece,
   ' My son, I have no change.'
   ' Then hand me down my old forty-four
   And I'll blow out my agurvatin' brains, Lord, Lord . . .'

7 John Hardy was lyin' on the broad river bank,
   As drunk as a man could be;
   Up stepped the police and took him by the hand,
   Sayin' ' Johnny, come and go with me, Lord, Lord . . .'

8 John Hardy had a pretty little girl,
   The dress she wore was blue.
   She come skippin' through the old jail hall
   Sayin' ' Poppy, I'll be true to you, Lord, Lord . . .'

9 John Hardy had another little girl,
The dress that she wore was red,
She came skippin' through the old jail hall
Sayin' ' Poppy, I'd rather be dead, Lord, Lord . . .'

10 They took John Hardy to the hangin' ground,
They hung him there to die.
The very last words that poor boy said,
' My forty gun never told a lie, Lord, Lord . . .'

142. CHARLES GUITEAU

From singing of Kelley Harrel, Victor 20797 B, or American Folk Music Folkways
Disc No. 16. SEE: Belden, 412; Brown II, 572; Freedman, 230; Laws, 176;
Randolph II, 29.

Hillbilly Style ♩ = 176

GUITAR- 2A, 4 or 5
BANJO- 1 or 4

Come all you Chris-tian peo-ple, wher-ev-er you may be, And
Chorus: My name is Charles Gui-teau, my name I'll nev-er de-ny, To

like-wise pay at-ten-tion to these few lines from me, On the
leave my ag-ed par-ents in sor-row for to die, But

thir-ti-eth day of June I am con-demned to die For the
lit-tle did I think, while in my youth-ful bloom, I'd be

mur-der of James A. Gar-field up-on the scaf-fold high.
car-ried to the scaf-fold to meet my fa-tal doom.

1 Come all you Christian people, wherever you may be,
And likewise pay attention to these few lines from me,
On the thirtieth day of June I am condemned to die
For the murder of James A. Garfield upon the scaffold high.
CHORUS:
My name is Charles Guiteau, my name I'll never deny,
To leave my aged parents in sorrow for to die,
But little did I think, while in my youthful bloom,
I'd be carried to the scaffold to meet my fatal doom.

273

2 I tried to play off insane, but found it would not do,
The people all against me, it proved to make no show.
Judge Cox passed the sentence, the clerk he wrote it down,
On the thirtieth day of June to die I was condemned. (CHO.)

3 And now I'm at the scaffold to bid you all adieu,
The hangman now is waiting, it's a quarter after two;
The black cap is on my face, no longer can I see,
But when I'm dead and buried, dear Lord, remember me. (CHO.)

143. MISTER MACKINLEY

Recorded and arranged by Alan Lomax from singing of Maynard Britton, Big
Creek, Ky. FROM: p. 256 of *Our Singing Country*, Lomax (Macmillan, N.Y., 1941).
Main reference: American Folk Music Folkways Disc, No. 20. Sung by Charlie
Poole. Additional stanzas from B. A. Lunsford.

Note: Other stanzas are sung to varying forms of these melodies

1 The pistol fires, MacKinley falls.
Doc says, ' MacKinley, I can't find that ball.'
In Buffalo, in Buffalo.

2 Zolgotz Zolgotz, you done him wrong,
Shot po' MacKinley when he was walking along
In Buffalo, in Buffalo.

3 Yonder comes the train, she's comin' down the line,
  Blowin' at every station, ' Mr. MacKinley's a-dyin'.'
  It's hard times, hard times.

4 Doctor on a horse, he tore down through Maine,
  Said to that horse, ' You've got to out-run this train,
  To Buffalo, to Buffalo.'

5 Doctor come a-runnin', takes off his specs,
  Says, ' Mr. MacKinley, you done passed in your checks,
  Bound to die, bound to die.'

6 MacKinley he hollered, MacKinley squawled,
  Doc says, ' MacKinley, I can't fin' that ball.'
  From Buffalo to Washington.

7 ' 'Tain't but one thing that grieves my mind,
  That is to die, an' leave my poor wife behind,
  I'm gone a long old time.'

8 ' Look-a here, you rascal, you see what you've done,
  You've shot my husband with that Ivor Johnstone gun;
  He'll be gone a long old time.'

9 ' Hush up, little children, now don't you fret,
  You'll draw a pension at your Poppa's death.
  He'll be gone a long old time.'

10 Forty-four boxes all trimmed in lace,
  ' Take him back to the baggage, where we can't see his face.'
  From Buffalo to Washington.

11 Roosevelt in the White House, he's doin' his best,
  MacKinley in the graveyard, he's takin' a rest;
  He's gone a long old time.

12 The engine she whistled all down the line,
  Blowin' at every station, ' MacKinley is dyin'.'
  From Buffalo to Washington.

13 Roosevelt in the White House, drinkin' out a silver cup,
  MacKinley in the graveyard, he'll never wake up,
  He's gone a long old time.

HARD TIMES AND THE HILLBILLY

144. PEG AN' AWL

SOME TUNES spread like spore-producing plants. When the climate is right, the spore case bursts open and a puff of wind carries the new germs far over the land, to make hundreds of new plants which continue the cycle. So it has been with this tune family. The Anglo-Scots branch, known as *Captain Kidd*, has been breeding new songs in England and America for at least four centuries (*see* earlier history of Captain Kidd, pp. 7-8). The Irish member of the family, a commonly known piper's jig, sometimes sung as *Johnny I Hardly Knew Ye*, became one of the most prolific song-producers in nineteenth-century America. In the North there was the whole *Johnny Comes Marchin' Home* family (*see* p. 98), and in the South, the *Crawdad* or *Sugar Babe* tribe. It is a very rare American singer, Negro or white, who does not know some variant.

The oddest member of the family is the present text, which might be called the first American song to deal with the problem of redundancy or mechanical unemployment. We shall probably never know when and where it was rhymed together. The dates it mentions seem far too early, for the first shoe-making machine did not come into use in America until 1858.

145. ROLL ON, BUDDY

AFTER the Civil War the Southern Appalachians were gradually opened up for industrial exploitation. The coal, mica, potash and lumber industries brought railroad spurs creeping into isolated valleys, and mountaineers, who had known modern technology largely in the form of the six-shooter, became familiar with railroad engines, dynamite and the shuttle and cage. At this time, too, many mountain folk first met Negroes and heard their music. Many an old-timer can recall being scared ' fitified ' by the first coloured man he ever saw— ' thort to my soul it was the boogerman ', yet friendly relations were soon established. I have met a number of Negroes living in remote mining camps, some quietly married to white women, whose songs and accent were those of the mountains.

Negroes introduced the guitar and the blues into the hills some time after the turn of the century, so recently in fact that the most complex of hillbilly guitar styles is still called ' nigger pickin' '. The mixed gangs who built the railroad swapped songs. One of the best white ballads concerns the Negro murderer *John Hardy*, and the finest Negro ballad, *John Henry*, is modelled upon a traditional mountain air, and has always been sung by both races. Finally, there are the hammer songs (*see* note to song 298, p. 551) which preceded *John Henry*, versions of which have crossed and recrossed the Jim Crow Line so frequently that it is impossible to tell which group has contributed most to the song. *Roll On, Buddy* is one of the white mountain cousins of this extensive song family.

146. PAY DAY

Way down yonder in Tennessee, they leased the convicts out,
Put them working in the mine against free labor stout.
Free labor rebelled against it, to win it took some time,
But while the lease was in effect, they made um rise and shine . . .

THIS is only one of a number of songs about the so-called ' Coal Creek War ', which erupted in the hills of Eastern Tennessee in the 1890's. The state of Tennessee, following a common Southern practice, was leasing its convicts out to private companies, in this case to the Tennessee Coal and Iron Corporation, for about sixty dollars a head per year. Convict labour depressed the wages of the free miners. After a number of fruitless appeals to the state government, angry mountain miners stormed a convict camp, released the Negro convicts and burned the stockade down. The state government replied by declaring martial law and building more stockades, and these again the miners captured and destroyed, assisting the prisoners to escape across the state line into Kentucky. At last troops were sent in, armed with cannon, and the miners, thoroughly aroused, fought a pitched battle that lasted several days.

In the end the mountain men were defeated and their leaders jailed. Those who could fled to Kentucky, where several old-timers informed me in confidence that they had 'fit in that air Cole Creek Rebellion '. Yet the miners' stand had won public support, for the next election brought a new administration which promptly abolished the lease system in Tennessee. I took this song down from the singing of the Kentucky banjo player Pete Steele, whose folks were miners. Pete couldn't tell me whether this powerful lament was composed during the Coal Creek War or during the mining disaster which, a few years later, took the lives of scores of miners in that place.

SOURCE: *Coaldust on the Fiddle*, G. G. Korson (University of Pa. Press, Philadelphia, 1943).

147. DOWN ON PENNEY'S FARM

. . . I hear people talkin' about the hard times they had in the depression, but most of us small farmers and sharecroppers and tenants here in the South have always had depression. In 1929, before the trouble on Wall Street, everybody was supposed to be prosperous, but we southern farmers didn't average more than 168 dollars that year all told, and a lot of us made less. After money for taxes, tools, fertilizer and interest on debts, we didn't have much for eatin' and buyin' overalls and payin' the doctor. And there was plenty of sickness. Our young ones sickened and died of pellagra and consumption . . .

The planter lives on the sweat of the sharecropper's brow,
Just how the sharecropper lives, the planter cares not how.

277

The sharecropper raises all the planter can eat
And then gets trapped down under his feet.
The sharecropper's wife goes to the kitchen, washtub and field,
Whilst the planter's wife enjoys herself in an automobile.
The planter's children dresses up and goes to school,
Whilst the sharecropper puts on rags and follows a mule.
When the sharecropper dies he has to be buried in a box,
Without any necktie or any socks,
Makes no difference how much the sharecropper raise,
The planter gets all of the praise.
No rich planter to be do I ever crave,
But I want to be something more than a planter's slave,
And now if anyone thinks this ain't the truth,
He can go to the South and get proof! . . .

QUOTE: John Hancocks, recorded by Alan Lomax.

148. COTTON MILL COLIC

When I die don't bury me at all,
Just hang me up on the spool room wall,
Place a knotter in my hand,
So I can spool my way to the Promised Land.
I got the blues,
I got them Winnsboro cotton-mill blues . . .

LATE in the nineteenth century, the New England cotton mills began moving south to find a fresh supply of free labour. White backwoodsmen who never saw cash from one year's end to the next, flocked into the mill towns, finding it mighty nice to have a few silver dollars chinking in their pockets every Saturday.

But soon the glamour of mill-town life began to wear off. The children and old women picked up a cough in the damp, lint-filled atmosphere of the mills where they were cooped up for so many hours away from the sunshine. The cheap new shoes and clothes went to pieces. The men hated ' being allus boogered about by some durned old mill boss . . .'

Old Man Sergeant, sittin' at the desk,
The damned old fool won't give us no rest,
He'd take the nickels off a dead man's eyes,
To buy a Coca-Cola and an Eskimo pie . . .

Prices went up and wages stayed down. When work was slack in the mill his family went hungry. When he listened to organizers and joined the union, he was black-listed. At Gastonia in 1929, at Huntsville in 1934—the deputies he drank with on Saturday night appeared with guns in their hands. He saw his union leaders shot down and his union brothers sent to jail. The mountains were now very far away. The milltown man picked up his cheap Sears & Roebuck guitar and made new songs, weaving rough rhymes to the old tunes . . .

Ever' morning' just at five
You gotta get up, dead or alive,
Ever' night when I go home,
A piece of cornbread and an old jawbone.
Ain't it enough to break your heart,
Have to work all day and at night it's dark,
It's hard times in the mill, my love,
It's hard times in the mill.

The best of all these cotton-mill songs is *Cotton Mill Colic*, recorded in a number of versions in the 1930's and '40s.

149. MY LAST OLE DOLLAR

THE LAND began to wear out. Farms got so poor ' it took two roosters to crow once '. The people came to town with their new folklore of hard times. Matching this song is a classic hard-luck story from North Carolina, collected by Lee Morris.

Hard luck just runs in my family. I mind the time I couldn't even buy a hen and chickens. Decided to kill myself. Scared my old pistol wouldn't work, so I brought me a gallon of kerosene, a piece of rope, bottle of rat poison. Rowed down to the lake to where some trees hung way out over the water.

So I stood up and tied the rope round my neck. Bid farewell to this hard old world. Poured kerosene all over myself, et that rat poison and set my clothes afire, figgerin' I'd shoot myself just when I kicked the boat out from under my feet.

But that durn pistol shot the rope in two. I fell in the river and put out the fire on my clothes and got to stranglin' and chokin' in that water, and throwed up the poison. Well from that I figgered my luck was changin', so I swum out and put up for the legislature. Durned if I didn't get elected, too!

QUOTE: As told by Lee Morris to Dudley Crawford. MS. of Federal Writers Project, N.C. Botkin IV, 465.

150. DOWN IN THE VALLEY

WHEN a mountaineer from the Smokies was sent to the state pen at Raleigh for moonshining or bushwhacking, he suffered more than the other prisoners. He found himself trapped in the dark and narrow valley of the prison, shut away from the sky and the stars and the fresh sweet winds of his native hills. Lowland water tasted so stale and flat, lowland air felt so close and stifling, that a man couldn't enjoy himself down in the valley, even outside the jailhouse! . . .

> I went down into the valley wunst and I declar I nigh sultered. 'Pears like there ain't enough air to go round, with all them people. And the water don't do a body no good; an' you cain't eat hearty, nor sleep good o' nights. Course, they pay big money down thar; but I'd a-heap ruther ketch me a big old coon fer his hide. Boys, I did hone fer my dog Fiddler, an' the times we'd have a-huntin', and the trout fishin' and the smell of the woods and nobody bossin' and jowerin' an' all. I'm a hill man all right and they needn't to glory their old flat land for me.

When he came courting his girl with his banjo, he recalled these lonely, prison-born feelings to make her feel sorry for him. From pity to love was for her a brief step, since love appeared to her already as the prison-house in which she would spend the rest of her life.

QUOTE: Kephart, p. 312.

151. THE RISING SUN BLUES

THE 'RISING SUN' occurs as the name of a bawdy house in two other traditional songs, both British in origin. The symbol is, indeed, an appropriate one. The melody can be linked with one setting of *Lord Barnard and Little Musgrove* (*see* page 316) and with other old traditional British tunes. Yet this song is, so far as I know, unique. I took it down in 1937 from the singing of a thin, pretty, yellow-headed miner's daughter in Middlesborough, Kentucky, subsequently adapting it to the form that was popularized by Josh White. The story, which concerns the sordid path that poverty has forced many poor country girls to follow, may date back to pre-Civil War days, when New Orleans was the true capital of the South and many country boys and girls landed there, after rafting all the way down the Ohio and Mississippi rivers.

152. MULE SKINNER BLUES

THE BIG gramophone companies took no serious notice of American folk music until after World War I. In those days, every company had a board of directors who listened to all records before they were released, and vetoed those they did not consider good music. Naturally, the raw, wild voices of American rural singers did not appeal to these urban dignitaries, and the hillbilly business, today responsible for a very large proportion of American disc sales and hit tunes, had a late and a fortuitous beginning.

When Ralph Peer of *Okeh* visited Atlanta in the early '20s, a local record dealer offered to buy a thousand copies of *Little Old Log Cabin* and *The Hen Cackled*, by Fiddlin' John Carson, if Peer would record it. Peer decided to risk his company's disapproval and cut the disc. 'It was so bad that we didn't even put a serial number on it,' he recalls. 'We thought that when the local dealer got his supply, that would be the end of it. He got his thousand records on Thursday, and that night he called New York on the phone and ordered five thousand more sent by express, and ten thousand by freight. When the national sale got to five hundred thousand we were so ashamed we had Fiddlin' John come up to New York and do a re-recording of the numbers.'

Other companies rushed into the field, recording with little discrimination any back-woods musicians they could find. Country musicians, looking for pay and public attention, were encouraged to form small instrumental combinations, so that when local radio stations began to open up in the South, expert string bands were ready to play for them.

These regional radio stations further fostered the development of accomplished Southern white folk musicians who now had the opportunity to perfect their skill. Nowadays hill-billy stars travel between dates by air plane and fill the biggest halls in the country with their fans. The first nationally popular hillbilly singer was a San Antonio railroad brakeman with a sob in his voice, by the name of Jimmy Rodgers. He specialized in a new type of song called the 'yodelling blues', a cross between the Negro blues and the Swiss yodel, popu-larized in the Middle West by touring Swiss groups in the nineteenth century. Jimmy's yodelling songs sounded as if they might have been composed by a lonesome Texas cowboy or a hobo kicked off a freight in Tucson or Albuquerque: his records sold in millions and his original *Blue Yodel* was followed by *Blue Yodels* numbered 1 to 9. (The present song is No. 9, recorded by Bill Monroe as the *Muleskinner's Blues*.)

Rodgers maintained his popularity by keeping his songs close to the interests of the working stiffs among whom he spent his life. When he died of tuberculosis in 1933, he had achieved his life's ambition—to own a guitar entirely covered in mother-of-pearl.

153. I DON'T WANT YOUR MILLIONS, MISTER

ONE OF THE EARLIEST and finest American folk love songs begins:

> I was born and raised in old Virginia,
> To North Carolina I did go,
> There I courted some pretty young woman,
> Her name and age I did not know.
>
> Her hair, it was some darksome color,
> And her cheeks were a rosy red,
> On her breast she wore white lilies,
> Many-a tear for her I've shed . . .

Some time in the 'twenties this lovely song was given a new shape. These were the years when hillbilly music had become the staple fare, catering for urbanized backwoods whites who wanted new songs which spoke of love in the most sentimental terms. They were the last Americans to learn the sorrows of divorce and unstable love affairs, and to discover the loneliness of a society in which the village, the clan and the family were in dissolution. Between 1920 and 1950 thousands of melancholy hillbilly songs told again and again the same sad stories of broken homes and unhappy love affairs. One of the best of these was *Greenback Dollar* (a new setting of *East Virginia*) in which some mountain girl, who 'run away from home with the wrong man,' tells of her desertion.

1 I don't want your greenback dollar,
  I don't want your diamond ring,
  All I want is your love, darlin',
  Won't you take me back again?

2 Once I had a darlin' sweetheart
  And he thought the world of me,
  Till a dark-eyed girl persuaded,
  And he cared no more for me.

3 Mama said we couldn't marry,
  Papa said it would never do,
  But if you ever learned to love me,
  I'd run away and marry you.

4 When the train pulled out from Nashville,
  And we said our last goodbye,
  You said, ' Go back home, my darlin',
  Go back home and do not cry.'

5 I'd rather be in some dark holler
  Where the sun refused to shine,   (the only traditional
  Than to see you with another,   stanza)
  And to know you'll never be mine.

6 I don't want your greenback dollar,
  I don't want your diamond ring,
  All I want is a .38 special
  To blow out your dirty brains . . .

Almost every mountain singer came to know *Greenback Dollar*, and no two people sang it in precisely the same way. During the Eastern Kentucky coal strike in the 1930's, the miners composed many songs to tell their story and to stiffen their fighting spirit. Jim Garland, one of the strike leaders of Coal Creek, Kentucky, rhymed together this new version of the old *East Virginia* and *Greenback Dollar*.

154. SIXTEEN TONS
155. DARK AS A DUNGEON

OCCASIONALLY, out of the roar of the jukeboxes, there comes the voice of a genuine folk poet with something real to say and the talent to command the attention of the nation. One of these singers is Merle Travis, the Kentucky miner's son, whom years of success in Hollywood have neither stained nor changed. Late in the '40's Travis decided to record some ballads which would speak for his mining family and friends ; he made an album for Capitol (*see* appendix) which is a landmark in the field. Along with adapted traditional pieces, he sang two original ballads, which conform so superbly to our native ballad tradition that they have already gone into oral circulation throughout the English-speaking world. Merle says . . .

I never will forget one time when I was on a little visit down home in Ebenezer, Kentucky. I was a-talkin' to an old man that had known me ever since the day I was born—and an old friend of the family, he says, ' Son, you don't know how lucky you are to have a nice job like the one you've got and don't have to dig out a livin' from under these hills and hollers, like me and your pappy used to.' When I asked him why he had never left and tried some other kind of work, he said, ' Nawsir, you just won't do that. If you ever get this old coal dust in your blood, you're just gonna be a plain old coal miner as long as you live.' He went on to say, ' It's a habit— sorta like chewin' tobaccer.'

QUOTE: Merle Travis.

144. PEG AN' AWL

As sung by The Carolina Tar Heels, American Folk Music Folkways Disc, No. 12.
SEE: Sharp II, 75 for another shoemaker's song.   Peter Kennedy says: similar bawdy ballad in Suffolk.

Pokerfaced ♩ = 176

GUITAR- 2A, 5C
BANJO- 1, 2

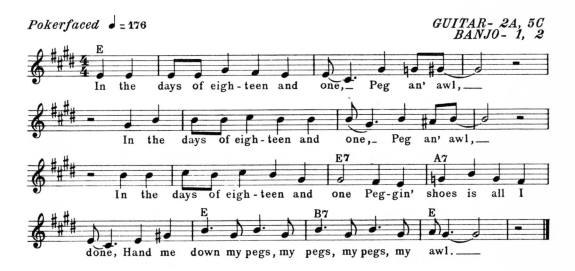

In the days of eigh-teen and one,_ Peg an' awl,_
In the days of eigh-teen and one,_ Peg an' awl,_
In the days of eigh-teen and one Peg-gin' shoes is all I
done, Hand me down my pegs, my pegs, my pegs, my awl.___

1 In the days of eighteen and one,
  Peg an' awl,
In the days of eighteen and one,
  Peg an' awl,
In the days of eighteen and one
Peggin' shoes is all I done,
  Hand me down my pegs, my pegs, my pegs,
                        my awl.

2 In the days of eighteen and two,   (3)
Peggin' shoes was all I'd do,
  Hand me down my pegs, my pegs, my pegs,
                        my awl.

3 In the days of eighteen and three,   (3)
  Peggin' shoes is all you'd see,
    Hand me down my pegs, my pegs, my pegs,
                        my awl.

4 In the days of eighteen and four,   (3)
  I said I'd peg them shoes no more,
    Throw away my pegs, my pegs, my pegs,
                        my awl.

5 They've invented a new machine,   (3)
  The prettiest little thing you ever seen.
    I'll throw away my pegs, my pegs, my pegs,
                        my awl.

6 Makes a hundred pair to my one,   (3)
  Peggin' shoes, it ain't no fun.
  Throw away my pegs, my pegs, my pegs, my awl.

145. ROLL ON, BUDDY

Collected and arranged by Alan Lomax. SEE: Brown II, 267; Lomax IV, 264;
Odum I, 252; White, 258. For excellent recording, see Merle Travis, *Nine Pound
Hammer*, reference in note for *Dark as a Dungeon*. For related Negro songs see
Ham and Eggs (No. 292), *East Colorado Blues*, this volume. For *Sugar Babe* reference,
see Brown III, 550.

Piano arrangement by DON BANKS.

CHORUS:
Well, roll on, buddy,
Don't you roll so slow,
Buddy, how can I roll,
When the wheels won't go?

1 Now some of these days, and it won't be long,
You gonna call my name and I'll be gone. (CHO.)

2 I wish I was a rich man's son,
I'd stand on the banks and see the work get done.
(CHO.)

3 But as it is, I'm a poor man's son,
   I'll wait in the cut, till the pay train comes. (CHO.)

4 I asked my captain just to gimme my time,
   'Go on, buddy, you're time behind.' (CHO.)

5 I asked my captain just to gimme one dime,
   'Go on, buddy, you're a dime behind.' (CHO.)

6 I told my captain my feet were cold,
   'God damn your feet, let the wheelers roll.'

CHORUS:
So roll on, buddy,
Don't you roll so slow,
When the sun goes down
You'll roll no more.

7 This nine pound hammer's just a little too heavy,
   Buddy, for my size, buddy, for my size. (CHO.)

8 It's a long way to Harlan, it's a long way to Hazard,
   Just to get a little booze, just to get a little booze.
                                                  (CHO.)

9 I'm goin' on the mountain, just to see my baby,
   And I ain't comin' back, and I ain't comin' back.
                                         (CHO.)

146. PAY DAY

Recorded and arranged by Alan Lomax from singing of Pete Steele, Hamilton, Ohio, 1938, AAFS 6B. FROM: p. 274 of *Our Singing Country*, Lomax (Macmillan, N.Y., 1941).

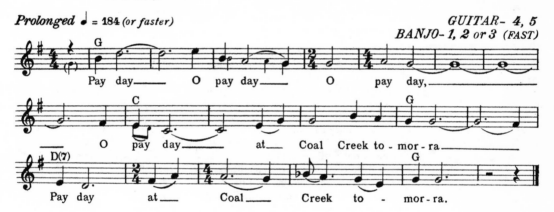

Prolonged ♩ = 184 *(or faster)*

GUITAR– 4, 5
BANJO– 1, 2 or 3 (FAST)

Pay day___ O pay day___ O pay day,___
___ O pay day___ at___ Coal Creek to-mor-ra___
Pay day at___ Coal___ Creek to-mor-ra.

1 Pay day—O pay day, O pay day,
   O pay day at Coal Creek tomorra,
   Pay day at Coal Creek tomorra.

2 Bye bye—O bye bye, O bye bye,
   O bye bye, good woman, I'm gone,
   Bye bye, good woman, I'm gone.

3 You gonna miss me, you gonna miss me,
                                gonna miss me
   You gonna miss me when I'm gone,
   You gonna miss me when I'm gone.

4 She's a rider, O she's a rider, O she's a rider,
   O she's a rider, but she'll leave that rail some-
                                             time,
   She's a rider, but she'll leave that rail sometime.

5 Pay day—O pay day, O pay day,
   O pay day won't come no more,
   Pay day won't come no more.

285

147. DOWN ON PENNEY'S FARM

FROM: p. 287 of *Our Singing Country*, Lomax (Macmillan, N.Y., 1941). As sung by the Bentley Boys, Columbia 1556. For similar songs, see Greenway FF 216 and note on *Hard Times*.

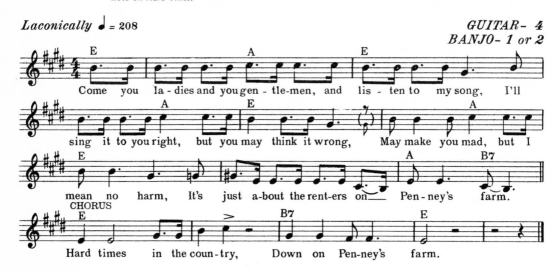

1 Come you ladies and you gentlemen, and listen to my song,
I'll sing it to you right, but you may think it wrong,
May make you mad, but I mean no harm,
It's just about the renters on Penney's farm.
CHORUS:
Hard times in the country,
Down on Penney's farm.

2 You move out on Penney's farm,
Plant a little crop of 'baccer and a little crop of corn,
Come around to see you, gonna 'plit an' plot,
Get a chattel mortgage on ever'thin' you got.   (CHO.)

3 Haven't old George Penney got a flatterin' mouth?
Move you to the country in a little log house,
Got no windows but the cracks in the wall,
He'll work you in the summer and starve you in the fall.   (CHO.)

4 George Penney's renters comin' to town
With their hands in their pockets and their heads hangin' down,
Go in the store and the merchant will say,
' Your mortgage is due and I'm lookin' for my pay.'   (CHO.)

5 Down in the pocket with a tremblin' hand,
' Can't pay you now, but I'll pay you when I can.' . . .
Then to the telephone, the merchant makes a call,
They'll put you on the chain-gang, can't pay at all.   (CHO.)

148. COTTON MILL COLIC

FROM: p. 291 of *Our Singing Country*, Lomax (Macmillan, N.Y., 1941). For background, see Greenway 121-46.

Quickly and evenly ♩ = 108

GUITAR– ANY ²⁄₄ STYLE
BANJO– 1 or 2

1 When you buy clothes on easy terms,
The collector treats you like a measly worm;
One dollar down and then, Lord knows,
If you don't make a payment, they'll take your
When you go to bed, you can't sleep,   [clothes.
You owe so much at the end of the week.
No use to colic, they're all that way,
Peckin' at your door till they get your pay.
CHORUS:
I'm a-gonna starve, ev'rybody will,
You can't make a livin' at a cotton mill.

2 When you go to work, you work like the Devil,
At the end of the week you're not on the level.
Pay day comes, you pay your rent,
When you get through, you've not got a cent
To buy fat-back meat, pinto beans;
Now and then you get a turnip green.
No use to colic, they're all that way,
You can't get the money to move away.

3 Twelve dollars a week is all I get—
How in the heck can I live on that?
I got a wife and fourteen kids,
We all have to sleep on two bedsteads.
Patches on my breeches, holes in my hat,
Ain't had a shave since my wife got fat.
No use to colic, ever'day at noon—
Kids get to cryin' in a different tune.

4 They run a few days and then they stand,
Just to keep down the working man.
We'll never make it, we never will,
As long as we stay in a roundin' mill.
The poor are gettin' poorer, the rich are gettin'
If I don't starve, I'm a son of a gun.   [rich,
No use to colic, no use to rave,
We'll never rest till we're in our grave.
FINAL CHORUS:
If I don't starve, nobody will,
You can't make a livin' at a cotton mill.

149. MY LAST OLE DOLLAR

FROM: p. 96 of *American Mountain Songs*, Richardson and Spaeth (Greenberg, 1927). Used by permission. SEE: Randolph IV, 114. For related songs, see *Sugar Babe*, American Folk Music Folkways Disc No. 62. This song family, which is related to Negro blues, reproduced itself in many variants during the first part of the 20th century.

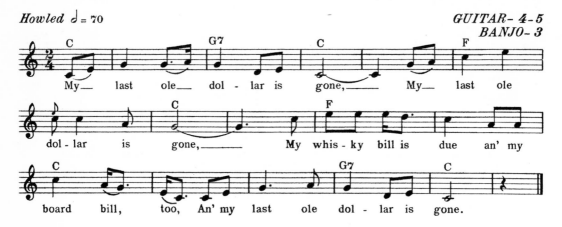

1 My last ole dollar is gone,
My last ole dollar is gone,
My whisky bill is due an' my board bill, too,
An' my last ole dollar is gone.

2 Oh darling, I'm crazy about you, (2)
I am crazy about you and another girl, too,
Oh darling, what shall I do?

3 Oh darling, won't you hold my head? (2)
Won't you hold my head for I'm almost dead?
Oh darling, won't you hold my head?

4 Oh darling, won't you go my bail?
Won't you go my bail and git me out of jail? (2)
Oh darling, won't you go my bail?

5 Oh darling, six months ain't too long! (2)
Six months ain't too long fer me to be gone,
Oh darling, six months ain't too long!

150. DOWN IN THE VALLEY

Collected and arranged by Alan Lomax. Based on *Little Willie*, p. 310 of *Our Singing Country* (Macmillan, N.Y., 1941). SEE: Belden, 488; Brown III, 330; Lomax IV, 310; Randolph IV, 284; Sandburg, 148.

Pulsing ♩ = 120, *or faster*

GUITAR } ANY WALTZ TIME STYLE
BANJO

Down in the val - ley, The val - ley so low, ____

Hang your head o - ver And hear the wind blow. ____

1 Down in the valley,
The valley so low,
Hang your head over
And hear the wind blow.

2 Little Willie's my darlin',
Little Willie's my dear,
If you think I don't love her,
Got a foolish idea.

3 She wrote me one letter,
She sent it by mail,
She sent it in care of
The Washington jail.

4 Gonna build me one steeple
On the mountain so high,
So I can see Willie
Passin' on by.

5 She said that she loved me
Just to give my heart ease,
Just as soon as my back was turned
She loved who she pleased.

6 I rapped on her window,
I knocked on her do',
She gave me short answer
' Don't knock there no mo'.'

7 Sittin' in the prison
With my back to the wall,
Old corn whisky
Was the cause of it all.

8 The judge said ' Stand up, George,
And dry up your tears;
You're sentenced to Raleigh
For twenty-two years.'

9 If I had of listened
To what mother said,
I'd 'a been there today, boys,
In her feather bed.

151. THE RISING SUN BLUES

Recorded and arranged by Alan Lomax from singing of Georgia Turner. FROM:
p. 369 of *Our Singing Country*, Lomax (Macmillan, N.Y., 1941). Tune related to
Lord Barnard and Lady Musgrove, see p. 316 this volume. A related song found in
Suffolk, England, by Peter Kennedy.

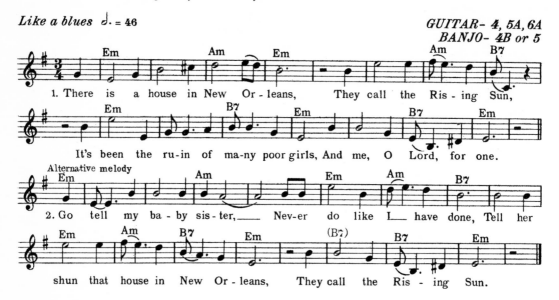

1. There is a house in New Orleans, They call the Ris-ing Sun,
It's been the ru-in of ma-ny poor girls, And me, O Lord, for one.

2. Go tell my ba-by sis-ter,___ Nev-er do like I___ have done, Tell her
shun that house in New Or-leans, They call the Ris-ing Sun.

1 There is a house in New Orleans,
They call the Rising Sun,
It's been the ruin of many poor girls,
And me, O Lord, for one.

2 Go tell my baby sister (brother),
Never do like I have done,
Tell her (him) shun that house in New Orleans,
They call the Rising Sun.

3 The only thing that a drunkard wants
Is a suitcase and a trunk,
The only thing that a rounder likes
Is to git on a great big drunk.

4 One foot is on the platform,
The other one on the train,
I'm going back to New Orleans
To wear that ball and chain.

5 I'm going back to New Orleans,
My race is almost run,
I'm going to spend the rest of my days
Beneath the Rising Sun.

6 Go tell my baby sister (brother),
Never do like I have done,
Tell her (him) shun that house in New Orleans
They call the Rising Sun.

152. MULE SKINNER BLUES

Blue Yodel 8, Jimmy Rodgers. Copyright Southern Music Publishing. Co. Used by permission. An excellent recording by the Monroe Brothers is the source of this version.

Piano arrangement by DON BANKS

new road line?'
2. Well,

1 ' Good mornin', Captain.' ' Good mornin', son.'
An' it's ' Good mornin', Captain.' ' Good mornin', son.'
' Do you need another mule skinner out on your new road line?'

2 Well, I like to work, I'm rollin' all the time,
An' I like to work, I'm rollin' all the time.
I can carve my initials on a mule's behind.

3 Well, it's ' Hey, little waterboy, bring your water 'round.'
An' it's ' Hey, little waterboy, bring your water 'round.
If you don't like your job, set that water-bucket down.'

4 It's T for Texas, T for Tennessee,
It's T for Texas, T for Tennessee,
It's T for Thelma, the gal who made a fool out of me.

153. I DON'T WANT YOUR MILLIONS, MISTER

By Jim Garland; copyright. Verses quoted from Randolph. SEE: Randolph IV,
207. For *East Virginia*, see Lomax IV, 144; Sharp II, 232.
Piano arrangement by DON BANKS

Smoothly ♩ = 76

GUITAR– 4, 5A IN WALTZ TIME
BANJO– 1, 5 (WALTZ TIME)

To be sung an octave lower

1. I don't want your mil-li-ons, Mis- ter, I don't

Note: Bring out these passages in the bass clef (like a response to the tune)

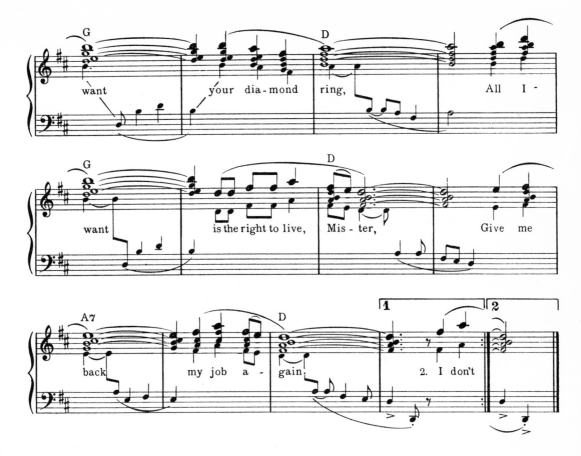

want your dia-mond ring, All I -

want is the right to live, Mis - ter, Give me

back my job a - gain. **2.** I don't

1 I don't want your millions, Mister,
I don't want your diamond ring,
All I want is the right to live, Mister,
Give me back my job again.

2 I don't want your Rolls-Royce, Mister,
I don't want your pleasure yacht,
All I want is food for my babies,
Give to me my old job back.

3 We worked to build this country, Mister,
While you enjoyed a life of ease,
You've stolen all that we built, Mister,
Now our children starve and freeze.

4 Think me dumb if you wish, Mister,
Call me green, or blue or red;
This one thing I sure know, Mister,
My hungry babies must be fed.

154. SIXTEEN TONS

By Merle Travis; copyright 1947 American Music Inc., Hollywood. Used by permission of American Music Inc. and author. SEE: *Folk Songs of the Hills*, Capitol 48001.

1 Now some people say a man's made out of mud,
  But a poor man's made out of muscle and blood,
  Muscle and blood, skin and bones,
  A mind that's weak, and a back that's strong.
  CHORUS:
  You load sixteen tons and what do you get?
  Another day older and deeper in debt.
  Saint Peter, don't you call me 'cause I can't go,
  I owe my soul to the company store.

2 I was born one mornin' when the sun didn't shine,
  I picked up my shovel and I walked to the mine,
  I loaded sixteen tons of number nine coal
  And the strawboss hollered, ' Well, damn my soul!'   (CHO.)

3 Now when you see me comin', you better step aside,
  Another man didn't and another man died;
  I've got a fist of iron and a fist of steel,
  If the right one don't get you, the left one will.   (CHO.)

294

155. DARK AS A DUNGEON

1. Come all you young fellows, so young and so fine,
   And seek not your fortune in a dark dreary mine.
   It will form as a habit and seep in your soul,
   'Till the stream of your blood runs as black as the coal.
   CHORUS:
   Where it's dark as a dungeon and damp as the dew,
   Where the danger is double and the pleasures are few,
   Where the rain never falls and the sun never shines,
   It's dark as a dungeon way down in the mines.

2. It's many a man I have seen in my day,
   Who lived just to labour his whole life away,
   Like a fiend with his dope and a drunkard his wine,
   A man will have lust for the lure of the mine.   (CHO.)

3. I hope when I'm dead and the ages shall roll
   My body will blacken and turn into coal,
   Then I'll look from the door of my heavenly home,
   And pity the miner a-digging my bones.   (CHO.)

PART III. THE WEST

THE WEST

. . . includes the states across the Mississippi, with the exception of Louisiana, parts of the Mid-West (which belong to the North) and the Spanish South-West. Western folk-song styles arose from the mingling of the Northern and the Southern backwoods traditions.

This blending occurred first in the Missouri territory which lay at the junction of the great routes from East to West and North to South and was also the jumping-off place for the explorers and settlers of the Far West: the songs of Pike County were carried all the way to California. In the Ozark mountains, the heart of this sub-region, there developed a back-woods folklore second only to that of the Appalachians in richness, but with a strong Yankee twang and a wildness and extravagance typically western.

The folklore of Eastern Texas, another western sub-region, is a different cultural amalgam —the Southern backwoods culture coloured by the mores of the plantation system—for Texas was the western refuge of the Southern slave holder. When the planters became cattle barons, their feudal attitudes spread, though in a softened form, across the whole West. At the same time the Texas cowboys carried their Southern backwoods songs north across the plains, where they acquired the Northern ballad style; thus, many cowboy songs are reworked lumberjack ballads with a strong Southern accent. On the plains, the singing voice grows more open and full as one moves north from Texas.

On the whole the West was settled by an overflow of adventurous, rebellious, and sometimes criminal males from both North and South, and its songs are notable for their easy-going virility. The old, fanciful ballads gave way to factual narratives, that reflect the awesome and lonely beauty of the West and the quiet valour of the men who conquered it. These Western riders were lonely bachelors and regarded women with a mixture of reverence and tenderness. Among them the *American Tragedy* ballad was replaced by brooding songs about death, by songs of rollicking humour, or by the sentimental ditties of the professional entertainers who toured western outposts . . .

In his last interview, Daniel Boone discoursed on the Westerner's love of ' elbow room ' . .

I first removed to the woods of Kentucky. I fought and repelled the savages and hoped for repose. Game was abundant and our path was prosperous. But soon I was molested by interlopers from every quarter. Again I retreated to the region of the Mississippi; but again these speculators and settlers followed me. Once more I withdrew to the locks of the Missouri—and here at last I hoped to find rest. But I was still pursued—for I had not been two years at the licks, before a damned Yankee settled down within a hundred miles of me . . .

To Boone and the men who followed him into the Mississippi wilderness every ' furriner ' represented a threat to their free-and-easy, unbuttoned way of life. Their loathing for citified strangers is set down in the most famous bit of Ozark folklore, the dialogue between the traveller and the Arkansas squatter . . .

Traveller: Hello, stranger.
Arkansas Squatter: Hello, yourself.
Traveller: Do you live around here?
Squatter: I don't live nowhere's else.
Traveller: Where does this road go to?
Squatter: It ain't gone nowhere since I been here.
Traveller: How far is it to the next tavern?
Squatter: It's upwards of some distance.
Traveller: How long will it take to get there?
Squatter: A hell of a while, if ye stay foolin' here.

As soon as the traveller showed that he could play a hoe-down tune in good style, the squatter's animosity vanished. Venison steaks and whisky appeared on the table and the stranger was invited to ' stay fur a week ', for his fiddling proved that he, too, was a rebel against the straight-laced morality of the ' settlements '. Perhaps the squatter had mistaken the traveller for one of the doleful Baptist circuit-riders who would take the first opportunity to preach at him . . .

. . . there sits an old grey-headed sinner bound for Hell. If he were there one week and then brought back to earth and thrown into a cauldron of boiling lead, seven times heated, why he would freeze to death in a minute. Yea, brethring, Hell is a tremendous hot place . . .

One of these prophets of doom caught up with an Arkansawyer who was cussing his ox-team out of a mud hole . . .

' My poor fellow,' he groaned, ' do you know where you're going?'
' Why, pigeon-wing,' says the squatter, ' I'm going home, I reckon.'
' No, sir, you air not.'
' Then where in tarnation am I a-goin'?'
' You're going straight to hell.'
' Well, I'll just turn this team round then, for I'll be damned if I go this road any further!'

The irreverent tone of this Arkansas anecdote is typical of the new West. It was a land of renegades and rebels and outlaws, which the doleful Baptists and the moralising Methodists were never able to tame completely. Indeed, the big West made folks more tolerant; it even changed the preachers, as the following Davy Crockett yarn shows. In the 1830's Davy was travelling through the Arkansas wilderness on his way to Texas, when he was flabbergasted to hear, deep in the virgin forest, the sound of a fiddle, playing a square-dance tune . . .

We checked our horses and listened and heard *Hail, Columbia, Happy Land*, played in fine style. ' That's fine,' says I. ' Fine as silk and a leetle finer,' says the other. ' But hark, the tune's changed.' We took another spell of listening, and now the musician struck up *Over the River to Charley*.

When we reached the crossing we were struck all of a heap at beholding a minister of the gospel seated in a sulky in the middle of the river, and playing for dear life on a fiddle. The horse was up to his middle in the water and it seemed as if the flimsy vehicle was ready to be swept away in the current. We thought he was mad and shouted at him, ' Turn back.' ' I can't.' ' Then how the devil will you get out?' ' I'm sure I don't know; come and help me.'

The men from the clearing took our horses and rode up to the sulky, and after some difficulty succeeded in bringing the traveller safe to shore. We then asked him what could have induced him to think of fiddling at a time of such peril, and he replied that he had remarked in his progress through life that there was nothing in universal nature so well calculated to draw people together as the sound of the fiddle; and he knew that he might well bawl until he was hoarse and no one would stir a peg; but they would no sooner hear the scraping of his cat-gut than they would quit all business and come to the spot in flocks. We laughed heartily at the knowledge he showed of human nature. And he was right.

The fiddling preacher whom Crockett encountered on the banks of the Washita was a typical member of the free-and-easy frontier communities of East Texas and the Ozarks. There the bear-hunter and the woodsman made their last stand against civilization. There they reached the western limits of their range. Ahead lay the great American desert, the treeless and waterless plains, where their woodlore could not help them, and their tree-to-tree guerilla tactics were of no avail against the savage tribes of horseback Indians. For the space of fifty years the American frontier paused in this trans-Mississippi woodland, reproducing there the log-cabin culture of the East, and storing up reservoirs of folklore which later on poured out songs and yarns to the whole West.

QUOTES: (1) *Tall Tales of Arkansas*, James Masterson (Chapman & Grimes, Boston, 1943) p. 116. From 19th century newspaper source. (2) Ibid. p. 118. (Original. A letter from Pete Whetstone, ST VII, 166, 1837). (3) *The Life of Davy Crockett, By Himself*.

BEYOND THE MISSISSIPPI
156. WE'RE COMING, ARKANSAS

THE WIND OF WORDS blown up by local and national patriots during these expansive years of western settlement has never been matched in the history of the English language. The Gargantua among our national huffers and puffers was General Buncombe, who addressed the House of Representatives in 1855 in the following terms . . .

Sir, we want elbow room—the continent—the whole continent—and nothing but the continent! And we shall have it! Then shall Uncle Sam, placing his hat on Canada, rest his right arm on the California coast, his left leg on the eastern seaboard, and whittle away the British power, while reposing his leg, like a freeman, upon Cape Horn!

Texan patrioteers bragged that the air of the Lone Star State was so pure that it revived corpses and that the climate was so fine that the natives lived to be six hundred years old before they permitted themselves to dry up and be blown away. Meanwhile the Arkansawyers boasted the wonders of their state . . .

The squatter had sold some bottom land to a Yankee farmer. 'How did you like things?' I said. 'Pretty well,' said he. 'The cabin is convenient, and the timber land is good; but that bottom land ain't worth the first red cent.' 'Why?' says I. 'Cause it's full of cedar stumps and Indian mounds,' said he, 'and it can't be cleared.' 'Lord,' said I, 'them ar " cedar stumps " is beets, and them ar " Indian mounds " ar tater hills.' As I expected, the crop was overgrown and useless. The soil is too rich, and planting in Arkensaw is dangerous. I had a good-sized cow killed in that same bottom land. The old thief stole an ear of corn, and took it down where she slept at night to eat. Well, she left a grain or two on the ground, and lay down on them; before morning the corn shot up, and the percussion killed her dead. I don't plant any more; natur intended Arkensaw for a hunting ground, and I go according to natur.'

The settlers poured into the rich bottom lands and the green Ozark hills, in buggies, carts and wagons, on horseback and afoot, many attracted by the news of the famous hot springs of Eureka, Arkansas, which would cure you ' whether you were sick or well '.

QUOTE: *The Big Bear of Arkansas*, T. B. Thorpe (1841).

157. BLUE
158. THE HOUND DAWG SONG

THE BACKWOODS FOLK of the South lived off game, and they thought more of a good hunting dog than they did of most people. Such was the opinion of Jim Doggett, the Arkansas squatter about his bear hound . . .

That gun of mine is a perfect epidemic among bar; if not watched closely, it will go off as quick on a warm scent as my dog Bowie-Knife will; and then that dog—whew! Why, the fellow thinks the world is full of bar, he finds them so easy. It's lucky he don't talk as well as think for with his natural modesty, if he should suddenly learn how much he is acknowledged to be ahead of all other dogs in the universe, he would be astonished to death in two minutes.

Strangers, that dog knows a bar's way as well as a horse jockey knows a woman's; he always barks at the right times, bites at the exact place, and whips without getting a scratch. I never could tell whether he was made expressly to hunt bar or whether bar was made expressly for him to hunt; anyway, I believe they were ordained to go together as naturally as Squire Jones says a man and woman is, when he moralizes in marrying a couple. In fact, Jones once said, said he, ' Marriage according to law is a civil contract of divine origin; it's common to all countries as well as Arkensaw, and people take to it as naturally as Jim Doggett's dog takes to bar.'

In the Mississippi Valley country which produced this story and the ballad of Old Blue, they tell about a possum dog that hunted to order. His master had boards of different sizes on which he dried the possum hides. When he wanted a hide of a certain size, he'd lean the correct board up against the cabin wall, and that smart possum hound would bring in an animal that fitted it exactly. Once the smart hound disappeared for a week, then came into the yard dragging a bear by the scruff of its neck. They saw right away what had happened. The old woman had put her new ironing board out to air, and that smart possum hound had gone off to find a possum with a hide big enough to fit it.

They tell a story about a boy who fell out of a tree on a possum hunt and broke his neck. ' Well,' said his father, ' it could-a been worse. He might have fell on one of the dogs!'

Many a time I've ' hollered ' a Southern shack so wretched that a Mexican peon would hesitate to live there, and watched fifteen or twenty vari-coloured, oddly-shaped hounds boil out from under the front gallery. These hounds might look hungry, flea-bitten, and uncared for, ' but stranger, if you want to stay healthy, don't go kickin' those dogs around '. A southern cracker thinks as much of his dogs as he does of his family.

Some say *The Hound Dawg Song*, a favourite Ozark mountain song, originated before the Civil War, when a country boy named Zeke Parish had a tussle with a townie who had kicked his dog. Old Aaron Weatherman, Swan Post Office, Taney County, Missouri, concurs—' I was there and knowed Zeke and his paw and the hound, too.' Some of his neighbours laugh at old Zeke and say that *The Hound Dawg Song* is a recently composed piece, while others swear that Daniel Boone brought the song to Missouri. It became universally popular at the time when Arkansas's favourite son, Champ Clark, who was candidate for the presidency of the United States, used it as his campaign song. Since that time civic organizations and booster clubs in both Arkansas and Missouri have claimed it for their state. The tune is the old fiddlers' favourite, *Sandy Land* or *Sally Anne* (see p. 230).

QUOTE: *The Big Bear of Arkansas*, T. B. Thorpe (1841).

159. LET'S GO A-HUNTIN'

AN OLD ENGLISH version of this south-western ballad runs, in part . . .

> ' O where are you going?' said Milder to Malder,
> ' O we may not tell you,' said Festle to Fose,
> ' We're off to the woods,' said John the Red Nose.
>
> ' What will you do there?' said Milder to Malder,
> ' We may not tell you,' said Festle to Fose,
> ' We'll hunt the cutty wren,' said John the Red Nose . . .

The ballad tells how this strange quintet shoot the cutty wren with bows and arrows, carry it home in four big wagons, use hatchets and cleavers to cut it up and a furnace to cook it and then feed the poor with its ribs. Obviously, the hunting of this tiny and inoffensive bird carries some deeper significance than the ballad presents. The song may be one of the many English poaching songs, in which exaggeration is used for satirical effect. A. L. Lloyd argues plausibly that it is a very old song of protest by the downtrodden and hungry British peasantry, and Greenway compares it, in this sense, with our own ballad of the Grey Goose. (*See Southern Folklore Quarterly*, XVIII, 3, p. 70.)

This curious song also has its roots in pre-Christian religious beliefs. Until recently the lads of certain villages on the Isle of Man ceremonially hunted the wren every year on St. Stephen's Day (December 26) and bore the small body through the village nailed to a long pole, while they sang this song. In the language of pagan symbolism the wren stood, probably, for the sun and for the old year, and its sacrifice during the winter solstice represented the death of the old year and opened a way for the renewal of life in the spring to come.

In New York State the wren song was once sung on St. Stephen's Day, but in most American versions a squirrel, a rat, or some other little animal takes its place, and the song becomes a nonsense piece for children. Its survival on the frontier, as far west as Texas, where this version was collected in the 1940's by my father, depended on its first lines, ' Let's go a-huntin' ', which was the refrain, the burden, the joyous chorus to every frontiersman's life.

160. BLOW THE CANDLE OUT

A PRETTY RED-HEADED GIRL from Missouri taught me this old Anglo-Scots courting song. She had learned it from her pioneer grandmother, who told her, ' It's not a bad sort of song, honey, but don't never sing it in mixed company.' In the south-eastern states such a prohibition would scarcely have been necessary; but in the Ozarks, with their infiltration of northern settlers, manners were somewhat freer, as this Missouri bundling story indicates.

One time there was some folks had a lot of company all at once, and the house was pretty crowded. After they got everybody settled down for the night, there was one boy and one girl left over, so they had to put 'em in the same bed. It ain't so bad as you might think, because they was in a big room with lots of beds, and grown folks a-sleepin' all round 'em. Just for the looks of the thing, the old woman put an old-fashioned bolster in the middle of the bed. A bolster is like a big long pillow, but stuffed a lot harder than common pillows are nowadays.

The boy didn't go to sleep for a long time, because he was thinking about that pretty girl in bed with him. He knowed the girl was awake too, but there wasn't nothing he could do about it. The moon was a-shinin' right on to the bed, and there was all them people right in the same room. Also the boy hadn't never seen the girl until that day, and didn't know what kind of girl she was or how she was going to act. He didn't want to raise no disturbance, and maybe get throwed right out of the house. So the boy just laid there, and finally went to sleep.

When he woke up next morning, the womenfolks was all dressed, and they was cooking breakfast. The girl acted pleasant enough, but she didn't talk much. Along that evening him and her went a-walkin' down by the spring branch, and they come to a fence without no gate in sight. ' I can jump over easy enough,' says the girl, ' but I'm afraid you'll have to go round.' The boy just stared at her. ' What are you talkin' about?' he says.

The girl kind of giggled. ' Well,' says she, ' a fellow that can't climb over a bolster ain't goin' to have much luck with a five-rail fence.'

QUOTE: *Southern Folklore Quarterly XIX*, 1955, 2. Randolph, *Tales from Arkansas*.

161. UH-UH, NO
162. BUFFALO BOY

THESE WESTERN courting songs are close in spirit to their bawdy English originals, but are infected, too, with the rowdy humour of such high-jinks as this Ozark frontier wedding . . .

Across one corner of the only room a sheet and bearskin were hung, and behind there was the bride's chamber. After resting awhile and groaning several times, the preacher rose and said, ' Let the candidates come forward at once.' At this there was a considerable fuss outside, and presently appeared two men, leading or rather holding back a tall, slim, barefoot son-of-a-gun, with a shocky head of red hair—and he was the groom; he came a-pawing and squealing and nickering and snorting like a four year old. His grooms had hold one on each arm, and were obliged to dig their heels in the dirt floor to hold him in. When the bride appeared he was worse than ever. At length they got him quieted enough to stand alone, and the ceremony proceeded—but now and then he would look sideways at the bride and squeal.

As soon as ' Amen ' was heard, he seized his newly-made wife under his arm, and at one jump disappeared with her under the bear skin. Further, deponent sayeth not, but about four months after, happening to pass

305

the same place, I stopped, and found him the father, or she the mother of a pair of twins. The squealing lover, following me to the fence said, ' Stranger, ain't I married some pumpkins? Twins and all alive. Git married, stranger, git married and see if you can beat that!'

QUOTE: ' A Wedding Frolic in Arkansas', ' Skyscraper ', *Southern Watch Tower* XVIII, 247 (July 15, 1848).

163. TWISTIFICATION

In the States, when a young man dances a set with a young lady he treats her to a glass of lemonade or ice-cream, but in Arkansas he gives his girl a chew of tobacco. A girl will dance with the raggedest, homeliest young man on the ground if he has a plug of store tobacco in his pocket.

They usually have very fine music at the dances. They have an old fiddle strung up with wire strings and two play on it. One plays with the bow and one beats time on the strings. There is but very few tunes they can play, but if a man can play one tune that is good for an all night dance . . .

A big bare-footed, long-haired, ragged sixteen-year-old boy backed up in the corner and said, ' Air you all ready?' The girl said, ' Yes ', and then she said, ' Now play us the old tune.' He started out pretty lively, when the boy, with a voice like a steamboat whistle said, ' Come and go—bring and fetch—ring and twist—take your partner by the craw and swing her all round old Arkansaw.' By that time they were going around so fast you could hardly tell the boys and girls apart, and I got so dizzy-headed and seasick I had to go out for fresh air.

When no fiddler was handy, the Ozarkians danced to mouth-music or play-party tunes, such as this present variant of *Charley Over the Water*.

QUOTE: *Three Years in Arkansas* (Donahue, Chicago, 1904), ' New Orleans Daily Picayune,' October 20, 1849.

164. LITTLE MATTHY GROVES

THE MAJORITY of the British ballads of courtly intrigue did not survive in America. *Little Musgrove*, the ballad par excellence of sexual jealousy, provides one notable exception to this rule. It has been in wide oral circulation in the U.S. for three hundred years, and yet this recently discovered version from the West can be compared for length and antiquity of style with the oldest and best British versions. Here then, is a story which did not perplex the folk of the frontier, but which they understood and appreciated in every detail.

In the old South and West, when a man discovered that his wife had been unfaithful, he lost face if he didn't use a bowie-knife or a six-gun on his rival; and no jury could be found which would not return a verdict of justifiable homicide in such a case.

The extremes of jealousy among frontiersmen are the theme of a familiar yarn about Mike Fink, the bully of the western rivers—a man so ferocious in battle that he acquired among a crew of eye-gougers and ear-chewers the horrendous nickname of ' Snapping turtle of the Ohio and the Big Snag of the Mississippi '. Here is how he taught his woman, Peg, ' a lesson '.

One autumn day, Mike raked together a huge pile of dried leaves and ordered Peg, at whom he had been casting his blackest glances, to lie down in it. ' Get in there or I'll shoot you,' he growled. Poor Peg obeyed and crawled into the leaf pile. Mike then deliberately set fire in four places to the leaves that surrounded his wife. In an instant the mass of leaves was on fire, aided by a fresh wind. Mike stood quietly by, enjoying the fun. Peg stood it as long as she could; but when the flames became too hot, she made a run for the river, her hair and clothing all on fire. In a few seconds she reached the water and plunged in, rejoiced to know she had escaped both fire and rifle. 'Thar,' said Mike. 'That'll larn ye not to be winkin' at them fellers on t'other boat.'

165. THE GIRL I LEFT BEHIND

ALONG WITH the old Scots ballads, the pioneers brought many pieces of the eighteenth century come-all-ye type into the Ozarks. Among them was this song of parting, which has been cherished by the restless, footloose Anglo-American tribe for almost three centuries. The narrator leaves Ireland for Scotland, or sails from England bound for Amerikay, sets off on horseback from Virginia to Tennessee, turns west from Tennessee to Texas or old Missouri, or starts across the plains from Texas to Salt Lake City or California. In British versions he often finds a new sweetheart whose gold destroys his love for the girl he left behind. News then comes that his parents and his old sweetheart have died of broken hearts.

In all American versions, however, the man is betrayed by the fickle girl he has left behind. To the lonely traveller in a strange land the first mail-coach brings the news that his sweetheart has married another man; he then takes to drink, to gambling, or to wandering the world in search of the girl he left behind. As the frontier rolled to the West, the place names were changed, but this story, doubtless repeated thousands of times in real life, remained unaltered.

The shift of guilt from the man to the woman in this ballad possibly reflects a variation between the sexual ratios in the two countries during this period. In Britain, constantly warring and colonizing, there were normally more marriageable women than men during these centuries, and men were sought after. In America, not only did women have more legal rights and more independence, but they were a scarce commodity and thus constantly tempted to break off one engagement when a better offer came along. Besides, a sensible girl knew, when her young man went west, that there were five chances in ten he might be killed or might not send for her. The wisest course for her was to find another sweetheart.

Regarded as a dream or a fantasy containing a wish, perhaps this ballad may have functioned in a number of ways. It expressed the unconscious wish of the man to be free of his sweetheart back home, on the ground that she has probably already been unfaithful to him; many men certainly did go west to escape irksome marriages. It voiced an even more positive wish on the woman's part that her husband or fiancé might never return from the West and thus that an unsatisfactory relationship might be brought painlessly to an end. Sung by men it accused all women of fickleness, and thus provided an excuse for promiscuity and drunkenness. Sung by women, it took fantasy revenge upon the men whom they resented as tyrants and suspected of infidelity; it warned the men that the singer might prove as unfaithful as the girl in the song. Transcending all these subconscious themes, however, the song speaks, more effectively than any other Western ballad, of the loneliness, the shattered loves and the homesickness that traced the faces of the pioneers with lines of sorrow.

166. I'M GOIN' AWAY TO TEXAS

ARKANSAS was admitted to the Union in 1835 and the next year Texas won her independence from Mexico. These two new Western territories became rivals, each boosting the attractions it offered to settlers and exaggerating the faults of the other area. There emerged a rich folklore of yarns and jokes for and against both states. Texas was said to be the refuge of all the scamps and rapscallions who had suddenly to decamp from their home towns; GTT (gone to Texas) became a national joke. The patriotic folks of the Ozarks went on to tell stories on Texas.

. . . A Texan died, and when he got to Heaven and they asked him where he came from, he said, proudly, ' Texas '. They invited him right in—' You been in Hell long enough,' said the recording angel . . .

The next Texan that died got to some big gates and stood there fanning himself with his Stetson hat, saying, ' Lord, I didn't know Heaven was so much like Texas.' The old watchman look at him sort of sad like and told him, ' My boy, this *ain't* Heaven.'

Vance Randolph, who found these anti-Texas stories in the Ozarks, also recorded a Missouri form of the old *Quaker's Courtship* in which the man is GTT and his young lady's attitude is—good riddance.

QUOTE: Randolph.

167. THE STATE OF ARKANSAS

TEXANS say that in the early days one fork of the big road west led to Arkansas, the other to Texas. On the latter road there was a sign reading, ' This road to Texas '. According to Texans, all who could read pressed on to the Lone Star State, while the others settled in Arkansas. Texas propaganda was so effective that Arkansas, the backwoods state, remained a sensitive spot on the national funny bone for a century—America's Yokumville. When an Irish navvy, who had come to Arkansas to work on the railroads, composed a satiric ballad about his experiences in the state, it was taken up by folk singers all across the South and Middle West. This version, like many of the best Arkansas stories, comes from a native of that state, Lee Hayes.

168. THE HORSE TRADER'S SONG

PETER KENNEDY's recent work in Great Britain has shown that the gipsies have lately been the most important carriers of British traditional songs and ballads; but, aside from my father's recordings from the gipsy woman in Forth Worth, Texas in 1904, or 1905,* little was known about the songs of American gipsies until Vance Randolph made this all-important find in the Ozarks. An old woman, who claimed to be a member of a band of gipsy horse traders, sang it to Randolph's informant in 1900, and it seems to give a picture of life in the group. The refrain line, ' I've been around this world,' occurs in a few other mountain banjo tunes of a similar character, all of them concerned with the lives of wanderers or criminals, hinting that this line may be one fragment of a genuine American gipsy song-lore, as yet unknown to us.

* *Git Along, Little Dogies, The Factory Girl, Careless Love.*

156. WE'RE COMING, ARKANSAS

FROM: *Texas Folk Songs*, William Owen (Texas Folklore Society, Dallas, 1950).
Used by permission. SEE: Lomax I, 283; Randolph III, 14. A related song is
Way Out in Idaho, Lomax IV, 269.
Piano arrangement by DON BANKS

1 They say there is a stream
  Where crystal waters flow,
  That'll cure a man sick or well
  If he will only go.

CHORUS:
We're coming, Arkansas,
We're coming, Arkansas,
Our four-horse team will soon be seen
On the road to Arkansas.

2 The men keep hounds down there,
   And hunting is all they care;
   The women plough and hoe the corn,
   While the men shoot turkey and deer. (CHO.)

3 The girls are strong down there,
   Clean and healthy and gay,
   They card and spin from morning till night
   And dance from night till day. (CHO.)

4 They raise their 'baccer patch,
   The women all smoke and chaw,
   Eat hog, and hominy and poke for greens
   Way down in Arkansas. (CHO.)

5 The roads are rough down there,
   You must take um ' done or raw ',
   There's rocks and rills and stumps and hills
   On the road to Arkansas. (CHO.)

The same song turned up again several hundred miles to the west in Idaho.

1 They say there is a land
   Where crystal waters flow,
   Where veins of purest gold are found
   Way out in Idaho.

2 We'll need no pick or spade,
   No shovel pan or hoe,
   The largest chunks are on the ground
   Way out in Idaho.

157. BLUE

As sung by Peggy Seeger. SEE: Brown III, 252; Lomax IV, 111; Randolph II, 382;
White, 207. A song known to whites and Negroes mainly from Mississippi Valley
west into Texas.

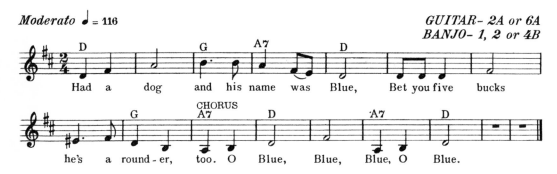

1 Had a dog and his name was Blue,
   Bet you five bucks he's a rounder, too.
   CHORUS:
   O Blue, Blue, Blue, O Blue.

2 Every night just about good dark,
   Blue goes out and begins to bark. (CHO.)

3 Blue treed a possum in a 'simmon tree,
   Blue looks at possum, possum looks at me. (CHO.)

4 Chased that possum out on a limb,
   Blue set down and talked to him. (CHO.)

5 Blue got sick and very sick,
   Called for the doctor to come right quick. (CHO.)

6 Called for the doctor and the doctor come,
   He says, ' Blue, your huntin' days are done.'
                                        (CHO.)

7 Old Blue died and he died so hard
   Scratched little holes in my back yard. (CHO.)

8 Dug his grave with a silver spade,
   Let him down with a golden chain. (CHO.)

9 When I get to heaven first thing I'll do
   Take my horn and blow for Blue. (CHO.)

10 Come on, Blue, come on, Blue.
   There's a possum in Heaven for me and you.
                                        (CHO.)

158. THE HOUND DAWG SONG

FROM: p. 278, Vol. III, *Ozark Folk Songs*, Vance Randolph (State Historical Society of Missouri, 1946-50). Used by permission.

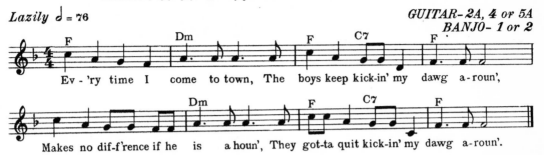

Lazily ♩ = 76

GUITAR— 2A, 4 or 5A
BANJO— 1 or 2

Ev-'ry time I come to town, The boys keep kick-in' my dawg a-roun',
Makes no dif-f'rence if he is a houn', They got-ta quit kick-in' my dawg a-roun'.

1 Ev'ry time I come to town,
The boys keep kickin' my dawg aroun',
Makes no difference if he is a houn',
They gotta quit kickin' my dawg aroun'.

2 Me an' Lem Briggs an' old Bill Brown
Took a load of corn to town,
My old Jim dawg, ornery old cuss,
He just naturally follered us.

3 As we driv past Johnston's store
A passel of yaps come out the door.
Jim he scooted behind a box,
With all them fellers a-throwin' rocks.

4 They tied a can to old Jim's tail
An' run him a-past the county jail,
That just naturally made us sore,
Lem, he cussed and Bill he swore.

5 Me an' Lem Briggs an' old Bill Brown
Lost no time a-gittin' down,
We wiped them fellers on the ground
For kickin' my old dawg, Jim, around.

6 Jim seen his duty there an' then,
He lit into them gentlemen,
He shore mussed up the court-house square
With rags an' meat an' hide an' hair.

7 Every time I come to town
The boys keep kickin' my dawg aroun',
Makes no difference if he is a houn',
They gotta quit kickin' my dawg aroun'.

159. LET'S GO A-HUNTIN'

FROM: p. 101 of *Our Singing Country*, Lomax (Macmillan, N.Y., 1941). Collected by J. A. Lomax in Fort Spunky, Texas. SEE: Flanders II, 58; Guide and Index (*Cutty Wren*); Opie, 367.

Evenly ♩ = 192

GUITAR— 2A, 4, 5A (WALTZ TIME)
BANJO— 1 (WALTZ TIME)

'Let's go a-hunt-in',' says Risk-y Rob. 'Let's go a-

hunt - in',' says Rob - in to Bob. 'Let's go a - hunt - in',' says

Dan - 'l and Joe. 'Let's go a - hunt - in',' says Bil - ly Bar - low.

1 ' Let's go a-huntin',' says Risky Rob.
  ' Let's go a-huntin',' says Robin to Bob.
  ' Let's go a-huntin',' says Dan'l and Joe.
  ' Let's go a-huntin',' says Billy Barlow.

2 ' What shall we hunt?' says Risky Rob.
  ' What shall we hunt?' says Robin to Bob.
  ' What shall we hunt?' says Dan'l and Joe.
  ' What shall we hunt?' says Billy Barlow.

3 ' Let's hunt coons,' says Risky Rob.
  ' Possum for me,' says Robin to Bob.
  ' Let's catch rabbits, says Dan'l and Joe.
  ' I'm huntin' rats,' says Billy Barlow.

4 ' How shall we divide him?' says Risky Rob.
  ' How shall we divide him?' says Robin to Bob.
  ' How shall we divide him?' says Dan'l and Joe.
  ' How shall we divide him?' says Billy Barlow.

5 ' I'll take shoulder,' says Risky Rob.
  ' I'll take thigh,' says Robin to Bob.
  ' I'll take back,' says Dan'l and Joe.
  ' Tail bone mine,' says Billy Barlow.

6 ' How shall we cook him?' says Risky Rob.
  ' How shall we cook him?' says Robin to Bob.
  ' How shall we cook him?' says Dan'l and Joe.
  ' How shall we cook him?' says Billy Barlow.

7 ' I'll fry mine,' says Risky Rob.
  ' I'll broil thigh,' says Robin to Bob.
  ' I'll bake back,' says Dan'l and Joe.
  ' Tail bone **raw**,' says Billy Barlow.

160. BLOW THE CANDLE OUT

Collected and arranged by Edna Crumpley. SEE: Ord, 95. Song known England, Ireland, Scotland, and often concerns a soldier, drafted into the army, who promises to marry his sweetheart after his term of service. Peter Kennedy points out this is a well-known Irish air, *The Winding Banks of Erne.*
Piano arrangement by MATYAS SEIBER

Swiftly and steadily ♩ = 92

GUITAR– 2A, 4, or 5C
BANJO– 1 or 2

1. It was late last Sat-ur-day eve - ning I

went to see my dear, The candles were all burning And the moon shone bright and clear. I rapped on her window To ease her of her pain, She rose and let me in And then barred the door again.

2. I

(Fine)

1 It was late last Saturday evening
I went to see my dear,
The candles were all burning
And the moon shone bright and clear.
I rapped on her window
To ease her of her pain,
She rose and let me in
And then barred the door again.

2 I like well your behaviour
And this I often say—
I cannot rest contented
While you are far away;
But the roads they are so muddy
I cannot roam about,
So roll me in your arms, love,
And blow the candle out.

3 Your father and your mother
In yonder room do lie,
A-huggin' one another
So why not you and I?
A-huggin' one another,
Without a fear or doubt
So roll me in your arms, love,
And blow the candle out.

4 And if we prove successful, love,
Please name it after me,
Hug it neat and kiss it sweet
And dap it on your knee.
When my three years are ended
And my time it is run out,
Then I will prove my indebtedness
By blowing the candle out.

161. UH-UH, NO

Collected from Lannie Sutton. Used by permission of Sam Eskin. SEE: Belden, 506; Brown III, 23; Index and Guide (*Madam, I Am Come to Court You* and *O No, John*); JEFSS IV. 297 (many English references); Reeves, 33, 140, 162; Sharp II, 249, 279. This song is a middlewestern cross between *Madam, I Have Gold and Silver*, and *No, Sir, No* (Brown III, 26 and Randolph III, 104). These are sung as comedy dialogues and occasionally game songs. Found commonly in England and all over U.S.

1 ' Madam, I have come for to court you,
Your affections for to gain,
If you'll give me good attention
Perhaps I'll come twice more again.'

CHORUS:
' Uh-uh, no, no, sir, no,'
All of her answers to me were no.

2 ' Madam, I have gold and silver,
Madam I have a house and land,
Madam, I have a world of plenty,
It'll be yours at your command.' (CHO.)

3 ' What care I for your gold and silver?
What care I for your house and land?
What care I for your world of plenty?
All I want is a handsome man.' (CHO.)

4 ' Madam, you seem for to dote on beauty,
Beauty is a thing that'll fade away.
Gather a red rose in the morning,
Then by noon, it'll fade away.' (CHO.)

5 ' The ripest apple will soon grow rotten,
The warmest love will soon grow cold,
A young man's promise is soon forgotten,
Pray, little miss, don't be so bold.' (CHO.)

6 The Texas boys, they ain't the fellers,
They don't know how to court the girls,
Turn their backs and hide their faces,
That ain't the way of the big wide world. (CHO.)

7 But the Arkansas boys, they're the fellows,
They know how to court a girl.
Hug them a lot and kiss them a-plenty,
This is the pretty way of the world. (CHO.)

162. BUFFALO BOY

Composite version of *The Mountaineer's Courtship*, the Stoneman Family, AFM 64, Folkways 253, and *Buffalo Boy*, Sam Hinton, La Jolla, Calif., AAFS 105 B. Collected by D. Emrich. Tune is a close relative of the *Go Tell Aunt Rhody* family, for which see Jackson I, 173; JEFSS XXXV, 257 (*The Country Courtship*); Randolph II, 347; Sharp II, 345. Recently found in Wilts, Dorset, Norfolk. See also: Index and Guide (*When Shall We Get Married?*); Reeves, 221; Williams, *Folk Songs of Upper Thames* (London, 1923).

Fast and poker-faced ♩ = 208

GUITAR– ANY ²⁄₄ STYLE
BANJO– 1-3

'O when are you comin' to court me, to court me, to court me, O when are you comin' to court me, my dear old Buffalo boy?'

1 ' O when are you comin' to court me, to court me, to court me,
O when are you comin' to court me, my dear old Buffalo boy?'

2 ' I guess I'll come on Sunday, Sunday, Sunday,
I guess I'll come on Sunday, that is if the weather is good.'

3 ' How long do you think you'll court me, court me, court me,
How long do you think you'll court me, my dear old Buffalo boy?'

4 ' I guess I'll court you all night, all night, all night,
I guess I'll court you all night, that is if the weather is good.'

5 ' And when shall we be married?'

6 ' O we'll be married on Sunday.'

7 ' What you gonna come to the weddin' in?'

8 ' I guess I'll come in my ox-cart.'

9 ' Well, who you gonna bring to the weddin'?'

10 ' I guess I'll bring my children.'

11 ' I didn't know you had any children.'

12 ' Why sure I've got five children, five children, five children,
Sure, I've got five children, maybe six if the weather is good.'

13 ' Well there ain't a-goin' to be no weddin', no weddin', no weddin',
There ain't a-goin' to be no weddin', not even if the weather is good.'

315

163. TWISTIFICATION

From singing of Lannie Sutton in Doxie, Oklahoma. Used by permission of Sam Eskin. SEE: Botkin I, 349. This is a western play-party version of *Weevily Wheat*, from Scots *Charlie Over the Water*.

Swinging ♩ = 208

GUITAR— 2A, 4
BANJO— 1-3

Way down yon-der in the ma-ple swamp, Wa-ter's deep and mud dy,
Chorus Five times five is twen-ty - five, Five times six is thir - ty,
Five times nine is for-ty - five, Five times ten is fif - ty,

There I met this pret-ty lit-tle miss, There I spied my hon - ey.
Five times sev-en is thir - ty - five, Five times eight is for - ty.
Five times e-lev-en is fif - ty - five, Five times twelve is six - ty.

1 Way down yonder in the maple swamp,
  Water's deep and muddy,
  There I met this pretty little miss,
  There I spied my honey.

CHORUS:
Five times five is twenty-five,
Five times six is thirty,
Five times seven is thirty-five,
Five times eight is forty.
Five times nine is forty-five,
Five times ten is fifty,
Five times eleven is fifty-five,
Five times twelve is sixty.

2 Take that little miss by her hand,
  Lead her like a pigeon,
  Make her dance one more reel,
  Scatter her religion. (CHO.)

3 Racoon's out a-choppin' wood,
  Possum, he's a-haulin',
  My old dog a-sittin' on a log,
  Splittin' his throat a-squawlin'. (CHO.)

164. LITTLE MATTHY GROVES

FROM: *Journal of American Folklore* XXX, 31, a Missouri version. SEE: Belden, 57; Brown II, 101, Child, No. 81; Creighton II, 43; Eckstorm, 150; Flanders I, 135; Gardner, 46; Mackenzie, 27; Randolph I, 124; Sharp I, 161. This ballad has been rarely reported in the last century from Great Britain, but has been found over entire U.S.

Freely ♩ = 112

GUITAR— 6A
BANJO— 4B or 2

On a high hol-i-day, on a high hol-i-day, The

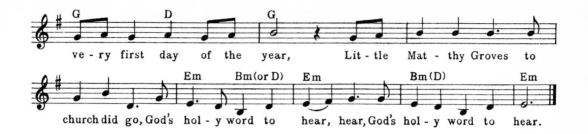

ve - ry first day of the year, Lit - tle Mat - thy Groves to
church did go, God's hol - y word to hear, hear, God's hol - y word to hear.

1 On a high holiday, on a high holiday,
The very first day of the year,
Little Matthy Groves to church did go,
God's holy word to hear, hear,
God's holy word to hear.

2 The first that came in was a gay ladie,
And the next that came in was a girl,
And the next that came in was Lord Arnold's
The fairest of them all . . .   [wife,

3 He stepped right up unto this one
And she made him this reply,
Saying, ' You must go home with me tonight,
All night with me for to lie.'. . .

4 ' I cannot go with you tonight,
I cannot go for my life;
For I know by the rings that are on your fingers
You are Lord Arnold's wife.' . . .

5 ' And if I am Lord Arnold's wife,
I know that Lord Arnold's gone away;
He's gone away to old England
To see King Henery.' . . .

6 A little footpage was standing by,
And he took to his feet and run;
He run till he came to the water-side
And he bent his breast and swum . . .

7 ' What news, what news, my little footpage?
What news have you for me?
Are my castle walls all toren down,
Or are my towers three?' . . .

8 ' Your castle walls are not toren down,
Nor are your towers three;
But little Matthy Groves is in your house
In bed with your gay ladie.' . . .

9 He took his merry men by the hand
And placed them all in a row,
And he bade them not one word for to speak
And not one horn for to blow . . .

10 There was one man among them all
Who owed little Matthy some good will,
And he put his bugle horn to his mouth,
And he blew both loud and shrill . . .

11 ' Hark, hark! Hark, hark!' said little Matthy
' I hear the bugle blow,   [Groves,
And every note it seems to say,
'' Arise, arise and go!'' ' . . .

12 ' Lie down, lie down, little Matthy Groves,
And keep my back from the cold,
It is my father's shepherd boys
A-blowing up the sheep from the fold.' . . .

13 From that they fell to hugging and kissing,
And from that they fell to sleep;
And next morn when they woke at the break of
Lord Arnold stood at their feet . . .   [day,

14 ' And it's how do you like my fine feather bed?
And it's how do you like my sheets?
And it's how do you like my gay ladie
That lies in your arms and sleeps?' . . .

15 ' Very well do I like your fine feather beds,
Very well do I like your sheets;
But much better do I like your gay ladie
That lies in my arms and sleeps.' . . .

16 ' Now get you up, little Matthy Groves,
And all your clothes put on;
For it never shall be said in old England
That I slew a naked man.' . . .

17 'I will get up,' said little Matthy Groves,
  'And fight you for my life,
  Though you've two bright swords hanging by
  And me not a pocket-knife.' . . .   [your side,

18 'If I've two bright swords by my side,
  They cost me deep in purse;
  And you shall have the better of the two
  And I will keep the worse.' . . .

19 The very first lick that little Matthy struck,
  He wounded Lord Arnold sore;
  But the very first lick that Lord Arnold struck,
  Little Matthy struck no more . . .

20 He took his ladie by the hand,
  And he downed her on his knee,
  Saying, 'Which do you like the best, my dear,
  Little Matthy Groves or me?' . . .

21 'Very well do I like your rosy cheeks,
  Very well do I like your dimpled chin;
  But better I like little Matthy Groves
  Than you and all your kin.' . . .

22 He took his ladie by the hand
  And led her o'er the plain;
  He took the broadsword from his side
  And he split her head in twain . . .

23 'Hark, hark, hark, doth the nightingale sing,
  And the sparrows they do cry;
  Today I've killed two true lovers
  And tomorrow I must die.' . . .

165. THE GIRL I LEFT BEHIND

Collected and arranged by Alan Lomax. SEE: Belden, 198; Brown II, 378; Lomax
I, 192; Randolph I, 283; Sharp II, 64. Often printed by broadside press in
Britain; recorded in Scotland, (Ord, 45) and England (JEFSS VIII, 262). In U.S.
it has been found from Virginia to California, with appropriate changes.
Piano arrangement by MATYAS SEIBER

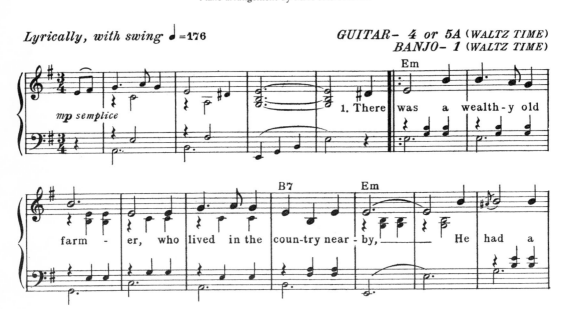

Lyrically, with swing ♩=176

GUITAR— 4 or 5A (WALTZ TIME)
BANJO— 1 (WALTZ TIME)

mp semplice

1. There was a wealth-y old farm-er, who lived in the coun-try near-by,____ He had a

1 There was a wealthy old farmer, who lived in the country nearby,
He had a lovely daughter on whom I cast an eye;
She was pretty, tall and handsome, indeed, so very fair,
There was no other girl in the country with her I could compare.

2 I asked her if she would be willing for me to cross over the plains,
She said it would make no difference, so I returned again,
She said that she would be true to me till death should prove unkind;
We kissed, shook hands and parted, I left my girl behind.

3 Out in a western city, boys, a town we all know well,
Where everyone was friendly and to show me all around,
Where work and money was plentiful and the girls to me proved kind,
But the only object on my mind was the girl I left behind.

319

4 As I was rambling around one day all down on the public square,
The mailcoach had arrived and I met the mailboy there,
He handed to me a letter that gave me to understand,
That the girl I left in old Texas had married another man.

5 I turned myself all around and about, not knowing what else to do,
I read on down a piece further to see if these words proved true.
It's drinking I throw over, card-playing I resign,
For the only girl that I ever loved was the girl I left behind.

6 Come all you ramblin', gamblin' boys, and listen while I tell,
Does you no good, kind friends, I am sure it will do you no harm,
If ever you court a fair young maid, just marry her while you can,
For if ever you cross over the plains, she'll marry some other man.

166. I'M GOIN' AWAY TO TEXAS

FROM: p. 61 of *Ozark Folk Songs*, Vance Randolph, Vol. III. Used by permission.
Related to *The Quaker's Courtship*, see p. 28.
Piano arrangement by MATYAS SEIBER

Faster, saucily

on an' just keep a-go-in', Fa-la-day,— fa-la-day,— Just go

on an' just keep a-go-in', Fa-la-did-dle-la-la-day.

1 *Man :*
　　I'm goin' away to Texas,
　　　　Oh dear me,
　　I'm goin' away to Texas,
　　　　Oh dear me.

Woman :
　　Just go on an' just keep a-goin',
　　　　Fa-la-day, fa-la-day,
　　Just go on an' just keep a-goin',
　　　　Fa-la-diddle-la-la-day.

2 *Man :*
　　When I get there, I'll write you a letter. (2)

Woman :
　　I don't want you nor none o' your letters. (2)

3 *Man :*
　　You'll be sorry for all this. (2)

Woman:
　　If I am, you never will know it. (2)

4 *Man :*
　　Some cold night you'll freeze to death. (2)

Woman :
　　If I do you never will know it. (2)

167. THE STATE OF ARKANSAS

Collected and arranged by Lee Hayes and adapted by Alan Lomax. SEE: Belden, 424; Brown II, 382; Laws, 220; Lomax I, 283; Randolph III, 25; Sharp II, 238; L.C. Record 35A. For main references see *Tall Tales of Arkansas*, Masterson, 255-268. According to Belden it was sung by Irish navvies imported to work on railroads in Ark.

1 My name is Charlie Brennan, from Charlestown I come,
I've travelled this wide world over, and many a race I've run,
I've travelled this wide world over, and some ups and downs I've saw,
But I never knew what misery was till I came to Arkansas.

2 I stepped behind the depot to dodge that blizzard wind,
Met a walking skeleton whose name was Thomas Quinn,
His hair hung down in rat-tails on his long and lantern jaw,
He invited me to his hotel, the best in Arkansas.

3 I followed my conductor to his respected place,
Where pity and starvation was seen in every face,
His bread it was corn dodger, his meat I could not chaw,
But he charged me half a dollar in the state of Arkansas.

Spoken: But I didn't like the work, nor the food, nor the swamp-angel, nor his wife, nor none of his children. So I went up to him and I told him, ' Mister, I'm quitting' this job. I want to be paid off.' He says to me, ' All right, son.' And he handed me a mink skin. He says, ' That's what we use for currency down here in Arkansas.' So I took it into a saloon to see if I could get me a pint of whisky. Put my mink skin on the bar, and be durned if the bartender didn't slip me that pint. Then he picked up my mink skin, blowed the hair back on it, and handed me three 'possum hides and fourteen rabbit skins for change . . .

4 I started back in Texas a quarter after five,
  Nothing was left but skin and bones, half dead and half alive,
  I got me a bottle of whisky, my misery for to thaw,
  Got drunk as old Abraham Linkern when I left old Arkansas.

5 Farewell, farewell, Thomas Quinn, and likewise his darling wife,
  I know she never will forget me in the last days of her life,
  She put her little hand in mine and tried to bite my jaw,
  And said, ' Mr. Brennan, remember me when you leave old Arkansas.'

6 Farewell, farewell, swamp-angels, to canebrakes and to chills,
  Fare thee well to sage and sassafras tea and corn-dodger pills,
  If ever I see that land again, I'll give to you my paw,
  It will be through a telescope from here to Arkansas.

7 O now I am a railroad man at a dollar and a half a day.
  An' there I 'low to work, boys, till I can get away,
  Then I'll go to the Cherokee mountains and marry me a squaw,
  Farewell to hog and hominy in the state of Arkansas.

168. THE HORSE TRADER'S SONG

As sung by Fred Woodruff, Ark., 1941, learned by him in 1900. FROM: p. 261 of
Ozark Folk Songs, Vance Randolph, Vol. III. Used by permission. Connected with
several recorded mountain banjo pieces with the refrain ' I been all over the
world.'

1 It's do you know those horse traders,
  It's do you know their plan?
  It's do you know those horse traders,
  It's do you know their plan?
  Their plan it is for to snide you
  And git whatever they can,
  Lord, Lord, I been all around this world.

2 They'll send their women from house to house ⎤
    To git whatever they can,   ⎬ (2)
    O yander she comes a-runnin', boys,
    With a hog-jaw in each hand,
    Lord, Lord, I been all around this world.

3 It's look in front of our horses, boys ⎤
    O yander comes a man,   ⎬ (2)
    If I don't git to snide him
    I won't get nary a dram,
    Lord, Lord, I been all around this world.

4 O now we stop for supper, boys, ⎤
    We've found a creek at last,   ⎬ (2)
    O now we stop for supper, boys,
    To turn out on the grass,
    Lord, Lord, I been all around this world.

5 Go saddle up your snides, boys, ⎤
    And tie 'em to the rack,   ⎬ (2)
    The first man that gets 'em
    Will pay us to take 'em back,
    Lord, Lord, I been all around this world.

6 Come on now, boys, ⎤
    Let's go git a drink of gin ⎬ (2)
    For yander comes the women, boys,
    To bring us to camp agin,
    Lord, Lord, I been all around this world.

PLAINSMEN AND '49ERS

169. THE TEXAS RANGERS

To BELONG to the Texas Rangers, a man had to be able to ' ride like a Mexican, trail like an Indian, shoot like a Tennessean, and fight like the very devil '. This small, highly mobile force, in which every man was as good as a small army, guarded the American settlements in Texas from Mexican raids and fought an unending battle with the Indians to extend the white man's domain into the plains. West of the ninety-eighth parallel of longitude, wood and water stopped and the boundless prairie began; of this land the well-mounted, war-like Comanche and Kiowa Apache Indians had been for two centuries the unquestioned masters.

This ballad tells of a battle in which sixteen rangers, armed with guns, lost their lives to Indians who fought with bows and arrows. A man with an old-fashioned single-shot rifle that took a minute to load was no match for an Indian who could lean under the neck of his fast-running pony and let fly twenty arrows in as many seconds. The Indian tactic was to circle the white on the gallop, shooting their arrows, and, having drawn their fire, ride in for the kill with their fourteen-foot lances. The Rangers were trained to fire by squads. The first shot had to count, for there was often no chance for a second. If the skirmish was lost, the dead were scalped and the living put to torture, at which the Plains Indians were experts.

In 1840 the newly invented Colt six-shooter came into the hands of the Rangers. At its first trial in the battle of Perdenales, Captain Hays and fourteen Rangers routed seventy Comanches.

In vain the Comanches tried to turn their horses and make a stand, but such was the wild confusion of running horses, popping pistols, and yelling Rangers, that they sought safety in flight . . .

Having equipped themselves with repeating weapons, the Rangers then gradually cleared the state of hostiles, but the battle for the plains had really been won by the English inventor, Samuel Colt, in his Massachusetts arms factory.

This song of the Texas Rangers was the first important ballad of the far West, and it made a great impression on the whole country. Sung by both sides in the Civil War, often reprinted in songsters, it became a standard part of the folk singer's repertoire in New England and the Southern Mountains. I learnt this version from two pretty young girls in Hazard, Kentucky, in 1934.

170. GREEN GROWS THE LAUREL

THIS REFRAIN was so much sung by the Irish-American troops who marched into Mexico during the 1846-8 war that Mexicans thenceforth called Americans ' gringos ' (from ' green grows '). However, this was only another stage in the long journey of a love song, once known in every part of the British Isles.

In popular English poetry the laurel stood for virginity and the rue for the loss of virtue. Old Lize Pace of Hyden, Kentucky, gave me the chorus in the form best known in the old country . . .

> Green grows the laurel and so does the rue,
> We'll (I'll) change the green laurel for the orange and blue . . .

Vance Randolph believes that the original phrase was ' origen (origane) blue ' and that ' origane ' means oregano, or marjoram, the herb whose blue flower symbolizes fidelity. An English folklorist also points out that orange and blue were the colours of a northern regiment. In any case, the girl is giving up her virginity in exchange for a faithful love.

This symbolism, however, was lost in later centuries. The Irish, because the ditty refers to both ' green ' and ' orange ', esteemed it as a patriotic love song and brought it to America where they did, indeed, ' exchange the green laurel for the red, white, and blue'.

In such fashion do the people emend their folk songs, as they pass from generation to generation, each one struggling to re-interpret lost meanings by the substitution of a word here and there. Further tangles result; further changes are made; and, eventually, a new song will flower up out of the humus of the old, if there is time enough and the song does not disappear. In this case time intervened in another fashion. The Oklahoma writer, Lynn Riggs, knew the refrain as ' Green grow the lilacs all sparkling with dew '. He wrote a folk musical entitled *Green Grow the Lilacs*—a cowboy love story which was used as the basis of the Broadway success *Oklahoma*.

171. ROOT, HOG, OR DIE

THE MACHINE that first licked the problems of the plains was the ox-drawn covered wagon, called the prairie schooner by sea-minded Americans of that day. The heroes of the overland trails were the bull-whackers, a race of rough giants who spurred their teams on with twenty-foot blacksnake whips, and kept the trade routes open, the forts supplied, and brought most of the wagon trains safely to Santa Fe, Oregon, and California, in spite of drought, Indians, quicksand, alkali deserts, and the snows of the Rocky Mountains.

The bull-whacker held that profanity was the only language his oxen could understand. A Christian general, shocked by the six-cornered oaths of his western teamsters, banned profanity on one campaign. Within fifty miles his supply train was stalled, nor did it move until the general ordered the drivers to ' cuss away as usual '.

Root, hog, or die, the refrain of the western bull-whackers' most notable song, states a hardboiled pioneer aphorism which means pitch into the job or take the consequences. In upstate New York I was told that both the saying and the song took their rise among the poor people who once combed the hill country near the Finger Lakes, digging for ginseng;

or them it was literally ' root, hog, or die '. In any case, the refrain cropped up in many nineteenth century American ballads.

Deep-water sailors off the coast of Maine sang:

> We hoisted up our sails and the wind began to blow,
> We cleared up our decks and then went below,
> We tumbled in our bunks, but scarce shut an eye,
> When 'twas, ' Turn out and reef, boys, root, hog, or die '.

Yet no other form of the song matches the epic power of these verses, roared out around a buffalo-chip camp-fire by the randy, rusty-throated, bull-whackers on the Red Cloud line.

172. WHOA! HA! BUCK AND JERRY BOY

ONCE THE WAY was open across the plains nothing could stay the westward rush of settlers. It is estimated that thirty-four thousand pioneers perished along the two thousand miles of the Oregon Trail—an average of seventeen dead for each mile; yet every spring more caravans formed on the banks of the Missouri. On the heels of the Oregon emigrants came the Mormons led by Brigham Young, who sought refuge for his persecuted flock in the wastes of Utah. Young, a visionary but an able planner and administrator as well, organized his wagon trains on modern military lines. He drilled his men in plains fighting, and each night held orientation lectures and entertainments, where fiddlers and bards raised the spirits of the trail-weary saints . . .

> Some men have got a dozen wives and others have a score,
> And the men that ain't got but one's a-lookin' out for more.
> Now young men, don't get discouraged, get married if you can,
> But take care don't get a woman that belongs to another man.
> Tittery-irie-aye . . .

It is pleasant to think of this simple folk, whose polygamous system populated a desert within two generations, chuckling over these lines, anticipating the fleshly joy that awaited them across the Rockies in Brigham Young's promised land.

173. SWEET BETSY

WHEN THE NEWS of Sutter's discovery of gold in Sacramento flashed across the country in 1849, the human freshet running across the plains became a flood. By July 8, 1851 the Indian traders at Fort Laramie on the Platte had watched 40,000 people, 10,000 wagons. 30,000 oxen, and 30,000 horses and mules pass by on the way west.

Yet, out of all this mighty human horde, the person who will be remembered longest is the figment of some western ballad-maker's imagination—a composite of all the young women who hopefully made the journey, dreaming of rich young husbands and golden teething rings for their babies. The ballad maker called her ' Sweet Betsy '. If she had kept a diary of her trip across the plains, she might have recorded the following impressions . . .

May 3, 1849. Fifteen miles to Bull Creek. The guide pointed out the continuous rise and fall of the track across what are rightly called the billows, or little ridges of the prairie. 'No, it's not high mountains ner great rivers ner hostile Injuns,' says Meek, 'that'll give us most grief. It's the long grind o' doin' every day's work regler an' not let-up fer nobody ner nothin'. Figger it fur yourself; 2100 miles—four months to do it in between April rains and September snows—123 days. How much a day and every cussed day?'

I saw the point. Seventeen miles a day.

'Yaas,' drawled the scout. 'And every day rain, hail, cholera, breakdowns, lame mules, sick cows, washouts, prairie fires, flooded coulees, lost horses, dust storms, alkali water. Seventeen miles every day—or you land in the snow and eat each other like the Donner party done in '46.'

May 13, 1849. Long pull. Here we are beginning to meet people who are turning back, discouraged. They had seen enough of the 'Elephant'. Graves are more frequent these last days. We saw whitening on the plains, bones of animals which had died on the way.

QUOTE: From '*49ers* by Archer Butler Hulbert (Little, Brown & Co., Boston, 1931), pp. 16, 41.

174. JOE BOWERS

PIKE COUNTY, MISSOURI, was once as big as an ordinary state, and the men of Pike County, known as dead shots and fly sports, dominated the early plains period. Greenhorns often tried to pass themselves off as Pikers to acquire a 'rep'. Yet the only son of Pike County likely to be remembered by posterity is the comic hero of this rather foolish ballad. Frank Swift, poet to a band of western Argonauts, is said to have composed it one night at a camp-fire on the prairie to tease one of the boys, whose name was Joe Bowers. For reasons already discussed (*see* p. 307) the ballad became the hit of the plains, and the bull-whackers sang it all the way from the Missouri to the Rocky Mountains. John Woodward of Johnston's Minstrels toured the country with it; ballad singers in every part of the land and on both sides in the Civil War laughed over it. Joe Bowers, meantime, had passed in his checks in a California gold camp, and Sally had died of a broken heart back home in Missouri.

In 1904-5 my father found the ballad everywhere among cowboys and miners, and other collectors have discovered it in the East and Middle West. As late as the thirties, Sally's awful red-haired baby used to send audiences into fits of laughter, but, with changing customs and a relaxing of sexual tensions, the joke does not seem nearly so funny to us today, and the song is hardly ever sung. During the mauve decade, however, Joe Bowers was one of our national folk heroes, and in 1897 the Missouri Legislature 'rared back' and passed a resolution to erect a monument to him. The bill never came up for a vote. It is probably better so. Joe's ballad monument will outweather bronze.

175. LOUSY MINER

FEW OF THE THOUSANDS of gold seekers struck it rich. Most miners endured the discomforts of camp life for nothing, as this fragment of a miner's diary and the accompanying song set forth.

July 10th. We made $3.00 each today. This life of hardships and exposure has affected my health. Our diet consists of hard tack, flour we eat half cooked, and salt pork, with occasionally a salmon which we purchase from the Indians. Our feet are wet all day, while a hot sun shines down upon our heads. After our days of labor, exhausted and faint, we retire—if this word may be applied to the simple act of lying down in our clothes—robbing our feet of their boots to make a pillow of them, and wrapping our blankets about us. The feet and the hands of a novice in this business become blistered and lame, and the limbs are stiff. Besides all these causes of sickness, the anxieties and cares which wear away the lives of so many men who leave their families to come to this land of gold contribute, in no small degree, to the same result.

Disappointed California miners, however, had the habit of turning up at the new gold and silver strikes which kept the West in a fever of excitement for the next forty years. From Pike's Peak, Colorado, to Virginia City, Nevada, from Cripple Creek to the Black Hills, through mountains, canyons and deserts to the burning heart of Death Valley roamed these prospectors, their minds agleam with the tales of gold and silver kicked up by horses' hooves, thrown up by gophers, found in the gizzards of chickens, and even in the new-dug graves of trail-weary prospectors.

QUOTE: *Life in the Diggings*, Daniel B. Woods (1849).

176. THE DREARY BLACK HILLS

As THE UNION PACIFIC railway pushed its tracks west across the high plains in the years after the Civil War, it carried with it a floating town, called Julesberg, where the railroad roughnecks amused themselves with drink, women and games of chance. Every few weeks this so-called Hell-on-Wheels packed up its portable saloons and parlourhouses and rolled west, and the swarm of gamblers, barkeeps, fancy ladies, and bad men moved with it. When they came to the foothills of the Rockies in Wyoming and heard rumours of gold in the Black Hills, these pioneers of the plains decided to strike roots and found a permanent Hell. They christened it *Cheyenne*, after the fiercest of the Plains Indian tribes.

Colonel Dodge, the hard-boiled railroad engineer, who had seen a good deal of life, remarked, ' Hell must have been raked to furnish the inhabitants of Cheyenne, and to Hell they must naturally return after graduating here.' Thus encouraged, Cheyenne boomed. It had innumerable saloons, a theatre, a busy Boot Hill and an energetic vigilante committee. One early settler recalls with pride that the morning he arrived in town he found four men hanging from as many lamp-posts.

Cheyenne became one of the capitals of the western cattle business and when, in 1874, Custer reported that there were rich gold fields in the Black Hills, Cheyenne boomed again. As usual, the Westerners disregarded the government's treaty which guaranteed that the Black Hills and Yellowstone Country were to remain forever the hunting ground of the Indians. A good many prospectors were well-feathered with Indian arrows, and Sitting Bull's warriors scalped Custer and his men at the battle of the Little Big Horn, but no one in Cheyenne was much concerned so long as the Black Hills stage kept running, and thirsty miners filled their saloons.

I suspect this song was born in one of the roaring nights of Cheyenne's gold-boom when an entertainer in the guise of ' the orphan of the Dreary Black Hills ' stepped before the footlights. His whining complaint must have drawn howls of laughter from the bearded miners and, by reminding them of the fears they had conquered, it heartened them for fresh adventures in Sitting Bull's country. The song was first published in a broadside in San Francisco, attributed to an entertainer named Dick Brown.

177. THE REGULAR ARMY-O

We heard of Sioux Indians all out on the plains,
A-killing poor drivers and burning their trains,
A-killing poor drivers with arrow and bow,
When captured by Indians no mercy they'd show . . .

THUS SANG the men of the Oregon Trail, looking nervously over their shoulders into the mysterious dark of the prairies. Now armed with repeating rifles, the Plains Indians were more dangerous than ever. A veteran officer of the Indian wars said, ' That our cavalry can still contend with the Indians on anything like equal terms is its highest commendation, for the Indian is his superior in every soldier-like quality . . . '

The government then put a bounty on buffalo, and soon the plains were whitened by the bones of these herds which had been the chief food supply of the tribes. By the 1870's only 25,000 untamed tribesmen were left between the Missouri River and California. This handful of stone-age men, armed with rifles, held the whole of America at bay for twenty years. Their leaders were brilliant, intrepid, and hopelessly misinformed. Sitting Bull, believing that the men of Montana and Wyoming belonged to different tribes and that his massacre of Custer's two hundred and fifty men had ended the white power on the plains, sent the United States commanding general this magnificently arrogant note.

I want to know what you are doing traveling on this road. You scare the buffalo away. I want to hunt in this place. I want you to turn back from here. If you don't I will fight you again. I want you to leave what you have got and turn back from here. I am your friend.

SITTING BULL

Armed thus by ignorance and by their indomitable spirit, the western Indians continued their hopeless battle. Some tribes, such as the Navaho, never did surrender. In the case of the Apache, the whites sued for peace. This ballad tells how the Indian wars looked to an Irish lad, who stepped off the boat straight into the arms of a recruiting sergeant. In the grim desert mountains along the border of Mexico, the Apaches, under Cochise and Geronimo, taught him that there was more to fighting than fists and shillelaghs.

178. LULU

ALONG WITH *Shenandoah*, which recounts an unconventional voyageur love affair at the head-waters of the Wild Missourye, *Lulu* was the favourite song of the hard-riding, hard-drinking western cavalryman. Life in the far West was actually a good deal less Puritanical than Owen Wister, Zane Grey, and the movies have ever let us know. At a Utah Army post in 1855 every officer except the colonel kept a squaw, and the company doctor had three— a mother and two daughters, the mother to do the housework. *Lulu* belongs to this background. She was a girl who could hold down a job in a frontier dance hall and handle a derringer like a man. Like so many of the girls who followed the army camps, the gold fields and the cowcamps, she probably found the right man and settled down to make good as a wife and mother in some little town like Wink or Dry Gulch or Big Spring.

169. THE TEXAS RANGERS

FROM: p. 245 of *Our Singing Country*, Lomax (Macmillan, N.Y., 1941) as collected and arranged by Alan Lomax. SEE: Belden, 336; Flanders I, 226; Laws, 122; Lomax I, 359; Randolph II, 170. Song is related to Catnach broadside, *Nancy of Yarmouth*, became current about time of the Battle of the Alamo, 1835, and spread back north-east and east, so is now current among folk singers in New England and Southern Mountains.

Freely ♩=160

GUITAR– 4, 5A
BANJO– 1 or 2

Come all you Tex-as Ran-gers,____ wher-ev-er you may be, I hope you'll pay at-ten-tion and lis-ten un-to me, My name is noth-ing ex-try, the truth to you I'll tell, I____ am a rov-ing Ran-ger and I'm sure I wish you well.

1 Come all you Texas Rangers, wherever you may be,
I hope you'll pay attention and listen unto me,
My name is nothing extry, the truth to you I'll tell,
I am a roving Ranger and I'm sure I wish you well.

2 'Twas at the age of sixteen I joined this jolly band,
We marched from San Antonio unto the Rio Grande,
Our captain, he informed us, perhaps he thought it right,
' Before you reach the station, boys, I'm sure you'll have to fight.'

3 I saw the Injuns coming, I heard them give a yell,
My feelings at this moment no human tongue can tell,
I saw their glittering lances and their arrows round me flew,
And all my strength it left me and all my courage, too.

4 We fought full nine hours before the strife was o'er,
The like of dead and wounded I never saw before,
And when the sun was rising and the Indians they had fled,
We loaded up our rifles and counted up our dead.

5 Now all of us were wounded, our noble captain slain,
   The sun was shining sadly across the bloody plain,
   Sixteen brave Rangers as ever roamed the West,
   Were buried by their comrades with arrows in their breast.

6 'Twas then I thought of mother, who to me in tears did say,
   ' To you they are all strangers, with me you'd better stay.'
   I thought that she was childish and that she did not know,
   My mind was fixed on ranging and I was bound to go.

7 I have seen the fruits of rambling, I know its hardships well,
   I have crossed the Rocky Mountains, rode down the streets of Hell,
   I have been in the great Southwest, where wild Apaches roam,
   And I tell you from experience, you'd better stay at home.

170. GREEN GROWS THE LAUREL

From the singing of Robin Roberts of Utah. SEE: Belden, 490; Brown III, 328,
444; Guide and Index (*The Orange and Blue*); JEFFS XVIII 70 (*We'll Change the Green
Laurel to the Bonnet So Blue* as a Prince Charlie song); JEFFS I, 246, 570; Ord, 182;
Randolph I, 273-5; Sharp II, 211.

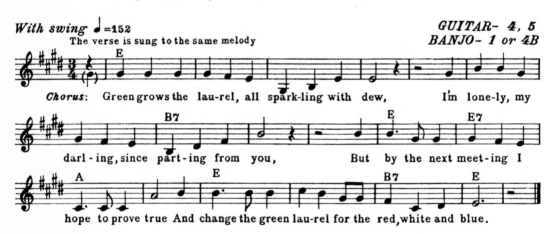

With swing ♩ =152   GUITAR— 4, 5
The verse is sung to the same melody   BANJO— 1 or 4B

Chorus: Green grows the lau-rel, all spark-ling with dew, I'm lone-ly, my
darl-ing, since part-ing from you, But by the next meet-ing I
hope to prove true And change the green lau-rel for the red, white and blue.

CHORUS:
Green grows the laurel, all sparkling with dew,
I'm lonely, my darling, since parting from you,
But by the next meeting I hope to prove true
And change the green laurel for the red, white and blue.

1 I once had a sweetheart but now I have none,
   Since she's gone and left me, I care not for none,
   Since she's gone and left me, contented I'll be,
   For she loves another one better than me. (CHO.)

332

2 I passed my love's window both early and late,
The look that she gave me would make your heart ache,
O the look that she gave me was painful to see,
For she loves another one better than me.   (CHO.)

3 I wrote my love letters in red rosy lines,
She wrote me an answer all twisted in twines,
Saying, ' Keep your love letters and I will keep mine,
Just you write to your love and I'll write to mine.'   (CHO.)

171. ROOT, HOG, OR DIE

Adapted and arranged by Alan Lomax from p. 430 of *American Ballads and Folk Songs*, Lomax (Macmillan, 1933). SEE: Belden, 334; Lomax I, 396.

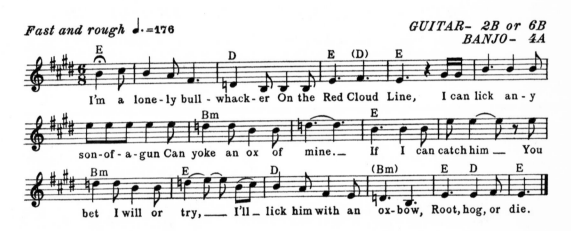

Fast and rough ♩.=176

GUITAR– *2B* or *6B*
BANJO– *4A*

I'm a lone-ly bull-whack-er On the Red Cloud Line, I can lick an-y son-of-a-gun Can yoke an ox of mine.— If I can catch him — You bet I will or try,— I'll — lick him with an ox-bow, Root, hog, or die.

1 I'm a lonely bull-whacker
On the Red Cloud Line,
I can lick any son-of-a-gun
Can yoke an ox of mine.
If I can catch him
You bet I will or try,
I'll lick with him an ox-bow,
Root, hog, or die.

2 Well, it's out upon the road
With a very heavy load,
With a very awkward team
And a very muddy road,
You may whip and you may holler,
If you cuss it's on the sly,
Then it's whack the cattle on, boys,
Root, hog, or die.

3 Now it's out upon the road
These sight are t'be seen,
The antelope and buffalo
The prairie all s'green,
The antelope and buffalo,
The rabbit jumps s' high,
Then it's whack the cattle on, boys,
Root, hog, or die.

4 Now every day at twelve
There's something for to do,
If there's nothing else,
There's a pony for to shoe;
I'll throw him down, boys,
Still I'll make him lie,
Little pig, big pig,
Root, hog, or die.

5 Now perhaps you'd like to know, boys,
  What we have to eat,
  A little piece of bread
  And a little dirty meat,
  A little black coffee
  And whisky on the sly,
  It's whack the cattle on, boys,
  Root, hog, or die.

6 There's hard times on Bitter Creek
  Never can be beat,
  It was root, hog, or die.
  Under every wagon sheet;
  We cleaned up all the Injuns,
  Drank all the alkali,
  And it's whack the cattle on, boys,
  Root, hog, or die.

7 There was good times in Salt Lake
  I never can pass by,
  That's where I met her,
  My China girl called Wi.
  She could smile, she could chuckle,
  She could roll her hog-eye,
  Then it's whack the cattle on, boys,
  Root, hog, or die.

8 O I'm a-goin' home
  Bull-whackin' for to spurn,
  I ain't got a nickel,
  And I don't give a durn.
  'Tis when I meet a purdy gal
  You bet I will or try,
  I'll whack her with my ox-bow,
  Root, hog, or die.

172. WHOA! HA! BUCK AND JERRY BOY

FROM: *Songs of the Mormons*, collected by Austin Fife, L.C. Album L 30, edited by
D. Emrich. Tune: *see Turkey in the Straw*, p. 95.

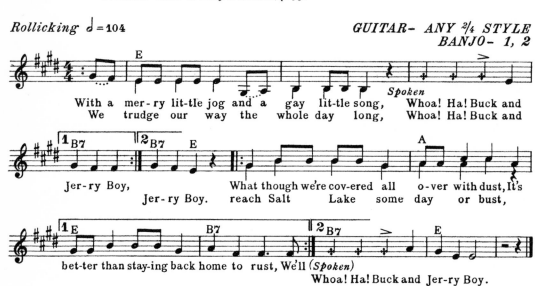

1 With a merry little jog and a gay little song,
    Whoa! Ha! Buck and Jerry Boy,
  We trudge our way the whole day long,
    Whoa! Ha! Buck and Jerry Boy.
  What though we're covered all over with dust,
  It's better than staying back home to rust,
  We'll reach Salt Lake some day or bust,
    Whoa! Ha! Buck and Jerry Boy.

2 There's a pretty little girl in the outfit ahead,
I wish she was by my side instead,
Look at her now with a pout on her lips,
As daintily with her fingertips
She picks for the fire some buffalo chips.

3 O tonight we'll dance by the light of the moon,
To the fiddler's best and only tune,
What though we're covered all over with dust,
It's better than staying back home to rust,
We'll reach Salt Lake some day or bust!

173. SWEET BETSY

FROM: p. 388 of *Cowboy Songs*, Lomax (Macmillan, N.Y., 1910, 1938) adapted by
Alan Lomax. As found by John A. Lomax in *Put's Golden Songster*, early 1900's.
The text never varies and it seems likely that it was spread by print. Set to that
ever-popular tune, *Villikens and His Dinah*. SEE: Belden, 343; Laws, 136.

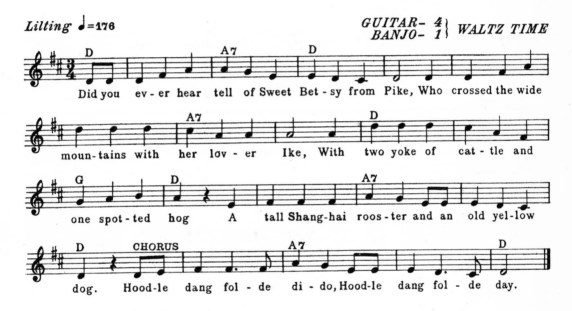

1 Did you ever hear tell of Sweet Betsy from Pike,
Who crossed the wide mountains with her lover Ike,
With two yoke of cattle and one spotted hog,
A tall Shanghai rooster and an old yellow dog.
CHORUS:
Hoodle dang fol-de di-do, hoodle dang fol-de day.

2 They swam the wide rivers and climbed the tall peaks
And camped on the prairies for weeks upon weeks,
Starvation and cholera, hard work and slaughter,
They reached California spite of hell and high water. (CHO.)

3 The Injuns come down in a wild yelling horde
And Betsy got skeered they would scalp her adored,
So behind the front wagon-wheel Betsy did crawl,
And fought off the Injuns with musket and ball.   (CHO.)

4 They camped on the prairie one bright, starry night,
They broke out the whisky and Betsy got tight,
She sang and she shouted and romped o'er the plain
And showed her bare bum to the whole wagon train.   (CHO.)

5 The wagon tipped over with a terrible crash
And out on the prairie rolled all sorts of trash,
A few little baby clothes, done up with care,
Looked rather suspicious, but 'twas all on the square.   (CHO.)

6 Sweet Betsy got up with a great deal of pain
And declared she'd go back to Pike County again,
Then Ike heaved a sigh and they fondly embraced,
And she travelled along with his arm round her waist.   (CHO.)

7 They passed the Sierras through mountains of snow,
Till old California was sighted below.
Sweet Betsy she hollered, and Ike gave a cheer,
'Saying, Betsy, my darlin', I'm a made millioneer.'   (CHO.)

8 A miner said, 'Betsy, will you dance with me?'
'I will that, old hoss, if you don't make too free.
But don't dance me hard, do you want to know why?
Doggon ye, I'm chock full of strong alkali.'   (CHO.)

9 Long Ike and Sweet Betsy got married, of course,
But Ike, who was jealous, obtained a divorce,
And Betsy, well satisfied, said with a smile,
'I've six good men waitin' within half a mile.'   (CHO.)

174. JOE BOWERS

FROM: *Texas Folk Songs*, William Owen (Texas Folklore Society).   Used by permission.   SEE: Belden, 341; Laws, 139; Lomax I, 375; Randolph II, 191.
Piano arrangement by MATYAS SEIBER

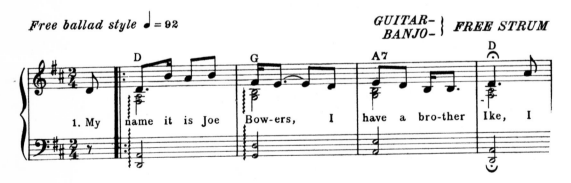

come from old Mis-sour-i, yes, all the way from Pike, I used to court a

pret-ty girl by the name of Sal-ly Black, I asked her to

mar-ry me, she said it was a whack. 2. But says
(Fine)

1 My name it is Joe Bowers, I have a brother Ike,
I come from old Missouri, yes, all the way from Pike,
I used to court a pretty girl by the name of Sally Black,
I asked her to marry me, she said it was a whack.

2 But says she to me, ' Joe Bowers, before we hitch for life,
You'd better get a little home to keep your little wife.'
I said, ' Sally, oh Sally, it's all for your sake,
I'll go out to California and try to raise a stake.'

3 At length I went to mining, put in my biggest licks,
Fell down upon the shining, just like a thousand bricks,
I worked both late and early, in rainstorm and snow,
It was all for my sweet Sally's sake, 'twas all the same to Joe.

4 At length there came a letter, it was from my brother Ike,
It came from old Missouri, yes, all the way from Pike,
It brought me the goldarnest news that you did ever hear,
My heart is almost busted, so please excuse a tear.

5 It said my Sal was false to me, her love for me had fled,
  She'd married a goldurn butcher, and the fellow's hair was red,
  And, readin' on, the letter said—it's enough to make me swear—
  That Sally had a baby, and the baby had red hair.

6 And now I've sung you quite enough about this durned affair,
  'Bout Sally and the butcher and the baby with red hair,
  Whether it was a boy or gal child the letter never said;
  It only said the durned thing's hair was inclined to be red!

175. LOUSY MINER

FROM: p. 24 of *Gold Rush Song Book*, Eleanora Black and Sidney Robertson (Colt Press, San Francisco, 1940). SEE: Botkin II, 863. Text comes from *Put's Golden Songster*. Tune is *Dark-Eyed Sailor*, a ballad popular in N.E.; known in England as *Fair Phoebe and Her Dark-Eyed Sailor*.

1 It's four long years since I reached this land
  In search of gold among the rocks and sand,
  And yet I'm poor when the truth is told,
  I'm a lousy miner,
  I'm a lousy miner in search of shining gold.

2 I've lived on swine till I grunt and squeal,
  No one can tell how my bowels feel
  With flapjacks a-swimming round in grease,
  I'm a lousy miner,
  I'm a lousy miner, when will my troubles cease?

3 I was covered with lice coming on the boat,
  I threw away my fancy swallow-tailed coat,
  And now they crawl up and down my back,
  I'm a lousy miner,
  I'm a lousy miner, a pile is all I lack.

4 My sweetheart vowed she'd wait for me,
  Till I returned, but don't you see?
  She's married now, so I am told,
  Left her lousy miner,
  Left her lousy miner in search of shining gold.

5 O land of gold, you did me deceive,
  And I intend you my bones to leave,
  So farewell home, now my friends grow cold,
  I'm a lousy miner,
  I'm a lousy miner, in search of shining gold.

176. THE DREARY BLACK HILLS

FROM p. 372 of *Cowboy Songs*, Lomax (Macmillan, N.Y., 1910, 1938). SEE: Belden, 349; Flanders I, 108; Laws, 263. Song has been found through West, and in Pa., Wyo., and Mo.

1 Kind friends, you must pity my horrible tale,
   I'm an object of pity, I'm looking quite stale,
   I gave up my trade, selling Right's Patent Pills,
   To go hunting gold in the dreary Black Hills.
   CHORUS:
   Don't go away, stay at home if you can,
   Stay away from that city, they call it Cheyenne,
   For big Wallipee* or Comanche Bills,
   They will lift up your hair on the Dreary Black Hills.

2 The roundhouse in Cheyenne is filled every night,
   With loafers and bummers of most every plight,
   On their backs is no clothes, in their pockets, no bills,
   Each day they keep starting for the Dreary Black Hills.   (CHO.)

3 One morning so early, one morning in May,
   I met Kit Carson a-goin' away,
   He was goin' away with Buffalo Bill,
   He was goin' a-minin' in the Dreary Black Hills.   (CHO.)

* Or ' Old Sitting Bull '.

339

4 I got to Cheyenne, no gold could I find,
   I thought of the lunch route I'd left far behind,
   Through rain, hail and snow, frozen plumb to the gills,
   They call me the orphan of the Dreary Black Hills. (CHO.)

5 Oh, I wish the man that started this sell,
   Was a captive, and Crazy Horse had him in Hell,
   There's no use of grieving or swearing like pitch,
   But the man that would stay here is a son-of-a-gun. (CHO.)

177. THE REGULAR ARMY-O

FROM: *Sound Off*, E. A. Dolph (Farrar & Rinehart, 1942), p. 6. Used by permission.

Lilting ♩.=120

GUITAR— 2B, 6B
BANJO— 4A

Three years a-go this ve-ry day I went to Gov-er-nor's Isle__ To stand for-ninst the can-non in true mil-i-tar-y style,__ Thir-teen A-mer-i-can dol-lars each month we'd sure-ly get To car-ry a gun and bay-o-net with a mil-i-tar-y step.__ There's Ser-geant John Mc-Caf-fer-ty and Cor-poral Don-a-hue,__ They make us march up to the crack in

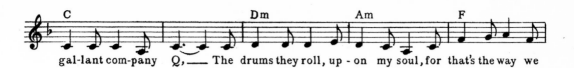

gal-lant com-pany Q,—— The drums they roll, up - on my soul, for that's the way we

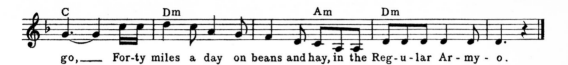

go,—— For-ty miles a day on beans and hay, in the Reg-u-lar Ar-my - o.

1 Three years ago this very day I went to Governor's Isle
To stand forninst the cannon in true military style,
Thirteen American dollars each mouth we'd surely get
To carry a gun and bayonet with a military step.
CHORUS:
There's Sergeant John McCafferty and Corporal Donahue,
They make us march up to the crack in gallant company Q,
The drums they roll, upon my soul, for that's the way we go,
Forty miles a day on beans and hay, in the Regular Army-o.

2 We had our choice of going to the army or the jail,
Or it's up the Hudson River with a copper take a sail,
So we puckered up our courage and with bravery did go,
And we cursed the day we marched away with the Regular Army-o. (CHO.)

3 When we went out to Fort Hobo they run us in the mill,
And there they made us take a bath, 'twas sure against our will,
With three full meals within our belts, each day we had our fill,
And we sat upon the dump cart and watched the tarriers drill. (CHO.)

4 There's corns upon me feet, me boys, and bunions on me toes,
And lugging a gun in the red-hot sun puts freckles on me nose,
And if you want a furlough, to the captain you do go.
He says, ' Go to bed and wait till you're dead in the Regular Army-o.' (CHO.)

5 We went to Arizona for to fight the Indians there,
We were nearly caught bald-headed, but they didn't get our hair,
We lay among the ditches in the dirty yellow mud,
And we never saw an on-i-on, a turnip, or a spud. (CHO.)

6 We were captured by the Indians and brought forninst the chafe.
Says he, ' We'll have an Irish stew,' the dirty Indian thafe!
But on the telegraphic wire we skipped to Mexico,
And we blessed the day we marched away from the Regular Army-o! (CHO.)

178. LULU

FROM : p. 263 of *Cowboy Songs*, Lomax (Macmillan, N.Y., 1910, 1938).

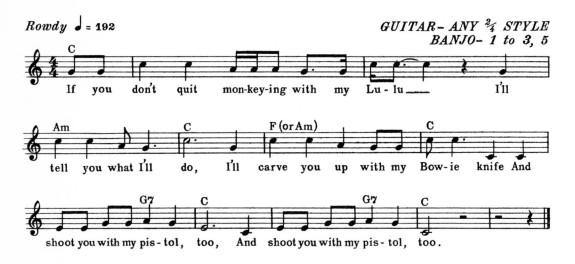

Rowdy ♩ = 192

GUITAR— ANY ²⁄₄ STYLE
BANJO— 1 to 3, 5

If you don't quit mon-key-ing with my Lu-lu___ I'll tell you what I'll do, I'll carve you up with my Bow-ie knife And shoot you with my pis-tol, too, And shoot you with my pis-tol, too.

1 If you don't quit monkeying with my Lulu
   I'll tell you what I'll do,
   I'll carve you up with my Bowie knife
   And shoot you with my pistol, too. (2)

2 My Lulu hugged and kissed me,
   She wrung her hands and cried,
   She said I was the sweetest thing
   That ever lived or died. (2)

3 My Lulu she's a dandy,
   She stands and drinks like a man,
   She calls for gin and brandy,
   And she don't give a damn. (2)

4 I seen my Lulu in the springtime,
   I seen her in the fall.
   She wrote me a letter in the winter-time,
   Says, ' Goodbye, honey '—that's all. (2)

5 I ain't gonna work on the railroad,
   I ain't gonna lie in jail,
   I'm goin' down to Cheyenne town
   To live with my Lulu gal. (2)

6 My Lulu had a baby,
   'Twas born on Christmas Day,
   She washed its face in brandy
   And called it Henry Clay. (2)

7 Lulu had twin babies,
   Born on Christmas Day,
   She mashed one's head with a rollin' pin,
   The other one got away. (2)

SOLDIERS AND RENEGADES

179. CHARLIE QUANTRELL

IN THE 'FIFTIES the West, indeed the whole nation, split over the issue of whether slavery ought to be extended into Kansas and Nebraska. Guerilla war broke out on the prairies and continued for a decade. Two folk heroes emerge from this period—one, the noble and fantastic John Brown, whose soul still marches on—the other, a lynx-eyed, handsome night-rider named Charlie Quantrell. The kind of story you hear about Quantrell depends upon the regional bias of the teller. To Missouri Confederates he was a noble patriot; to Kansas abolitionists he was an arsonist and a sadistic killer. Maryland-born, he and his brother came to the Missouri country when Kansas was still a territory. There, say his friends, a band of thirty abolitionist ' red-legs ' ambushed the Quantrells, killed his brother, and left Charlie for dead. When he had recovered from his wounds, Quantrell slipped into Lawrence, Kansas, the abolitionist stronghold, discovered the identity of his brother's murderers, and vowed vengeance on them.

Yankee historians bring Quantrell on the scene as a bandit who hung about Independence, preying on the California emigrants. Whatever his incentive, he became the most notable leader in the guerilla warfare of the West. His band of bush-whackers, which included the James and Younger boys, harrassed the Union Army and terrorized the Kansas abolitionists until, in desperation, Federal troops seized the female relatives of the best known night-riders and held them as hostages in Kansas City. One day the jail building collapsed, killing and wounding some of these women, and Quantrell played upon this incident to inflame his undisciplined freebooters. Descending by night from their hideout in the Missouri hills, they took Lawrence by surprise, burnt the town and killed a hundred and fifty civilians. Quantrell afterwards swore that he had accounted personally for twenty-eight of his brother's murderers.

Quantrell refused to surrender when the South laid down her arms. He disappeared, some say to die by an assassin's hand in Kentucky. But piney woods folks believe that Quantrell hid out in East Texas and was the brains behind the James and the Youngers, who were never bandits, but loyal Confederates, seizing Federal funds so that Quantrell could finance the re-opening of the war!

The Quantrell ballad shows how folk-song can completely triumph over history. The composer made Quantrell the hero of the Irish outlaw ballad, *Brennan on the Moor*, changing the Irish text so little that the western badman uses a blunderbuss and steals five thousand pounds!

343

180. THE BRASS MOUNTED ARMY

IRVIN WILEY, in his *Plain People of the Confederacy*, gives a vivid picture of the conditions which produced this Missouri soldier's song. The majority of Confederate soldiers were poor whites who owned no slaves and whose lack of education and social position condemned them to march in the rear ranks. Accustomed to the free, lazy life of the backwoods, they hated military discipline and loathed the ' fuss and feathers ' of the upper-class officers who often behaved as if they were characters out of a novel by Sir Walter Scott. The privates of one outfit seized their pompous colonel and rode him through camp on a rail until he promised to be more civil to them.

It riled these frontiersmen, accustomed to the democratic drinking habits of the frontier, to see their officers guzzle whisky while they themselves went dry. Somehow they set up mobile stills and manufactured liquor, lovingly termed Tanglefoot, Red Eye, Bust Skull, or Rock Me to Sleep, Mother. The Chaplains moaned, ' Drunkenness is so common among our troops as not to excite comment.'

The hungry army became a plague to southern farmers, but where protests by the big planters brought disciplinary action, the foragers continued to prey upon the small farmers without punishment. This further evidence of favouritism soured Johnny Reb, who already felt that it was a rich man's war. ' How can we go into battle,' wrote one private, ' and fight to keep the enemy back off the rich man, who, because he owns twenty Negroes, is permitted to stay at home with his family and save his grain, but the poor man must suffer in the army for something to eat, while his family suffers at home . . .'

For these and other causes, more than a hundred thousand men deserted from the Confederate Army before the war's end. Even so, rebel fighting morale remained high. The troops marched ragged and barefoot, but joked about their hardships. ' In our outfit, a man with one hole in his pants is a captain; two holes, a lieutenant; and the one with no seat in his breeches is a private . . .'

QUOTE: *Plain People of the Confederacy*, Bell Irvin Wiley (La. State University Press, 1943).

181. THE BATTLE ON SHILOH'S HILL

BEFORE THE BATTLE, *Shiloh* was the name of a little log chapel lost in the woods on the western side of the Tennessee River on the border of Mississippi. Two days later it had become a word of horror both north and south, as the scene of the bloodiest battle that ever took place on the North American continent. Six thousand men had been killed and twice that number wounded.

The folks at home trembled for their loved ones as they read the news stories . . .

As I sit tonight writing this epistle, the dead and wounded are all around me. The knife of the surgeon is busy at work, and amputated legs and arms lie scattered in every direction. The cries of the suffering victims and the groans of those who patiently wait for medical attention are most distressing to anyone who has any sympathy with his fellow men. All day long they have been coming in, and they are placed upon the decks and within the cabins of the steamers, and wherever else they can find a resting place. I hope my eyes may never again look upon such sights . . .

This Missouri folk singer's report of the battle reflects the terror of the scene. It is impossible to say whether the composer was a northern or southern sympathizer. The bloody field of Shiloh reminded the whole nation that in war no one is ever really the victor.

QUOTE: *The North Reports the Civil War*, J. Cutler Andrews (University of Pittsburgh Press, 1955), p. 175.

182. COLE YOUNGER

TEDDY BLUE, in his rowdy and delightful book of cowboy reminiscences, *We Pointed Them North*, remarks that the Civil War was the principal cause of western gunfights.

> The Texans and the Missourians was on the side of the South, and oh, but they were bitter. That was how a lot of them got killed, because they were filled full of that old dope about the war and they wouldn't let an abolitionist arrest them. The marshalls in those cow towns on the trail were usually Northern men, and the Southerners wouldn't go back to Texas and hear people say, ' He's a hell of a fellow. He let a Yankee lock him up.' Down home, one Texas Ranger could arrest the lot of them, but up North you'd have to kill them . . .

If the Texas cowboys were bitter, the Ozark bush-whackers were vengeful and vindictive. Most of them considered that they had never been whipped. When Quantrell's night-riders, professional gunmen such as Clay Allison and hundreds of touchy, trigger-happy Texas cowboys, rode into abolitionist towns like Abilene and Dodge City, all hell broke loose. The peaceful citizens then called in the pistoleers who had fought on the Union side—men like Wyatt Earp, Bat Masterson, Billy Tilighman and Pat Sugrue, who never went for their guns unless they were shooting to kill. Wild Bill Hickock, the most spectacular of these cowtown marshalls, had served as a scout for the union army, fought equally well with his fists or his six-guns and was never whipped in any sort of scrap. He did not know, himself, how many men he had killed. Once he shot two men simultaneously, one coming in the front door of a saloon and the other, who was gunning for him through the back door, with a mirror shot over his shoulder. Wild Bill soon tamed Abilene, and the other marshalls, calling on the assistance of Judge Lynch, sobered up the Texas cowpunchers in other western towns. The Missouri gangs, however, presented another problem.

The James boys, the Youngers, and the Daltons, who had ridden with Quantrell, had no interest in making a ' rep '. They were out after money, and they felt that the banks and the railroads, as northern enterprises, were fair game. Many disgruntled southern Democrats of Missouri sympathized; others were afraid to talk; and the tangle of the Ozarks provided perfect hide-out country. With their companions, the Youngers, the James boys robbed, ran, and marauded successfully for more than a decade, perfecting a technique for train robbery and bank-busting that was still being practised by John Dillinger, Pretty Boy Floyd, and Clyde Barrow as late as the 1930's.

QUOTE: *We Pointed Them North*, E. C. Abbott ('Teddy Blue') and H. H. Smith (University of Oklahoma Press, 1954). Reprinted by permission of Mrs. H. H. Smith.

183. JESSE JAMES

THE JAMES BOYS were brought to trial several times in the state of Missouri, but the courts, influenced by the strong pressure of Jesse's Democratic friends and by the sight of the heavily armed bravos in the courtroom, kept dismissing the cases.

Jesse James led a charmed life, until one day, without reason, he brutally tortured a member of the Ford connexion. Robert Ford, one of Jesse's trusted gunmen, swore vengeance. He received a secret promise from the Governor of Missouri that his life would be spared if he assassinated the outlaw. He then paid a friendly visit to James, who was living under the alias of Howard in a little clapboard house in St. Joseph, Missouri.

Jesse wore his two six-guns at all times, but one day, when he wished to dust a picture in his front parlour, he took off his gun-belt and turned his back on his traitorous friend. Ford cocked his pistol and, though the outlaw heard the sound and made as if to turn, he was too late. Ford's bullet crashed into the back of his skull and Jesse James fell dead. Ford was acquitted of the murder, collected the $10,000 reward, and hastily left Missouri, while Jesse's friends mourned and respectable Missourians breathed easier.

Soon after the killing of James a ten foot poem set to music came out and was sung on the streets of Springfield quite frequently. It caused many tears to be shed; it was Mark Anthony at the bier of Caesar. An old blind woman used to stand in front of the court-house in Springfield and sing it by the hour. Mourners would drop coins in her tin can. She went up to Richmond, Missouri, and was singing her sad song with tears in her voice when she found herself slapped and knocked into the middle of the street. Bob Ford's sister happened to be passing that way . . .' (From the *Missouri Leader*, October 18, 1933 . . .)

This story explains why no one has ever been able to discover or, perhaps, ever dared to reveal the identity of Billy Gashade, the anonymous composer of the James ballad. Certainly, he was one of the most successful propagandists on record, for the ballad quickly spread to every part of the United States, and caused Jesse's crimes to be forgotten, and only his generosity and his betrayal to be remembered. Possibly the ballad helped to bring about the final act in the tragedy, for although Ford changed his name and took work in an obscure gambling-house in Creede, Colorado, he was shot down there by an unknown assassin.

179. CHARLIE QUANTRELL

FROM: p. 144 of *Cowboy Songs*, Lomax (Macmillan, N.Y., 1910, 1938). A new ballad using *Brennan on the Moor* as model. SEE: Creighton II, 232; Lomax IV.

1 It is of a fearless highwayman, a story I will tell,
   His name was Charlie Quantrell and in Kansas he did dwell;
   It was on the Nebraska prairies he commenced his wild career,
   And many wealthy gentlemen before him stood with fear.
   CHORUS:
   Charlie Quantrell-o, Charlie Quantrell-o,
   O bold, gay, and daring stood old Charlie Quantrell-o.

2 A brace of loaded pistols he carried both night and day,
   Though he never robbed a poor man while out on the highway,
   But what he taken from the rich, like toffs and like best,
   He always did divide it with the widows in distress. (CHO.)

3 As Charles went out to walk one day, 'twas early on one morn,
   He met the Mayor of Casmeyer, just outside of town.
   Now the Mayor knew his features. 'Your name,' he said, 'must be,
   Yes, your name is Charlie Quantrell, you must come along with me.' (CHO.)

4 Now Charles's wife to town had gone, provisions for to buy,
   When she saw her Charlie taken, she began to weep and cry.
   'O I wish I had a dollar,' he says, no sooner had he spoke,
   Than she handed him a blunderbuss from underneath her coat. (CHO.)

347

5 Now with his loaded blunderbuss, the truth it must be told,
It caused the mayor to tremble and it robbed him of his gold,
Five thousand pound were there laid down, and then pre-empted there,
And with his horse and saddle to the mountains did repair.   (CHO.)

6 Now Charlie, being an outlaw, upon the mountains high,
With infantry and cavalry to take him they did try,
But he hid among the brush that grew upon the field
And received nine dreadful wounds before that he would yield.   (CHO.)

7 It was at a little prairie, a place they call Lamar,
Where Charlie and his comrades were forced to suffer sore.
The jury found them guilty and the judge gave this reply,—
' For robbing on the highway you are condemned to die.'   (CHO.)

8 ' Now farewell, dear wife and my little children three,
And you, my aged father, who sheds tears for me,
And likewise my dear old mother,' who tore her hair and cried,
Saying, ' It were better, Charlie, in your cradle you had died.'   (CHO.)

180. THE BRASS MOUNTED ARMY

FROM: p. 273 of *Ozark Folk Songs*, Vance Randolph, Vol. II. Used by permission.

1 O whisky is the monster that ruins great an'
                                        small,
But in old Kirby's army, Headquarters gets it all.
CHORUS:
O how do you like the army?
The brass mounted army,
The high-falutin' army,
Where eagle buttons rule.

2 They drink it when it's plenty,
Although they think it hard,
But if a private touches it,
They put him under guard.   (CHO.)

3 Our army is more richer
Than when the war begun,
Furnishes three tables,
An' then they set but one.   (CHO.)

4 The first is richly laden
Of chicken, goose an' duck,
The next is pork an' mutton,
The third is pore old buck.   (CHO.)

5 Our generals eat the poultry,
They git it very cheap,
Our colonels and our captains
Devours the hogs and sheep.   (CHO.)

6 Our soldiers git so hungry
They're bound to press a pig,
The biggest stump in Dixie
They're sure to have a dig.   (CHO.)

7 On every big plantation
Or a big holder's yard,
Just to save his property
Our generals place a guard.   (CHO.)

8 An' now my song is ended
It's beautiful and true,
The pore men and the widders
Must have a line or two.   (CHO.)

9 For there no guard is stationed,
Their fence is often burned,
Their property's molested,
As long ago we learned.   (CHO.)

181. THE BATTLE ON SHILOH'S HILL

FROM: p. 273 of *Ozark Folk Songs*, Vance Randolph, Vol. II. Used by permission.

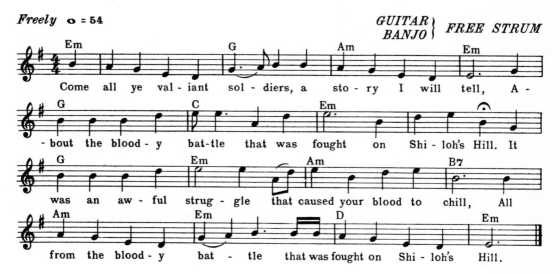

1 Come all ye valiant soldiers, a story I will tell,
About the bloody battle that was fought on Shiloh's Hill.
It was an awful struggle that caused your blood to chill,
All from the bloody battle that was fought on Shiloh's Hill.

2 'Twas on the sixth of April, about the break of day,
The drums an' fifes was playin' for us to march away,
My feelin's at that moment I do remember still,
When first my feet was trompin' on the top of Shiloh's Hill.

3 About the hour of sunrise the battle first began,
Before the day was ended we fought 'em hand to hand,
The horrors of that battle did my soul with anguish fill,
The wounded men and dyin' all laid on Shiloh's Hill.

349

4 They was men from every nation laid on them bloody plains,
They was fathers, sons and brothers all numbered with the slain,
The wounded men was cryin' for help from everywhere,
An' others was a-dyin' an' offerin' God their prayer.

5 Very early the next mornin' we was called to arms again,
Unmindful of the wounded, unuseful to the slain,
The battle was renewed agin, ten thousand men was killed,
An' from their deadly wounds the blood ran like a rill.

6 An' now my song is ended about them bloody plains,
I hope the sight to mortal man may ne'er be seen again,
I'll pray to God my Saviour, consistent with His will,
To save the souls of them brave men who fell on Shiloh's Hill.

182. COLE YOUNGER

As sung by Edward L. Crain, American Folk Music, Folkways Disc, No. 15. Apparently Crain learned song word for word from the original edition of *Cowboy Songs*, p. 106, and set his own tune. SEE: Laws, 171; Lomax I (1910 Edition), 106; Randolph II, 14.

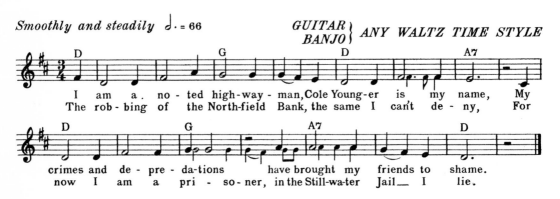

1 I am a noted highwayman, Cole Younger is my name,
My crimes and depredations have brought my friends to shame.
The robbing of the Northfield Bank, the same I can't deny,
For now I am a prisoner, in the Stillwater Jail I lie.

2 'Tis of a bold high robbery, a story I will tell,
Of a California miner who unto us fell,
We robbed him of his money and bid him go his way,
For which I will be sorry until my dying day.

3 And then we started homeward, when Brother Bob did say,
' Now, Cole, we'll buy fast horses and on them ride away;
We'll ride to avenge our father's death and try to win the prize,
We'll fight those anti-guerillas until the day we die.'

350

4 And then we rode towards Texas, that good old Lone Star state,
But on Nebraska's prairies the James boys we did meet,
With knives and guns and pistols we all sat down to play,
A-drinkin' of good whisky, boys, to pass the time away.

5 A Union Pacific railway train was the next we did surprise,
And the crimes done by our bloody hands bring tears into my eyes,
The engineer and the fireman killed, the conductor escaped alive,
And now their bones lie mouldering beneath Nebraska's skies.

6 Then we saddled horses, north-westward we did go,
To the God-forsaken country called Minnesot-i-o,
I had my eye on the Northfield Bank, when brother Bob did say,
' Now Cole, if you undertake the job, you'll surely rue the day.'

7 But I stationed out my pickets and up to the bank did go,
And there upon the counter I struck my fatal blow.
' Just hand us over your money and make no further delay,
We are the famous Younger boys, we spend no time in play.'

8 The cashier, being as true as steel, refused our noted band,
'Twas Jesse James that pulled the trigger that killed this noble man.
We run for life, for death was near, four hundred on our trail,
We soon were overtaken, and landed safe in jail.

9 I am a noted highwayman, Cole Younger is my name,
My crimes and depredations have brought my name to shame,
And now in the Stillwater Jail I lie, a-wearin' my life away,
Two James boys live to tell the tale of that sad and fatal day.

183. JESSE JAMES

From singing of B. L. Lunsford, L. C. Record 97B1, collected by A. Moser.
SEE: Belden, 401; Laws, 170; Lomax I, 152-8; Randolph II, 18. Song was
composed immediately after James was shot, 1882. Spread rapidly and widely
and folk variants have been collected throughout Mid-West, West, and South.
The air of this version is from the Smoky Mountains.

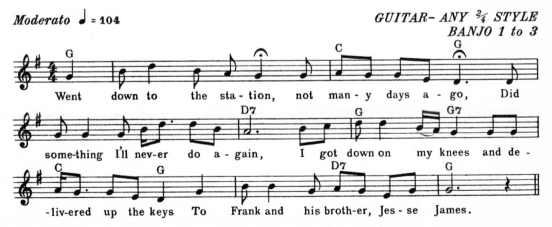

Moderato ♩ = 104

GUITAR– ANY ²⁄₄ STYLE
BANJO 1 to 3

Went down to the sta - tion, not man - y days a - go, Did
some-thing I'll nev-er do a - gain, I got down on my knees and de-
-liv-ered up the keys To Frank and his broth-er, Jes - se James.

CHORUS

Poor__ Jes-se, good-bye, Jes-se, Fare-well,__ Jes - se James, Ro-bert
Ford caught his eye and he shot him on the sly And he laid poor Jes-se down to die.

1 Went down to the station, not many days ago,
   Did something I'll never do again,
   I got down on my knees and delivered up the keys
   To Frank and his brother, Jesse James.
   CHORUS 1:
   Poor Jesse, good-bye, Jesse,
   Farewell, Jesse James,
   Robert Ford caught his eye and he shot him on the sly,
   And he laid poor Jesse down to die.

2 O Jesse was a man and friend to the poor,
   He would never see a man suffer pain,
   But with his brother Frank, he robbed the Chicago Bank,
   And he stopped the Glendale train.   (CHO.)

3 O the people in the west, when they heard of Jesse's death,
   They wondered how he came to die.
   It was Ford's pistol ball brought him tumbling from the wall,
   And it laid poor Jesse down to die.
   CHORUS 2:
   O Jesse leaves a wife, she's a mourner all her life,
   And the children, they were brave,
   But the dirty little coward, he shot Mister Howard,
   And he laid poor Jesse in his grave.

4 Now Jesse goes to rest with his hands upon his breast,
   And the devil will be upon his knees,
   He was born one day in the county of Clay,
   And he came from a solitary race.   (CHO. 1 and 2)

5 This song it was made by Billy Gashade,
   As soon as the news did arrive,
   He said there was no man with the law in his hand
   Who could take Jesse James when alive   (CHO. 1 and 2)

COWBOYS

184. WAKE UP, JACOB

THE SHRILL YELL of the camp cook woke post-Civil War Texans to the realization that they were potential millionaires. Their longhorn cattle, left to run wild in the brush of South Texas, had multiplied until they threatened to be a pest. Meantime, the skyrocketing population of the East and the reservation Indians needed ' beef, heap beef '. The steer that was worth five dollars in Texas (if anybody owned him) would fetch fifty dollars on the eastern markets. Texas cattlemen, impoverished by four years of war, took out their stub pencils and figured. Five million cattle roamed the mesquite and chapparel thickets south of San Antonio. Delivered at the railheads, these vast herds would bring something like two hundred million dollars. The Texans promptly disappeared in the brush and began branding cattle. A new era in the West had begun.

185. THE RAILROAD CORRAL

THE GREAT BREEDING-GROUND of the longhorn, the mustang, and the cowboy lay in the V-shaped tip of Southern Texas south of San Antonio—a low-lying, sub-tropical plain in which every bush carried a thorn and every beast wore horns or a stinger. The Mexicans had run ranches in this country until the gringos won the war in 1848. In the years that followed, Texas cowboys adopted the Mexican vaquero's costume, acquired his savvy of cattle and horses, and stole his herds, but, because there was little market, the longhorns continued to run wild in the brush. Spawn of fighting bulls of Spain, grown savage in their fight for survival, and armed with an eight- to twelve-foot spread of needle-pointed horns, they were by far the most dangerous animals in that savage country. A longhorn bull once charged the American army and scattered several companies like chaff.

Roping one of these critters in the brush required nerves of rawhide. The longhorns could run like deer. They hid in small bunches in the jungles of cactus, mesquite, black locust and yucca, into which a movie cowboy couldn't even crawl. The Texas cowhunter had to run his horse through this hellish thicket, ducking and dodging, until his loop snaked out and stopped the longhorn, throwing him hard enough to stun him. At the branding fire, the punchers got kicked so often and so fast that ' it looked like the critters were all feet '.

Yet these stubborn animals performed magnificently on the trail. Steel-hoofed, rangy, inured to every hardship, they ' could walk to Hell and back again '. The swiftest rivers, the highest mountains, the driest deserts never daunted them. After three or four months on the trail, through broiling heat or blizzard, they strode proudly into their northern pastures, fatter than when they left Texas.

In the spring of 1866, herds totalling 250,000 cattle crossed the Red River, bound north-west for the nearest railhead at Sedalia, Missouri (where ragtime originated). But the Texans had counted without the Ozark roughnecks. Now that the Civil War was over, these bush-whackers were unemployed and hungry. They charged down out of their hills upon the Texan herds, stampeded the cattle, and in some cases lynched the cow-punchers. That ended trail driving eastward towards St. Louis.

The few herds that set out from South Texas next year headed straight north across the flat plains, where the trailing was easy, without knowing where they would end up. An Illinois cattle buyer named J. J. McCoy saw the solution to the problem. He sought for help from the officials of the *Kansas Pacific* which made connexions between Kansas and Chicago. Their decision to help McCoy build a cattle shipping station on the K.P. Railroad was to make Chicago the ' cow and hog butcher to the world '.

For his shipping terminus McCoy chose Abilene, Kansas, which at the time was , a small dead place, consisting of about one dozen log huts and the inevitable saloon '. He sent his riders out into the plains to contact the longhorn herds that were straggling north-ward, while he put the townsfolk to work building cattle pens. When the first herds rolled into Abilene, the Kansans drove them down the main-street, six-guns firing and cowboy hats sailing into the blue Kansas sky. The boom was on. In the next five years a million and a half head of Texas cattle were shipped out of Abilene, and Wild Bill Hickock, the most deadly gunman in the West, had to be appointed city marshall to keep order among the whisky-happy cowboys in its saloon. By 1880 the Texans had shipped five million cattle to market from Kansas railheads, and trailed another five million north to stock the vast western ranges.

186. I'M BOUND TO FOLLOW THE LONGHORN COWS

' Ma ', said the nester girl, ' do cowboys eat grass ? '
' No, honey, ' said the nester lady, ' they're part human. '

ROSS SANTEE tells how a cowpuncher's career began . . .

I always wanted to be a cowpuncher. When I was a little kid on the farm in East Texas, I couldn't think of nothin' else. Most kids, I guess, is that-away, but they never could knock the idea out of me. That was all farmin' country, even then. But once in a while someone would drive a bunch of cattle by our place. I couldn't have been more'n eight years old when I followed one bunch off. It didn't make any difference to me that I was the only one afoot. I had a long stick, an' was busier than a bird dog, drivin' drags. I had an uncle livin' down the road about four miles. He happened to see me goin' by his place.

' Whatcha doin', kid?'

' A-workin' stock,' says I.

He finally talked me into going back home with him . . . and I stuck it out till I got to be fifteen. Then I pulled out for good. I've never been home since . . .

Thus, thousands of spirited American boys thumbed their noses at home, mother, the church and respectability, escaped hypocritical and repressive Victorian America, and rode off to live in the unbuttoned, free-and-easy, masculine world of the cattle range. There, the old, simple code of the frontier prevailed. A cowboy was respected for his skill on the job and his loyalty and generosity to his friends, his toughness and his courage. He was better liked if he had a good sense of humour and knew how to crack a joke and sing a song. He was admired for his ability in handling horses, cattle, six-guns and men. But he could amuse himself as he pleased, and no one took any notice, so long as he stuck with the cattle and didn't back down in a fight. The cowboy met life ' head on with a recklessness and wildness of spirit and real relish for conquering it '. He charged after it ' as if it were something to be roped in a hurry before it got away '.

As this ballad indicates, it was hard for a cowboy to quit the range and settle down. Many of the old-timers kept drifting and stayed poor, but could never quite give up the life. A stove-up bronco-buster once wrote my father . . .

I wouldn't take anything for what I have saw, but I wouldn't care to travel the same road again. I wish I had never saw a cow ranch. And yet I'd rather be on one and work for wages than do anything you could name. It's a wild, free life, where your closest friend is on your hip. If your old horse can make it to the Mexican lines and you get back without any holes in your hide, that is real living. 'Tis the violent kind, but some people love it beyond a doubt . . .

QUOTE: *Cowboy*, Ross Santee (Cosmopolitan Books, 1928).

187. A COWBOY'S LIFE

The lumberman's life is a wearisome life,
Some say it's free from care,
But we chop down the pine from morning till night
In the middle of the forest so drear . . .

So RAN A MAINE woodsman's complaint that later drifted out onto the cattle range. The weather was the biggest complaint of both the cowboy and the lumberjack. Texas outfits scorned to carry tents, and the men took the prairie storms on their Stetsons. Teddy Blue remembers a frightening night in a plains hailstorm when he had to strip the saddle off his horse and hide beneath it for hours. Heat lightning played across the horns of the herd in an eerie blue glow, beads of static electricity formed on the manes of the horses and rolled down the moustaches of the riders, and balls of fire occasionally knocked a man off his horse. Blue northers would blow up out of nowhere and send the cattle stampeding, while the half-frozen cowboys pursued them through the black, stormy night.

188. THE OLD CHISHOLM TRAIL

PEOPLE HAVE THE IDEA that one big cattle trail ran north from Texas. Actually there were several trails, each with its roots spread wide over south Texas, wandering in wide bands across the plains, narrowing at the easy river crossings, converging again at the Kansas shipping point most popular at the particular epoch, and then sprangling out again into many branches through the northern prairie. Somehow the Old Chisholm (or Chizzum) Trail got the reputation of being the first one, and its name was attached to this song, which was said to have a verse for every mile of the way between Texas and Montana.

The cowboys sang ballads like this one in sheer exuberance when they were rounding up cattle, or in order to keep themselves awake during the long night guards. Teddy Blue explains another and more tragic necessity for cowboy song . . .

That night it come up an awful storm. It took all four of us to hold the cattle and we didn't hold them, and when morning came there was one man missing. We went back to look for him, and we found him among the prairie-dog holes, beside his horse. The horse's ribs was scraped bare of hide, and all the rest of horse and man was mashed into the ground as flat as a pancake. The only thing you could recognize was the handle of his six-shooter. His horse stepped into one of them holes and both went down before the stampede . . .

The awful part of it was that we had milled them cattle over him all night, not knowing he was there. That was what we couldn't get out of our minds. And after that, orders were given to sing when you were running with a stampede, so the others could know where you were as long as they heard you singing, and if they didn't hear you they would figure that something had happened. After a while this grew to be the custom on the range, but you know, that was still a new business in the seventies and they was learning all the time.

The cowboys were not particular about what they sang on those wild midnight rides or during the long, dreary night watches. They sang hymns, ballads, the sentimental songs of the day, and plenty of bawdy ditties. When they ran out of songs, two men on guard would make up verses, answering one another, back and forth across the herd, ranting any sort of jingle to keep themselves awake and quiet the cattle. Special cowboy favourites were *Lorena*, *The Cowboy's Lament*, *Little Black Bull Come Down the Medder*, which Lincoln had liked. Teddy Blue recalls that *Bury Me Not on the Lone Prairie* was sung to death in the '80s.—' It was a saying on the range that even the horses nickered it and the coyotes howled it; it got so they'd throw you in a creek if you sang it . . .'

QUOTE: Abbott.

189. GO ON, YOU LITTLE DOGIES

THE TEXAS LONGHORN was a nervous animal and a light sleeper. Any sudden or mysterious noise or movement could ' spook ' a whole herd and send it thundering off in a stampede that would kill cattle and run off many pounds of valuable tallow. Cattle rustlers took advantage of the nervousness of the longhorn, by creeping close to the cattle at night and suddenly popping a blanket or firing a gun to cause a stampede and in the confusion steal part of the herd.

During the day the cowpunchers kept their cattle moving at a steady pace with a series of strange, high-pitched and rather musical cries (known as cattle calls) which served to reassure, direct and spur on the herd. At night, they found that singing soothed the cattle. Whether it was the sound of a familiar human voice that had the effect or whether cattle actually respond to music in some way, no one can be quite sure, although many a dairy farmer swears that the music on the radio in his cowshed increases his milk yield, and here the singing milkmaids of the Hebrides concur.

Frank King, an old-time Texas trail driver, said, ' If the rider is moving around slow, and ain't makin' any noise, and happens to step against one of the critters, it will wake up startled, and jump into the herd and frighten all them that are close. This often causes a stampede. Now, the cowhand is ridin' around singin' or whistlin' in a sorta low voice, he wakes them cattle nearest to him in a sorta lazy way and they go back to sleep when he passes on . . .'

Mr. King's ingenious theory jibes with the opinions of most old-time cowmen. The night herding songs, they said, covered up disturbing noises, such as the creaking of saddle leather, the rattle of rocks under the horses hooves or the sudden, sharp yelp of a coyote, and thus provided a sort of protective blanket of familiar sounds beneath which the cattle rested securely. There is a yarn about a cowboy who played his fiddle on night guard and about one old blue steer who seemed to like music, and followed the fiddler round the herd, as long as the tune lasted.

QUOTE: *Longhorn Trail Drivers*, Frank King (privately printed, copyright, 1940), p. 49.

190. RUN ALONG, YOU LITTLE DOGIES
191. PUT THE OLD MAN TO SLEEP
192. THE OLD MAN'S LAMENT

THE HISTORY of this ballad shows the endless fascination of the song-hunter's job. In the early 1900's my father met a gipsy woman in Forth Worth, Texas, who gave him *Git Along, Little Dogies*. A dogie was a little orphan calf ' whose mammy had died in a bog-hole and whose daddy had run off with another cow '. Sick and feeble, their young bellies swollen by a too early diet of grass, these little ' dough-guts ' trailed along in the drag of the herd, and often had to be carried across a saddle-pommel by their cowboy foster-fathers. The dogie lullaby was the most original cowboy song, everyone agreed. According to romantic commentators it sounded like ' a cross between the lonely howl of the coyote and the wild song of the plains Indians '. Reworked by Billy Hill, it became a Tin Pan Alley hit in the 1930's.

Then one day Frank Sullivan, from Idaho, came into the Library of Congress Archives with a song he had learned on the northern ranges (*see Run Along, Little Dogies*). This song had an unfamiliar chorus, which underlined the bastard origin of the dogie. At the time I attributed this chorus to the somewhat thinner and cruder cowboy tradition of the North; but the next summer, I met a French-Canadian lumberjack who sang the full ballad about an old man rocking a baby that was none of his own, which sounded like the parent of the Sullivan piece. As this ballad had a much less polished lyric than the cowboy song I had grown up with, I was not at all sure which song was the original, until I landed in Dublin in 1950. There, in my very first Irish *ceilidhe* (*kaley* or sing-song), Seamus Ennis sang me *The Old Man's Lament* in the form printed here.

Not many days later, Mrs. Cronin, an eighty-year-old Cork singer, ran her incredibly sensitive voice over an ancient Irish lullaby . . . (*see* p. 374).

Here, at last, was the source of my father's dogie song, and the importance of the song to the western Irish was soon explained. In that impoverished land, where pretty girls were so often given in marriage to rich old men, the ancient Celtic independence of women still asserted itself and the young bride of an old man might (in ballads, at least) go off ' to

357

balls and plays ' with younger men and laugh at her old husband. Everyone in the west of Ireland greatly appreciated this theme.

Seamus Ennis later discovered the end of the little dogie trail among his oldest informants in the far west. When he sang them Mrs. Cronin's lament they nodded. This, they told him gravely, was the oldest of all songs, the lullaby that the Virgin sang when she rocked the Holy Babe to sleep in Bethlehem long, long ago. Indeed, Joseph was the man about whom it could be said . . . 'Yes, I'm rocking the cradle and the child not my own' . . .

Of course, this is but recreative hindsight on the part of the tellers of old tales and recreative use of an old theme on the part of the northern cowboy who made the original dogie song—yet who can deny the kinship between the carpenter, Joseph, and the cowboy tenderly carrying the tired dogie across the pommel of his saddle?

193. NIGHT HERDING SONG

HARRY STEPHENS, bronco-buster and cowboy poet, recalls how he composed this classic among western songs . . .

Years ago, in 1909 up in the Yellowstone, I got me a job herding stage-coach horses. Now every cowboy knows that one of the hardest jobs on earth is to hold a bunch of nervous horses together at night. Back in them times when they didn't have so many fences and corrals, you had as many as two to four men on a night shift, depending on the size of the herd. Well, we had so many different calls and yells that I thought we might as well have a kind of a song to it . . .

It turned out that I had this herd of horses all to myself day and night for a while. So bein' by myself and havin' nothin' better to do, ridin' around there all night on my own, I got me a start on this song and went ahead and put it together after several nights of riding.

I didn't have so much of a tune for it. In fact, cowboy songs didn't run to no regular tunes. You'd hardly ever hear cowboys singin' together much. Generally each one of um had such a different kind of a tune that each one would have to sing by himself. See, they all come from different places, they knew the songs different. So mostly they'd kind of recite things. Some of them boys couldn't carry a tune less'n they pack it over their shoulders in a gunny-sack. So they'd kindly just say it or speak it off, like I'm doin' . . .

194. DONEY GAL
195. I'M A-LEAVIN' CHEYENNE

THE HORSES the Spaniards brought to America were descended from the Moorish, desert-adapted *Barb*. Some of these Spanish ponies ran wild in the South-West and from them came the mustang breed on which the Indians hunted the buffalo and the Texans the long-horns. The cowboy's mustang was a small, tough mount with the eyesight and agility of a cat. He could follow a wild steer through the brush like a hound, and at night on a stampede he could carry his rider safely at breakneck speed over rocky terrain or flats, riddled with prairie dogholes, where a fall meant almost certain death beneath the hooves of the longhorns.

Every man in a cow outfit had his assigned string of mounts which remained his as long as he kept his job, and not even the boss could ride them without the cowboy's permission. Few cowhorses were completely broken to the saddle, and they pitched every time they were saddled. The cowboys enjoyed the sport and bragged about how hard their horses bucked . . . ' That hoss could pitch more ways than a Chinaman could write . . . He threw me so high that I saw the courthouse steeples in three counties and the nearest of them was thirty miles off . . .'

According to the old western adage, ' There wasn't but two things a cowboy was afraid of—a decent woman and bein' afoot.' Like the plains Indians, they spent their lives on horseback. In fact . . .

The ranchman saw a lot more of his horse than he did anybody else including his wife, and naturally he got attached to him. So when you hear these sentimental ballads about men and their horses in the Old West, you can know that they have foundation in an actual state of affairs.

A good cow horse knew more about the man on his back than the man himself knew. He could sense his disposition and his mood and know which way he was going to turn. He knew when the old boy had been drinking too much and could pilot him back to the outfit without any direction whatsoever. Those horses knew as much about handling a bunch of cattle as any man. A roping horse or a cutting horse can do his stuff without the rider ever touching the reins. A cutting horse can cut a cow out of the herd after she has been spotted without his boss telling him a thing, and a roping horse will keep a steer in position until the rope is thrown, and pull back on the rope after it is around the steer's neck, holding it taut and tight and keeping the steer down until he is tied.

That kind of horse was invaluable to any ranchman—such a horse meant the difference between failure and prosperity in the ranching business, and the agility and spirit and toughness of a cow pony sometimes meant the difference between life and death for a man.

Doney Gal is a modern piece, perhaps the last of the genuine cowboy ditties; *I'm A-leavin' Cheyenne* was the cowboy's last dance of the evening—his *Home, Sweet Home* or *Goodnight, Ladies*—and is to be sung with the drawling swing of the fiddle on the notes.

QUOTE: *Big Spring*, Shine Phillips (Prentice-Hall, N.Y., 1943), p. 128. Used by special permission of the author.

196. ON THE TRAIL TO MEXICO

THE WESTERN COWMEN were not all Texans, by any means. The romance of the West and the stories of the fortunes to be made there drew men from all over America and the world. Owen Wister's Virginian came from an old tidewater family. Billy the Kid was born in New York City. Many young English aristocrats invested their money in the cattle business. Australian miners, Irish railroad workers, Scots lumberjacks, French-Canadian trappers, Negro ex-slaves, Mexican vaqueros, all these types and more took up the cowboy trade, and left their mark somewhere on the songs, though the Texan brand stands out most clearly in the herd. As an old puncher remarked, ' Texas taught Wyoming and Montana.'

Some book-learnt folklorists have recently taken to saying that there were few genuine cowboy folk songs, that most so-called cowboy songs were the work of educated poets or were mere imitations of popular songs. This position stems from such discoveries as the following: *Bury Me Not on the Lone Prairie* is a parody of (though I should say an improvement on) the English *Bury Me Not in the Deep, Deep Sea*; a frontier minister composed *Roll On, Little Dogies*; the cowboys sang *Lorena* and other hit songs of the period; many cowboy songs are reworkings of older folk ballads (*see* pp. 380, 382).

To my mind these critics have merely pointed to the fact that the West was a cultural melting pot—that cowboys followed the practice of all folk composers and put new wine in old bottles. Yet the western songs were not parodies, most of them. Sometimes they *look* like parodies on paper, but, when they are *sung*, they do not remind you of their originals, as parodies do: *they put the originals out of your mind entirely*. Like Teddy Blue, who was born in England, but talked, rode and thought like a Texan, these songs had been thoroughly westernized. That this evocative and self-consistent body of oral literature could have been created in thirty or forty years (for the open range period lasted only from 1865 to 1900) and under constantly changing conditions, is a marvellous example of how quickly a folk culture can grow up when it is needed.

After the Texan, the lumberjack contributed most to cowboy balladry. This ballad, probably are make of the eastern *Canada-I-O* (*see* p. 114), is a vast improvement upon it, since it recounts a drama, instead of a series of complaints. Its relative, the familiar *Buffalo Skinners*, ranks as the best ballad of the West. At last, the two main streams of American folk songs, the northern and the southern, had met and merged on the western plains, and this marriage of styles produced songs which reflected the lonely grandeur of the landscape and the wild freedom of western life.

197. WHEN I WAS A COWBOY

AMONG SOUTH TEXAS Negroes, my father and I found several variants of this ditty of Leadbelly's, all of which seemed to be composites of *Longhorn Cows* (*see* p. 368) and the lusty British ballad, *Our Goodman*, that begins—

> I come home the first night drunk as I could be,
> I found a hoss in my stable where my hoss ought to be . . .

Many of the early cow outfits in the prairie country around Houston, especially, started up in slavery times, and Negroes learned the cattle trade. Some became champion cowboys. The greatest bull-dogger who ever lived was a giant black man who would leap off his horse, wind his arms round the horns of a steer, sink his teeth in the animal's nose, and twist the head round to throw the animal.

Negro cowboys evidently did a good deal of the singing on the trail. Teddy Blue's favourite song was one he first learned from John Henry, 'the top nigger in Ab Blocker's outfit '. Blue calls Blocker the greatest of the Texas trail men and implies that old Ab had a number of Negroes on his payroll. John Henry's song began . . .

> I'se gwine North with the Blocker Seven Herd,
> And Mister Ab is a-movin' like a bird . . .

Using the Negro's tune, Blue and his comrades made up rhymes about every river they crossed between Texas and Wyoming.

Leadbelly never worked on a ranch and the stanzas he added to this old Negro cowboy song are fantastic and unreal; nevertheless, the tune and the rhythm and the spirit are genuine, and the song stands for an important chapter in the history of western song, neglected by historians.

QUOTE: Abbott.

360

198. THE WILD RIPPLING WATER
199. MY LOVE IS A RIDER

THIS WESTERN VERSION of the old English *Soldier and the Lady* and Belle Starr's love song will have to stand for a whole family of rowdy songs that filled the cowboy's off-duty hours with sounds of joy, but would burn the paper they were printed on. Cowboys were not such plaster saints as the movies and the cartoons have made them out to be. When they hit Dodge City or Cheyenne after six or eight months on the trail, they headed for fun spots plainly marked with swinging doors and little red lights. Teddy Blue, who rode the trail from Texas to Montana in the '70s and '80s, is almost the only western rider who has told this side of the story with candour. He recalls . . .

In Miles City that summer I found a lot of new friends and some old ones. There were girls that I had seen in a lot of different places along the trail. They followed the trail herds. The madams would bring them out from Omaha and Chicago and St. Paul; you would see them in Ogallala and then again in Cheyenne. But when the herds was all gone and the beef was shipped, the town was dead. The girls would go back where they came from and the gamblers would go with them . . . When our outfit came down to Miles City in the fall of '83, there was some new girls there, too, fresh from the East, and they was afraid of us wild Texas cowpunchers. But they got over that. Those were the days when I didn't have a care in the world. I had plenty of good horses to ride, and the girls said I was the best-looking cowboy on Powder river, and they cleaned me down to my spurs . . .

Some of those girls in Miles City were famous, like Cowboy Annie and Connie the Cowboy Queen. Connie had a two hundred and fifty dollar dress embroidered with all the different brands —they said there wasn't an outfit from the Yellowstone down to the Platte and over in the Dakotas, too, that couldn't find its brand on her dress.

Things were different down South from what they were up North. The Texas men couldn't be open and public about their feelings towards those women, the way we were . . . I suppose those things would shock a lot of respectable people. But we wasn't respectable and we didn't pretend to be, which was the only way we was different from some others . . .

A night or two before we left town that fall, we were all together with the girls, and there was a dance going on and not enough women to go around, which was the usual way of it in that country . . . So one of them went in a back room and he came out with a pair of women's ruffled drawers pulled on over his pants. So Cowboy Annie turned to me . . . and I said yes, naturally. So she pulled them off and I put them on over my pants. And we all paraded down the street. The whole town turned out to see us . . .

After that, going back to the mouth of the Musselshell, I made up a song about Cowboy Annie that went:

> Cowboy Annie was her name,
> And the Bar N outfit was her fame,
> And when the beef is four years old,
> We'll fill her pillowslips with gold . . .

I still had Cowboy Annie's ruffled drawers that she gave me that night, and I put them on a forked stick and carried them that way to the Musselshell, like a flag. And before we left, my girl took one of her stockings off and tied it around my arm, you know, like the knights of old. I had my flag hanging on the wall of the cabin until Harry Rutter got sore one day and tore it down and throwed it in the stove. He said it wasn't decent. And no more it was.

QUOTE: Abbott.

361

200. THE DYING COWBOY

I'm wild and woolly and full of fleas,
I ain't been curried below the knees,
I'm a wild she wolf from Bitter Creek,
And it's my night to howl—WHOOPIEEE!

WHEN A COWPUNCHER hit town at the end of the trail, the first place he headed for was the barber's shop. An old-time cowtown barber remembers that on Saturday he would cut enough cowboy hair to stuff a mattress. After his haircut, the puncher would ' take his biennial bath ', slick up his boots, put on a fancy shirt and head for a barroom. No bottles were permitted on the range within a hundred yards of a cowcamp, and though occasionally a cowboy might break the rule on the job, most cattlemen who rode into Abilene, Dodge City, Ellsworth or Cheyenne, were as dry as a desert in a sandstorm. After several interior applications of liquid variously known as ' Tangle Leg ', (which left you weaving from side to side), 'Forty Rods' (which brought you to your knees within forty rods of the bottle), ' Cheyenne Lightning ' (which struck you down on the spot), or ' Tarantula Juice ' (which simply poisoned you), a joyous spirit pervaded the cowman. He sometimes invited his pony into the saloon for a drink or a game of billiards. The idea struck him that it would be amusing to run the town marshall up a tree. Mirrors drew him irresistibly; he could not look into one without pulling his six-gun and shattering his own image with bullets. All western barkeeps recognized this impulse and kept spare mirrors on hand.

However, the numbers of fatal shootings in the West have been multiplied tenfold by eye-witnesses, and at least a thousand-fold since by western movies and magazines. Teddy Blue, who had a taste for romance, says that he saw men wounded in saloon fracases, but never anyone killed outright—and Teddy had his fun in Dodge City and Cheyenne at their wildest. Nevertheless, cowboys did die with their boots on in those tough cow towns; a good many of them were just foolish kids, who stopped a bullet for reasons that Teddy Blue explains . . .

I was never really bad. I never had a reputation as a bad man, only when I was a kid—oh, I was just stinking to kill somebody, because most all the men I associated with had shot somebody, but as I told you, a kid's the most dangerous thing alive.

I carried a chip on my shoulder for years, and I got into my share of fights. But after I got over that early foolishness, I wasn't looking for fights, I was looking for fun and that I believe was the case with nine-tenths of them. They were out there for months on end, on the trail or living in some cow camp, eating bad food, sleeping in wet clothes, going without everything that means life to a man—though that was all they ever talked or thought about—and when they hit the bright lights of some little cow town, that looked like gay Paree to them, they just went crazy.

QUOTE: Abbott.

201. THE SAILOR CUT DOWN IN HIS PRIME

FOR MANY CENTURIES, the theme of love-that-kills grew steadily more important among our guilt-ridden ancestors. In the nineteenth century, when the denial of sensuality reached its peak, this theme was stripped of all its trappings, religious and secular. Thus the central image of this ballad is of a young person on his death bed or upon the operating table, how he dies there and is buried. The final murmur of pity or shout of rowdy defiance by his mourners is a prelude to the rebellion against sexual mores that burst out in the jazz of the 'twenties.

Nevertheless, the ballad collector of the eighteenth century, though he might have been struck by the magnificent vulgarity of the funeral, where all the prostitutes in town turned out as mourners, would never have supposed that this street ballad would have so many offshoots. Stall balladeers printed it so often in Great Britain during the early nine-teenth century that we cannot be sure which was the song's source. Joyce has the earliest dated publication—a fragment said to have been current in Cork in 1790. By 1850 broadsides called *The Unfortunate Rake, The Irish Rake, The Unfortunate Lad, The Rakish Young Fellow, St. James Hospital,* and *The Rambling Boy* had appeared in Great Britain. In a number of these songs it is clear that the rake was dying of syphilis . . .

> Had she but told me before she disordered me,
> Had she but told me of it in time,
> I might have got salts and pills of white mercury,
> But now I'm cut down in the height of my prime . . .

A derivative ballad with a female victim appeared in Britain at the same period, various-ly titled *The Bad Girl's Lament, One Morning in May* and *The Young Girl Cut Down in Her Prime* (*see* p. 193). This young lady died of dissipation and was also interred with military honours Both songs spread to America, along with a rowdy sailor ballad *Wrap Me Up In My Tarpaulin Jacket* (circa 1830, *see* p. 444) . . .

> Get six jolly fellows to carry me
> And let them be good and drunk,
> When they carry me 'long in my coffin,
> Then they will let me fall with a bump.
>
> Let them all start cursing and swearing,
> Like men that are going to go mad,
> Just tip a glass over my coffin
> Saying, ' There goes a brave jolly lad.'

The American sense of propriety vastly increased the importance of the ballad. For the religious-minded, the song became a morality, for the rebellious, a rallying song; but, once the American censor had removed the prostitutes and the syphilis from the story (*see* p. 193 for a trace that remains), the ballad could fit any pioneer environment in which a young person died tragically, on the job or off it. There was no scarcity of such situations. The lumberjack, drowned in the river drive . . .

One day I was walking out on the mountain,
A wood robin was singing, I happened to spy
A handsome young lumberjack on the banks of the river,
All dressed in white linen and laid out to die . . .

The young western miners dying of silicosis . . .

'Twas once in the saddle I used to go dashing,
'Twas once as a cowboy I used to be brave,
But ain't it a pity I came to Butte City,
To work for Jim Brennan, and now to my grave . . .

Among the cowboys it became the most popular of all songs, with a score of versions . . .
The Negro *St. James Infirmary*, closely linked with *The Bad Girl's Lament*, retains more of the
hospital stink of the original song than any other American form . . . In Dorset, England,
I met an old codger named Charley Wills, who roared out this song, and told me that as
late as World War II the naval police would not permit it to be sung in a pub.

202. BILLY THE KID

. . . THIS PSYCHOPATHIC western gunman, born in New York City in 1859 and christened William H. Bonney, established his 'rep' in Silver City, New Mexico, at the age of twelve, by shooting down a man who insulted his mother, and kept it bright by murdering a total of twenty-one men, 'not counting Mexicans and Indians', before he was killed himself at the age of twenty-one. Legend made of him a handsome, gallant daredevil. The truth is that he never killed a man unless he had the drop on him, and was, in fact, 'a nondescript, weasel-eyed, narrow-chested, stoop-shouldered, repulsive-looking creature, with all the outward appearance of a cretin.' Yet if Billy was inferior physically, he proved the truth of the western saying that the Colt revolver made all men equal.

He thought nothing of taking human life. His reputation won him a job in 1879 as gunman for the big ranchers of New Mexico in their range war with small cattlemen, and he earned his salary by mowing down an unknown number of the opposition. After a quarrel with old man Chisum, in which Billy threatened his employer's life, he became a cattle rustler and desperado. His former friend, Pat Garrett, who knew Billy's taste for pretty Mexican girls, traced him to the home of one of his sweethearts, caught the Kid unprepared and shot him down. He died with a Colt .41 in one hand and a butcher knife in the other. The rest is legend and this ballad, composed long after the event.

203. TYIN' A KNOT IN THE DEVIL'S TAIL

. . . IS A BALLAD from the dude ranch period and the sort of haywire song the guide serves up to his Eastern charges round some nice, comfortable camp-fire in the mountains. A ranch poet, desperate to find something to match the tourists' idea of the wild and woolly West, remade the Charles Badger Clark poem, which began . . .

'Way high up in the Mokiones, among the mountain tops,
A lion cleaned a yearling's bones and licks his thankful chops;
And who upon the scene should ride, a-trippin' down the slope,
But High-Chin Bob, of sinful pride and maverick hungry rope.
   'O glory be to me,' says he, 'and fame's unfadin' flowers.
   I ride my good top-hawse today and I'm top hand of the Lazy J,
   So, kitty-cat, you're ours.'

Old-time westerners claim that greenhorns forced them to invent a tall-tale West. The famous scout, Jim Bridger, the first white man to view the wonders of Yellowstone, was called a liar when he told the plain truth about what he had seen. Thereupon he lied about mile-high mountains of clear glass, through which he could see petrified stone forests where petrified birds flew, singing petrified songs in the putrified air—and his listeners swallowed the story and were happy.

184. WAKE UP, JACOB

FROM: p. 3 of *Cowboy Songs*, Lomax (Macmillan, N.Y., 1910, 1938). Arranged by J. A Lomax.

Piano arrangement by DON BANKS

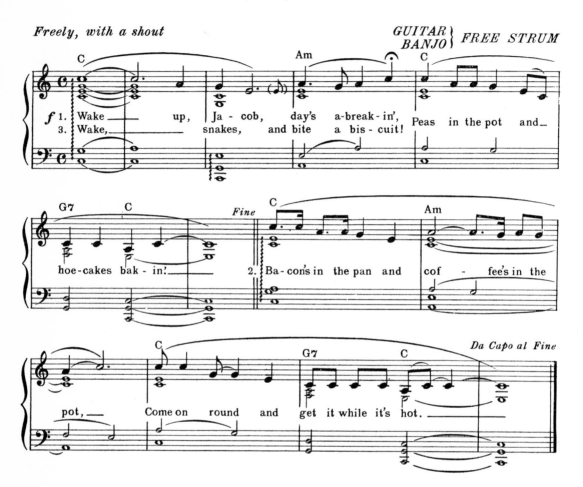

1 Wake up, Jacob, day's a-breakin',
  Peas in the pot and hoe-cake's bakin'.

2 Bacon's in the pan and coffee's in the pot,
  Come on round and get it while it's hot.

3 (*Shouted*) Wake, snakes, and bite a biscuit!

185. THE RAILROAD CORRAL

FROM: p. 42 of *Cowboy Songs*, Lomax (Macmillan, N.Y., 1910, 1938). Tune: *The Irish Washerwoman*.

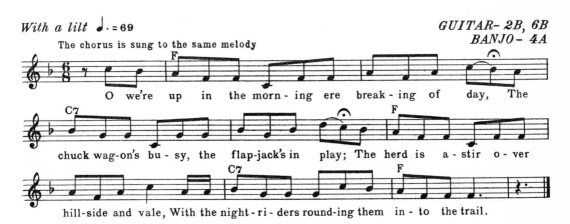

With a lilt ♩. = 69

GUITAR – 2B, 6B
BANJO – 4A

The chorus is sung to the same melody

O we're up in the morn-ing ere break-ing of day, The chuck wag-on's bu-sy, the flap-jack's in play; The herd is a-stir o-ver hill-side and vale, With the night-ri-ders round-ing them in-to the trail.

1 O we're up in the morning ere breaking of day,
The chuck wagon's busy, the flapjack's in play;
The herd is astir over hillside and vale,
With the nightriders rounding them into the trail.
CHORUS:
So come take up your cinches, come shake out your reins,
Come wake your old bronco and break for the plains,
Come roust out your steers from the long chapparal,
For the outfit is off to the railroad corral.

2 The sun circles upward. The steers as they plod,
Are pounding to powder the hot prairie sod,
And it seems when the dust makes you dizzy and sick,
That we'll never reach noon and the cool, shady crick.
CHORUS:
But tie up your handkerchief, play up your nag,
Come dry up your grumbles and try not to lag,
Drive up your steers from the long chapparal,
For we're far on the road to the railroad corral.

186. I'M BOUND TO FOLLOW THE LONGHORN COWS

FROM: p. 19 of *Cowboy Songs*, Lomax (Macmillan, N.Y., 1910, 1938). Arranged by Alec Moore, ex-cowpuncher of Austin, Texas, and by J. and A. Lomax.

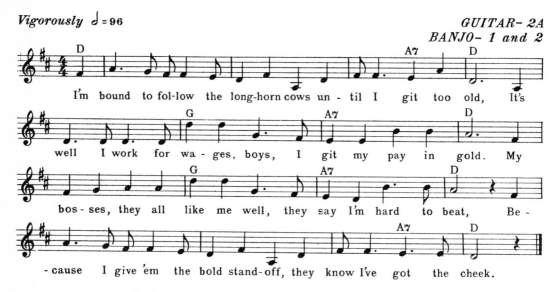

Vigorously ♩ = 96

GUITAR— 2A
BANJO— 1 and 2

I'm bound to fol-low the long-horn cows un - til I git too old, It's well I work for wa - ges, boys, I git my pay in gold. My bos - ses, they all like me well, they say I'm hard to beat, Be - cause I give 'em the bold stand-off, they know I've got the cheek.

1 I'm bound to follow the longhorn cows until I git too old,
It's well I work for wages, boys, I git my pay in gold.
My bosses, they all like me well, they say I'm hard to beat,
Because I give 'em the bold stand-off, they know I've got the cheek.

2 Yes, I'm a rowdy cowboy, just off the stormy plains,
My trade is cinchin' saddles and pullin' bridle reins,
O I can tip the lasso, boys, it is with graceful ease,
I can rope a streak of lightnin' and ride it where I please.

3 Now when we git them bedded down, we think it's for the night,
Some horse will shake a saddle and give the herd a fright,
The herd will rise up to its feet and madly dash away,
'It's movin' time, to the lead, my boys,' you'll hear some cowboy say.

4 And when we git them rounded up and just about quieted down,
The storm's a-risin' in the west, and fire plays on their horns,
The foreman says, ' Stay with 'em, boys, your pay will be in gold '—
I'm bound to follow the longhorn cows, until I git too old.

5 One night way up in Kansas, I had a pleasant dream,
I dreamed I'se back in Texas, boys, down by some pleasant stream,
My love was right beside me, boys, she'd come to go my bail,
But I woke up broken-hearted with a yearling by the tail.

6 Now if I had a little stake, I soon would married be,
But another week and I must go, the boss said so today.
My girl must cheer up courage and choose some other one,
For I'm bound to follow the longhorn cows until my race is run.

368

187. A COWBOY'S LIFE

FROM: p. 15 of *Cowboy Songs*, Lomax (Macmillan, N.Y., 1910, 1938). SEE:
Rickaby, 43; Doerflinger, 211. Last two references for *The Lumberman's Life* of
which this is a Western re-working. Originated in New Brunswick, current in
Maine before 1850's.

Piano arrangement by MATYAS SEIBER

Howled ♩ = 96

GUITAR- 1, 2A
BANJO- 1

A cow-boy's life is a wea-ry, drea-ry life, Some say it's free from care, Round-ing up the cat-tle from morn-ing till night In the mid-dle of the prai-rie so bare. Half past four, the nois-y cook will roar, 'Whoop-a-whoop-a - hey!' Slow-ly you will rise with sleep-y feel-ing eyes, The

sweet dream-y night has passed a-way.

1 A cowboy's life is a weary, dreary life,
   Some say it's free from care,
   Rounding up the cattle from morning till night
   In the middle of the prairie so bare.
   CHORUS:
   Half past four, the noisy cook will roar,
   ' Whoop-a-whoop-a-hey!'
   Slowly you will rise with sleepy feeling eyes,
   The sweet dreamy night has passed away.

2 The wolves and owls with their terrifying howls
   Disturb us in our midnight dream,
   As we lie on our slickers on a cold, rainy night,
   Way over on the Pecos stream.   (CHO.)

3 Spring-time sets in, double trouble will begin,
   The weather is so fierce and cold.
   Our clothes are wet and frozen to our necks
   And the cattle we can scarcely hold.   (CHO.)

4 The cowboy's life is a dreary, dreary life,
   He's driven through the heat and cold,
   While the rich man's a-sleeping on his velvet couch,
   A-dreaming of his silver and his gold.   (CHO.)

188. THE OLD CHISHOLM TRAIL

FROM: p. 192 of *It's an Old Wild West Custom*, Duncan Emrich (Dial Press, N.Y., 1951). Used by permission. Tune arranged by Alan Lomax. SEE: Brown III, 248; Lomax I, 28-37; Randolph II, 174.

Rowdy ♩ = 104   *GUITAR— ANY VIGOROUS* 2/4 *STYLE*
                                                              BANJO— 1, 3

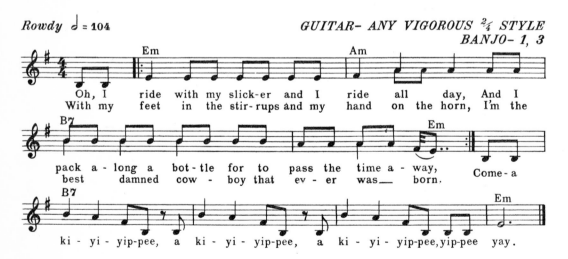

Oh, I ride with my slick-er and I ride all day, And I
With my feet in the stir-rups and my hand on the horn, I'm the

pack a-long a bot-tle for to pass the time a-way,   Come-a
best damned cow-boy that ev-er was— born.

ki - yi - yip-pee, a ki - yi - yip-pee, a ki - yi - yip-pee, yip-pee yay.

1 Oh, I ride with my slicker and I ride all day,
  And I pack along a bottle for to pass the time away,
  With my feet in the stirrups and my hand on the horn,
  I'm the best damned cowboy that ever was born.
  CHORUS:
  Come-a ki-yi-yippee, a ki-yi-yippee, a ki-yi-yippee, yippee-yay.

2 Oh, I know a girl who's a-going to leave her mother,
  All the devils down in Hell couldn't stir up such another,
  She rides on a pinto and she works on the drag,
  With her petticoats a-flopping like a pair of saddlebags. (CHO.)

3 Oh, I'm out night herding on the Lone Squaw Butte,
  When I run my sights on a lone coyote,
  He's a-helling and a-yelling and as he drifts by
  I snakes out my lasso and I loops him on the fly. (CHO.)

4 Oh, the shorthorns rattle and the longhorns battle,
  Never had such a ride around the locoed cattle;
  I'll trade my outfit as soon as I can,
  And I won't punch cows for no damned man. (CHO.)

5 It's along 'fore daylight, they start in to feed,
  The steers all a-dragging, with the pointers in the lead;
  They head on north where the grass grows green,
  And now for the biscuits and the bacon and the beans. (CHO.)

6 No chaps, no slicker, and she pours down rain,
  And I swears to my boss I'll never night herd again,
  Oh, I'll head back south and marry me a squaw,
  And live all my life on the sandy Washitaw. (CHO.)

7 Oh, I jumped on my bronco, I raked him down the flank,
  He starts in to pitching and I landed on the bank;
  Well, I leaps to my saddle and I gives a little yell,
  Oh, the leaders broke the country and the cattle went to hell. (CHO.)

8 Oh, Abilene city is a dang fine town,
  We'll all liquor up and twirl those heifers round;
  Then back once more with my bridle and my hoss,
  For old John Chisum is a damned fine boss. (CHO.)

9 I never hankered for to plough or hoe,
  And punching steers is all I know.
  With my knees in the saddle and a-hanging to the sky,
  Herding dogies up in Heaven in the sweet by-and-by. (CHO.)

189. GO ON, YOU LITTLE DOGIES

Recorded and arranged by John and Alan Lomax from singing of Dick Devall, Reed, Oklahoma. SEE: Lomax I, 4.

1 As I walked out one bright summer's mornin',
I met a gay cowboy come ridin' along,
His hat throwed back and his spurs was a-jinglin',
As I approached him he was singin' this song.

CHORUS:
O hoop-an-li-ay, go on, you little dogies,
O hoop-an-li-o, Wyomin's your home,
It's whoopin' an' yellin' an' drivin' the dogies,
Ever makin' sad fortunes where it's none of our
own.

2 Now some boys tries the trail for pleasure,
But them that does gits it awfully wrong,
You never see the like of the trouble they give us,
While we roll those longhorn cattle along. (CHO.)

3 You're gonna make beefsteak for Uncle Sam's
' It's beef, heap beef,' I hear them call.   [Injuns,
Roll on, roll on, roll on, you damn dogies,
You're gonna be beefsteak long before fall. (CHO.)

4 You was born and raised below the Nueces,
Where the mesquite and cactus and chapparal grow,
So fill yourselves up with grass in Kansas
And roll your tails for old Idaho.

CHORUS:
Hoop-li-ay-aye, go on, you little dogies,
Hoop-li-ay-aye, Wyomin's your home,
Its whoopin' an' cussin' and damnin' them dogies,
To our soul's perdition, but none of their own.

190. RUN ALONG, YOU LITTLE DOGIES

FROM: pp. 240-2 of *Our Singing Country*, Lomax (Macmillan, N.Y., 1941), arranged by Alan Lomax from singing of Frank Sullivan, who learned it from cowboys in Idaho, 1910.

1 As I looked out of my window,
I saw a cowboy come riding along,
His hat was shoved back and his spurs kept
a-jingling
And as he drew near me, he was singing this song.

CHORUS:
Hush-ie-ci-ola, little baby, lie easy,
Who's your real father may never be known.
O it's weeping, wailing, rocking the cradle,
And tending a baby that's none of your own.

2 When spring comes along, we round up the
dogies,
We stick on their brands and we bob off their
tails,
Pick out the strays, then the herd is inspected
And then the next day we go on the trail.

CHORUS:
Singing hoop-pi-o-hoop! run along, you little
dogies,
For Montana will be your new home,
Oh, it's whooping, swearing, driving the dogies,
It's our misfortune we ever did roam.

3 Oh, it's worst in the night just after the round-up
  When dogies are grazing from the herd all around,
  You have no idea of the trouble they give us,
  To the boys who are holding them on the bed
                    ground. (CHO.)

4 Oh, some think we go up the trail for pleasure
  But I can tell them that they are dead wrong.
  If I ever got any fun out of trailing,
  I'd have no reason for singing my song. (CHO.)

191. PUT THE OLD MAN TO SLEEP

Collected from Mrs. Elizabeth Cronin, Cork, Ireland, and arranged by Seamus Ennis.

GUITAR— 1 or 6A
BANJO— 1 or 4B

Transliteration: Kwir a kho-lla, kwir-a kho-lla, kwir-a kho-lla   un shan-dwin-na,___ kwir-a

Gaelic: Luir a chod-la, cuir a chod-la, cuir a chod-la   an sean-cluine-(e),___ luir-a

kholl-ay___ nig-a khus-a_____ ag-us bag jokh dhur tan dwin-na _____

chodl-e,___ nigh a cho-sa_____ ag-us bog deoch do'r tsean duin-e _____

TRANSLATION OF GAELIC
Put to sleep, put to sleep,
  put to sleep the old man.
Put him to sleep, wash his feet
  and draw a drink for the old man.

374

192. THE OLD MAN'S LAMENT

Collected and arranged by Seamus Ennis, Dublin. Song is common in North and Western Ireland, frequently printed on broadsheets.

Dreamily and freely ♩ = 116

GUITAR– 2A
BANJO– 4B or 1 (WALTZ)

1 The other evening I chanced to go roaming,
Down by the clear river I joggled along.
I heard an old man making sad lamentation,
About rocking the cradle and the child not his own.
CHORUS:
Ee-i-o, my laddie, lie easy,
Perhaps your own daddy might never be known.
I'm weeping and weary with rocking this cradle,
And nursing a baby that's none of my own.

2 I'm sorry, my neighbours, I married this fair one,
She favours the neighbours and none of her own,
She goes out every evening to balls and to parties
And leaves me here rocking the cradle alone. (CHO.)

3 Come all you young fellows that want to get married,
Take my advice, leave the weemen alone;
For it's by the Lor' Harry, if ever you marry,
They'll leave you there rocking the cradle alone. (CHO.)

193. NIGHT HERDING SONG

FROM: p. 60 of *Cowboy Songs*, Lomax (Macmillan, N.Y., 1910, 1938).
Composed by Harry Stephens.
Piano arrangement by DON BANKS

1 O slow up, dogies, quit your roving around,
You've wandered and trampled all over the ground.
O graze along, dogies, and feed kinda slow,
And don't forever be on the go.
Move slow, little dogies, move slow.

2 I have circle-herded, trail-herded, cross-herded,
 too,
But to keep you together that's what I can't do,
My horse is leg-weary and I'm awful tired,
But if I let you get away, I'm sure to get fired,
Bunch up, little dogies, bunch up.

3 O say, little dogies, when you goin' to lay down,
And quit this forever shiftin' around?
My limbs are weary, my seat is sore,
O lay down, dogies, like you've laid before,
Lay down, little dogies, lay down.

4 O lay still, dogies, since you have laid down,
Stretch away out on the big open ground,
Snore loud, little dogies, and drown the wild
 sound
That will all go away when the day rolls round,
Lay still, little dogies, lay still.

194. DONEY GAL

FROM: p. 11 of *Cowboy Songs*, Lomax (Macmillan, N.Y., 1910, 1938). Recorded and arranged by John A. Lomax from singing of Louise Henson, San Antonio, Texas. For related song: Randolph II, 238. Used by special permission of the author.

Piano arrangement by DON BANKS

1 We're alone, Doney gal, in the rain and hail,
   Drivin' them dogies on down the trail.
   CHORUS:
   It's rain or shine, sleet or snow,
   Me an' my Doney gal are on the go,
   It's rain or shine, sleet or snow,
   Me an' my Doney gal are bound to go.

2 A cowboy's life is a weary thing,
   For it's rope and brand and ride and sing.
   CHORUS:
   We'll ride the range from sun to sun,
   For a cowboy's work is never done,
   He's up and gone at the break of day
   Drivin' the dogies on their way.

377

3 Over the prairies, lean and brown,
On through the flats where there ain't no town.
CHORUS:
We travel down that lonesome trail,
Where a man and his horse seldom ever fail,
For day and night in the rain or hail
He'll stay with his dogies out on the trail.

Repeat first chorus.

195. I'M A-LEAVIN' CHEYENNE

New words and music by Ross Whitmire and Alan Lomax. For other variants
see: Lomax I, 12; Sandburg, 12.
Piano arrangement by MATYAS SEIBER

I'm a-rid-in' Old Paint and I'm a-lead-in' Old Fan, My foot's in my stir-rup, my bri-dle's in my hand.

CHORUS
Good-bye, my lit-tle do-ney, I'm a-leav-in' Chey-enne, Chey-enne - a, Chey-

enne, I'm a-leav-in' Chey-enne. Chey--enne.

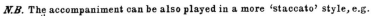

N.B. The accompaniment can be also played in a more 'staccato' style, e.g.

etc.

1 I'm a-ridin' Old Paint and I'm a-leadin' Old Fan,
My foot's in my stirrup, my bridle's in my hand.
CHORUS:
Goodbye, my little doney, I'm a-leavin' Cheyenne,
Cheyenne-a, Cheyenne, I'm a-leavin' Cheyenne. (2 or 3 *times.*)

2 Old Paint's a good pony and he paces when he can,
Saddle him in the mornin', an' he'll pi—itch to beat the band. (CHO.)

3 The grass is a-risin' all over this land,
I'm sorry, young lady, I'm o—off to Montan'. (CHO.)

4 I've bridled old Paint and I've saddled old Fan,
I'm sorry, little doney, my po—ony won't stand. (CHO.)

196. ON THE TRAIL TO MEXICO

Adapted by Alan Lomax from singing of H. Knight, Sterling City, Texas. Lomax I,
41 and 335 (*Boggy Creek*). see: Laws, 136. Song is a cowboy variant of the
Caledoni-o, Canada-i-o, Range of Buffalo family, see note on *Canada-i-o.*

1 It was out in old West Texas in the spring of '83,
That a highly noted cow drover came steppin' up to me,
Sayin', ' How do you do, young fellow, and how would you like to go-o,
And spend one summer pleasantly on the trail to Mexico?'

2 Now me bein' out of employment, boys, to the drover I did say,
' A-goin' out to New Mexico depends upon the pay.
If you'll pay me good wages and transportation, too,
I think, sir, I will go with you and stay the summer through.'

3 With all the drover's flattering talk, he enlisted quite a train,
Some ten or twelve in number, strong and able-bodied men,
Our trip it was a pleasant one, o'er the road we had to go,
Until we crossed old Boggy Creek out in New Mexico.

4 And there our pleasures ended and our troubles they began,
The first hard storm that hit us, oh, how the cattle ran!
While running through thorns and stickers we had but little show,
And the Indians watched to pick us off in the hills of New Mexico.

5 The summer season ended and the drover would not pay,
  Said we had been extravagant, were in debt to him that day;
  But bankrupt law among cowboys, I tell you will not go,
  So we left that drover's bones to bleach out in New Mexico.

6 And now we've crossed old Boggy Creek and homeward we are bound,
  No more in that cursed country will ever we be found.
  Go home to our wives and sweethearts, tell others not to go,
  To that God-forsaken country in the hills of Mexico.

197. WHEN I WAS A COWBOY

FROM: p. 210 of *Negro Folk Songs as Sung by Lead Belly*, Lomax (Macmillan, copyright 1936). SEE: Lomax I, 39. © Ludlow Music, 1959.

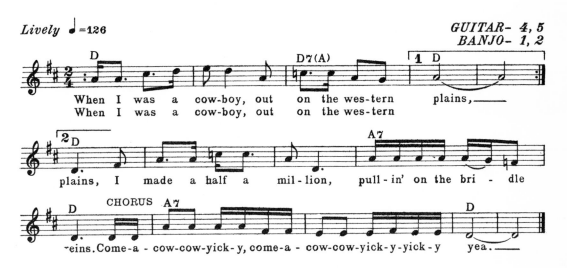

1 When I was a cowboy, out on the western plains, (2)
  I made a half a million, pullin' on the bridle reins.
  CHORUS:
  Come-a-cow-cow-yicky, come-a-cow-cow-yicky-yicky-yea.

2 O the hardest battle was ever on the western plains, (2)
  When me an' a bunch of cowboys run into Jesse James. (CHO.)

3 When me an' a bunch of cowboys run into Jesse James, (2)
  The bullets was a-fallin' just like a show'r of rain. (CHO.)

4 O the hardest battle was ever on-a Bunker Hill, (2)
  When me an' a bunch of cowboys run into Buffalo Bill. (CHO.)

5 When your house catch a-fire and they ain't no water roun', (2)
  Throw your jelly out the window, let the doggone shack burn down. (CHO.)

198. THE WILD RIPPLING WATER

FROM: p. 183 of *Cowboy Songs*, Lomax (Macmillan, N.Y. 1910, 1938). Lomax adaptation from the Gant Family, Austin, Texas. SEE: Belden, 239, links song with the *Lovers' Conversation* of Theocritus, 27th Idyll; Brown III, 24; Index (*The Nightingale*); Randolph I, 268; Reeves, 85; Sharp II, 192. Boccaccio uses same theme in 4th story of 5th day of *Decameron*. Occurs in English balladry as far back as 17th century, printed as *Nightingale Song* or *Soldier's Rare Musik and Maid's Recreation*, Roxburghe Ballads IX, 170. Found in modern currency England and southern U.S.

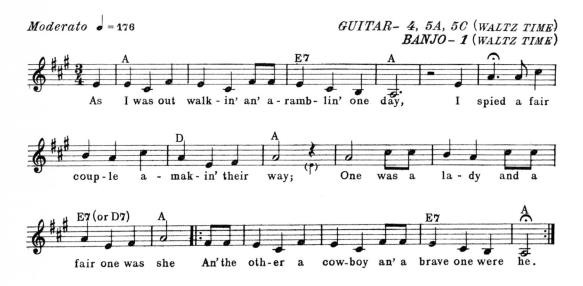

1 As I was out walkin' an' a-ramblin' one day,
   I spied a fair couple a-makin' their way;
   One was a lady and a fair one was she,
   An' the other a cowboy, an' a brave one were he.   (2)

2 Says, ' Where are you goin', my pretty fair maid?'
   ' Jest down by the river, jest down by the shade,
   Jest down by the river, jest down by the spring,
   See the wild ripplin' water an' hear the nightingale sing.'   (2)

3 They hadn't been there but an hour or so,
   Till he drew from his satchel a fiddle and bow;
   He tuned his fiddle all on the high string,
   An' he played this tune over an' over again.   (2)

4 ' Now,' said the cowboy, ' I should have been gone.'
   ' No, no,' said the pretty maid, ' jest play one more song.
   I'd rather hear the fiddle played on that one string
   As to see the water glide an' hear the nightingale sing.'   (2)

5 He tuned up his fiddle and he rosined his bow;
   He played her a lecture, he played it all o'er;
   He played her a lecture that made the valley ring.
   ' Hark! Hark!' said the fair maid. ' Hear the nightingale sing.'   (2)

6 She said, ' Dear cowboy, will you marry me?'
He said: ' Dear lady, that could never be.
I have a wife in Arizona, an' a lady is she;
One wife on a cow-ranch is plenty for me.' (2)

7 ' I'll go to Mexico, I'll stay there one year;
I'll drink sweet wine an' I'll drink lots of beer.
If I ever return, it will be in the spring,
To see the bright ripplin' water, hear the nightingale sing.' (2)

8 ' Come all you young maidens, take warning from me;
Never place your affections in a cowboy too free;
He'll go away an' leave you like mine did me;
Leave you to rock cradles, sing ' Bye-o-babee.' (2)

199. MY LOVE IS A RIDER

FROM: p. 267 of *Cowboy Songs*, Lomax (Macmillan, N.Y., 1910, 1938). SEE: Randolph II, 228. This often bawdy song is sometimes attributed to Belle Starr, the cowgirl bandit. Also claimed by a cowboy named Hatch, who came into Platte City, Nebraska in 1882 with a trail herd.

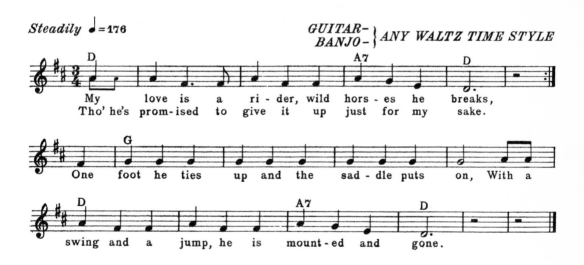

1 My love is a rider, wild horses he breaks,
Though he's promised to give it up just for my
One foot he ties up and the saddle puts on, [sake.
With a swing and a jump, he is mounted and gone.

2 The first time I met him, 'twas early last spring,
Riding a bronco, a high-headed thing,
He tipped me a wink as he gaily did go,
For he wished me to look at his bucking bronco.

3 The next time I saw him, 'twas late in the fall,
Swinging the girls at Tomlinson's ball,
He laughed and he talked as we danced to and fro,
Promised never to ride on another bronco.

4 He made me some presents, among them a ring,
The return that I made him was a far better thing,
'Twas a young maiden's heart, I'd have you all know;
He's won it by riding his bucking bronco.

5 My love has a gun, and that gun he can use.
　　But he's quit his gun fighting as well as his booze;
　　And he's sold off his saddle, his spurs and his rope,
　　There'll be no more cow-punching and that's what
　　　　　　　　　　　　　　　　　I hope.

6 My love has a gun that has gone to the bad,
　　Which makes poor old Jimmy feel pretty damn sad,
　　For the gun it shoots high and the gun it shoots low,
　　And it wobbles about like a bucking bronco.

7 Now all you young maidens where'er you reside,
　　Beware of the cowboy who swings the rawhide,
　　He'll court you and pet you and leave you and go
　　In the spring up the trail on his bucking bronco.

200. THE DYING COWBOY

Adapted and arranged by Alan Lomax. FROM: p. 417 of *Cowboy Songs*, Lomax
(Macmillan, N.Y., 1910, 1938). SEE: Belden, 393 (shows its publication in
Wayman's Song Sheets and wide distribution from Nova Scotia to Tennessee,
the Mid-West and Far West); Laws, 131. SEE ALSO: *One Morning in May* and
St. James Hospital, Sharp II, 164.

Smoothly ♩.=52

GUITAR- 5A, 6A, 2A
BANJO- 1, WALTZ TIME

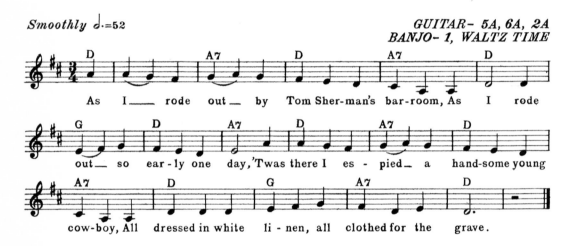

As I rode out by Tom Sherman's bar-room, As I rode out so ear-ly one day, 'Twas there I es-pied a hand-some young cow-boy, All dressed in white li-nen, all clothed for the grave.

1 As I rode out by Tom Sherman's bar-room,
　　As I rode out so early one day,
　　'Twas there I espied a handsome young cowboy,
　　All dressed in white linen, all clothed for the grave.

2 'I see by your outfit that you are a cowboy,'
　　These words he did say as I boldly stepped by.
　　'Come sit down beside me and hear my sad story,
　　For I'm shot in the breast and I know I must die.

3 'Then beat your drum slowly and play your fife lowly,
　　And play the dead march as you carry me along,
　　And take me to the graveyard and throw the sod o'er me,
　　For I'm a young cowboy and I know I've done wrong.

4 ' 'Twas once in the saddle I used to go dashing,
  'Twas once in the saddle I used to go gay,
  But I first took to drinking and then to card-playing,
  Got shot in the body and I'm dying today.

5 ' Let sixteen gamblers come handle my coffin,
  Let sixteen young cowboys come sing me a song,
  Take me to the green valley and lay the sod o'er me,
  For I'm a poor cowboy and I know I've done wrong.

6 ' Go bring me back a cup of cool water
  To cool my parched lips,' this cowboy then said.
  Before I returned, his soul had departed
  And gone to his Maker—the cowboy lay dead.

7 We swung our ropes slowly and rattled our spurs lowly,
  And gave a wild whoop as we carried him on,
  For we all loved our comrade, so brave, young and handsome,
  We all loved our comrade, although he'd done wrong.

201. THE SAILOR CUT DOWN IN HIS PRIME

Recorded by Alan Lomax from singing of Charlie Wills, Dorset, England.
This form, which may be oldest, is associated with the town of Bristol. SEE:
Belden, 392; Index (*St. James Hospital*); Randolph, 179; Reeves, 188; Scarborough, 94; Sharp II, 164.

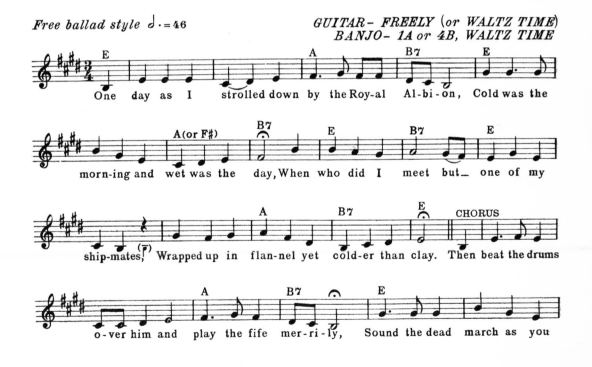

Free ballad style ♩. = 46

GUITAR– FREELY (or WALTZ TIME)
BANJO– 1A or 4B, WALTZ TIME

One day as I strolled down by the Roy-al Al-bi-on, Cold was the
morn-ing and wet was the day, When who did I meet but one of my
ship-mates, Wrapped up in flan-nel yet cold-er than clay. Then beat the drums
o-ver him and play the fife mer-ri-ly, Sound the dead march as you

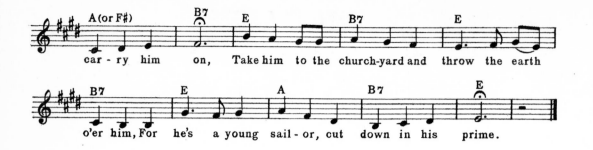

car - ry him on, Take him to the church-yard and throw the earth o'er him, For he's a young sail - or, cut down in his prime.

1 One day as I strolled down by the Royal Albion,
Cold was the morning and wet was the day,
When who did I meet but one of my shipmates,
Wrapped up in flannel yet colder than clay.
CHORUS:
Then beat the drums over him and play the fife merrily,
Sound the dead march as you carry him on,
Take him to the churchyard and throw the earth o'er him,
For he's a young sailor, cut down in his prime.

2 He asked for a candle to light him to bed with,
Likewise a flannel to wrap round his head;
For his poor head was aching, his poor heart was breaking,
For he was a sailor cut down in his prime. (CHO.)

3 His poor old father, his good old mother,
Oft-times had told him about his past life,
When along with those flash girls his money he'd squander,
And along with those flash girls he took his delight. (CHO.)

4 And now he is dead and he lies in his coffin,
Six jolly sailors shall carry him along,
And six jolly maidens shall carry white roses,
Not for to smell him as they pass him by. (CHO.)

5 At the top of the street you will see two girls standing;
One to the other they whispered and said:
' Here comes a young man whose money we've squandered,
Here comes a young sailor cut down in his prime.' (CHO.)

6 On the top of his headstone you'll see these words written:
' All you young men take a warning by me,
And never go courting with the girls in the city,
Flash girls in the city were the ruin of me.' (CHO.)

202. BILLY THE KID

FROM: p. 136 of *American Ballads and Folk Songs*, Lomax (Macmillan, N.Y., 1934). As sung by Frank Crummitt. SEE: Lomax, I, 140.

Smoothly ♩ = 208

GUITAR— ANY ¾ STYLE
BANJO— 4B or 1

I'll sing you a true song of Bil-ly the Kid,
I'll sing of the des-per-ate deeds that he did, Way out in New Mex-i-co,
long, long a-go, When a man's on-ly chance was his own for-ty-four.

1 I'll sing you a true song of Billy the Kid,
I'll sing of the desperate deeds that he did,
Way out in New Mexico, long, long ago,
When a man's only chance was his own forty-four.

2 When Billy the Kid was a very young lad,
In old Silver City he went to the bad,
Way out in the West with a gun in his hand
At the age of twelve years he killed his first man.

3 Fair Mexican maidens play guitars and sing
A song about Billy, their boy-bandit king,
How ere his young manhood had reached its sad end,
He'd a notch in his pistol for twenty-one men.

4 'Twas on the same night when poor Billy died,
He said to his friends, ' I'm not satisfied.
There are twenty-one men I have put bullets through,
And Sheriff Pat Garrett must make twenty-two.'

5 Now this is how Billy the Kid met his fate,
The bright moon was shining, the hour was late;
Shot down by Pat Garrett, who once was his friend,
The young outlaw's life had now come to its end.

6 There's many a man with a face fine and fair,
Who starts out in life with a chance to be square,
But just like poor Billy he wanders astray
And loses his life in the very same way.

203. TYIN' A KNOT IN THE DEVIL'S TAIL

FROM: p. 406 of *American Ballads and Folk Songs*, Lomax (Macmillan, N.Y., 1934).
SEE: Cisco Houston, Folkways FP 22; Laws, 141; Charles Badger Clark poem
'Way High Up in the Mokiones,' published in *Sun and Saddle Leather*, 1915.
Piano arrangement by DON BANKS

1 Way high up in the Syree peaks,
  Where the yellow pines grow tall,
  Sandy Bob and Buster Jiggs
  Had a round-up camp last fall.

2 They took their horses and their runnin' irons,
  And maybe a dog or two,
  And they 'lowed they'd brand all the long-eared
  That came within their view.   [calves

3 Well, many a long-eared dogie
  That didn't hush up by day,
  Had his long ears whittled and his old hide
  In a most artistic way.   [scorched

4 Then one fine day said Buster Jiggs,
  As he throwed his cigo down:
  ' I'm tired of cow biography
  And I 'lows I'm goin' to town.'

5 They saddles up and they hits them a lope,
  Fer it weren't no sight of a ride,
  An' them was the days when an old cow hand
  Could oil up his old insides.

6 They starts her out at the Kentucky bar
  At the head of the whisky row,
  And they winds her up at the Depot House,
  Some forty drinks below.

7 They sets her up and turns her around
  And goes her the other way,
  And to tell you the Lord forsaken truth
  Them boys got drunk that day.

8 Well, as they was a-headin' back to camp
  And packin' a pretty good load,
  Who should they meet but the Devil, himself,
  Come prancin' down the road.

9 Now the Devil he said: ' You cowboy skunks,
  You better go hunt your hole,
  'Cause I come up from the hell's rim-rock
  To gather in your souls.'

10 Said Buster Jiggs: ' Now we're just from town
  An' feelin' kind o' tight,
  And you ain't gonna get no cowboy souls
  Without some kind of a fight.'

11 So he punched a hole in his old throw-rope
  And he slings her straight and true,
  And he roped the Devil right around the horns
  He takes his dallies* true.

12 Old Sandy Bob was a reata†-man
  With his rope all coiled up neat,
  But he shakes her out and he builds him a loop
  And he roped the Devil's hind feet.

13 They threw him down on the desert ground,
  While the irons was a-gettin' hot,
  They cropped and swallow-forked his ears
  And branded him up a lot.

14 And they pruned him up with a dehorning saw
  And knotted his tail for a joke,
  Rode off and left him bellowing there,
  Necked up to a lilac-jack oak.

15 Well, if you ever travel in the Syree peaks
  And you hear one helluva wail,
  You'll know it's nothin' but the Devil himself,
  Raisin' bell about the knots in his tail.

* turns of the rope around the saddle horn.   † lasso.

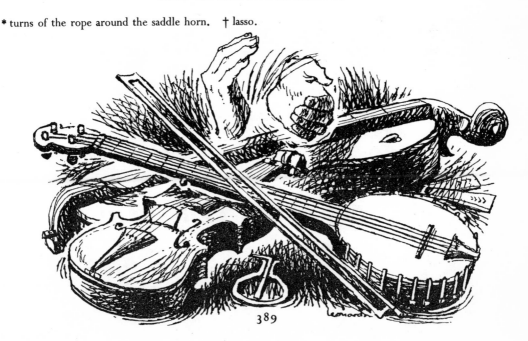

389

PRAIRIE FARMERS

204. IN KANSAS

' Now give me your honest opinion of western Kansas,' Father asked. ' Well—sir, Parson,' began Johnston. ' This here country is the '' short grass country ''. From the one-hundredth meridian, which we are now a-settin' on, clean through to the foot hills and on south and west, it is a desert and will not raise nothing but grass, unless you irrigate it. It is a land of sand burrs, soap weeds, cacti, badgers, owls and coyotes—everything out here needs thorns, claws, or some kind of stickers. Sometimes I think we need fish hooks to help hang on with when the wind blows. This here country is the '' American Desert ''.'

' What do you stay here for then?' asked the Father.

' That is a fair question,' admitted the other. ' I reckon I am like the coyotes, rattlesnakes and prairie dogs,' said he. ' I have always been a triflin' sort of a cuss and maybe livin' out here in this place is good enough for me—serves me right, good place to do penance. Maybe when I die, it will kind o' hurry the Devil to find some punishment for me that I ain't already been used to from livin' in Kansas.'

QUOTE: *Wild West Exaggerations*, Eli Perkins (alias Melville Landon) (Cassell, 1891).

205. THE LITTLE OLD SOD SHANTY

THE ORDINARY sod house had grave faults. Its few windows permitted little light and air for ventilation. The immaculate housekeeper abominated them because they were hard to keep clean. The dirt and straw kept dropping on everything, and few of the sod-covered houses really turned water. A heavy rain came, soaked into the dirt roof, and soon, little rivulets of muddy water were running through the sleepers' hair. One pioneer woman remembered frying pan-cakes with someone holding an umbrella over her and the stove . . . When the roof was well-soaked, its weight was immense. The heavy rafters sank deeper and deeper into the soggy walls until occasionally the roof caved in, or the walls collapsed, burying the people underneath the ruins.

The pioneer parody of the Irish music-hall song *The Little Old Log Cabin in the Lane* tells the rest of the story.

QUOTE: *The Sod House Frontier*, Dick Everett (Appleton-Century-Crofts Inc., N.Y., 1937), p. 110.

206. THE RED RIVER SHORE

He rode till he came in three miles of the place,
Then he turned himself all around,
And there he espied some seven iron men
Come hastening from the town.

Get down, get down, Lady Margaret, he said,
And hold the bridle in your hand,
Till I turn back to yonder's green
And fight them seven iron men . . .

THESE VERSES occur in an American form of the ancient Anglo-Scandinavian ballad *Hildebrand* or *Earl Brand*, a tragic tale of bride capture. *The Bold Soldier*, a comic eighteenth century descendant of that ancient piece, gave rise to the present song which contains the basic plot of hundreds of western films—the story of a poor, but honest cowpuncher who runs away with the rancher's or squatter's daughter. It also hints at the solution life provided for the conflict between the squatters and the ranchers that troubled the plains country for a generation.

The cowboys had gentled the great American desert, and millions of square miles of virgin grain-land invited the land-hungry people of the East. They came with a rush. Between 1879 and 1890 the population of Kansas grew from 300,000 to a million and a half—of Texas from 800,000 to two millions and a quarter. Other prairie states developed at the same speed. The plains passed out of the control of the rancher kings into the hands of the settlers, but not before a good deal of blood had been shed.

The settlers' barbed-wire fences doomed the open range. Cattlemen cut the wire and shot at the posthole diggers. But the antagonism between the two groups ran deeper than land and politics. Two opposing ways of life were in conflict. The cowboy spent his money freely and welcomed all strangers at the chuck wagon. He liked a good horse, a good time, a bottle of whisky, a pretty girl, and he would risk his life to defend his honour. He despised the nester, or squatter, as a poor rider, a pennypincher, a coward, a thick-skinned peasant, and a man who sometimes refused hospitality or asked to be paid for a meal. The nesters hated and feared the swashbuckling cowboys, who carried guns, mistreated their horses, quarrelled over trifles, preferred the saloon to the church, wasted their money, and had scant regard for either property or propriety.

Sooner or later, however, a cowboy would see some nester girl ' who was prettier than a calf looking through a paling fence ', or he would notice how ' the pore little barefooted thing made a five-toed track on her way to Sunday school '. Next day he might ride up to the sod shanty, pitch her little brother a half-dollar to open the gate for him and present the family with half a beef out of his boss's herd. If things went smoothly, this lonesome cowboy who saw a woman maybe once in nine months, and whose steady diet consisted of sourdough bread, beefsteak, and coffee, might be sitting down to a meal of smothered chicken, hot biscuits and home-made jelly, fresh vegetables, buttermilk, and apple pie, while a certain feminine heart began to gallop under a polka-dot dress. In the ranch bunk-house the cowpoke would begin to dream of salt-rising biscuits, served hot out of the oven by a pair of small freckled hands. The deed was as good as done, and the Wild West would soon lose another cowboy to the nesters.

SOURCE: *Folkways on Bear Creek.*

207. HOG DROVERS

IN THE NEIGHBOURHOOD where I was born and reared the better class of people in the country did not believe in dancing. Regular dances, where the music was furnished by a fiddler, were held, for the most part, only in the homes of the rough element. They were generally accompanied by card-playing, and frequently by drunkenness and fighting. The better class ranked dancing, in the moral scale, along with gambling and fishing on Sunday. The church rules forbade dancing, and there was no thought of evading the letter of the law. Therefore, if the boy or girl danced a single quadrille to the music of a violin he had ' broke over,' as the common expression was, and knew that at the next protracted meeting he was a fit subject for re-conversion, and that the preacher's pointed words were aimed straight at him; while, on the other hand, he might dance to the time of his own singing from seven in the evening to three o'clock the next morning, and suffer therefrom no qualms of conscience. It was not dancing; it was only playing.

The invitations to these parties were by word of mouth, and delivered by one or more young men on horseback, who were said to ' get up ' the party. All of the eligible young people within a radius of from three to five miles were invited.

The playing would begin as soon as four or five couples had arrived, and would continue, with only short intermissions for breathing spells, until midnight to three o'clock in the morning. It consisted of keeping step to the singing, and at the same time going through various movements; swinging partners by one hand or both; advancing, retreating and bowing.

. . . as in this American variant of the old English children's game *Here Come Three Dukes*.

QUOTE: JAFL XXIV, No. XCIII, 1911, p. 295. *Missouri Play Party*, Mrs. L. D. Ames.

208. TIDEO

A TEXAS swinging play.

. . . The music of these dances carried forward a sort of afterglow into the next day for those who went about their work. The beat and melody kept time with the rhythm and beat of the horses' hooves, the swish and impact of a chopping axe, and the squeal of saddle or harness. The mind, constricted by the drudgery of daily work, was, for a time, released, lifted out of itself and transported into a magic world of enjoyment. There was always much to remember; the aroma of a faint perfume, the touch of a sweetheart's hand, the bright smile of a beaming face in the glow of lamplight . . .

QUOTE: *Folkways on Bear Creek*, p. 145.

209. LORD LOVEL

The romances of Sir Walter Scott exercised a tremendous influence on the imagination of the old South and South-West, and boys and girls were brought up to live and love by the rose-coloured canons of chivalry as Scott defined it then. Countless Rowenas pined palely while their Quentins and Lochinvars galloped away to the Civil War, to fight Indians, or simply to punch steers north to Cheyenne or Chicago. So it was that from Maryland to West Texas, rural American Ivanhoes contested in tournaments, which matched Scott's descriptions as nearly as the law allowed.* So it was that medieval ballads like *Lord Lovel* survived among the ranching and farming folk of the Great Plains.

* See J. A. Lomax, *Adventures of a Ballad Hunter*, p. 15 (Macmillan, 1947).

210. THE HELL-BOUND TRAIN

WE HAD camp meetings every summer out east of town under a big brush arbor, and everybody in Big Spring went. It wasn't fitten if you didn't. People came from way up on the prairies to our camp meetings and cow outfits sometimes rode in. When we had all-day meetings and dinner-on-the-ground and camp-meetings we would have a big picnic spread, and all the women in town would try to outdo each other with what they cooked up.

Preaching at those camp meetings would hit a pitch of emotionalism and fervour which was probably very good for our citizens, especially the ones that lived on lonely mesas all year and just kept penning their emotions up. They could really let them out in camp meeting in the singing, and the praying had the amen corner.

Once I saw one of these preachers knock his watch off the pulpit and jump down on it—carried away, that's all. They would ask everybody who was saved to hold up his hand in order to make those who were still lost sheep aware of it . . . A lot of people stumbled to the altar by these means just to get rid of the stigma. As soon as the special revivalist left town, they started shooting up the Klondike again . . . One old drunk cowhand went to a camp meeting and got religion every night. When they would call for mourners, he would waddle and swagger down the aisle to the mourner's bench, where he would howl like a lone wolf.

I remember one case where a pious sister approached a well-cargoed cowhand and said, ' What are you going to do when you approach the Lord with whisky on your breath?'

The old boy looked up and said, ' Lady, when I approach the Lord, I'm goin' to leave my breath here!'

QUOTE: *Big Spring*, Shine Phillips, p. 73.

211. COLORADO TRAIL

A MAN of the Old West hardly ever got downhearted about anything unless something happened to the woman he loved and was married to. They were a quiet, solemn kind of lot, mighty short on kissing and all that stuff women are supposed to set such store by, but I reckon they loved their wives as much as any men that ever lived, even if they rarely said so. And the women must have known it with a woman's intuition. Anything like a divorce was unheard of, and what these women went through in remote ranch houses, far from any of their kind, with the most primitive equipment for their housekeeping and even for existence, was plenty. That pioneer female who once said that Texas was heaven for men and horses, but hell on women and dogs, spoke a mouthful. But women stuck it out and brought up large families, one way or another. If they hadn't stuck it out, I doubt if the men would have . . .

QUOTE: *Big Spring*, Shine Phillips, pp. 41, 131.

212. SPRINGFIELD MOUNTAIN
(Texas version)

WESTERN RANCH HANDS had plenty of snake trouble. Not only were western rattlesnakes more poisonous than their eastern cousins, but they were considerably more sociable. Sometimes at night they crawled into a man's blankets for warmth and he would wake in the morning to find a pair of cold eyes staring into his. And, as the Yankee rattlesnake stories travelled west, they grew taller and taller . . .

393

Rattlesnakes? Yes, sir, I have seen rattlesnakes. Some years ago I had a meadow on the prairie of three hundred acres, and when it came haying-time, rattlesnakes were so thick there that of seven Irishmen I sent to mow it one morning, five were bitten so that they died instantly.

Well now, I had a pair of boots made of the toughest bull's hide, doubled, and I put them on one fine morning and taking a scythe, went into the meadow and began to mow.

The snakes came at me a dozen at a time, and whenever they struck their fangs into the tough leather, it held them fast. I took no notice of them but kept on mowing till they hung in such numbers about my legs that the weight became troublesome, and then I stopped mowing and cut them off with the scythe. I had to do this about once in a half hour, and when I went home to dinner the boys picked off enough heads to fill a peck measure heaping full. I kept this up for a fortnight, and by that time, I can tell you, snakes were getting rather scarce in that particular meadow.

QUOTE: Dorson, from *A Summer Cruise on the Coast of New England*, Robert Carter (Boston, 1864).

213. FOD

As a COMPANION PIECE to this western variant of *Springfield Mountain*, here is the story of a lonely railroad telegrapher in a small depot who taught a rattler to be assistant operator . . .

Soon as I would make a letter, he'd raise his tail and try to imitate the dots and dashes and spaces with his rattles. He had a little trouble with the letter ' P ' which consists of five dots. He seemed to lose control of his tail muscles on that one. But he finally mastered the ' P ' and his Morse was a joy to listen to.

But the biggest lift he gave me was in helping me report trains. As you know, a snake's tongue when extended from his mouth is sort of like a radio antenna. Leander would crawl on the telegraph table in the depot's bay window, stick his head out, poke his tongue out some more and get the vibration of a train thirty-five miles away. Then he would come over to the table where I was sleeping, touch my face tenderly with that sensitive tongue of his, and I knew that it was time to rouse up and exchange signals with that train crew and report their passing . . .

QUOTE: ' Greenhouse', Paul Flowers, in *The Commercial Appeal*, Memphis, Tenn. Reprinted *Illinois Central Magazine*, Vol. 32, 1944.

204. IN KANSAS

From singing of G. Graham, San Jose, Calif., 1938, recorded by S. Robertson, AAFS—3818 A 3. SEE: Belden, 428; Randolph III, 7. Missouri version said to have been written by Beecher, after Civil War, based on a popular song in 1844. Probably song derived from the Irish *The Praties They Grows Small*, which became known in 1848 potato famine.

Piano arrangement by DON BANKS

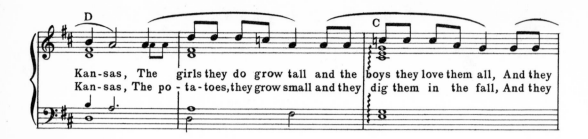

CHORUS:
All who want to roam in Kansas, (2)
All who want to roam, go and get yourself a home,
Be contented with your doom in Kansas.

1 O the girls they do grow tall in Kansas, (2)
The girls they do grow tall and the boys they
love them all,
And they marry 'em in the fall in Kansas.

2 The potatoes they grow small in Kansas, (2)
The potatoes they grow small and they dig
them in the fall,
And they eat them tops and all in Kansas.

3 O they chew tobacco thin in Kansas, (2)
O they chew tobacco thin and it dribbles
on their chin
And they lick it back again in Kansas.

In Ozark Folk Songs, Vance Randolph reports these stem-winding stanzas, sung about Arkansas, pronounced Arkán-sas

1 O the chickens they grow tall in Arkansas, (2)
The chickens they grow tall and their meat
is full of gall,
They eat um guts and all in Arkansas.

2 O they make polecat pie in Arkansas, (2)
O they make polecat pie and the crust is
made of rye,
You must eat it if you die in Arkansas.

3 The roosters they lay eggs in Arkansas, (2)
The roosters they lay eggs as big as whisky kegs,
An' there's whiskers on their legs in Arkansas.

4 The people never wed in Arkansas, (2)
The people never wed, or so I've heard it said,
They just tumble into bed in Arkansas.

205. THE LITTLE OLD SOD SHANTY

Sung by Clyde (Slim) Wilson, Missouri, 1936. LC record AAFS 3199B-1.
SEE: Botkin V, 742; Lomax I, 405; Randolph II, 219. A western setting of the popular minstrel song *The Little Old Log Cabin in the Lane*. John A. Lomax says it was composed in 1888 by Linden Baker of Kernilt, West Va., after his brother returned from spending several years in Kansas.

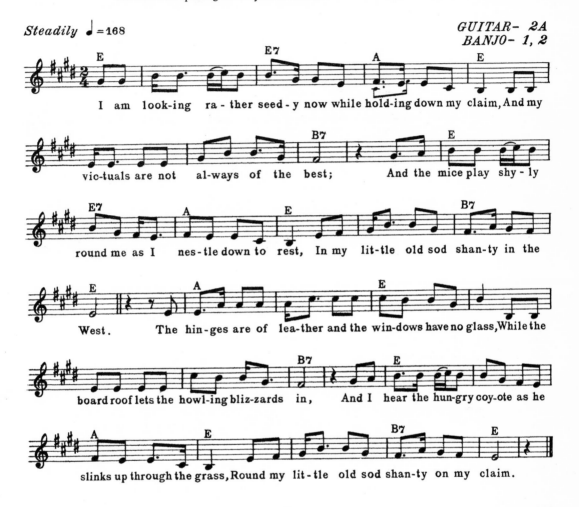

Steadily ♩ = 168

GUITAR– 2A
BANJO– 1, 2

I am look-ing ra-ther seed-y now while hold-ing down my claim, And my vic-tuals are not al-ways of the best; And the mice play shy-ly round me as I nes-tle down to rest, In my lit-tle old sod shan-ty in the West. The hin-ges are of lea-ther and the win-dows have no glass, While the board roof lets the howl-ing bliz-zards in, And I hear the hun-gry coy-ote as he slinks up through the grass, Round my lit-tle old sod shan-ty on my claim.

1 I am looking rather seedy now while holding down my claim,
And my victuals are not always of the best;
And the mice play shyly round me as I nestle down to rest,
In my little old sod shanty in the West.
The hinges are of leather and the windows have no glass,
While the board roof lets the howling blizzards in,
And I hear the hungry coyote as he slinks up through the grass,
Round my little old sod shanty on my claim.

2 Yet I rather like the novelty of living in this way,
   Though my bill of fare is always rather tame,
   But I'm happy as a clam on the land of Uncle Sam
   In the little old sod shanty on my claim.
   But when I left my eastern home, a bachelor so gay,
   To try and win my way to wealth and fame,
   I little thought I'd come down to burning twisted hay
   In the little old sod shanty on my claim.

3 My clothes are plastered o'er with dough, I'm looking like a fright,
   And everything is scattered round the room,
   But I wouldn't give the freedom that I have out in the West
   For the table of the eastern man's old home.
   Still I wish some tender woman would pity on me take,
   And relieve me from the mess that I am in;
   The angel, how I'd bless her, if this her home she'd make
   In the little old sod shanty on my claim.

4 And we would make our fortunes on the prairies of the West,
   Just as happy as two lovers we'd remain;
   We'd forget the trials and troubles we endured at the first,
   In the little old sod shanty on my claim.
   And if fate should bless us with now and then an heir,
   To cheer our hearts with honest pride of fame,
   O then we'd be contented for the toil that we had spent
   In the little old sod shanty on our claim.

206. THE RED RIVER SHORE

FROM: p.298 of *Cowboy Songs*, Lomax (Macmillan, N.Y., 1910, 1938), arranged from singing of Mrs. Minta Morgan, Bells, Texas. This cowboy romance is a western version of *New River Shore* (Brown II, 286), which is in turn connected with *Locks and Bolts* (Brown II, 285). There is another similar broadside-style ballad, *The Bold Soldier* (Brown II, 287), which is often connected with *The Douglas Tragedy* (Child, No. 7). Randolph I, 303 mentions a *White River Shore*. SEE: Belden, 103; JEFFS I, 108.

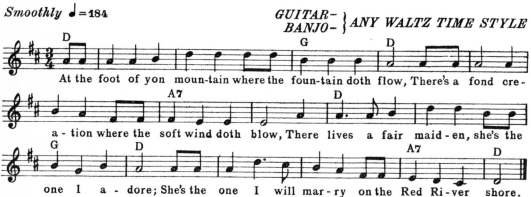

Smoothly ♩=184

GUITAR—
BANJO— } ANY WALTZ TIME STYLE

At the foot of yon moun-tain where the foun-tain doth flow, There's a fond cre-a-tion where the soft wind doth blow, There lives a fair maid-en, she's the one I a-dore; She's the one I will mar-ry on the Red Ri-ver shore.

1 At the foot of yon mountain where the fountain doth flow,
   There's a fond creation where the soft wind doth blow,
   There lived a fair maiden, she's the one I adore;
   She's the one I will marry on the Red River shore.

2 I asked her old father if he'd give her to me.
' No sir, she shan't marry no cowboy,' said he.
So I jumped on my bronco and away I did ride,
A-leaving my true love on the Red River side.

3 She wrote me a letter and she wrote it so kind,
And in this letter these words you could find,
' Come back to me, darling, you're the one I adore,
You're the one I would marry on the Red River shore.'

4 So I jumped on my bronco and away I did ride,
To marry my true love on the Red River side.
But her dad knew the secret, and with twenty and four
Came to fight this young cowboy on the Red River shore.

5 I drew my six-shooter, spun around and around,
Till six men were wounded and seven were down,
No use for an army of twenty and four,
I'm bound for my true love on the Red River shore.

6 Such is the fortune of all womenkind,
They are always controlled, they are always made mind,
Controlled by their parents until they are wives,
Then slaves of their husbands the rest of their lives.

207. HOG DROVERS

Arranged by Alan Lomax from singing of John A. Lomax, who learned it in
central Texas in the 80's. Singing directions come from Botkin I, 205. SEE:
Gomme II, 257; Newell, 232; many European versions. Song is kin to *Knights
of Spain, Three Dukes A-riding.*

With a swing ♩=176

GUITAR– 2A, 4 (WALTZ TIME)
BANJO– 1 (WALTZ TIME)

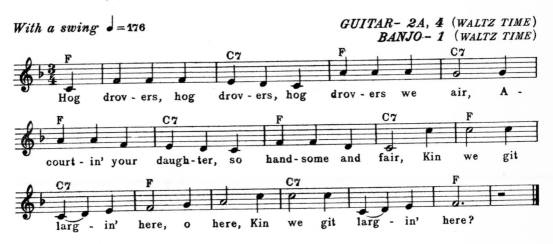

Hog drov-ers, hog drov-ers, hog drov-ers we air, A-
court-in' your daugh-ter, so hand-some and fair, Kin we git
larg-in' here, o here, Kin we git larg-in' here?

*(A man and a woman sit side by side in two chairs. A
circle of couples marches around singing, while two men
approach.)*
* are

1 Hog drovers, hog drovers, hog drovers we air,*
A-courtin' your daughter, so handsome and fair,
Kin we git largin' here, o here,
Kin we git largin' here?

(*Man sings.*)

2 This is my daughter and she sets by my side,
And none of you hog drovers kin have her
                                    for your bride,
And you can't git largin' here, o here,
And you can't git largin' here.

(*Two men sing.*)

3 Don't care for your daughter, much less for
                                    yourself,
We'll go on a piece further and better ourselves,
And we don't want largin', *etc.*

(*Two new men come marching and singing.*)

4 Gold miners, gold miners, *etc.*

(*Man sings.*)

5 This is my daughter and she sets by my side,
And one of you miners kin have her for your
By bringing another one here, o here,   [bride,
By bringing another one here.

(*Girl in chair chooses one of the two gold miners. Second gold miner chooses a new girl for chair in centre. She chooses a girl to march with him. The circle begins its march again with two cowboys approaching and singing.*)

6 Cowboys, cowboys, *etc.*

(*Man in chair.*)

7 This is my daughter and she sets in my lap,
And none of you cowboys kin take her from
                                    her pap, *etc.*

(*The game continues as above. School teachers are accepted ; oil drillers not accepted ; farmers usually accepted, etc.*)

208. TIDEO

Arranged by Alan Lomax from the singing of John A. Lomax, who learned it in
central Texas in the 80's. SEE: Botkin I, 332 ; Randolph III, 313 (he supposes
that *Tideo* may originally have been *Toddy-o*).
Piano arrangement by DON BANKS

Come jingle at the windows,
Tideo!
Jingle at the windows,
Tideo!
Jingle at the windows,
Tideo!
Come jingle at the windows low.

1 Skip one window, Tideo! (3)
Come jingle at the window low. (CHO.)

2 Skip two windows, Tideo! (3)
Come jingle at the windows low. (CHO.)

And so on through 3 and 4 windows, etc.

209. LORD LOVEL

Collected and arranged by John and Alan Lomax from singing of the Gant Family, Austin, Texas, 1935. SEE: Barry, 139-49; Belden, 52; Child No. 75; Flanders III, 215; Guide and Index; Randolph I, 113; Sharp I, 146. This was probably the most common Child ballad in America during 19th century. Printed in many song books and broadsides, and widely parodied, especially by 19th century English comedian, Sam Cowell. American texts seem to be derived from a London broadside print, but singers are constantly reworking the text, as in this version.

Smoothly ♩ = 152

GUITAR— *2A or 4, WALTZ STYLE*
BANJO— *1 or 4B*

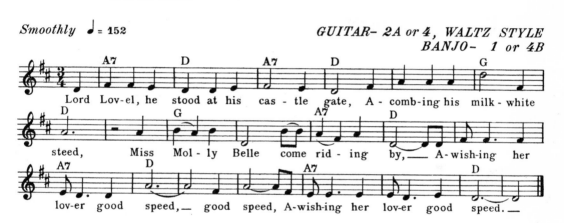

Lord Lov-el, he stood at his cas-tle gate, A-comb-ing his milk-white steed, Miss Mol-ly Belle come rid-ing by,— A-wish-ing her lov-er good speed,— good speed, A-wish-ing her lov-er good speed.—

1 Lord Lovel, he stood at his castle gate,
A-combing his milk-white steed,
Miss Molly Belle come riding by,
A-wishing her lover good speed, good speed,
A-wishing her lover good speed.

2 ' O where are you going, Lord Lovel?' she cried
' O where are you going?' cried she.
' I'm going away for a year and a day,
Strange countries for to see, to see,' . . .

3 He hadn't been gone but a very short while,
Not four months to a day,
Till something strange came over his mind
About his loving Mollee, Mollee . . .

4 He mounted all on his milk-white steed
And rode till he came to the town,
And there he heard the death bells a-ringing,
And the people mournin' all round, all round . . .

5 ' O who is dead?' Lord Lovel, he cried,
' O who is dead?' cried he.
' I do not know, but I will declare,
They call her the loving Mollee, Mollee ' . . .

6 ' Go open the coffin,' Lord Lovel, he cried,
' Go open the coffin,' cried he,
' And I'll bid adieu to this wide world
And go with my loving Mollee, Mollee ' . . .

210. THE HELL-BOUND TRAIN

Words by J. W. Pruitt. Tune by Alan Lomax. SEE: Lomax I, 236; Randolph IV, 23.

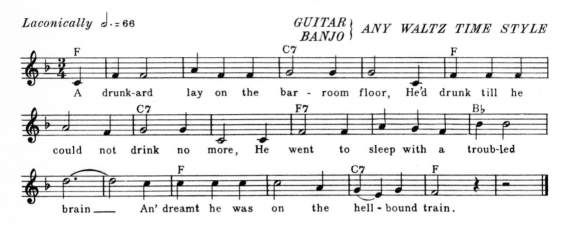

Laconically ♩. = 66

GUITAR }
BANJO } ANY WALTZ TIME STYLE

A drunk-ard lay on the bar - room floor, He'd drunk till he could not drink no more, He went to sleep with a troub-led brain ___ An' dreamt he was on the hell - bound train.

1 A drunkard lay on the bar-room floor,
He'd drunk till he could not drink no more,
He went to sleep with a troubled brain
An' dreamt he was on the hell-bound train.

2 The fireman, he was a crazy tramp,
An' the headlight, it was a brimstone lamp,
The tank was full of lager beer
An' the Devil himself was the engineer.

3 The train it flew at an awful pace,
The brimstone a-burnin' both hands and face,
An' worse an' worse the roadbed grew,
An' faster an' faster the engine flew.

4 He blowed the whistle an' rung the bell,
An' the Devil says, ' Boys, the next stop's Hell.
An' all the passengers yelled with pain
An' begged the Devil to stop the train.

5 But the Devil laughed at their misery,
He hollered an' roared an' yelled with glee.
' You paid your fare with the rest of my load
An' you got to ride to the end of the road.'

6 ' You robbed the weak and done wrong to the poor,
Turned hungry folks away from your door,
You laid up gold till your purses bust,
You ruined young gals with your beastly lust.

7 ' You mocked at God in your stubborn pride,
You murdered an' killed an' cheated an' lied,
You double-crossed partners, an' cussed an' stole.
You belong to me both body an' soul.

8 ' You paid your fare at Shamrock's bar,
An' now you'll ride in the Devil's car,
An' here's one time when I am no liar,
I'll carry you all to the land of fire.

9 ' Your bones will burn in the flames that roar,
You'll scorch an' sizzle from rind to core—'
Then the bar-room rang with an awful scream,
As the drunkard woke from his terrible dream.

10 Down on his knees on the bar-room floor,
He prayed as he never had prayed before,
His prayers an' vows was not in vain,
An' he rode no more on the hell-bound train.

211. COLORADO TRAIL

FROM: *The American Songbag*, Carl Sandburg (Harcourt, Brace, 1927). Used by permission. SEE: Brown II, 626.

Piano arrangement by DON BANKS

1 Eyes like a morning star,
  Cheeks like a rose,
  Laura was a pretty girl,
  God Almighty knows.

2 Weep, all ye little rains,
  Wail, winds, wail,
  All along, along, along
  That Colorado Trail.

212. SPRINGFIELD MOUNTAIN

(Texas version)

FROM: p. 194 of *Cowboy Songs*, Lomax (Macmillan, N.Y., 1910, 1938); Randolph II, 167. Davis notes many variants in Virginia. SEE: *Springfield Mountain*, p. 13.

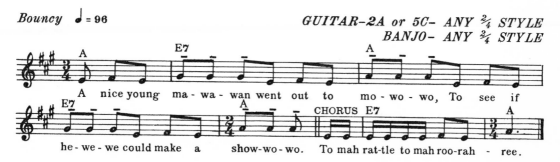

1 A nice young ma-wa-wan went out to mo-wo-wo,
To see if he-we-we could make a sho-wo-wo.
CHORUS:
To mah rattle to mah roo-rah-ree.

2 He scarce had mo-wo-woed all round his fie-wee-weeld,
When up jump-a come-a rattle come-a sna-wa-wake, and bit him on the he-we-weel. (CHO.)

3 'Now Johnny, dear-weer-weer, what made you go-wo-wo
All down in the fie-wee-weeld, so fur to mo-wo-wo?' (CHO.)

4 'Now Sally, mi-wi-wine, I thought you kno-wo-woed,
The grass was ri-wi-wipe and had to be mo-wo-woed.' (CHO.)

5 Then John he di-wi-wied, gave up the gho-wo-wost,
And straight to glo-wo-wory he did po-wo-wost. (CHO.)

6 Come all young me-we-wen and warning ta-wa-wake,
Don't never get bi-wi-wit by a pizenous sna-wa-wake. (CHO.)

213. FOD

Collected by C. Todd and R. Sonkin as adapted and arranged by the King Family, Visalia, Calif., Okie emigrants to Calif. from Missouri. AAFS 8 BI. SEE: Botkin V, 792; Brown III, 221; White, 203. This is a white remake of Negro animal jingles popular in blackface minstrel era. Tune is one of the Middlewestern variants of the *Rattlesnake Song*, which has also contributed to *Fod*. SEE: Lomax V, 28.

Piano arrangement by DON BANKS

Sung fast and poker-faced ♩ = 120

GUITAR- *4 or 1*
BANJO- *1, 2*

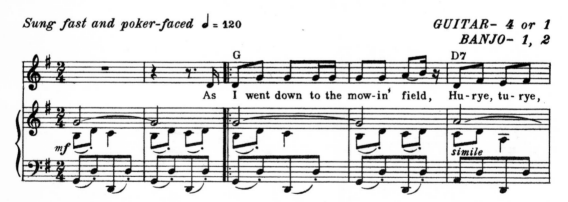

As I went down to the mow-in' field, Hu-rye, tu-rye,

1 As I went down to the mowin' field,
   Hu-rye, tu-rye, fod-a-link-a-dye-do,
   As I went down to the mowin' field,
   Fod!
   As I went down to the mowin' field,
   A big black snake got me by the heel,
   Tu-rolly-day.

2 Well, I fell down upon the ground, (3)
   I shut both eyes and looked all around.

3 I set upon a stump to take my rest, (3)
   I looked like a woodchuck on his nest.

4 The woodchuck grinned a banjo song (3)
   And up stepped a skunk with the britches on.

5 The woodchunk and skunk got into a fight, (3)
   The fumes was so strong they put out the light.

6 They danced and they played till the chimney
                               begin to rust, (3)
   It was hard to tell which smelt the wust.

RAILROADERS AND HOBOES

214. SHE'LL BE COMIN' AROUND THE MOUNTAIN

IN AMERICA, the railroad itself became folklore. From the Catskills to the Cascades the continent was strung with steel like a great harp, singing of money and power to the railroad barons but, for the poor, making a different music. The mule-skinner in the Mississippi bottoms timed his long days by the whistle of the passing trains. The mountaineer, penned up by his southern hills, heard the trains blowing down in the valley and dreamed of the big world ' out yonder '. The blue-noted whistles made a man miss pretty women he'd never seen. Boys in hick towns, lost on the prairie, heard the locomotives snorting and screaming in the night and knew they were bound to small-town stagnation only for the lack of a railroad ticket. You leaned back in your plush seat. The old conductor punched your yellow ticket, while the wheels began to chuckle over the sleepers, and you became a member of the select company to which Marco Polo, Columbus, Stanley and the Wandering Jew belonged. Americans had always had an itching heel. When railroads came along, they began to travel so far and so often that, in the words of the old blues, ' their feet got to rolling like a wheel, yeah, like a wheel '.

In the early days when hoggers of temperament and daring like Casey Jones were risking their lives to set records, every famous engineer designed his own whistle. When the steam ripped through his four, five or six barrel quill, everybody knew who had his hand on the throttle that day. Casey Jones would make his whistle ' say prayers or scream like a Banshee '. One Georgia engineer contrived a whistle that could laugh like a man and kept the hills echoing with wild laughter as he raced by. Another southern engineer could name the stations passed with the blasts on his quill.

One Sunday night in Kentucky, a church service was interrupted by a passing train whose engineer played *How I Love Jesus* on his whistle. After the train had gone by the preacher opined, ' Only a religious man could whistle a hymn that pretty.'

No subject, not even the little dogie, has produced so much good American music as the railroad—our best ballads, *John Henry*, *Casey Jones*, and *The Old '97*; a cycle of powerful worksongs for every aspect of railroad building; spirituals like *This Train* and *All Night Long*: love songs like *Down in the Valley* and *Careless Love*: blues verses without number, indeed the blues might be said to be half-African and half-locomotive rhythm; endless jazz tunes and pop songs such as *Yancey's Special*, *Blues in the Night*, *The Chattanooga Choo-Choo*, *The Fireball Mail*, and *Tuxedo Junction*. Two of the most vivid sermons ever preached on American soil were entitled—*The Black Diamond Express to Hell* and *The White Flyer to Heaven*. What a ship on the sea is to an Englishman, a droshky on the snow to a Russian, a horse on the desert to an Arab, the iron horse became to the men of North America. This early western railroad ditty, anonymously composed, put the original hymn tune (*The Old Ship of Zion*) out of the minds of most of us; it catches the jubilation of that halcyon day when the first steam engine came whistling and snorting into a horse-and-buggy town on the prairies.

406

215. A RAILROADER FOR ME

THERE WERE COWBOYS who bragged they ' could rope anything that could walk, run or fly ', and they proved it by lassoing coyotes, rattlesnakes, turkey buzzards, eagles, buffalo, wild cats, mountain lions, and grizzly bears. The day the first iron horse came rumbling across the plains a cowboy rode his skittish pony up alongside it and threw his lariat straight and true. It settled around the big black smokestack, the cow horse squatted, the saddle girths broke, and the cowboy seemed to sprout wings. When he woke up all patched and bandaged on the saloon pool table, he grinned. ' Well, doc, they say there's always a hoss a feller can't ride, and now I've met a critter that can't be roped.'

The day of Lochinvar on a paint horse had come to an end. The country girls began to roll their eyes at the grease-smudged engineer. The railroader took the place of honour in ditties that had once celebrated the charms of the sailor, the lumberjack, and the cowboy. Meanwhile the cracker-barrel philosopher studied the thing over, spat and observed, 'Well, boys, you know an engineer ain't nothin', really, but a fireman with his brains baked out. '

216. JERRY, GO AN' ILE THAT CAR

Damn be the president, my name's Mike,
I put my hand to it, I drive the spike!

OLD-TIMERS tell about a forthright Irish railroader who, without knocking or removing his hat, strode into the office of the president of the line and asked for a pass. The executive gave Pat a lecture on etiquette and told him to come back again and behave more politely next time. Two hours later, Pat knocked on the door. This time his manners were perfect.

'Now my good man, what can I do for you?' asked the president.

'You can go to hell,' says Pat. 'I got a job and a pass on another railroad.'

Such were the Irishmen who built the early railroads and they stayed behind, in section gangs, to keep the tracks in repair and the trains running on time. Today their descendants have gone on to better jobs, and the deeds of these hard-handed, hard-drinking, Irish railroad builders have been largely forgotten. Their best memorials are the ribbons of gleaming track that span the continent and a few fragmentary ballads like this one of Larry O'Sullivan, the section boss, which was found by Carl Sandburg, and is reprinted here with his permission from *The American Songbag*.

217. DRILL, YE TARRIERS

'THERE'S AN IRISHMAN buried under every tie of that road,' said the grizzled old railway construction engineer, thinking of the part the Irish had played in building America's railroad lines.

The gangs of Irish muckers and rock drillers, who dug and blasted out the right of way for so many American railroads, east and west, were known as 'tarriers', and they soon had a song composed in their honour. Written in 1888 by the vaudeville team of Connelly and Casey, this piece had such an authentically Irish swing that the Harps sang it on all sorts of jobs up and down the country. The story is a repeater in American folklore, for there is a similar yarn from the Rockies about two dynamiters who were lowered into a deep canyon on a blasting job.

Wall, them fellers ketched the dynamite all right, and put 'er in an' lit their fuse, but afore we could haul 'em up she went off. Great guns! 'twas wuss'n forty thousand Fourth o' Julys. A million coyotes an' tin pans an' horns an' gongs ain't a sarcumstance. The hull gorge fur ten mile bellered an' bellered, an' kep' on bellerin' wuss'n a corral o' Texas bulls. I foun myself on my back a-lookin' up, an' the las' thing I seed wuz two o' them fellers a-whirlin' clean over the mountain. When we all kinder come to, the boss looked at his watch, 'n' tole us all to witness that the fellers was blown up just at noon, an' was only entitled to half a day's wages, an' had quit 'thout notice.

QUOTE: *The Crest of the Continent*, Ernest Ingersoll (Hooper, Chicago, 1885), pp. 196-200.

218. WAND'RIN'

THE RAILROAD added a new character to American folklore. His name was Weary Willie, the tramp. When he heard a locomotive whistle moaning blue notes down in the freight yards, Willie felt that a change in scenery was called for. However, he had no intention of paying tax to the railroad barons. One famous tramp claims to have spent just a shade over seven dollars for 500,000 miles of free train rides.

These primitive American tourists suffered all the risks and discomforts of pioneers. Accommodations varied. Sometimes the hoboes found an empty boxcar and a friendly brakie and travelled de luxe. An unused freight car with sides but no top was windier, but still comfortable. The cat-walk on top of a freight car made a good bed, but a man had to hang on in his sleep.

If the brakies were hostile, there were various places a tramp could sneak a ride. Just over the bumpers between freight cars is a narrow steel ledge where a man can stand and hold on for some hours, risking a fall between the cars if a bucking freight breaks his grip. Real old train barnacles balance a narrow plank on the steel struts below a passenger car and thus steal high-speed rides across country, just a few inches above the gravel and with death only a split second away. A tramp who can take punishment crawls into an empty battery box below a pullman car and lies in this narrow, dusty coffin for a transcontinental trip. Some hoboes break in to the animal cars and sleep among the sheep and cattle, or hide in the coal piles on the engine tenders. One professional searched for years for a way to conceal himself below the boiler of the engine.

Holbrook, in his *Story of the American Railroads*, estimates that in the nineties there were about 60,000 tramps riding the trains. After the twentieth century began, the number had risen to perhaps fifteen times that number, and during the Depression, about a million men were hoboing round the country by rail. Hardly a freight passed without a group of men perched on the top of every car, the police not daring to interfere. At various times the vagrants held conventions and elected their own kings.

This fraternity cooked their mulligan stews in the waste spaces along the railroad tracks, and rhymed together many songs—among them one of the most beautiful of American folk songs, discovered by Carl Sandburg in Minnesota, and reprinted by his special permission.

SOURCE: Botkin VIII, pp. 221 ff.

219. AROUND A WESTERN WATER TANK

TOM KROMER, who has hoboed all over the country, describes how it feels to catch a fast drag (a fast freight train), a double-header (a train with two engines attached for speed), when she is highballing (speeding) out of town on a dark night . . .

. . . We crawl on our hands and knees and ease up towards the yards. It is so dark you can hardly see your hands in front of you. We hear this drag give the highball (starting whistle). We ease up as close as we can get without being seen by the bulls (railroad police). . . . I can see her coming now. This is a manifest (a fast freight). She won't lose any time where she is going. This old stiff (bum of a low type) picks up his bundle and starts back towards the jungle.

' This one is too hot,' he says. ' There will be another drag tomorrow. I do not like to sell pencils.'

I judge my distance. I start running along this track. I hold my hand up to the side of these cars. They brush my fingers as they fly by. I feel this step hit my fingers and dive. My fingers get hold of it. I grab it as tight as I can. I think my arms will be jerked out of their sockets. My ribs feel like they are smashed. I hang on. I made it. I am bruised and sore. I climb to the top. The wind rushes by and cools the sweat on my face. I cannot believe I made this drag she is highballing it down the tracks so fast . . . But just the same, I am glad I am here on the top and not smashed all to hell underneath those wheels that sing beneath me . . .

QUOTE: *Waiting for Nothing*, Tom Kromer (Knopf, 1935). Used by permission of the publishers, Alfred A. Knopf, Inc.

220. THE WABASH CANNON BALL

THE YOUNGEST of the Bunyan boys, Cal S. Bunyan, built the most wondrous railroad in the world; the Ireland, Jerusalem, Australian, and Southern Michigan Line. It took the largest steel mill in the country two years, said Swede Hedquist, operating on a schedule of a thirty-six-hour day and a nine-day week to produce one rail for Cal. Each tie was made from an entire redwood tree. The train had seven hundred cars. It was so long that the conductor rode on a twin-cylinder, super-de luxe motorcycle to check tickets. He punched each ticket by shooting holes through it with a .45 calibre automatic. The train went so fast that after it was brought to a dead stop it was still making sixty-five miles an hour. After two months of service, the schedule had been speeded up, so that the train arrived at its destination an hour before it left its starting point.

One day Cal said to the engineer, ' Give her all the snuss she's got.' That was the end of the I.J.A. & S.M. Railroad. The trains travelled so fast that the friction melted the steel rails and burned the ties to ashes . . . When it reached the top of the grade, the engine took off just like an airplane and carried itself and the seven hundred cars so far into the stratosphere that the law of gravity quit working. That was years and years ago, but the I.J.A. & S.M. is still rushing through space, probably making overnight jumps between the stars, by Jupiter!

Old-time hoboes had a name for this Flying Dutchman of a train. They called her *The Wabash Cannon Ball*, and they said there was no station in America that had not heard her lonesome whistle.

221. THE BIG ROCK CANDY MOUNTAINS

Hallelujah, I'm a bum,
Hallelujah, bum again,
Hallelujah, give us a handout
Revive us again!

MAC McCLINTOCK, who claims to be the author of this song, as well as of the original *Big Rock Candy Mountains* quoted below, played clarinet in the first IWW (Industrial Workers of the World) street band, became their principal song-busker, edited the first edition of *The Little Red Songbook*, and tried out Joe Hill's first song (*The Preacher and the Slave*) when Joe brought it into the Wobbly meet-hall in Portland in 1910. Mac had already been around. When he was fourteen he ran way from his Knoxville, Tennessee, home to join a travelling circus. The circus folded in 1896 and Mac went on the bum . . .

It was in New Orleans that I found singing in saloons could be profitable. A bunch of Limey sailors were having a bit of a sing-song and I ventured to join in one of the choruses. I was immediately invited to grab a glass and sit in. They kept dropping coins into my pockets at odd intervals, and I woke up next morning with nearly four bucks in small change. So when I hit the road again I was no longer a moocher of pokeouts at back doors. In a strange town I searched for sounds of ' revelry by night ', and there were few saloon crowds that would refuse to listen to a kid who wanted to sing.

But my new trade of singing for my supper brought new dangers on the road and in the jungles. As a ' producer ' I was a shining mark; a kid, who could not only beg handouts but who could bring in money for alcohol, was a valuable piece of property for the jocker that could snare him. The decent hoboes were protective as long as they were around, but there were times when I fought like a wildcat or ran like a deer to preserve my independence and my virginity, and on one occasion I jumped into the darkness from a box-car door—from a train that must have been doing better than thirty miles an hour. I lay in the ditch where I landed until picked up by a section gang next morning.

In *The Big Rock Candy Mountains*, McClintock tells how a jocker lured a country boy away from home by telling him ' ghost stories ' about lemonade springs and such. After many a thirsty mile the punk is disillusioned.

> The punk rolled up his big blue eyes
> And said to the jocker, ' Sandy,
> I've hiked and hiked and wandered, too,
> But I ain't seen any candy.
> I've hiked and hiked till my feet are sore,
> I'll be God-damned if I hike any more
> To be————————————————
> In the Big Rock Candy Mountains.

Fifty years of re-working by other balladeers have obscured the raw irony of McClintock's original song, but have graced it with age-old Utopian fantasies which inspired the song *Oleana* (*see* p. 77). One source lay near at hand in the South-west . . .

In his letters to Charles V of Spain, Pizarro reported the discovery of a wonderful town in Peru called Juaja in which no one was permitted to labour, where men lived to be six hundred years old and finally died of laughter. ' To be in Juaja ' came to mean ' to live without care '. Plays and romances which spread to all parts of Spanish America were composed about Juaja . . . The Chilean *Romance de Ciudad Deliciosa* described a city where walls were of cheese, beams of taffy, doorposts of caramel and roofs were shingled with fritters steeped in honey, refreshed each morning by a rain of pear syrup . . .

A Mexican ballad, popular as far north as New Mexico, celebrated the 'City of I Don't Know Where'. Its streets were paved with precious metals, its wells filled with olive oil, its churches were made of sugar. Roasted ducks flew through the air.

Was it a Mexican or a Scandinavian hobo who told these wonder tales at the hobo jungle fire where the road kid McClintock was listening? Or did these old Utopian motives come from English, Celtic, or German sources? Since the folk fantasy of the roast pig running about squeaking ' Eat me ' was common to the whole of hungry West Europe, we shall probably never know.

SOURCE: Greenway, p. 203.

222. PIE IN THE SKY

BY 1900 THE AMERICAN frontier had come to an end, and with it the authority of the Spartan frontier code and the Puritan religious tradition. Hundreds of thousands of men who went west to seek their fortunes found that the best lands, mining sites and tracts of timber had already been taken up. They drifted from job to job as casual labourers, living in vermin-infested bunkhouses when they had a job, and sleeping in hobo jungles when they were unemployed. The low wages and the low standards of living which their pioneer ancestors had accepted as temporary hardships along the road to personal success, now looked as if they might become permanent conditions for their whole class. The freeborn American working man had become surplus labour for giant industrial combines. Viewed from a bed in the cinders along the railroad tracks, the American system was not working any more; religion, as analysed in the popular atheistic tracts of Robert Ingersoll, was a myth, created to keep the gullible in line.

The Industrial Workers of the World, formed in 1906 with the avowed intention of taking over industry for the benefit of the workers, supplied an organized outlet for these currents of discontent. The man who carried a red card became a dedicated fighter for the rights of his class to good jobs at decent pay. He was willing to go to jail, to face the guns and clubs of company cops and to die, if necessary, for his cause. In the lives of these lonely hoboes, ex-cowpunchers, seamen, lumberjacks, and farm hands, a sense of comradeship and of identification with the working-class of the world replaced the old ties of community, family, and religion. A body of rough, but pungently ironic and highly singable parodies did more than speeches and principles to give the IWW members their emotional unity.

From the beginning, music played an important role in the IWW or 'Wobbly' organizing drive. IWW Organizers and the Salvation Army were fighting each other for converts along Spokane's skid roads. The Army bands drowned out the Wobbly speakers, until Jack Walsh and Mac McClintock brought out their own band. Then they convulsed their hard-boiled audience with irreverent parodies of favourite Salvation Army tear jerkers, ' In the sweet bye and bye . . .' becoming ' You will eat bye and bye . . .'

A Scandinavian immigrant named Joe Hill composed this as well as many other songs in the Wobbly *Little Red Song Book*. Virtually nothing is known about this mysterious man up to the time of his arrest in Salt Lake City in 1914 on a murder charge. Joe Hill denied his guilt, claiming a frame-up by state authorities who wanted to run the IWW out of Utah. He was tried by a hostile court and convicted on circumstantial evidence, so doubtful that President Wilson twice wired the governor of Utah to reconsider the case. Hill refused to testify in his own defence and spent his time in jail writing poetry and painting. From the death cell he sent his last message to his Wobbly friends . . . ' Don't mourn for me, organize.'

The next morning he faced the rifles of his executioners without the usual blindfold and shouted the orders to the firing squad himself. His last will, written in his death cell the night before his execution, is touched with genuine and poignant magic . . .

> My will is easy to decide
> For there is nothing to divide.
> My kin don't need to fuss and moan,
> ' Moss does not cling to a rolling stone.
> My body? Ah, if I could choose,
> I would to ashes it reduce,
> And let the merry breezes blow
> My dust to where some flowers grow.
> Perhaps some fading flower then
> Would come to life and bloom again.
> This is my last and final will,
> Good luck to all of you.—Joe Hill.

Surely, if some heavenly visitor had decided to intervene in the troubled life of America in this period, he would have behaved like Joe Hill, would have been misunderstood like him, and would have died like him.

223. WILLIE THE WEEPER

Back in the days of America's rough-and-tumble innocence—when the saloon was the first building to be erected in a western town and when you had only to push open the swinging door to enter a national club where whisky came at five cents a throw with all the free lunch you could swallow—taking dope was not regarded as a much more serious habit than drinking or chewing tobacco. Since every weakness of the flesh condemned the sinner to hellfire, cocaine and opium addicts were only a degree more vicious than the man who went on a Saturday night bender. At first, many Americans on the frontier did not realize that these drugs were habit-forming and destructive. At least, my informants from the Mississippi Delta have told me that before World War I you could buy cocaine tablets in the drugstore as freely as you wished, and that the Negro mule-skinners passed their cocaine boxes around like their plugs of tobacco. Everyone helped himself. Perhaps these out-door workers had a high resistance to the harmful effects of drugs.

In this epoch, the snow-birds and hop-heads of the West had their own folky ballads, as boastful, as optimistic, and as unashamed as so many cowboy songs. *Take a Whiff on Me*, *The Ballad of Cocaine Lil*, and *Willie the Weeper*, composed in the raggy style of those days, gave rise later to a whole school of jazzy songs like *Minnie the Moocher* and *Calling the Vipers*.

214. SHE'LL BE COMIN' AROUND THE MOUNTAIN

SEE: Brown III, 534; Jackson IV, 148, 211; White, 94. A secular reworking of the folk hymn *Old Ship of Zion*.

Lively ♩ = 138

GUITAR— 4
BANJO— 1-3

She'll be com-in' a-round the moun-tain when she comes, She'll be com-in' a-round the
moun-tain when she comes, She'll be com-in' a-round the moun-tain, She'll be
com-in' a-round the moun-tain, She'll be com-in' a-round the moun-tain when she comes.

1 She'll be comin' around the mountain when she
               comes, (2)
She'll be comin' around the mountain, (2)
She'll be comin' around the mountain when
               she comes.

2 She'll be drivin' six white horses, *etc.*

3 We will all go out to meet her, *etc.*

4 We will have chicken an' dumplin's, *etc.*

5 She'll be reelin' an' a-rockin', *etc.*

6 We'll shout glory hallelujah, *etc.*

215. A RAILROADER FOR ME

Recorded by C. Todd and R. Sonkin. Arranged by Russ Pike, Okie camp, Visalia, Calif., who brought it from Southern Missouri. LC Record. Additional verses from Randolph III, 259. SEE: Belden, 262; Gomme, 153; Randolph II, 351, III, 64; Sharp II, 381. In Missouri it is called *I Will Not Marry a Guerilla*. Compare with *The Roving Gambler*, Lomax II, 150.

An easy swing ♩. = 72

GUITAR— 2A or 4 (WALTZ TIME)
BANJO— 1 (WALTZ TIME)

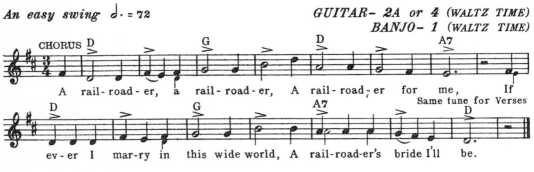

A rail-road-er, a rail-road-er, A rail-road-er for me, If
ev-er I mar-ry in this wide world, A rail-road-er's bride I'll be.

CHORUS:
A railroader, a railroader,
A railroader for me,
If ever I marry in this wide world,
A railroader's bride I'll be.

1 Now I would not marry a blacksmith,
He's always in the black,
I'd rather marry an engineer
That throws the throttle back. (CHO.)

414

2 I would not marry a farmer,
  He's always in the dirt,
  I'd rather marry an engineer
  That wears a striped shirt. (CHO.)

3 I would not marry a cowboy,
  A-ridin' the western plain,
  I'd rather marry an engineer
  Who wears a big watch-chain. (CHO.)

4 I would not marry a sheriff
  For he is sure to die,
  But I would marry a railroader
  Who has them pretty blue eyes. (CHO.)

5 I would not marry a preacher,
  He preaches too much hell,
  But I would marry a railroader
  Who rings the engine bell. (CHO.)

6 I would not marry a gambler
  Who's always drinkin' wine,
  But I would marry a railroader
  Who drives the forty-nine. (CHO.)

7 Father, oh dear father,
  Forgive me if you can,
  If you ever see your daughter again
  It'll be with a railroad man. (CHO.)

216. JERRY, GO AN' ILE THAT CAR

FROM: p. 361 of *The American Songbag*, Carl Sandburg (Harcourt, Brace, 1927).
Used by permission. As sung by Gunny Sack Riley, Albuquerque, New Mexico,
1884 on the Santa Fe. SEE: Belden, 445. For cowboy version, see *Forty Years a
Cowboy*, Abbott, p. 231.
Piano arrangement by DON BANKS

cin - ter back, An' Jer-ry, go an' ile that car-r-r!' 2. For
shim-min' up the ties, It's 'Jer-ry, wud yez ile that car-r-r!'

1 Come all ye railroad section men
An' listen to my song;
It is of Larry O'Sullivan,
Who now is dead and gone.
For twinty years a section boss,
He never lost a car-r
Oh it's ' J'int ahead and cinter back,
An' Jerry, go an 'ile that car-r-r!'

2 For twinty years a section boss,
He worked upon the track,
And be it to his cred-i-it,
He niver had a wrack.
For he kept every j'int right up to the p'int,
Wid the tap of the tampin' bar-r;
And while the byes was a-shimmin' up the ties,
It's ' Jerry, wud yez ile that car-r-r!'

3 'Twas in November, in the winter time
An' the ground all covered wid snow,
' Come, put the hand-car-r on the track
An' over the section go!'
Wid his big sojer coat buttoned up to his throat,
All weathers he wud dare—
An' it's ' Paddy Mack, will yez walk the track,
An' Jerry, go an' ile that car-r-r!'

4 ' Give my rispicts to the Roadmas-ther,'
Poor Larry he did cry,
' And lave me up, that I may see
The ould hand-car-r before I die.'
They lay the spike-maul upon his chist,
The gauge an' the ould claw-bar-r,
And while the byes do be fillin' the grave,
' O Jerry, go an' ile that car-r-r!'

416

217. DRILL, YE TARRIERS

As sung by Bess B. Lomax and recorded by Alan Lomax. SEE: *Famous Songs and Their Stories*, J. J. Geller (MacAuley, 1931).

Vigorously ♩ = 160

GUITAR— 1, 2A, 4, 7B
BANJO— 5A or B

Ev - 'ry morn-ing at sev - en o' - clock There's twen - ty tar - ri - ers a - work-in' on the rock; And the boss comes a - long and he says, 'Kape still, And come down heav - y on the cast - iron drill.' And drill, ye tar - ri - ers, drill. Drill, ye tar - ri - ers, drill, It's work all day for the su - gar in your tay, Down be-hind the rail-way, And drill, ye tar-ri-ers, drill! And blast! And fire!

1 Every morning at seven o'clock
There's twenty tarriers a-workin' on the rock;
And the boss comes along and he says, 'Kape still,
And come down heavy on the cast-iron drill.'
CHORUS:
And drill, ye tarriers, drill.
Drill, ye tarriers, drill,
It's work all day for the sugar in your tay,
Down behind the railway,
And drill, ye tarriers, drill!
And blast! And fire!

2 Now our new foreman was Gene McCann,
By God, he was a blamey man.
Last week a premature blast went off
And a mile in the air went Big Jim Goff. (CHO.)

3 Next time pay day comes around,
Jim Goff a dollar short was found;
When asked what for, came this reply,
' You're docked for the time you was up in
the sky.' (CHO.)

4 The boss was a fine man down to the ground
And he married a lady six feet round;
She baked good bread and she baked it well
And she baked it hard as the holes in Hell. (CHO.)

218. WAND'RIN'

Adapted from p. 188 of *The American Songbag*, Carl Sandburg (Harcourt, Brace, 1927). Used by permission. This finest of American hobo songs has grown out of *My Father's a Lawyer* (*see* p. 134).

Piano arrangement by DON BANKS

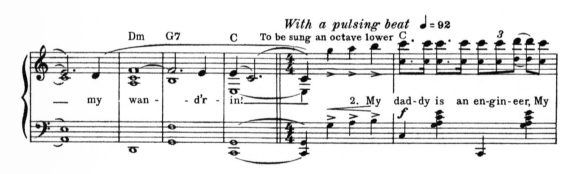

1 I've been wand'rin' early,
I've been wand'rin' late,
From New York City
To the Golden Gate.

CHORUS:
And it looks like
I ain't never gonna cease my wand'rin'.

2 My daddy is an engineer,
My brother drives a hack,
My sister takes in washin',
And the baby balls the jack.* (CHO.)

3 I've been workin' in the army,
I've been workin' on the farm,
And all I've got to show
Is just this muscle in my arm. (CHO.)

4 Snakes in the ocean,
And fish in the sea,
And the blonde-headed women
Make a monkey out of me. (CHO.)

* an early jazz step

219. AROUND A WESTERN WATER TANK

Collected and arranged by J. and A. Lomax. FROM: p. 28, *American Ballads and Folk
Songs* (Macmillan, N.Y., 1934). SEE: Brown III, 428; Laws, 221; Lomax II, 28.
A common hobo song which takes many forms and has been frequently recorded
by western and hillbilly singers.

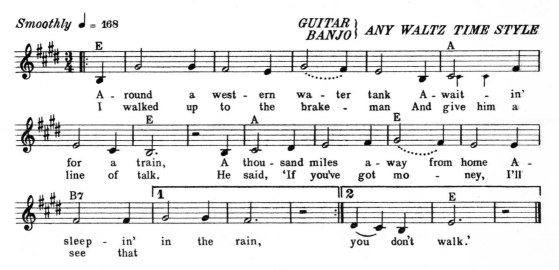

1 Around a western water tank
  A-waitin' for a train,
  A thousand miles away from home
  A-sleepin' in the rain,
  I walked up to the brakeman
  And give him a line of talk.
  He said, ' If you've got money
  I'll see that you don't walk.'

2 ' I haven't got a nickel,
  Not a penny can I show.'
  ' Get off, get off, you railroad bum—'
  And he slammed the boxcar door.
  He put me off in Texas,
  A state I dearly love.
  Wide open spaces all round me,
  The moon and stars above.

3 Standing on the platform
  Smoking a cheap cigar,
  A-listenin' for the next freight train
  To catch an empty car.

My pocket-book was empty,
My heart was full of pain,
A thousand miles away from home,
A-bummin' a railroad train.

4 I next got off in Danville,
  Got stuck on a Danville girl.
  You can bet your life she was out of sight,
  She wore those Danville curls.   [sight,
  She took me in her kitchen,
  She treated me nice and kind,
  She got me in the notion
  Of bummin' all the time.

5 As I left the kitchen
  And went down in the town,
  I heard a double-header blow
  And she was western bound.
  My heart began to flutter
  And I began to sing,
  ' Ten thousand miles away from home
  A-bummin' a railroad train.'

6 I pulled my cap down over my eyes,
  And walked on down the tracks,
  Then I caught an empty car
  And never did look back.

220. THE WABASH CANNON BALL

Collected and arranged by Alan Lomax. SEE: Botkin VII, 462; Randolph IV, 363.
Perhaps the song is a remake of the post Civil War *Uncle Sam's Farm* (*see* Brown
III, 474) but still it is a genuine hobo ballad which became a favourite of hillbilly
singers in the 1930's, and has been frequently recorded and considerably altered in
recorded transmission.

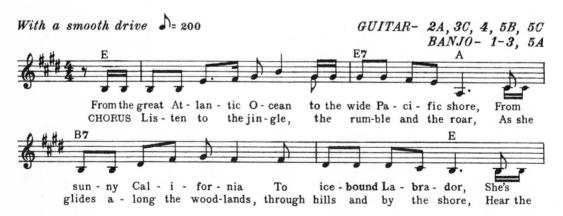

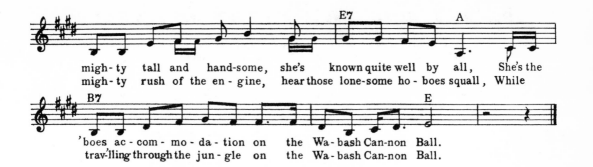

migh-ty tall and hand-some, she's known quite well by all, She's the
migh-ty rush of the en-gine, hear those lone-some ho-boes squall, While

'boes ac-com-mo-da-tion on the Wa-bash Can-non Ball.
trav-'lling through the jun-gle on the Wa-bash Can-non Ball.

1 From the great Atlantic Ocean to the wild Pacific shore,
   From sunny California to ice-bound Labrador,
   She's mighty tall and handsome, she's known quite well by all,
   She's the 'boes accommodation on the Wabash Cannon Ball.
   CHORUS:
   Listen to the jingle, the rumble and the roar,
   As she glides along the woodlands, through hills and by the shore,
   Hear the mighty rush of the engine, hear those lonesome hoboes squall,
   While travelling through the jungle on the Wabash Cannon Ball.

2 This train, she runs to Memphis, Mattoon, and Mexico,
   She rolls through East St. Louis and she never does it slow,
   As she flies through Colorado, she gives an awful squawl,
   They tell her by her whistle—the Wabash Cannon Ball.   (CHO.)

3 Our eastern states are dandy, so the people always say,
   From New York to St. Louis and Chicago by the way,
   From the hills of Minnesota where the rippling waters fall,
   No changes can be taken on the Wabash Cannon Ball.   (CHO.)

4 Now here's to Boston Blackey, may his name forever stand,
   And always be remembered by the 'boes throughout the land,
   His earthly days are over and the curtains round him fall,
   We'll carry him home to victory on the Wabash Cannon Ball.   (CHO.)

221. THE BIG ROCK CANDY MOUNTAINS

FROM: p. 278 of *Folk Song : U.S.A.*, Lomax (Duell, Sloan & Pearce, 1947). The probable author is Mac McClintock, but the song has been re-worked frequently, receiving new material from folk legends about Utopian lands.

INTRODUCTION:

On a summer's day in the month of May,
A burly little bum come a-hiking,
Travelling down that lonesome road
A-looking for his liking.

He was headed for a land that was far away,
Beside them crystal fountains—
' I'll see you all this coming fall
In the Big Rock Candy Mountains.'

1 In the Big Rock Candy Mountains
You never change your socks,
And little streams of alcohol
Come a-trickling down the rocks.
The box cars are all empty
And the railroad bulls are blind,
There's a lake of stew and whisky, too,
You can paddle all around 'em in a big canoe
In the Big Rock Candy Mountains.
CHORUS:
O — the buzzing of the bees in the cigarette
Round the soda-water fountain,   [trees
Where the lemonade springs and the bluebird sings
In the Big Rock Candy Mountains.

2 In the Big Rock Candy Mountains,
There's a land that's fair and bright,
Where the hand-outs grow on bushes
And you sleep out every night,
Where the box cars are all empty
And the sun shines every day,
O I'm bound to go, where there ain't no snow,

Where the rain don't fall and the wind don't blow
In the Big Rock Candy Mountains.
CHORUS:
O — the buzzing of the bees in the cigarette
Round the soda-water fountain,   [trees
Where the lemonade springs and the bluebird sings
In the Big Rock Candy Mountains.

3 In the Big Rock Candy Mountains
The jails are made of tin
And you can bust right out again
As soon as they put you in;
The farmer's trees are full of fruit,
The barns are full of hay,
I'm going to stay where you sleep all day,
Where they boiled in oil the inventor of toil
In the Big Rock Candy Mountains.
CHORUS:
O — the buzzing of the bees in the cigarette
Round the soda-water fountain,   [trees
Where the lemonade springs and the bluebird sings
In the Big Rock Candy Mountains.

222. PIE IN THE SKY

Composed by Joe Hill. Tune *Sweet Bye and Bye*.

Hymn style ♩ = 92

GUITAR 4
BANJO- 1 and 2

Long-haired preach-ers come out ev-'ry night, __ And they tell you what's wrong and what's right, __ When you ask them for some-thing to eat, __ They will an-swer in voi-ces so sweet: __ 'You will eat, __ bye and bye, __ In that glor-ious land a-bove the sky, __ Work and pray, __ live on hay, __ You'll get pie in the sky when you die.' __

1 Long-haired preachers come out ev'ry night,
  And they tell you what's wrong and what's right,
  When you ask them for something to eat,
  They will answer in voices so sweet:

CHORUS:
' You will eat, bye and bye,
In that glorious land above the sky,
Work and pray, live on hay,
You'll get pie in the sky when you die.'

2 O the starvation army they play,
  And they sing and they clap and they pray,
  Till they get all your coin on the drum,
  Then they'll tell you when you're on the bum.
                                    (CHO.)

3 Holy Rollers and Jumpers, come out,
  And they holler, they jump and they shout.
  ' Give your money to Jesus,' they say,
  ' He will cure all diseases today.'   (CHO.)

4 If you fight hard for children and wife,
  Try to get something good in this life,
  You're a sinner and a bad man, they tell,
  When you die you will sure go to Hell.   (CHO.)

5 Working men of all countries, unite,
  Side by side we for freedom will fight,
  When the world and its wealth we have gained
  To the grafter we will sing this refrain:

CHORUS:
You will eat bye and bye
When you've learned how to cook and fry,
Chop some wood, 'twill do you good,
And you'll eat in the sweet bye and bye.

223. WILLIE THE WEEPER

SEE: Lomax II, 184; Randolph III, 272; (Robert Gordon found over thirty versions
with a hundred different verses. Randolph heard it in Kansas in 1908); Sandburg,
204 (this and other snow-bird songs). Cab Calloway's *Minnie the Moocher* is a re-
working of this ballad formerly popular among college boys and jazzmen.
Piano arrangement by DON BANKS

1 Hark to the story of Willie the Weeper,
  Willie the Weeper was a chimney sweeper,
  He had the hop habit and he had it bad,
  O listen while I tell you 'bout a dream he had.

2 He went to the hop joint the other night,
  When he knew the lights would all be burning
                                        bright,
  I guess he smoked a dozen pills or more,
  When he woke up, he was on a foreign shore.

3 Queen o' Bulgaria was the first he met,
  She called him her darlin' and her lovin' pet,
  She promised him a pretty Ford automobile
  With a diamond headlight an' a silver steerin'
                                        wheel

4 She had a million cattle, she had a million sheep,
  She had a million vessels on the ocean deep,
  She had a million dollars, all in nickels and dimes
  She knew 'cause she counted them a million times.

5 Willie landed in New York one evenin' late,
  He asked his sugar for an after-date,
  Willie he got funny, she began to shout,
  BIM BAM BOO!—an' the dope gave out.

THE LAST WEST

224. TALKIN' BLUES
225. TALKIN' DUSTBOWL BLUES

THE AMERICAN taste for darn fool ditties and for crazy, surrealist, and rather cynical humour, culminates in the talking blues genre. Such songs began to appear on hillbilly recordings in the 'twenties and 'thirties, and it was from them that Woody Guthrie took his inspiration. The present early text shows that the talking blues is, ultimately, of Negro derivation. Most of the stanzas come from the *Po' Mourner* set, the barber shop quartet song in which the leader intones humorous verses against a background of rhythmic chords. Speaking in rhythm over a sung accompaniment is a common device among Negro preachers and blues singers (Lead Belly, for instance), and some early records exist of Negroes ' talking ' a story over, or to, their guitars.

The talking blues, however, with its delayed climax and its double or triple cracker on the end of the jokes, is a modern, white folk creation, put to the purposes of acid social comment by Woody Guthrie.

226. HARD TRAVELLIN'

WOODY WRITES:

I was born in western Oklahoma and drug up in the Texas Panhandle. That's where the wheat grows, where the oil flows, where the dust flows and the farmer owes—where you hunt for wood and dig for water— where you can look farther and see less—where there's more weather and less climate, more crops and less groceries than any other dadburned place in the universe.

Then the dust storms come. Dust was so thick you sometimes found yourself runnin' your tractor and ploughs upside down. The buzzards had to wear goggles and fly backwards. You could easy lose your wife and wake up huggin' your mother-in-law. Sometimes the dust would settle, but the debts wouldn't.

I decided it would be better in California, so I kissed the family goodbye and swung into a Santa Fe cattle car and whistled down the line. For the last few years I've been a rambling man. From Oklahoma to California and back, by freight train, and thumb—I've been stranded and disbanded, busted and disgusted with people of all sorts, shapes, sizes and calibres—folks that wandered all over the country, looking for work, down and outers, and hungry half the time. I slept with their feet in my face and my feet in theirs, with Okies and Arkies that were rambling over the states of California and Arizona like a herd of lost buffalo with the hot hoof and empty mouth disease. Pretty soon I found out I had relatives under every railroad bridge between Oklahoma and California.

Walking down the big road, no money, no job, no home, no nothing, nights I slept in jails, and the cells were piled high with young boys, strong men and old men. They talked and they sung and they told the story

426

of their lives—how it used to be, how it got to be, how the home went to pieces, how the young wife died or left, how Dad tried to kill himself, how the banks sent out tractors and tractored down the houses. So somehow I picked up an old rusty guitar and started to picking and playing the songs I heard and making up new ones about what folks said.

QUOTE: Woody Guthrie, recorded by Alan Lomax.

227. PRETTY BOY FLOYD

THE HERO of this recent American Robin Hood ballad was a soft-spoken, blue-eyed young fellow from the Oklahoma sand-hill country named Pretty Boy Floyd, who kept all the sheriffs, bank presidents, and FBI agents in the South-West in a sweat during the 'thirties. Sometimes he notified the sheriff when he was going to rob a bank. Then he would roar into town right on schedule, driving a car loaded down with sub-machine guns. As he was a dead shot and known to enjoy potting an officer as much as doing a bank job, the sheriff and his deputies often went fishing on the appointed day. The poor folks of the sand-hills hero-worshipped Pretty Boy and protected him, for reasons that Woody explains.

. . . There's been many-a time that I set around with my head hanging down, broke, clothes no good, old slouchy shoes, no money to spend on the women, sleeping in some barn of a place like an old white-faced steer, and seeing other people all fixed up with a good, high-rolling car, and good suits of clothes and high-priced whisky and more pretty gals than one. Even had money to blow on damn fool necklaces and bracelets around their necks and arms.

. . . So I would set there by the road and think—just one of them diamonds would buy a little farm with a water well and a gourd dipper and forty acres of good bottom land and some chickens to wake me up in the morning. That whole picture would go through my head every time I seen a drunk man with his woman a-driving a big Lincoln Zephyr down the road. Yes sir, all that was tempting, mighty tempting.

. . . I reckon that's how it went with old Charley Floyd. He was born and raised right down in there where I was. I talked to lots of people that knowed him personal. Said he wasn't much of a bad feller. Fact, some of them respected him lots more than they did the sheriff and his deputies. Anyhow, something went wrong and Pretty Boy went to packing shooting irons, blowing his way into the banks where the people's money was. Grabbed up big sacks of it and took it out and scattered it everywhere, give it to the poor folks up and down the country.

. . . Pretty Boy had the right idea, but the wrong system. The outlaw is in his grave today. Jesse James, Billy the Kid, Cole Younger and Belle Starr, all of them in their graves, but we still sing about them. You hear songs about those fellers, springing up everywhere like flowers in the right early spring. That's the way it was with my piece. It tells tales I heard concerning his life and what kind of a man he was. We never had a governor that was half as popular as Pretty Boy. Back in them times, you couldn't come down in my part of Oklahoma and say nothing against him. If you did, something was liable to hit you, son, and it wouldn't be no train . . .

QUOTE: Woody Guthrie, recorded by Alan Lomax.

228. HARD TIMES

WOODY SAYS:

If you never been in jail, without a single friend to your name, and stood around there like a lost dog in a hard rain, why then you won't get the full meaning out of any jailhouse song. I know. I've been where I could hear all them things. If all the jails I been in was all put together, it would make a hard rock hotel as big as the Capitol building. And this is the best jailhouse song I ever heard sung. *The Birmingham Jail* don't say enough. *The Prisoner's Song* don't say much, either. *Moonlight and Skies* brags too much on the deputies. Of course, lots of officers are honest and straight, but there's a hell of a lot of them that are ten times worse crooks and thieves than the fellers they beat up and throw in jail. And them's the kind of jailers this song tells about. It's been sung in every buggy, lousy jail from New Jersey to Portland, Oregon, from the days of the Revolution to the present.

QUOTE: Woody Guthrie, recorded by Alan Lomax.

229. HARD, AIN'T IT HARD

WOODY REMEMBERS:

. . . When I got out of jail, I made a run for a bottle of liquor and a pretty woman. I met her in a saloon, I had a couple of shots under my belt and was rearin' to step. She was one-eyed, but that didn't matter none. I had two eyes and she looked mighty good to me through both of 'em. I felt like a man coming up out of the grave when I stepped out of that jail. I had seventy-one dollars saved up and would have blowed seventy-one hundred if I'd of had it, just for a crack at that one-eyed girl. Her one eye was as pretty as a picture.

So I slipped my guitar into position and I played her my old Okie love song. You might think it was a mighty funny kind of a serenade. You might think it was too hard-boiled and sad to soften up a woman's heart. But that woman was pretty hard-boiled and pretty sad herself. She had had her heart broke as many times as my old uncle's wheat field, and it was broke every spring in planting time. She didn't want no mushy, sissyfied, jukebox lullaby, she wanted a song as real as the oak bar she was leaning against. So I rattled out my old song about how hard it is to love someone who never did love you, and by the end of the first chorus she was smiling through that one eye of hers. And there are a lot of choruses to that song.

QUOTE: Woody Guthrie, recorded by Alan Lomax.

230. FIDDLE-I-FEE
231. THE KICKIN' MULE

WAVE AFTER WAVE of emigrants—'49ers, Pikers, cowboys, prairie farmers, Okies*—carried the old ballads and songs into the Far West. Some ballads were dressed up in chaps and Stetson hats and rode the range like veterans. Other songs could not match the vaster magic and mystery and loneliness of the western country. Those that did survive were often flattened out, tunewise, losing their modal character; meanwhile they gained a kind of hard-boiled cheerfulness which gave them a modern ring and renewed their popularity. On the whole, the songs which best survived the long treks to the West were the funny

* The migratory labourers from Oklahoma and other South-Western states who came west to pick crops during the depression.

428

ones, the darn-fool ditties, the songs of crazy humours. These songs satisfied the western appetite for a good joke and matched the confident, breezy good humour of people who had pulled up stakes and were starting life over again in a new country. Here are two eastern folk songs recorded recently in California from folk-singers. The first is a children's rhyme traditional in Kentucky and North Carolina; the second concerns that long-eared, unpredictable, hard-working critter, known to Americans variously as the barnyard yodeller, the hard-tail, the jug-head, the long-eared chum and the Missouri humming bird. Most rural Americans have spent a good part of their working lives staring at the rear end of a mule. With a healthy respect for his heels, they christened their most potent drink mule or white mule. They gave his name to various humble machines and men that do the hard jobs—the small donkey engine, the farm tractor, the sod-busting plough and the fourth Negro waiter on dining-cars. You can not only work as hard as a mule, you can be as stubborn or as stupid as a mule. But in another view you can be as smart as a mule, as Richard Dorson reports in this Maine tall story . . .

My father brought up a couple of army mules after the last war to work on the farm. Those mules were too cussed lazy to do any work, but my brother Jimmy and I made up our minds we'd teach 'em. We put green glasses on 'em and fed 'em shavings, but still they wouldn't work. Then one morning we led 'em out and hitched 'em head on to the plow and showed them a big sign nailed on the plow ' WORK!' It took the hired man five gallons of oil to keep the plow point from heating, those mules tore over the ground so fast. They plowed 165 acres that day; we hauled water for three days to cool the ground. The hired man planted corn. After he had planted three acres he looked around to see how he was doing. The ground was still so hot that when the corn came up it popped; the old man thought it was snowing and froze to death.

The prime bit of American mule-lore is the Miss Liza song, a laugh-getter for the last seventy-five years between the Carolinas and California, here printed as sung by Henry King and family, who were minstrels to the Okie migrant camps in *Grapes of Wrath* days.

QUOTE: *Southern Folklore Quarterly*, VIII, 4, 1944, p. 283,' Maine Master Narrator ', Richard Dorson.

232. TALKING COLUMBIA
233. ROLL ON, COLUMBIA

AT THE TIME that Steinbeck was speaking for the Okies in *The Grapes of Wrath*, Woody, the dusty-headed folk-poet, was singing for them over a one-horse radio station in Los Angeles. He always claimed that he learned to play the guitar while he was broadcasting. His Okie fans would write him encouraging letters—' Keep it up, Woody; you almost made D this morning!'

When I met him in New York in 1939, however, he had mastered the Carter Family style, and could convulse an audience with his delayed-action, Will Rogers humour. Woody made a great success broadcasting and recording his songs; but he felt uncomfortable about eating well and sleeping soft, when his people were still ' wandering around over the West like a herd of locoed buffaloes', and one day he blew out of New York without saying goodbye to the ' phoney, big-shot producers ' and took to the highway again with his guitar.

This was the era of the drive to harness the rivers of the North-West for cheap public power. The choice between buying electricity from public and private sources lay with the voters and the Bonneville Power Administration was battling the private power outfits for votes. The big private companies were flying in Hollywood stars to draw the public to their meetings, when the Bonneville people called me to locate Woody. They wanted him for ' a public relations consultant ', they said.

Woody hitch-hiked into Portland and signed on. For a month he had a car and a chauffeur at his disposal, and he did the Columbia River basin in style, soaking in the scenery, the statistics, and the issues—and writing songs. He sat on the soft green banks and the big blue river talked to him. He looked at the Columbia River with the wonder that had filled the hearts of his pioneer ancestors who had come into that country along the Oregon Trail a hundred years before . . .

> The world has seven wonders, so the travelers always tell,
> Some gardens and some towers, I guess you know them well,
> But now the greatest wonder is in Uncle Sam's fair land,
> It's the King Columbia River and the Big Grand Coulee Dam.

Woody viewed the lush, green, irrigated fields and orchards along the river with the sunburnt eyes of an Okie . . .

> It's a mighty hard road that my poor hands has hoed,
> My poor feet has traveled a hot dusty road,
> Out of your dustbowl and westward we rolled,
> Lord, your desert is hot and your mountains are cold,
> Green pastures of plenty from dry desert ground,
> From the Grand Coulee Dam where the waters run down,
> This land I'll defend with my life, if need be,
> 'Cause my pastures of plenty must always be free . . .

The ballads poured out of Woody's typewriter with the fresh flow of the river he had come to love. Twenty-six ballads were composed and recorded in twenty-six days. Soon over the radio and through public address systems the people in the Bonneville area were listening to a voice they could believe in—a rural voice, harsh, ironical, humorous, truthful, with the heart-beat of the south-western guitar pulsing behind it. Apparently Bonneville voters agreed with him that ' twenty million salmon fish couldn't be wrong', for when they went to the polls, they voted overwhelmingly for public power; and some of his Bonneville ballads are sung today by people in the North-West who never heard his name.

The minstrel still has a place amongst us. Whether he sings for the King or the U.S. Government is not the question, if his songs, like Woody's, are honest, and composed in traditional modes. Woody has never tried to be original, in the sense of the sophisticated songwriter. Like all folk poets, he uses familiar tunes, re-works old songs, adding new lines and phrases out of the folk-say of the situation that demands the new song. He feels that his function is to sum up and crystallize popular sentiment, to act as the voice of the common man. Although his songs are conversational in tone, they have a truth, an authenticity, and a punch which no other poet of this age can match.

234. STAND TO YOUR GLASSES

> If you want to know where the privates are
> I'll tell you where they are,
> Up to their ears in mud . . .

IN THE ARMIES of other lands soldier-singers celebrated the romance of the fighting man and of war, but in our armies of citizen-soldiers, who abhor war and regard it as an interruption of more pleasant activities, few such songs have ever been recorded. We have left it to the professionals, to the West-Pointers, to sentimentalize over the soldier's life.

Especially in the last two wars, our communally-composed-and-transmitted soldier-songs have derided the whole of the military apparatus—from the mess-hall to the supreme commander. *Mademoiselle from Armentieres*, with its hundreds of bawdy and anti-disciplinary stanzas, laughed at World War I. *Bless 'Em All* groaned lewdly over World War II.

Of all our recent soldiers' ditties, the parodies of the Air Corps are by far the best, and William Walloch, in his article in the *Western Folklore Quarterly* (Vol. XII), has published a sufficient number of rhymes from the last two wars to indicate that a true folk-song tradition exists among our flyers.

The men who bombed Germany had their version of *Down In the Valley* . . .

> Down in Ruhr valley, valley so low,
> Some chairborne bastard said we must go . . .

They put Casey Jones in a bomber and sent him out on a mission . . .

> When they woke Casey up it was black as sin,
> Operations told Casey that the target's Berlin,
> Casey could tell by the lines on his map
> That this was gonna be his final lap.
>
> The major said, ' Boys, there'll be some flak,'
> Casey could tell by this that he wouldn't be back.
> He turned to his crew and this is what he said,
> ' We're gonna make it to Berlin, but we'll all be dead.'

431

Another stanza to the tune of *The Wreck of the Old '97*, tells the end of the story . . .

> He was going downwind making ninety miles an hour,
> When his aircraft fell off in a spin.
> He was found in the wreck with his hands on the throttle,
> And his body all covered with gin.

The birdmen of World War I sung a variant of the old sea-going ballad *Wrap Me Up In My Tarpaulin Jacket* (*see* p. 363), which parodied lines from hobo songs . . .

> I'm going to a better land, they jazz there every night,
> Bourbon grows on bushes, so everyone stays tight,
> They've torn up all the calendars, they've busted all the clocks,
> And little drops of whiskey come trickling down the rocks . . .

Flyers in the Korean War hummed their own form of this song over the swoosh of their jet planes, producing the cynical ballad printed here. It is probable that not long after the blast-off of the first American ship bound for Sirius, some groggy crew member will be chanting an unrespectable and unprintable ballad over the intercom. Behind the perspex of their space helmets the crew will join in the chorus.

NOTE ON TALKING BLUES

The banjo or guitar accompaniment for talking blues is very simple. You merely 'talk' the blues in rhythm against a steady background (usually 2/4 or 4/4 of simple plucking, rhythmic strumming, scratching, or single string picking). Chord progressions are basic and usually in a major key (C and G are especially good). You use mostly those chords found directly to the left and directly under the key chord you have chosen. (*See* chord chart in Appendix II, p. 601.) Occasionally the blues chords are played, but the modal and relative minor chords are rarely found in talking blues. The talking is done in a monotonous, somewhat lackadaisical tone of voice, but has upbeats and offbeats, just as if it had a tune.

The last small phrases are done *out* of rhythm with the accompaniment as an afterthought or comment on what has gone before. Variation in the accompaniment is achieved mainly by mixing up (1) chords, (2) bass notes, (3) strokes. The guitar continues the rhythm and chord changes even when the talking stops.

224. TALKIN' BLUES

FROM: Various recorded sources.

GUITAR--4
BANJO- 1

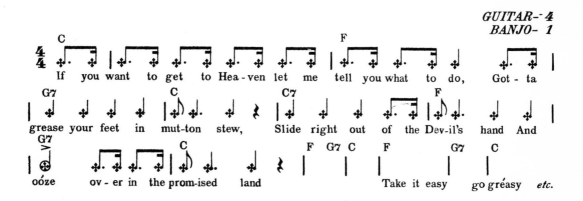

If you want to get to Hea-ven let me tell you what to do, Got-ta grease your feet in mut-ton stew, Slide right out of the Dev-il's hand And ooze ov-er in the prom-ised land Take it easy go greasy *etc.*

1 If you want to get to Heaven let me tell you what to do,
  Gotta grease your feet in mutton stew,
  Slide right out of the Devil's hand
  And ooze over in the promised land . . .
     Take it easy . . . go greasy.

2 Standing in the corner by the mantelpiece,
  Up in that corner was a bucket of grease,
  I stuck my foot in that bucket of grease,
  And went a-slipping up and down that mantelpiece,
     Huntin' matches . . . cigarette stubs.

3 Down in the henhouse on my knees,
  Thought I heard a chicken sneeze,
  Nothin' but a rooster saying' his prayers,
  Thankin' God for the hens upstairs,
     Rooster preachin' . . . hens singin' . . . little banty keepin' time.

4 I got a gal just over the hill,
  She won't kiss like her sister will,
  Never takes a bath, not even a rub,
  'Fraid she'll slide through a hole in the tub,
     Awful skinny . . . bony . . . cut a man like a razor.

5 Ain't no use-a me workin' so hard,
  I got a gal in the rich folks' yard,
  When she kills a chicken she sends me the feet,
  Thinks I'm workin', I'm walkin' the street,
     Pickin' up stubs . . . beggin' fer matches.

6 Ain't no a-use me workin' so hard,
  I got a woman in the rich folks' yard.
  When they kill a chicken she sends me the head,
  Thinks I'm workin' when I'm layin' up in bed,
     Dreamin' about her . . . and two other women.

7 When I get to eating pork chops, I can't stop,
   Ain't no gravy I can't sop,
   Grab that bone in both my hands
   And listen to my lips go flippety-flop
     Born likin' it . . . slicker the better.

225. TALKIN' DUSTBOWL BLUES

Composed by Woody Guthrie in Calif., late 1930's. Used by permission Guthrie Foundation.

Woody said . . .

You talk this piece off. They say it's four-four time. If that is out of your calibre, try 38 time or 16 gauge, anything—just play chords and talk. (For style see p. 432).

1 Back in nineteen twenty-seven
   Had a little farm and I called that heaven,
   Prices up, the rain come down,
   Hauled my crops all in to town.
     Got th' money . . . bought clothes and
                       groceries,
     Fed the kids . . . raised a big family.

2 But the rain quit and th' wind got high,
   Black old dust storm filled th' sky,
   I traded my farm for a Ford-machine
   Poured it full of this gasolene.
     And started . . . rockin' and a-rollin'
     Out to the California . . the old fruit bowl.

3 Way up yonder on a mountain road
   Had a hot motor and a heavy load,
   Goin' purty fast, wasn't even stopping,
   Bouncin' up and down like popcorn a-poppin',
     Had a breakdown . . . nervous bust-down,
     Mechanic feller there said it was eng-ine
                 trouble.

4 Way up yonder on a mountain curve,
   Way up yonder in the Piney wood,
   I give that rollin' Ford a shove,
   Gonna coast just far's I could,
     Commenced a-rollin' . . . pickin' up speed,
     Come a hairpin turn . . . and I didn't
               make it.

5 Man alive, I'm a-tellin' you
   The fiddles and guitars really flew,
   That Ford took off like a flyin' squirrel,
   Flew half-way round the world.
     Scattered wives and children
     All over the side of that mountain.

6 Got to California so dadgum broke,
   So dadgum hungry I thought I'd choke,
   I bummed up a spud or two,
   Wife fixed up some 'tater stew.
     Shoved the kids full of it
     Looked like a tribe of thy-mometers runnin'
              around.

7 Lord, man, I swear to you
   That was shorely a mighty thin stew,
   So damn thin, I really mean
   You could read a mag-a-zine.
     Right through it . . . Look at pictures, too,
     Purty whisky bottles . . . naked women.

Always have thought, always have figgered
If that damn stew had been a little bit thinner,
Some of those politicians . . . the honest ones
Could of seen through it.

226. HARD TRAVELLIN'

Composed by Woody Guthrie. Used by permission Guthrie Foundation.
Probably derived from a Negro spiritual.
Piano arrangement by DON BANKS

435

I been a-hav-in' some hard trav-ell-in', Way down the road,

I been a-hav-in' some hard trav-ell-in', Hard ram-bl-in', hard gam-bl-in',

I been a-hav-in' some hard trav-ell-in', Lord.

1. I been a-havin' some hard travellin',
   I thought you knowed,
   I been a-havin' some hard travellin',
   Way down the road,
   I been a-havin' some hard travellin',
   Hard ramblin', hard gamblin',
   I been havin' some hard travellin', Lord.

2. I been a-workin' in a hard rock tunnel,
   I thought you knowed,
   I been a-leanin' on a pressure drill,
   Way down the road,
   Hammer flyin', air hose suckin',
   Six feet of mud, I sure been a-muckin',
   I been havin' some hard travellin', Lord.

3. I been a-workin' that Pittsburgh steel,
   I thought you knowed,
   I been workin' that red-hot slag,
   Way down the road,
   I been a-blastin', I been a-firin',
   I been a-duckin' red-hot iron,
   I been havin' some hard travellin', Lord.

4. I been hittin' some hard harvestin',
   I thought you knowed,
   I been hittin' some rough handlin',
   Way down the road,
   Cut that wheat and stack that hay,
   Tryin' to make about a dollar a day,
   I been havin' some hard travellin', Lord.

5. I been hittin' that Lincoln Highway,
   I thought you knowed,
   I been a-hittin' that sixty-six,
   Way down the road,
   Heavy load and a worried mind,
   Lookin' for a woman that's hard to find,
   I been havin' some hard travellin', Lord.

227. PRETTY BOY FLOYD

Composed by Woodie Guthrie. Used by permission Guthrie Foundation.

Sostenuto ♩ = 76

GUITAR- ANY ²/₄ STYLE
BANJO- 1 or 2

Come and ga-ther 'round me, child-ren, A sto-ry I will tell A-bout Pret-ty Boy Floyd, the out-law, Ok-la-hom-a knew him well.

1 Come and gather 'round me, children,
A story I will tell
About Pretty Boy Floyd, the outlaw,
Oklahoma knew him well.

2 It was in the town of Shawnee
On a Saturday afternoon,
His wife beside him in the wagon,
As into town they rode.

3 There a deputy sheriff approached him
In a manner rather rude,
Using vulgar words of anger,
And his wife, she overheard.

4 Pretty Boy grabbed a log chain,
The deputy grabbed his gun,
And in the fight that followed
He laid that deputy down.

5 Then he took to the trees and timber
To live a life of shame,
Every crime in Oklahoma
Was added to his name.

6 Yes, he took to the river bottom
Along the river shore,
And Pretty Boy found a welcome
At every farmer's door.

7 The papers said that Pretty Boy
Had robbed a bank each day,
While he was setting in some farmhouse,
Three hundred miles away.

8 There's many a starving farmer
The same old story told,
How the outlaw paid their mortgage
And saved their little home.

9 Others tell you 'bout a stranger
That come to beg a meal,
And underneath his napkin
Left a thousand-dollar bill.

10 It was in Oklahoma City,
It was on a Christmas Day,
There came a whole carload of groceries
With a note to say:

11 ' You say that I'm an outlaw,
You say that I'm a thief,
Here's a Christmas dinner
For the families on relief.'

12 Yes, as through this world I've rambled
I've seen lots of funny men,
Some will rob you with a six gun,
And some with a fountain pen.

13 But as through your life you'll travel,
Wherever you may roam,
You won't never see no outlaw
Drive a family from their home.

228. HARD TIMES

FROM: p. 138 of *American Ballads and Folk Songs*, Lomax (Macmillan, 1934). SEE Belden, 433; Brown III, 419; Lomax I, 176. Recorded N.J.; Appalachians; Tex.; Oreg. This song has probably been sung in most American jails in varying forms. It comes from a tradition of broadside ballads, which satirize the weaknesses of merchants, preachers, women, etc., using this *Hard Times* refrain since early 19th century.

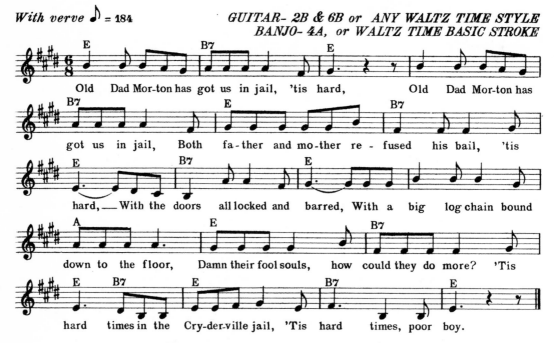

With verve ♪ = 184

GUITAR– 2B & 6B or ANY WALTZ TIME STYLE
BANJO– 4A, or WALTZ TIME BASIC STROKE

Old Dad Morton has got us in jail, 'tis hard, Old Dad Morton has got us in jail, Both father and mother re - fused his bail, 'tis hard,— With the doors all locked and barred, With a big log chain bound down to the floor, Damn their fool souls, how could they do more? 'Tis hard times in the Cry-der-ville jail, 'Tis hard times, poor boy.

1 Old Dad Morton has got us in jail, 'tis hard,
Old Dad Morton has got us in jail,
Both father and mother refused his bail, 'tis hard,
With the doors all locked and barred,
With a big log chain bound down to the floor,
Damn their fool souls, how could they do more?
'Tis hard times in the Cryderville jail,
'Tis hard times, poor boy.

2 The chuck they give us is beef and cornbread, 'tis hard,
The chuck they give us is beef and cornbread,
As old as hell and heavy as lead, 'tis hard,
With the doors all locked and barred.
We pop it down inside of our cells
Just like the pop from Heaven to Hell.
'Tis hard times in the Cryderville jail . . .

3 The lice and the chinches* are long as a rail, 'tis hard,
The lice and the chinches are long as a rail,
They raise their bristles and shake their tails, 'tis hard,
With the doors all locked and barred.

* bed bugs.

438

I said, ' Mister jailer, please lend me your knife,
For the bugs in your jail have threatened my life.'
'Tis hard times in the Cryderville jail . . .

4 Old Judge Simpkins will read us the law, 'tis hard,
Old Judge Simpkins will read us the law,
The damndest fool judge that you ever saw, 'tis hard,
With the doors all locked and barred.
He'll send you away for a year or two,
For making a barrel of the mountain dew,
'Tis hard times in the Cryderville jail . . .

5 And here's to the sheriff I'd like to forgot, 'tis hard,
And here's to the sheriff I'd like to forgot,
He's the damndest old rascal in the whole blame lot, 'tis hard,
With the doors all locked and barred.
Your pockets he'll pick and your clothes he will sell,
Get drunk on the money, God damn him to hell.
'Tis hard times in the Cryderville jail . . .

229. HARD, AIN'T IT HARD

Original treatment of *Tavern in the Town* by Woody Guthrie. Copyright 1952,
Ludlow Music, Inc., N.Y. and Essex Music, Ltd., London. Used by permission.
SEE: Belden, 201-7; Randolph I, 229. For another root see Randolph III, 249;
Sharp II, 76. Song stems from *Butcher's Boy* tradition, universal in Britain and
America for about two centuries. The Cornish lyric form *Tavern in the Town* has
become a standard community song. Another independent English variant to this
tradition is English *Died for Love*, Guide and Index; Reeves, 40, 90.

1 There is a house in this old town,
Where my true love lays around,
Well, he takes other women right down on his knee,
And he tells them a little tale that he won't
               tell me.

CHORUS:
It's hard and it's hard, ain't it hard,
To love one that never did love you.
It's hard and it's hard, ain't it hard, great God,
To love one that never will be true.

2 Well, the first time that I seen my true love,
He was a-walkin' past my door,
And the last time I seen his false-hearted smile,
He was dead on his coolin' board.   (CHO.)

3 Now don't go to drinkin' and a-gamblin',
Don't go there your sorrows to drown,
That hard liquor place is a lowdown disgrace,
It's the meanest damn place in this town.   (CHO.)

4 Now who's a-gonna kiss your ruby lips,
And who's a-gonna hold you to their breast,
Who's a-gonna talk the future over,
While I'm a-ramblin' in the West?   (CHO.)

230. FIDDLE-I-FEE

SEE: Brown III, 172; Newell, 115 for European background; Randolph III, 36; Sharp II, 310. Other farmyard types common in England—*Farmer's Boy*, *The Old Sow*, and *Old MacDonald*. Based on a version by Sam Hinton.

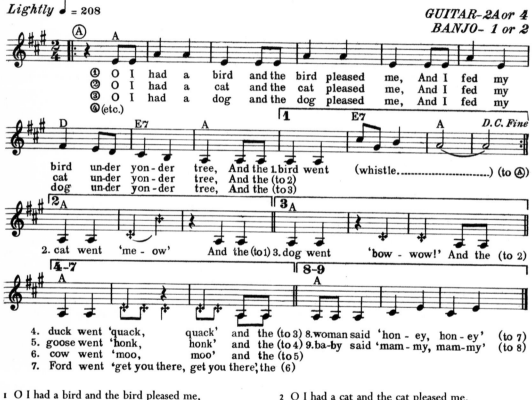

1 O I had a bird and the bird pleased me,
And I fed my bird under yonder tree,
And the bird went . . . (Whistle) *or* Fiddle-i-fee.

2 O I had a cat and the cat pleased me,
And I fed my cat under yonder tree,
And the cat went . . . ' me-ow '
And the bird went . . . (Whistle) *or* Fiddle-i-fee.

3 O I had a dog and the dog pleased me,
And I fed my dog under yonder tree,
The dog went ' bow-wow '
And the cat went . . . ' me-ow '
And the bird went . . . (Whistle) *or* Fiddle-i-fee.

Subsequent stanzas are formed by adding, successively, any or all of the following phrases:

> 4 The duck went ' quack, quack '.
> 5 The goose went ' honk, honk '.
> 6 The cow went ' moo, moo '.
> 7 The Ford went ' get you there, get you there '.
> 8 The woman said ' honey, honey '.
> 9 The baby said ' mammy, mammy '.

231. THE KICKIN' MULE

Recorded by Charles Todd and Robert Sonkin from singing of Henry King and Family, Visalia, Calif. AAFS 96 B-1. SEE: Brown III, 567; White, 157, 227. A universally popular folk song among southern white singers, this has distinct overtones from provincial theatre and minstrel show backgrounds.

1 As I went down to the huckleberry picnic,
Dinner all over the ground,
Skippers in the meat was nine foot deep
And the green flies walking all around.
The biscuits in the oven was a-baking,
Beefsteak frying in the pan,
Pretty gal sitting in the parlour,
Lord God A'mighty, what a hand I stand!
CHORUS:
Whoa there, mule, I tell you,
Miss Liza, you keep cool,
I ain't got time to kiss you now,
I'm busy with this mule.

2 My uncle had an old mule,
His name was Simon Slick,
'Bove anything I ever did see
Was how that mule could kick.
Went to feed that mule one morning
And he met me at the door with a smile,
He backed one ear and he winked one eye
And he kicked me half a mile. (CHO.)

3 This mule he am a kicker,
He's got an iron back,
He headed off a Texas railroad train
And kicked it off the track.
He kicked the feathers off a goose,
He pulverized a hog,
He kicked up three dead chinymans
And swatted him a yellow dog. (CHO.)

4 When I seen Miss Dinah the other day,
She was bent all over her tub,
And the more I'd ask her to marry me,
Well, the harder she would rub.
CHORUS:
Well, whoa there, mule, I tell you,
Whoa there, mule, I say,
Just keep your seat, Miss Liza Jane,
And hold on to that sleigh.

232. TALKING COLUMBIA *

Composed by Woody Guthrie. Used by permission Guthrie Foundation.

1 I was down along the river, just sittin' on a rock,
Lookin' at the boats in the Bonneville lock,
An' the gate swings open, the boat sails in,
Toots the whistle, she's go-one again!
    Gasolene goin' up, wheat comin' down.

2 Filled up my hat-brim, drunk a little taste,
Thought about a river, just goin' to waste,
I thought about the dust, 'n thought about the sand,
I thought about the people, 'n thought about the land . . .
    Ev'rybody runnin' around a-all over creation,
    Just lookin' for some kind of a little place.

3 Pulled out my pencil 'n I scribbled this song,
Figgered all o' them salmon jes' couldn't be wrong,
C's them salmon fish are mighty shrewd,
    They got senators . . . politicians, too . . .
    Jus' like a president . . . they run ever' four years.

4 You jes' watch this river 'n pretty soon
E-ev'rybody's gonna be changin' their tune . . .
The big Grand Coulee 'n the Bonneville Dam'll
Build a thousand factories f'r Uncle Sam . . .
    'N ev'rybody else in the world.

    Makin' ev'rything from sewin' machines
    To a-tomic bedrooms, 'n plastic . . .
    E-ev'rything's gonna be made outa plastic.

5 Uncle Sam needs wool, Uncle Sam needs wheat,
Uncle Sam needs houses 'n stuff to eat,
Uncle Sam needs water 'n power dams,
Uncle Sam needs people 'n the . . . people need land.

    Don't like dictators none much myself,
    What I think is the whole world oughta be run by
    Ee-lectricity . . .

* For style see p. 432.

233. ROLL ON, COLUMBIA

Composed by Woody Guthrie. Used by permission Guthrie Foundation.
Tune: Adaptation of *Irene Goodnight*.

Moderato ♩ = 138

GUITAR-
BANJO- } *ANY WALTZ TIME STYLE*

Green Doug-las fir where the wa-ters cut through, Down her wild moun-tains and can-yons she flew, Ca-na-dian North-west to the o-cean so blue, It's roll on, Co-lum-bia, roll on!___ Roll on,___ Co-lum-bia, roll on, Roll on,___ Co-lum-bia, roll on! Your pow-er is turn-ing our dark-ness to dawn, So roll on, Co-lum-bia, roll on!___

1 Green Douglas fir where the waters cut through,
Down her wild mountains and canyons she flew,
Canadian North-west to the ocean so blue,
It's roll on, Columbia, roll on!
CHORUS:
Roll on, Columbia, roll on,
Roll on, Columbia, roll on!
Your power is turning our darkness to dawn,
So roll on, Columbia, roll on!

2 Other great rivers add power to you,
Yakima, Snake and the Klickitat, too,
Sandy Williamette and Hood river, too,
Roll on, Columbia, roll on! (CHO.)

3 Tom Jefferson's vision would not let him rest,
An empire he saw in the Pacific North-west,
Sent Lewis and Clark and they did the rest, so
Roll on, Columbia, roll on! (CHO.)

4 At Bonneville now there are ships in the locks,
The waters have risen and cleared all the rocks,
Ship-loads of plenty will steam past the docks, so
Roll on, Columbia, roll on! (CHO.)

5 And on up the river is Grand Coulee Dam,
The mightiest thing ever built by a man,
To run the great factories and water the land, it's
Roll on, Columbia, roll on! (CHO.)

234. STAND TO YOUR GLASSES

Song and note material from *Western Folklore Quarterly* XII, 4, 1953, p. 240
'American Air Force Parodies', William Walloch. Collected in the airmen's
mess, 8th Bomber Wing in Korea, 1954. Related to *Wrap Me Up in My Tarpaulin
Jacket*, see note on *Sailor Cut Down in His Prime*; see also *The Dying Aviator*,
Tommy's Tunes (E. MacDonald, London, 1917), a popular song of the Flying
Corps in World War I.

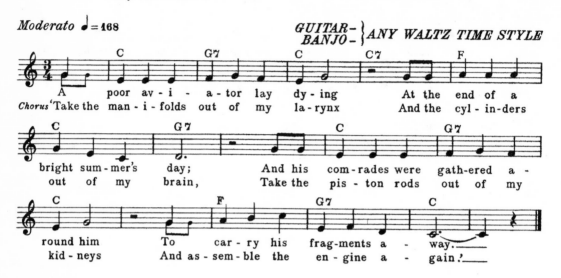

1 A poor aviator lay dying
   At the end of a bright summer's day;
   And his comrades were gathered around him
   To carry his fragments away.

2 O his bird was piled on his wishbone,
   And his engine was wrapped round his head,
   And he wore a spark plug on each elbow,
   'Twas plain he would shortly be dead.

3 O he spit out a valve and a gasket,
   As he stirred in the sump where he lay,
   And to his sorrowing comrades
   These brave parting words he did say:

4 'I'll be riding a cloud in the morning,
   With no Merlin before me to curse,
   So come along and get busy,
   Another lad will soon need the hearse.

CHORUS: (To the same tune.)
   'Take the manifolds out of my larynx,
   And the cylinders out of my brain,
   Take the piston rods out of my kidneys,
   And assemble the engine again.'

5 With rusted fifties and dud rockets,
   With pilots as old as they seem,
   We fly these worn-out Mustangs
   Against the MIG 15.

6 Forgotten by the country that bore us,
   Betrayed by the ones we hold dear,
   The good have all gone before us,
   And only the dull are still here.

7 So, stand to your glasses steady,
   This world is a world full of lies,
   Here's a toast to those dead already,
   And here's to the next man to die.

PART IV. THE NEGRO SOUTH

Spirituals I   Work Songs
Spirituals II   Ballads
Reels   Blues

THE NEGRO SOUTH

. . . . includes the Negro ghettos of certain Northern cities as well as the areas of large Negro population in the South; however, the region is not a geographic so much as a social phenomenon, created by racial and economic pressures. Negro folklore grew behind the barbed-wire fence of segregation.

The slaves, brought to the United States from many parts of Africa, continued to dance and make music as their ancestors had done, though not as freely as in Brazil or Haiti where African tribal music still survives. In the United States the tribes were mixed and African languages and ceremonies were forbidden, and the slaves filled this cultural vacuum by acquiring the rudiments of Anglo-American folk song, British country dancing, and European harmony, and adapting them to West African patterns (*see* pp. 487, 493).

Whatever they sang was intensely functional. Leader-chorus work songs to lighten the heavy burden of forced labour—dancing songs to quicken their spirits on their rare holidays— spirituals to replace their lost African religions and to console them during the ordeals of physical torment and spiritual degredation they suffered during three centuries. The words of their songs were even more oblique than those of the whites, since the slaves had to conceal their true emotions, but the music spoke for them without equivocation.

The Negroes came from cultures where women played an important role in the economy and were expected to enjoy their sexual lives as much as the men. Much West African music is a frank dramatization of sexual life and aggressive activities, and the African dance of possession provides outlets for a wide range of violent, sometimes psychotic emotions. American Negro dance music was, in its beginnings, joyously sensual, and it has remained so to a considerable degree in jazz, even beneath the melancholy surface of the blues, for, in spite of American moral and religious pressures, the sexual mores of the Negro folk group have been more permissive than those of whites at the same social level. Musically speaking, this permissiveness is expressed in the open, liquid, easily blending Negro voice—in its driving musical beat—in its erotic, syncopated rhythms, and in the melting decorations of the melodies.

Their songs and song forms, though largely derived from the folklore of their masters, were markedly African. One or two lines could serve a Negro singer, with his skill at improvising rhythmic variations, in place of a long ballad. Endless repetitions of these song fragments quickly lent a high polish to group songs, replete with choral passages, easy to harmonize and easy to remember. The music normally dominated the words, for Afro-American folk song remained basically choral and instrumental in character. Deprived of his drums and *sanzas*, the Negro used his hands and feet for rhythmic effects. He devised crude rattles and scrapers and perfected the banjo. As soon as he was permitted, he mastered the European instruments one after another—violin, bass, the horns, the reeds, the piano, and began teaching white folk and urban musicians how to play in the Afro-American fashion.

SPIRITUALS—I

235. JACOB'S LADDER

IN WEST AFRICA the Gods of the river, of the thunder, of the sea, of the wind, of love, of death and of ancestral spirits accompanied, punished, and protected every individual in his daily life. Their worship filled the year with brilliant ceremonial and encouraged every person to express himself, in songs, in dance, and in acts of self-dramatization. In America all these local, tribal, and personal protectors were far away, powerless and dumb, and the satisfactory pattern of ritual and dance and song was shattered. African *vaudou* (which continued to flourish in Catholic areas such as Haiti and Louisiana) survived in Protestant areas only in scraps of black magic. The slaves, impressed by the power of the white man's God and feeling the need of some fixed point in a situation deprived of most human values, embraced the faith of their Protestant masters and became ardent Baptists and Methodists.

Some planters did not allow their slaves to hold religious meetings, fearing, quite correctly, that Christian-Democratic ethics would put rebellious ideas into their heads. Other planters encouraged the conversion of their slaves so long as ' obey your masters ' was made the primary religious doctrine. Many sincere white Christians welcomed their black slaves into the fellowship of Christ, and, as time passed, this condition became more and more general. By the time of the Civil War, the vast majority of the slaves were practising Christians, and their African approach to religion attracted the whites to the singing meetings where spirituals like *Jacob's Ladder* were born. An ex-slave recalls . . .

At night, especially in the summertime, the old folks would get together and talk until bed time. Sometimes somebody would start humming an old hymn and then the next door neighbor would pick it up. In this way it would finally get around to every house and then the music started sure enough! Soon everybody would be gathered together, and such singing! Some would get happy and start shouting.

Steady yourselves, children,
Let's find the keys,
Let's find them tonight!

As soon as the white folks heard the singing they came running. Sometimes they would ask old Uncle Link to sing one of their favorite songs, or they would just sit and listen until everything got quiet and we all went to bed. Ours was considered the most religious plantation in that part of the country, and ol' Mars let us go round on Sundays and hold meetings at the other plantations. Then when it was our day, the slaves from the other places would come in flocks, and the singing and the shouting would set the world on fire, look like.

My grandmother was named Eve. She was a Christian from head to foot. It didn't take much to get her started, but when she called on God, she made the heavens ring. Aunt Charlotte used to cry most of the time when she got happy. Aunt Kate was a tall, portly woman, and it took some good ones to hold her when she got started. The old ones in them times walked over benches and boxes with their eyes fixed on heaven.

The white preacher had taught Uncle Link to fill the stand when he was unable to come. I remember one morning Uncle Link got up there. Mistress read the scripture off to him and he started preaching. I don't know how he could preach so much, for he couldn't read. He just remembered everything she read to him. Anyhow, he warmed up pretty soon, the spirit struck him and he set the place on fire that day. Lord, it looked like the very heaven would come down. My mistress cried and took her handkerchief and wiped my mother's eyes. She said it was the first time she had felt the presence of God since the little church had been built.

QUOTE : Fisk.

448

236. WHEN THE SAINTS GO MARCHIN' IN

THE BACKWOODS WHITES, who owned few slaves, often brought them to their summer revival meetings, where the Negroes contributed to the singing and to the general excitement. This contemporary account of a camp meeting in frontier Alabama captures the irony inherent in this moment of the human comedy . . .

> The hollow square of the encampment was filled with people listening to the mid-day sermon and its dozen accompanying exhortations. The excitement was intense. Men and women rolled about on the ground, or lay sobbing and shouting in promiscuous heaps. More than all, the Negroes sang and screamed and prayed. Several, under the influence of what is technically called ' jerks ' were plunging and pitching about with convulsive energy. The object of all seemed to be to see who could make the greatest noise.
>
> In another part of the square a dozen old women were singing. They were in a state of absolute ecstasy as their shrill pipes gave forth . . .
>
> > I rode on the sky,
> > Quite ondestified I,
> > And the moon it was under my feet.
>
> ' Glor-ee! ' yelled a huge Negro woman, as in a fit of the jerks she threw herself convulsively from her feet, and fell ' like a thousand bricks ' across a diminutive old man in a little round hat who was speaking consolation to one of the mourners.
>
> ' Good Lord have mercy!' ejaculated the little man earnestly and unaffectedly as he strove to crawl from under the sable mass which was crushing him.
>
> ' Whar's John Dobbs? You, Sukey!' cried an old lady in black silk, screaming at the Negro woman. ' Sukey, if you don't hunt up your Mass' John in a minute and have him here to listen to this 'sperience, I'll take you up when I git home and give you a hundred and fifty lashes, madam, see ef I don't. Blessed Lord! . . .'

The white camp meeting hymn, *The Old Ship of Zion*, crossed the race line on some such occasion, yet this was just the beginning of its story. Negro folk singers have used the melody to create a whole family of spirituals—*The Gospel Train*, *The Whole Round World*, *Way Beyond the Sun*, and, best known of all, *The Saints*, which, through an irony of history, has become an international hot jazz standard. The New Orleans jazz men, most of whom came from good religious homes, would never jazz up the normal spiritual, but *The Saints* was an exception since the Holy Rollers had already turned it into a red-hot revival tune.

QUOTE: *Simon Suggs Attends Camp Meeting*, Johnson Hooper.

237. WHEN THE STARS BEGIN TO FALL

NOT ALL the planters, by any means, gave their slaves licence to worship freely and as they pleased. The most familiar motif in the reminiscence of ex-slaves is the story of the secret religious meetings with an iron pot on the floor to keep the sound in the room. This pot (which they believed muffled the sound) was probably a survival from Africa, where the spirits of the helpful dead inhabit pots of water in the *vaudou* temples. But the secrecy of the gatherings at which it played a part indicates that they were sometimes rebellious as well as religious in character. The ex-slaves have been understandably reluctant to speak of these matters, but the fact is that slave uprisings, large and small, were a normal, though carefully hidden aspect of life in the pre-war South.

These abortive rebellions, which on one or two occasions involved thousands of slaves, were always put down with savage violence; the Negroes who participated were beheaded, hung, shot, or beaten to death, for the white South was always fearful that a true slave revolution would take place. Every slave knew that his nervous masters were watching him and that his slightest act, if no more than an angry look or a sullen word, might bring him a merciless lashing. Even the spirituals, as the following slave tale shows, were censored. Thus their symbolism became all the more evocative, cryptic, and intense, communicating to all those who were oppressed the hopeful message that they would one day be free and their oppressors punished . . .

Our white folks when they had camp meetings would have the colored folks come and sing over their mourners. You know they still say that colored folks can beat the whites singing. We sat way in the back with the white folks in front. Then sometimes they would let us have evenings in the church and we'd sit in front with the patterollers* behind. The colored preachers would tell us to obey our mistress and master. That's mostly all they knowed how to say. But if they said something else, the patterollers might stop them. One time we were singing 'Ride on, King Jesus, no man can hinder thee,' when the patterollers told us to stop, or they would show us whether we could be hindered or not. They said you was crazy if you got religion.

The white folks was afraid the niggers get to thinkin' they was free if they had their own churches. But we had our meetings anyhow, singing and praying like a good old-time revival. We would take pots and turn 'em upside down in the middle of the floor to keep the sound in the room, and keep the white folks from meddling. You know, the sound will stay right in the room if you turn a pot over. We'd sing the old-time hymns then, the ones the children done done away with now.

> My Lord, he called me, called me by the lightning,
> The trumpet sounds within my soul, I ain't got long to stay here.
> Steal away, steal away.

And I've heard them pray for freedom. I thought it was foolishness then, but the old-time folks always felt they was to be free. It must have been something revealed to them. Back there, if they'd catch you writing, they'd break you of it if they had to cut your fingers off; and still they knew they would be free.

QUOTE: Fisk.

* The white patrols, set up in every neighbourhood after the Nat Turner rebellion, to control the activities of the slaves.

238. MANY THOUSANDS GONE

THIS IS ONE of the spirituals of resistance, whose ante-bellum origin has been authenticated. Runaway slaves who fled as far north as Nova Scotia, after Britain abolished slavery in 1833, transmitted it to their descendants; and it is still in oral circulation there. At the time of the Civil War an abolitionist took it down from Negro Union soldiers.

I asked one of these blacks, one of the most intelligent of them, where they got these songs.
' Dey make 'em, sah.'
' How do they make them?'
After a pause, evidently casting about for an explanation, he said:
' I'll tell you: it's dis way. My master call me up an' order me a short peck of corn and a hundred lash. My friends see it and is sorry for me. When dey come to de praise meeting dat night, dey sing about it. Some's very good singers and know how; and dey work it in, work it in, you know, till dey get it right; and dat's de way.' (July 9, 1862.)

QUOTE: *Scenes in the Life of Harriet Tubman*, Sarah Bradford (W. J. Moses, N.Y., 1869).

239. KEEP A-INCHIN' ALONG

THE SONG-MAKERS were illiterates, but they were born orators; they read the book of earth, finding there a world of dew-bright images.

Now you talk about hard times, I have had hard times. I started ploughing at eight years old. I was barefooted as a duck. And I used to work in the tobacco patch catching worms off leaves. Marster would come behind me, and if he would find a worm I would have to bite its head off. I remember my sister broke old Marster's clock. He tied a rope round her neck and whipped her I don't know how long. There stood my mother, there stood my father, and there stood all the children and none of them could come to her rescue. But I seen the clod put on Marse after Freedom come. We all knew that the children of Israel was four hundred years under bondage and God looked down and seen their suffering and brought them out, and that he would do the same for us.

The first Sunday school I went to was after the war, under an old oak tree. We used to carry our dinner and stay there from eight till four in the evening. In slavery they used to teach the Negro that they had no soul. They said all they needed was to obey their mistress. One old sister was shouting in the back of the church and her mistress was up in front and she looked back and said, ' Shout on, old nig', there is a kitchen in heaven for you to shout over, too.'

I am no mathematician, no biologist, neither grammarian; but when it comes to handling the Bible, I knocks down verbs, breaks up prepositions and jumps over adjectives. I am a God-sent man. All the education I got, it was out in the fields. That was my fountain pen and pencil. The blade of my hoe was my pen, and my slate was the ground. Now the law says, ' Black and white shan't mix.' Who made that law? They made it. I made a law with my hoe, that all weeds must die that I hit . . .

QUOTE: Fisk.

240-1. ROLL, JORDAN, ROLL
(A Negro and a white version)

SINCE EACH OF THESE songs is a good representative of its type, detailed comparison can show what the Negro contributed to the white spirituals he adapted . . . In the *first* line the Negro affirms his faith in a personal God (' yes, my Lord '); he has visited Heaven in his vision and has listened to ' old Jordan roll ' while he sat, in lordly informality, in the kingdom—a vivid, charming, human experience.

In contrast, the white song presents a severe, patriarchal God, preceded by doom-sounding trumpets and a storm heralding death and the end of the world. To the faithful he offers no pleasurable reward, but the opportunity to praise a masterful Deity in eternal hallelujahs. The language, though vivid enough, is wooden, literary, and impersonal (' we ' instead of ' I ').

The Negro leader begins, as usual, with the refrain, which the group takes up. At the end of the first phrase—which is composed of a magnificent pattern of big, round vowels—the leader hits a triumphant high note while the words present the image of the great river of Christianity rolling timelessly and irresistibly on. In the second responsorial line the chorus has its opportunity to reaffirm this vision. Then all together on a positive, downward-swooping cadence, supported by a roaring masculine bass note at the very end, they say, ' I want to go to Heaven when I die,' making death into a positive act of faith. Why? Just to sit there and listen to ' old '—my old, my dear old, my familiar old—river of time rumble on in a sustained chord of heavenly enthusiasm.

In the verse the Negro leader takes a quiet, softer, more intimate tone, telling of his personal experience. In response comes a roar of yea-saying from the chorus, descending to another resounding and reassuring bass note from the men. In another soft, melodic line from the leader, the patterning of the ' i ' sound is matched by catchy syncopation. Then the chorus, participating in the vision and using a series of vowels that grows steadily rounder and more open, again perfectly combines melody and text.

The white spiritual, while noble and beautiful in its rather severe way, falls short of the Negro song at most points. The words are occasionally awkward to sing—' the seventh trumpet speaks '. The important third chorus line is long and pedestrian in metre. The melody does not soar and descend in response to the image of the heavenly river, but maintains a rigid and restrained middle course that corresponds to the severity of the white vision. The speech sounds do not flow with the melodic cadence as in the Negro song, but frequently interfere with it so that the words must be forced out through the notes, rather than intoned through them.

Where the Negroes took the white hymns they did not copy them; rather they touched them with magic and transformed them into eternal works of art. The majority of their finest hymns are original creations and their titles—*Go Down Moses*, *Nobody Knows*, *Steal Away*, *Joshua Fit the Battle of Jericho*, *Deep River*, *Little David*, *Swing Low*—make up a roster of the best American melodies, and match the finest songs in any language.

235. JACOB'S LADDER

Adapted by Alan Lomax. SEE: Brown III, 594; Johnson; Randolph II, 336; Sears; Sharp II, 295; White, 59. One of the old spirituals which emerged from white tradition, but was early remade by Negroes.
Piano arrangement by MATYAS SEIBER

1 We are climbin' Jacob's ladder, (3)
Soldiers of the cross.

2 Every new round we go higher, (3)
Soldiers of the cross.

3 I'm gonna ride in the golden char'ot, (3)
Soldiers of the cross.

4 I'm gonna sit at the welcome table, (3)
Soldiers of the cross.

In the 1940's a new set of words was put to this magnificent hymn, making it into a powerful appeal for peace and world brotherhood . . .

1 We are buildin' one big union,　(3)
People of this world.

2 Every new day we grow stronger,　(3)
People of this world.

3 We are black and white together,　(3)
People of this world.

236. WHEN THE SAINTS GO MARCHIN' IN

Similar to *Old-Time Religion* (Brown III, 674) and *Old Ship of Zion* (Brown III, 659).
SEE: Hampton, 200; Sears; White, 93.

1 O when the saints go marchin' in,　(2)
Lord, I want to be in that number
When the saints go marchin' in.

2 O when the sun refuse to shine, *etc.*

3 O when the moon goes down in blood, *etc.*

4 O when the stars have disappeared, *etc.*

5 O when they crown Him Lord of all, *etc.*

6 O when the day of judgement comes, *etc.*

237. WHEN THE STARS BEGIN TO FALL

Adapted by Alan Lomax. SEE: Jackson IV, 154; Johnson; Sears.
Piano arrangement by MATYAS SEIBER

CHORUS:
My Lord, what a mornin'! (3)
When the stars begin to fall!

1 You'll hear the sinner moan
To wake the nations underground,
Lookin' to my God's right hand
When the stars, the stars begin to fall. (CHO.)

2 You'll hear the gambler groan, *etc. as in* (1) (CHO.)

3 You'll hear the sinner pray, *etc. as in* (1) (CHO.)

4 You'll hear the Christian sing, *etc. as in* (1)
(CHO.)

5 You'll see my Jesus come,
His chariot wheels roll round,
Lookin' to my God's right hand
When the stars, the stars begin to fall.   (CHO.)

238. MANY THOUSANDS GONE

FROM: *Slave Songs of the U.S.*, W. F. Allen, C. P. Ware and L. McK. Garrison
(A. Simpson & Co., N.Y., 1867; Peter Smith, N.Y., 1929). SEE: Creighton II,
279; *Religious Folk Songs of the Negro as Sung at Hampton Institute*, Nathaniel Dett
(Schirmer, N.Y., 1927); *Afro-American Folk Songs*, H. E. Krehbiel (Schirmer,
N.Y., 1914) p. 18; Sears. Sung by Negro troops in South-East during Civil War.

Slow march or freely ♩ = 48   GUITAR⎫
                                   BANJO⎭ *FREE OR RHYTHMIC STRUM*

No more auc-tion block for me, Ma-ny thou-sands gone.

1 No more auction block for me,
No more, no more,
No more auction block for me,
Many thousands gone.

2 No more peck o' corn for me, *etc.*

3 No more driver's lash for me, *etc.*

4 No more pint of salt for me, *etc.*

5 No more hundred lash for me, *etc.*

6 No more mistress call for me, *etc.*

239. KEEP A-INCHIN' ALONG

Adapted by Alan Lomax. SEE: Johnson; Odum I, 89; Sears. An ante-bellum spiritual seldom sung in last generation.

Slow rock ♩=112

GUITAR– 7A, 7B
BANJO– 5

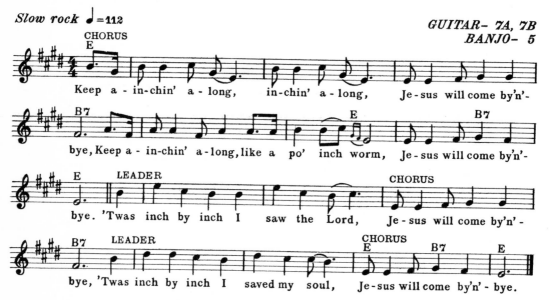

Keep a-inchin' a-long, inchin' a-long, Je-sus will come by'n'-bye, Keep a-inchin' a-long, like a po' inch worm, Je-sus will come by'n'-bye. 'Twas inch by inch I saw the Lord, Je-sus will come by'n'-bye, 'Twas inch by inch I saved my soul, Je-sus will come by'n'-bye.

CHORUS:
Keep a-inchin' along, inchin' along,
Jesus will come by'-'n'-bye,
Keep a-inchin' along, like a po' inch worm,
Jesus will come by'-'n'-bye.

1 'Twas inch by inch I saw the Lord,
Jesus will come by'-'n'-bye,
'Twas inch by inch I saved my soul,
Jesus will come by'-'n'-bye. (CHO.)

2 Down in the valley when my Lord come by,
I thought to my soul I would rise and fly. (CHO.)

3 When I get to Heaven, be able to tell,
Two archangels gonna toll the bell. (CHO.)

4 When I get to Heaven, ain't I gonna shout?
Nobody there to put me out. (CHO.)

5 Heaven so high, Heaven so high,
Nobody there but the sanctified. (CHO.)

6 Ever since my Lord set me free,
This old world's been a Hell to me. (CHO.)

7 Sometimes I hang my head and cry,
  But I'm gonna serve God till I die. (CHO.)

8 Old Pharaoh thought he had me fast,
  But the sea dried up and let me pass. (CHO.)

9 Jordan river is chilly and cold,
  Chills the body, but not the soul. (CHO.)

10 There's a fire in the East, fire in the Wes',
   There's fire among us Methodes'. (CHO.)

240. ROLL, JORDAN, ROLL

Especially adapted and arranged. SEE: Brown III, 667; Hampton, 165; Johnson;
Sears; White, 87.

Piano arrangement by DON BANKS

457

CHORUS:
Roll, Jordan, roll,
Roll, Jordan, roll,
I want to go to Heaven when I die
To hear old Jordan roll.

1 O preacher, you oughta been there,
Yes, my Lord,
A-sittin' in the kingdom
To hear old Jordan roll.

2 O brother, you oughta been there, *etc.* (CHO.)

3 O sister, you oughta been there, *etc.* (CHO.)

4 O sinner, you oughta been there, *etc.* (CHO.)

241. ROLL, JORDAN, ROLL

FROM: p. 247 of *Original Sacred Harp*, attributed to J. G. and A. W. McCurry,
a setting for four voices. SEE: Brown III, 667; Jackson II, 193, III, 127, IV, 180.

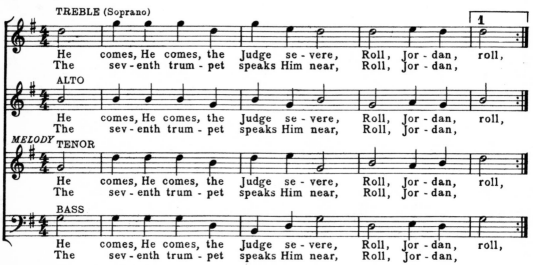

1 He comes, He comes, the Judge severe,
   Roll, Jordan, roll,
   The seventh trumpet speaks Him near,
   Roll, Jordan, roll.
   CHORUS:
   I want to go to Heaven, I do,
   Hallelujah, Lord,
   We'll praise the Lord in Heav'n above,
   Roll, Jordan, roll.

2 His lightnings flash, His thunders roll,
   How welcome to the faithful soul. (CHO.)

SPIRITUALS—II

242. WADE IN THE WATER

THE NOTES on earlier songs have not quite explained the supreme pleasure Negroes felt in singing the spirituals, nor the noble beauty of the songs, which strokes the heart as a single, clear feeling.

First of all, the West African Negroes were skilful in blending their voices in simple chords and in creating independent rhythmic parts. In America, listening to European chordal music performed on the parlour organ or by bands, or by the singing schools, they quickly learned to use a rudimentary European harmonic system, and made it their own by experimenting with their newly acquired techniques. Since singing sacred songs was the main artistic outlet permitted by their Calvinistic masters, the slaves poured their creativity into this art. They soon found that when they sang, the whites recognized their superiority as singers, and listened with respect. Thus, singing in chorus gave the Negroes status, which no other activity afforded. Otherwise they were tools, sexual objects, domestic appliances, and a source of wealth.

Yet the slaves occupied a position of moral superiority to their masters. They bore the burdens of the weakness and sadism of these white men and they knew it. While many of the planters drank, gambled, fornicated, danced, ate to excess, quarrelled, beat and sometimes killed their human work animals, their black chattels lived lives of want, forbearance and suffering. The faith of the slaves, therefore, was not lip service to Christian dogma. They sublimated their anger in profound conversion experiences; they felt washed clean of sin and expressed this joy in the poetic images of the spirituals.

Their songs proclaimed that some day justice would triumph and that an end for sorrow and shame would come, whether on earth or in Heaven. They rang with a passionate belief in the goodness of man and they voiced his endless longing for freedom. Thus, when the slaves sang the traditional white verses, they gave them a new and subtle power (*see* p. 451).

243. WHEN I'M GONE

244. SOON I WILL BE DONE

SOMETIMES the makers of the spirituals became so hopeless that they longed to die; but this was not the neurotic death wish of the whites, but a longing for release from real suffering. The ex-slaves remind us of the horrors of that bygone day . . .

There was an old man who belonged to Dr. Selby and he said if he ever got free he wasn't ever going to get up any more, and, after he got free, he really stayed there till he starved to death and died. He was an old man, but he was just so happy to know that he could lay in bed and nobody could make him get up, he wouldn't even get up to eat. You sho' couldn't lie in bed in old Mister Selby's place. He'd whip niggers most to **death**...

... Whenever they got ready to whip a darkey, unless there was a written statement not to draw blood, they would strap them down on their stomach with their hands straight out, fasten feet and legs, and with a piece of leather with holes cut in it, they'd give him three dozen—that meant three hundred. Then they had a pot of red pepper with salt in it; they would rip open the blisters and rub this liquor in. In order to work you had to wrap yourself in a sheet or something drenched in oil, and they would make you work all right. It was awful to hear 'em hollering and begging for mercy. If they hollered, ' Lord, have mercy!' Marse Jim didn't hear 'em, but if they cried, ' Marse Jim, have mercy!' then he made 'em stop the beating. He say, ' The Lord rule Heaven, but Jim Smith rule the earth.'

About 1861 some of the slaves learned to read, but a woman named Fredonia told the white folks that their niggers was going to rise and kill them. They caught these slaves and took them out on the road and whipped them nearly to death, and the preacher, Henry King, they knocked him over and cut his head off. They showed the head to the others and said that they would put them in the same fix if they didn't stop talking about being free.

QUOTES: (a) Botkin VII, 163; (b) Fisk.

245. BLIND MAN

One day when I was down in the public square I met my old master. I had not seen him for nearly thirty years. He said to me, ' Charlie, do you remember me lacerating your back?' I said, ' Yes, Mars'.' ' Have you forgiven me?' I said, ' Yes, I have forgiven you.'

There were a lot of people gathering around because we were a little distance apart and talking loud. I was never scared of nobody, so when he asked me the next question, ' How can you forgive me, Charlie?' I said, ' Mars, when we whip dogs we do it just because we own them. It is not because they have done anything to be whipped for, but we do it just because we can. That is why you whipped me. I used to serve you, work for you, almost nursed you, and if anything had happened to you I would have fought for you, for I am a man among men. What is in me, though, is not in you. I used to drive you to church and peep through the window to see you all worship, but you ain't right yet, Marster.'

He held out his hand to me and almost cried and said, ' Charlie, come to see me and I will treat you nice. I'm sorry for what I did.'

I said, ' That's all right, Marster, I done left the past behind me.'

I had felt the power of God and had tasted his love, and this had killed all the hate in my heart years before this happened. Whenever a man has been killed dead and made alive in Jesus Christ, he no longer feels like he did when he served the Devil.

The Negro convert felt that he and all fellow human beings were like the blind man by the wayside, crying out, ' Lord, show me the way!' When the way was shown to him, the ' love come tumbling down ' into his heart.

QUOTE: Fisk.

246. I COULDN'T HEAR NOBODY PRAY
247. HOLD THE WIND

WHEN THE SLAVES received Christianity, they discovered themselves to be sinners. Not only were their sexual practices and their love of amusement sins, but in order to exist under slavery, they were often forced to lie, steal, fornicate, and betray their brothers. Worst of all, they were filled with anger; sinned against, they were themselves heavy with sin— down in the valley, surrounded by shadows. Faced with personal disintegration, they pinned

461

all their faith in their new religion. Told that the Christian God would cleanse them, they demanded clear proof of their spiritual rebirth in visions as vivid as African *vaudou* had brought to their ancestors.

The seeker after religion prayed night and day, until a heavenly visitor came in a dream and cleansed him of sin. When he recounted this dream, he was admitted to the church, but, more importantly, he gained a sense of personal worth and security, denied him as a slave. He was now God's man, and doubt was put behind him. The religious experience that follows is typical of those that sustained the slave, and that gave rise to a great many spirituals such as *Hold the Wind*.

I was a slave and started to pray when I was nine years old. My mistress was mean to me and I was a stubborn child. One day she said, ' I am going to kill you. Go and eat and come back to me. I am going to kill you.' I started out to eat, but when I got to the steps of the kitchen, I, a nine-year-old child, fell down and prayed to God, saying, ' Lord, I don't want to be killed. Save me.' I went to the kitchen and ate nothing, and, when I came back in the house, she didn't touch me. From then on I prayed more and more.

Now I was a great dancer when I grew up, and in spite of my praying, I went to dances. One night I went to a dance but I didn't feel right, and strange to say, everytime I got on the floor to dance a round, the fiddle string would break. All of a sudden, while I was in my place ready to dance, I heard a voice on the inside that said, ' Do you remember the promise you made to me?' I thought that everybody heard the voice, it was so loud. I ran out of the room and hid myself and started to praying. It was while praying that I died and found myself at the greedy jaws of Hell!

I saw the Devil, a terrible club-footed man, with red eyes like fire. I saw a big wheel that seemed full of souls and, as it turned, the cry of ' Woe, woe!' was pitiful. I saw my own body, black with smoke, burning in the flames. Then old Satan set his hell-hounds after me, and I saw myself come out of myself, and I was a little angel and began to fly. I sailed just high enough and fast enough to keep out of their reach. I looked to the East and saw a man standing looking at me as I flew. He sounded a trumpet and the hell-hounds tucked their tails and left off running after me.

A voice came to me saying, ' My little one, I have given you eternal life. I looked upon you in the dust of earth and blessed you with everlasting life. You are fixed, pre-fixed and bought at the Lamb sale and caught up in the election and ready for the building.'

I came to the building where I saw God. He sat writing, and without stopping He said to me, ' I shod you with the Gospel of Peace at the greedy jaws of Hell. Your name is written on the Lamb book of life. Go back in yonder world and stay till I come.' When He spoke these words, the whole place seemed to sound in a moan, ' Amen!' I looked about me and saw a green pasture filled with sheep, all pure white and of the same size.

I know my God and rejoice in Him every day. Trusting in His name, I am not afraid of Hell-fire, for I have been killed dead and made alive again and I am fire-proof, rejoicing every day and waiting for Him to carry me home . . .

QUOTE: Fisk.

248. THE OLD ARK'S A-MOVERIN'

Reverend:	When the ole spirit hit you, honey, I'm gonna tell you the truth, you're not of yourself. I've knowed it to trip people, send um to the floor.
His wife:	I've hollered myself—' Oh!' it hurt me so.
Reverend:	Once I had to help pick up a woman that had the spirit and it hit me—' Wham!'—like that, so I couldn't help but holler out ' Glory!'
His wife:	But you never really hurt nobody if you got the spirit, no matter how much you shout.
Reverend:	I don't know about that. I grabbed my first wife one time when she was shoutin'. Then I didn't

	have no religion. That woman jerk me across every bench in church. I turnt her loose. I said I'll never grab that fool again.
His wife:	That's cause you didn't have religion. You didn't know how to handle her. Or let her be. Now I have a friend, when she gets happy at church, she runs. Run and laugh. Did you ever hear the Holy Spirit laughin'? And Lord, she'll run up and down the aisle till she feel satisfied, just *laughin'* hard as she can. Diggy-diggy-diggety-dig! She'll have her own way over everyone and everything. And don't you touch her. She don't like that. Just let her be—to shout . . .
Reverend:	Better let her alone! I 'member one time old Deacon Jones got to shoutin' so that he actually flew around the altar, not a hand or foot touchin'.

These good Baptists would be shocked to learn that they were describing the American survival of the West African, pagan *saut* or possession, in which a *vaudou* god mounts a worshipper. While thus possessed or ' happy ' (as Americans put it) the West African ' horse of the God ' dances, leaps, heals, prophesies, speaks the divine language, and may, according to the nature of his rider, eat fire, climb a tree like a snake, etc.

The Negro slaves and their descendants performed a religious dance called the ' shout ' which vividly recalls African dance types. As the group sang a repetitive choral spiritual, such as this, the worshippers shuffled counter-clockwise round the church house in single file, weaving their hips, rocking back and forth from heel to toe, clapping their hands and stamping the floor till the whole building boomed like a big drum. Sometimes a couple ' shouted ' face to face and every dancer might ' shout ' in his own style. All were carefully observed by an old deacon, called the watchman ; if the ' shouters ' crossed their feet or lifted them off the floor, he would call out . . .

Look out, sister, how you walk on the Cross,
Your foot might slip and your soul get lost . . .

Shouting in this old-fashioned African sense had disappeared in most churches by 1900, only to be revived in an even more frenetic style by the Holy Rollers; but the old sisters of the church still get happy and shout (dance, weep, or move in religious hysteria) all over the church when ' the old ark's a-moverin' '.

QUOTE: Lomax recording.

249. DESE BONES GWINE RISE AGAIN

When white folks go to meetin'
They never crack a smile,
But when colored folks in church
You'll hear um laugh er mile . . .

THE WEST AFRICAN lives with his gods on terms of intimacy. He appeals to them, reviles them, tricks them, laughs at their follies. In this spirit the Negro slave humanized the stern religion of his masters by adopting the figures of the Bible as his intimates. Untaught country preachers, with a natural genius for humour, did not hesitate to make their congregations laugh as well as weep. A slave preacher once prayed as follows . . .

O mah God an' mah father, ain't you see how dis groun' do trimble same like judgement day? Come down hyuh, Lawd, an' help po' people in dere trial and tribbilation, but o, do Mass Gawd, be sho an' come yo'self an' doan sen' Yo' Son, because dis ain' no time for chillun . . .

463

Heaven itself was not spared by the ironic and healing laughter of the Negro. Old Massa is telling his slave about the dream he had last night . . .

' It was like this. I dreamed I went to Nigger Heaven last night, and saw there a lot of garbage, some old torn-down houses, a few old broken down, rotten fences, the muddiest, sloppiest streets I ever saw, and a big bunch of ragged, dirty niggers walkin' around.'

' Umph, umph, Massa,' said Ike. ' You sho' musta et de same thing I did las' night, 'case I dreamed I went up to de white man's paradise, an' de streets was all of gol' an' silver, and dey was lots o' milk an' honey dere, an' putty pearly gates, but dey wasn't a soul in de whole place.'

Yet, when these same yarn spinners grew serious, they could express their view of things in the noble language of the prophets. An old slave here speaks about the creation . . .

God looked down through the scope of time and saw every generation, even down to this day. Then God conceived the idea of making man. He stooped down and took a handful of clay, but the earth mourned and God made a contract with the earth, saying, ' Weep not, for lo, I will repay every atom.'

Like a small number of other spirituals, this epic song of creation was parodied by the minstrel shows and later by college students until it lost some of its original grandeur. Even so, it retains a vision of the beginnings of things that is verdant and charming.

QUOTE: ' Juneteenth ', J. Mason Brewer in *Tone the Bell Easy* (Texas Folklore Society, 1932). Ed. F. Dobie.

250. DIDN'T IT RAIN

IN THEIR FOLK SONGS and tales the Negroes polished up the haloes of the prophets and brightened the heavenly plumage of the angels, meanwhile giving them feet of clay and a broad Southern accent. The Noah legend provided the Negro with a basis for much apocryphal folklore. Ermenie Vogelin tells us that the lion was sea-sick during the entire cruise of the Ark and once bit Captain Noah. Ham turned black and became the progenitor of the Negro race when he mocked at his father's nakedness; but he did not lose heart; he stripped the possum's tail and made strings for the first banjo—and that is why the possum's tail is bare to this day.

Zora Hurston reports one of the most amusing Noah stories. It seems that old John, the trickster slave, died at last by drowning in the great flood that destroyed Johnstown, Pennsylvania. John went on to Heaven, but he carried his big mouth with him . . .

. . . He took a seat on de bench and commenced to tune up his harp. By dat time, two angels come walkin' by where John was settin', so he throwed down his harp and tackled 'em. ' Say,' he hollered. ' Y'all want to hear 'bout de big flood Ah was in down on earth? Lawd, Lawd. It sho' rained, and talkin' 'bout water!'

Dem two angels hurried off from him jus' as quick as they could. He started to tellin' another one and he took to flyin'. After a while John went over to Ole Peter and said, ' Thought you said everybody would be nice and polite. Ah jus' walked up to a man as nice an' friendly as Ah could be and started to tell 'im 'bout all dat water Ah left back there in Johnstown and instead of him turnin' me a friendly answer, he said, "Shucks! You ain't seen no water," and walked off and left me standin' by myself.'

' Washe a *ole* man wid a crooked walkin' stick?' Peter ast John.

' Yeah.'

' Did he have whiskers down to here?' Peter measured down to his waist.

' He sho did,' John tol' him.

' Aw shucks,' Peter tol' im, ' dat was Ole Noah. You can't tell *him* nothin' 'bout no flood.'

QUOTE: Hurston, p. 29.

251. SAMSON

CHILLUN, Samson was one man that walked in the way of the Lord. Satan tried all his tricks to make him turn aside. He put the whole Philistine army in the way, but old Samson took the jawbone of the ass and kilt so many Philistines that they had to start a new graveyard to hold um all.

Samson was just fine till he started haulin' Miss Delilah round everywhere he go. Miss Delilah was doin' just what Satan told her. She started to beggin' Samson, ' Man, you the strongest thing. How'n the world did you git so strong?' An' she kept on pickin' at him till Samson told, told her that it was his hair.

When old Samson took his nap that afternoon, Miss Delilah roached his hair plumb bald. Cut every hair off, and when Samson come to, he felt low. He was too weak to swing a cat. The Philistines grab him and put out both his eyes. They hooked him to a plow with a mule and made him plow. I'll tell you, it looked pretty black for old Samson.

Then one day when all them Philistines was drinkin' and mockin' ol' Samson, the Lord touched his head and the hair just shoot out again. Samson taken up the posts that helt up the place, took um up under his arms and started walkin' down the Lord's road. The whole meetin' house fall down, and that's the way them Philistines meet their end. Just like the wicked always gonna end in dust and death . . .

QUOTE: *Negro Folk Sermons*—a thesis by John Henry Faulk (University of Texas).

465

252. JOHN THE REVELATOR

> Some say that John was a Baptist,
> Some say he was a Jew,
> But the Holy Bible tell us
> That John was a preacher, too . . .

JOHN, as the fore-runner and prophet of Christ's coming, has always been a folk hero among a people that had to live on hope. The preachers, especially, felt themselves to be John the Baptists for their flocks. The name had another significance, for old John was the slave who always talked his way out of every predicament. At last, one day, Old John tried his master's short patience too far and they were about to hang him . . .

So John called Jack and told him says, ' Ole Massa is gointer hang me under that persimmon tree. Now you get three matches and get in the top of the tree. Ah'm gointer pray and when you hear me ast God to let it lightning Ah want you to strike matches.'

Jack went on out to the tree. Ole Massa brought John on out with the rope around his neck and put it over a limb. ' Now John,' said Massa. ' Have you got any last words to say?'

' Yes, sir. Ah want to pray.'

' Pray and pray damn quickly. I'm clean out of patience with you, John.'

So John knelt down. ' O Lord, here Ah am at de foot of de persimmon tree. If you're gointer destroy ole Massa tonight with his wife and chillun and everything he got, lemme see it lightnin'.'

Jack up the tree struck a match. Ole Massa caught hold of John and said, ' John, don't pray no more.'

John said, ' O yes, turn me loose so Ah can pray. O Lord, here Ah am tonight callin' on Thee and Thee alone. If you're gointer destroy Ole Massa tonight, his wife and chillun and all he got, I want to see it lightnin' again.'

Jack struck another match and Ole Massa started to run. He give John his freedom and a heap of land and stock. He run so fast that it took an express train running at the rate of ninety miles an hour and six months to bring him back, and that's how come niggers got they freedom today.

QUOTE: Hurston.

253. RISE UP, SHEPHERD

CHILLUN, the Lord been havin' so much trouble with ol' Satan stealin' his sheep right outa the fold that he decided to send somebody down to look after um. He can't send Adam, because he been caught once, himself. Can't send Moses because he get riled too easy. So he called Jesus, his only Son.

He told little Jesus He was gonna have a rocky, dangerous time. Old Satan was just as slick as an eel. But little Jesus just smiled and ask when was He suppose to start the job. He never minded the danger, and the Lord never had to tell Him what to do. Little Jesus knows what to do.

But the Lord sort of hated to see Jesus go. He say, ' O my Son, you know they ain't nothin' in the world old Satan won't do to aggravate you. Is you sho you don't mind?'

Jesus say, ' Father, I loves them sheeps, and I wants to see them saved. Old Satan won't prank with me. I'll watch them sheeps and I'll save every one. Don't you worry.'

Chillun, it was a happy day for this old world when the Lord sent little Jesus down. No matter how bad the weather got, no matter how hard the storms blow, little Jesus was always watchin' after His sheeps . . .

QUOTE: Faulk.

466

254. THE HOLY BABY

IN THE OLD DAYS religious Negroes held ' watch meetings ' on Christmas Eve. They preached and prayed until midnight, and then, when the hour of the Saviour's birth was announced, they sang and shouted and worshipped together until dawn. Among the carols sung on these occasions was *The Song of the Twelve*. Versions of this ancient mystic song have been recorded everywhere in Europe. Archer Taylor (*Journal of American Folklore*, LXII, p. 382) suggests that its origin may be found in Sanskrit, but that all European versions are probably derived from a Hebrew chant for Passover (*Echod mi Yodea*, first printed in Prague in 1526). The earliest known English translation of the Jewish religious folk song appeared in the seventeenth century, but a number of distinct forms soon developed (*The Twelve Days of Christmas*, *The Dilly Song*, *The Twelve Apostles*, etc., *see* p. 245).

A quartet of Negro convicts recorded this version for my father in the Arkansas Penitentiary in 1935.

255. THIS TRAIN

IN HIS VISIONS the Negro has seen many roads leading to Heaven. Sometimes he mounts a golden chariot or rides on a prancing white horse. He climbs Jacob's ladder rung by rung, runs down the King's highway with the hell-hounds snapping their jaws at his heels, or inches along like a poor inch worm. Modern singers have him talking to the angels through the royal telephone, with a line running ' to the church-house and the receiver in my heart '. Ever since the first locomotive whistle split the quiet air of the South and the black engine thundered down the rails, snorting steam and fire like the horses of the Apocalypse, the righteous have been ' buying tickets on the snow-white heavenly express for glory '. For the gambler, the back-biter, the crap-shooter, and other back-sliding sinners, the Black Diamond Express, manned by Satan, was booked and bound for the lower regions.

QUOTE: Faulk.

256. THE DOWNWARD ROAD

I was a wild thing when I was young. Why I was more on dancing than my old Missy, and she taught me to dance. But after I joined the church, I didn't have the desire to dance no more. For a long time, you know, I could not git ahold of religion, cause I wanted to dance, but now I know what my religion did for me. It cleared my soul for all eternity. Dancing was an injury to me, I see it now . . .

When the church became the leading institution in the Southern Negro community, the preachers, as they have for so many centuries in our misfortunate folk culture, took up the cudgels against all the folk-arts which were not practised within the confines of the Church. They dared not speak of the worst ills of the South. Instead they let loose the power of their magnificent folk oratory against petty vice and the pleasures of everyday life; and thus we find the Negro convert attacking his own creativity and despoiling his own culture at the behest of the preacher, as this heart-rending folk song from North Carolina tells us . . .

I was born in North Carolina and raised up as a slave,
And no one ever told me I had a soul to save.
Until I had the fever, it brought me near my grave,
And many a Christian told me I had a soul to save.

I went to hear the gospel, to see if it was true,
I laughed and mawked the preacher, and I picked my banjo too.
Until he called for mourners, and tears stood in my eyes.
I bowed beneath the altar and I laid my banjo by.

I prayed for sovereign mercy, and Jesus filled my cup,
I went home rejoicing and I burned my banjo up.
Brother, will you meet me on that delightful shore?
We will praise the Lord forever, where banjos are no more.

Wherever one goes in the South, one finds old, broken instruments hanging by the wall, and old men who tell you, ruefully, ' I turnt all that devilish music by when I joined the church . . . ' These men, independent of spirit and creative though they were, could not hold out against the most important institution in their community speaking to them in terms like these . . .

God has done got angry on his Throne. He got tired of all his chillun dancin', drinkin' and fiddlin' themselves on the road to hell. He decided he gonna wipe the human race off the earth. But Li'l Jesus, he ask for time. He beg his Father for time to walk the earth and find the folks who ought to be saved . . .

Chillun, Jesus knock on the door, but nobody answer. He knock again. He hear somebody stirring around in there and finally he got to the window and look under the shade. All the folks in there drinkin', shootin' dice, dancin'. Gal come to the do' and say, ' Git on 'way from here, preacher man. We ain't got no time for religion here. If you don't want to dance and have a time, don't get in our way.' And po' Jesus walk off sad. He leave that house and he won't come back. Those folks bound straight for hell in time of judgement. They on that downward road, that big, broad, smooth, crowded road . . . that old highway Satan smoothed out for the sinner . . .

QUOTES: (a) Fisk. (b) (Song) *North Carolina Folklore*, Vol. 3, p. 638. (c) Faulk.

257. ALL NIGHT LONG

UP UNTIL the ministers of Montgomery began their remarkable stand in 1956, other-world-liness had been the official policy of the Negro church in the South. During Reconstruction, the Church emerged as the only permitted community organization, drawing the vast majority of the respectable and stable Negro citizens into its membership. It offered them the consolation of Christianity for their sorrows. It became a social centre where the folk could meet with a minimum of white interference in all sorts of recreational and beneficial activities. It was the stage upon which the talented competed for leadership and the creative could command an audience. Its preachers became the spiritual, intellectual, social, and political leaders of the community. As Richard Wright has put it, 'Our churches are where we dip our tired bodies in cool springs of hope, where we retain our wholeness and humanity, despite the blows of death from the Boss.'

By and large, therefore, the characteristics of Negro folk religion, as developed by the slaves, were perpetuated into our own times. Only since the 'twenties have the younger and intellectual members of the Baptist and Methodist churches turned against the emotionalism of the service, begun to mock at the apocalyptic and other-worldly eloquence of the old-fashioned minister, and grown ashamed to sing the spirituals. This change, though recent, has been rapid. Nowadays, one can only rarely hear a folk sermon or spiritual; pedantic pastors have replaced the fire-eating visionary revivalists, and book-instructed choirs have silenced the fine congregational singing. The desire to worship like respectable white folks has almost shut off this creative flow, which now finds its main outlet in the services of the Holiness cults.

This evolution is understandable and, perhaps, necessary to the developing dignity of the American Negro, but what a pity that so much that is artistically fine should perish out of a desire to conform. One of the most important tasks that lies before the Negro is to discover how to develop for his own benefit and pleasure the heritage of eloquence, passion, and truth created by his ancestors in the folk sermon and the folk spiritual. Nothing he can learn from books, from white culture, or buy from the amusement industry can match these folk arts in expressive power.

242. WADE IN THE WATER

Collected and arranged by Alan Lomax. SEE: Sears. A slave song, still fairly common in rural Negro churches during the 30's, it has been recorded by Negro quartets.

Piano arrangement by DON BANKS

With a slow rock ♩=90

GUITAR— 7A, 7B
BANJO— 5

CHORUS:
Wade in the water,
Wade in the water, children,
Wade in the water,
God's gonna trouble the water.

1 'Member one thing an' it's certainly sho',
    Wade in the water,
Judgement's comin' an' I don' know,
    Wade in the water. (CHO).

2 Up on the mountain, Jehovah, he spoke,
  Out of his mouth came fire and smoke. (CHO.)

3 I heard a rumblin' up in the sky,
  Must a-been Jesus passin' by. (CHO.)

4 Down in the valley, down on my knees,
  Askin' my Lawd to save me, please. (CHO.)

5 You can hinder me here, you can hinder me
                                        there,
  But the Lawd in Heaven will hear my prayer.
                                        (CHO.)

6 The enemy's great, but my Captain's strong,
  I'm marching to the city and the road ain't long.
                                        (CHO.)

7 I tell you once and I tell you twice,
  My soul's been anchored in Jesus Christ. (CHO.)

8 You may baptize Peter and baptize Paul,
  But the Lord-God-er-mighty gonna baptize
                                    um all. (CHO.)

9 Matthew, Mark, Luke and John,
  Tell me where my Saviour gone? (CHO.)

10 My Lawd spoke in a 'ponstrous voice,
   Shook the world to its very jois'. (CHO.)

11 Rung through Heaven and down in Hell,
   My dungeon shook and my chains, they fell.
                                        (CHO.)

243. WHEN I'M GONE

Adapted by Alan Lomax. SEE: Randolph II, 331 (minstrel version). A song
found in eastern states a generation ago. Probably still current.

Joyously ♪=138 *or* 176

GUITAR- 4, 7B
BANJO- 5 *or* 1-2

(Verses sung to same melody)

CHORUS:
It'll be Lawd, Lawd, Lawd, when I'm gone, (2)
It'll be Lawd, Lawd, Lawd, (2)
It'll be Lawd, Lawd, Lawd, when I'm gone.

1 I'm gonna fly from mansion to mansion, when I'm gone, (2)
  I'm gonna fly from mansion to mansion, (2)
  I'm gonna fly from mansion to mansion, when I'm gone.

2 I'll be done with 'bukes and 'buses, when I'm gone, *etc.*

471

3 I'll be done with troubles and trials, when I'm gone, *etc.*

4 I'm gonna walk and talk with Jesus, when I'm gone, *etc.*

5 I'm gonna set at the welcome table, when I'm gone, *etc.*

6 I'm gonna drink and never get thirsty, when I'm gone, *etc.*

244. SOON I WILL BE DONE

A song from South-East, probably still known to rural Negroes.

CHORUS:
Soon I will be done with the troubles of the world,
Troubles of the world, the troubles of the world,
Soon I will be done with the troubles of the world,
Goin' home to God.

1 I want to meet my mother,   (3)
  Goin' home to God.   (CHO.)

2 I want to see my Jesus,   (3)
  Goin' home to God.   (CHO.)

3 No more weepin' and wailin', (3)
  Goin' home to God.   (CHO.)

245. BLIND MAN

Collected and arranged by Alan Lomax. Recorded from singing of Negroes in South-West during the 30's. Josh White reports that the blind men he led in the 20's sang this. SEE: Johnson; Sears.

Moaned ♩=80

GUITAR- 7C
BANJO- (IF AT ALL) 5

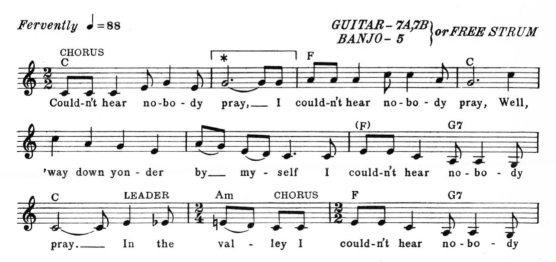

Blind man stood on the way and cried, Blind man stood on the way and cried, Cry-in'
'Wo,____ Lord, show me the way!' Blind man stood on the way and cried.

1 Blind man stood on the way and cried, (2)
Cryin' 'Wo—Lord, show me the way!'
Blind man stood on the way and cried.

2 Preacherman stood on the way and cried, *etc.*

3 My mother stood on the way and cried, *etc.*

4 My deacon stood on the way and cried, *etc.*

Other verses ad. lib. can be formed by substituting father, brothers, etc.

246. I COULDN'T HEAR NOBODY PRAY

Collected and arranged by Alan Lomax, from the singing of Texas Negroes in 1920's. SEE: *Religious Folk Songs of the Negro*, Hampton (T. P. Fenner, Hampton Press, 1909); Johnson; Sears.

Fervently ♩=88

GUITAR- 7A,7B
BANJO- 5 } or FREE STRUM

CHORUS
Could-n't hear no-bo-dy pray,__ I could-n't hear no-bo-dy pray, Well,
'way down yon-der by__ my-self I could-n't hear no-bo-dy
pray.__ In the val-ley I could-n't hear no-bo-dy

LEADER   CHORUS

473

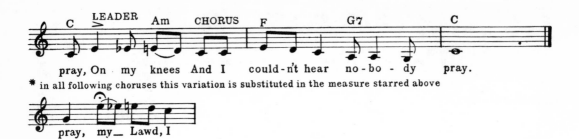

pray, On my knees And I could-n't hear no-bo-dy pray.

* in all following choruses this variation is substituted in the measure starred above

pray, my_ Lawd, I

CHORUS:
Couldn't hear nobody pray,
I couldn't hear nobody pray,
Well, 'way down yonder by myself
I couldn't hear nobody pray.
(*Repeated ad. lib.*)

1 In the valley
   I couldn't hear nobody pray,
On my knees
   And I couldn't hear nobody pray. (CHO.)

2 Callin' Jesus,
   So lonesome, (CHO.)

3 In the mornin',
   In the evenin', (CHO.)

247. HOLD THE WIND

Collected and arranged by Alan Lomax, from the singing of a Negro blacksmith
in Louisiana State Penitentiary, 1933. SEE: Johnson; Sears.

CHORUS:
Hold the wind, hold the wind,
Hold the wind, don't let it blow,
Hold the wind, hold the wind,
Hold the wind, don't let it blow.

474

1 You may talk about me just as much as you please,
Hold the wind, don't let it blow,
I'm gonna talk about you on the bendin' of my
knees,
Hold the wind, don't let it blow. (CHO.)

2 If you don't believe I been redeemed,
Just follow me down to the Jordan stream. (CHO.)

3 My soul got wet in the midnight dew,
And the mornin' star was a witness, too. (CHO.)

4 When I get to Heaven, gwine walk and tell,
Three bright angels go ring them bells. (CHO.)

5 When I get to Heaven, gwine be at ease,
Me and my God gonna do as we please. (CHO.)

6 Gonna chatter with the Father, argue with the Son,
Tell um 'bout the world I just come from. (CHO.)

248. THE OLD ARK'S A-MOVERIN'

Collected and arranged by Alan Lomax. Heard in country Negro churches in
South-West in 1930's. Verses from a number of sources. This song of Civil War
vintage. SEE: Johnson; Sears.

Rocking ♩=69

GUITAR- 4, 5A or 7B
BANJO- 5A

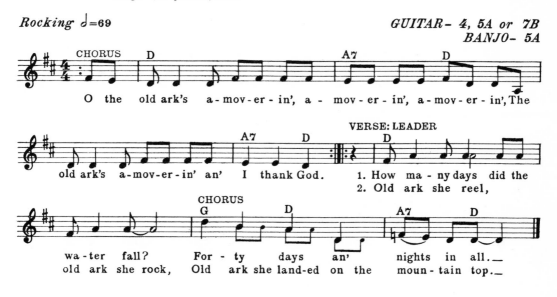

CHORUS:
O the old ark's a-moverin', a-moverin', a-moverin',
The old ark's a-moverin' an' I thank God.

1 How many days did the water fall?
Forty days an' nights in all. (CHO.)

2 Old ark she reel, old ark she rock,
Old ark she landed on the mountain top. (CHO.)

3 See that sister dressed so fine,
She ain't got Jesus on her mind. (CHO.)

4 See that brother lookin' so gay,
Old death gwine come an' carry him away. (CHO.)

5 See them children dressed in white,
It must be the chillun of the Israelite. (CHO.)

6 See the children dressed in red,
It must be the children that Moses led. (CHO.)

7 Look at that sister comin' 'long slow,
She's tryin' to get to Heaven fo' they close the
do'. (CHO.)

8 'Tain't but the one thing on my mind,
My sister's gone to Heaven, left me behind. (CHO.)

249. DESE BONES GWINE RISE AGAIN

FROM: p. 597 of *American Ballads and Folk Songs*, Lomax (Macmillan, N.Y., 1934).
SEE: Arnold, 148; Brown III, 580; Sandburg, 470; Sears; White, 83. Two or three spirituals have been based on Ezekiel's prophesy. This one was secularized early, and has been sung by college students with comic intent for a considerable time.

With spirit ♩=100

GUITAR- 4, 7B
BANJO- 5

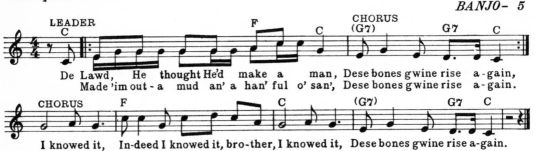

De Lawd, He thought He'd make a man, Dese bones gwine rise a-gain,
Made 'im out-a mud an' a han' ful o' san', Dese bones gwine rise a-gain.

I knowed it, In-deed I knowed it, bro-ther, I knowed it, Dese bones gwine rise a-gain.

1 De Lawd, He thought He'd make a man,
Dese bones gwine rise again,
Made 'im outa mud an' a han'ful o' san',
Dese bones gwine rise again.
CHORUS:
I knowed it,
Indeed I knowed it, brother,
I knowed it,
Dese bones gwine rise again.

2 Thought He'd make a woman, too,
Didn' know 'xactly what to do. (CHO.)

3 Took a rib from Adam's side,
Made Miss Eve for to be his bride. (CHO.)

4 Put um in a gyarden fine and fair,
Tole um to eat whatever was dere. (CHO.)

5 But to one tree they mus' not go,
Must leave de apples dere to grow. (CHO.)

6 Sarpint quoiled around a chunk,
At Miss Eve his eye he wunk. (CHO.)

7 First she took a little pull
Then she filled her apron full. (CHO.)

8 Adam took a little slice,
Smack his lips an' say 'twas nice. (CHO.)

9 De Lord He spoke with a 'ponstrous voice,
Shook de world to its very jois'. (CHO.)

10 'Stole my apples, I believe.'
'No, Marse Lord, I 'spec' it was Eve.' (CHO.)

11 'Out of this garden you must git,
Earn yo' livin' by yo' sweat.' (CHO.)

12 He put an angel at de do',
Tol' um never come dere no mo'. (CHO.)

13 Of this tale there is no mo',
Eve et the apple and Adam de co'. (CHO.)

250. DIDN'T IT RAIN

Collected and arranged by Alan Lomax. SEE: Brown III, 617; Odum II, 129, White, 141. This song, which contains fragments of Negro sermons on Noah and has been used by itinerant religious balladists for disaster songs, was recently repopularized by Sister Rosetta Tharpe's Decca record, and by gospel-song publications.

A jazzy spiritual ♪ = 200

GUITAR— 7A, 7B
BANJO— 5 or 1-2

Now did-n't it rain, chil-lun, God's gonna 'stroy this world with wa-ter, Now did-n't it rain, my Lord, Now did-n't it rain, rain, rain. Well, it rained for-ty days and it rained for-ty nights, There was-n't no land no-where in sight, God sent a ra-ven to car-ry the news, He histe his wings and a-way he flew.

CHORUS:
Now, didn't it rain, chillun,
God's gonna 'stroy this world with water,
Now didn't it rain, my Lord,
Now didn't it rain, rain, rain.

1 Well, it rained forty days and it rained forty nights,
There wasn't no land nowhere in sight,
God sent a raven to carry the news,
He histe his wings and away he flew. (CHO.)

2 Well, it rained forty days 'n forty nights without stoppin',
Noah was glad when the rain stopped a-droppin'.
God sent Noah a rainbow sign,
Says, ' No more water, but fire next time.' (CHO.)

3 They knocked at the window and they knocked at the do',
They cried, ' O Noah, please take me on board.'
Noah cried, ' You're full of sin,
The Lord's got the key and you can't get in.' (CHO.)

477

251. SAMSON

FROM: p. 6 of *Our Singing Country*, Lomax (Macmillan, N.Y., 1941).
Piano arrangement by DON BANKS

A jazzy spiritual ♩ = 144

GUITAR – 7A, 7B
BANJO – 5

VERSE

De - li - lah was a wo - man fine and fair,
De - li - lah, she gained old Sam - son's mind,

Ve - ry pleas-ant look-in' and coal-black hair,
When he saw the wo-man and she looked so

fine. He said, 'An'

CHORUS
To be sung an

With a beat

octave lower

f if I had -'n my way', He said, 'An' if I

had -'n my way', He said, 'An' if I had -'n my

1 Delilah was a woman fine and fair,
  Very pleasant lookin' and coal-black hair,
  Delilah, she gained old Samson's mind,
  When he saw the woman and she looked so fine.
  CHORUS:
  He said, ' An' if I had'n my way,   (3)
  I'd tear the buildin' down.'

2 Read about Samson from his birth,
  The strongest man that ever lived on earth,
  Read away down in ancient times,
  He killed three thousand Philistines.   (CHO.)

3 Stop an' let me tell you what Samson done,
  He looked at the lion an' the lion run,
  But Samson killed that lion dead
  And the bees made honey in the lion's head.
                                          (CHO.)

4 They bound him with a rope and, while walking
                                          along,
  He looked down and saw an old jawbone,
  He moved his arms, the rope snap like thread,
  When he got through killin', three thousand
                                  was dead.   (CHO.)

5 Samson's wife, she talked so fair,
  Samson told her, ' Shave off my hair,
  Shave my hair as clean as my hand,
  And my strength will become like a nachul man.'
                                          (CHO.)

6 They shaved his hair like the palm of his hand,
  And his strength became like a nachul man,
  Took po' Samson to the judgement hall,
  Bound him and chained him against the wall.
                                          (CHO.)

7 He called a little boy about three feet tall,
  Says, ' Place my hands up against the wall.'
  He placed his hands up against a wall
  And he tore that buildin' down.
  CHORUS:
  He said, ' And now I got my way,   (3)
  And I'll tear this buildin' down.'

252. JOHN THE REVELATOR

FROM: p. 22 of *Our Singing Country*, Lomax (Macmillan, N.Y., 1941). A song known along the eastern coast, not common in the West.
Piano arrangement by DON BANKS

1 My Lord called John while he was a-writin',
My Lord called John while he was a-writin',
My Lord called John while he was a-writin'
'O John, John,

Seal up your book, John,
An' don't you write no more,
O John, John,
An' don't you write no more.'

2 He wrote the Book of Revelations while he
was a-writin', *etc.*

3 He wrote the book of Seven Seals while he
was a-writin', *etc.*

253. RISE UP, SHEPHERD

SEE: Hampton, 173; Sears.

A pulsing beat ♩ = 138

GUITAR– 4 or 5A
BANJO– 5

1 There's a star in the east on Christmas morn,
  Rise up, shepherd, and foller,
  It'll lead to the place where the Saviour's born,
  Rise up, shepherd, and foller.
  CHORUS:
  Leave your sheep and leave your lambs,
  Rise up, shepherd, and foller,
  Leave your ewes and leave your rams,
  Rise up, shepherd, and foller.

Foller, foller,
Rise up, shepherd, and foller,
Foller the star of Bethlehem,
Rise up, shepherd, and foller.

2 If you take good heed to the angel's words,
  You'll forget your flocks and forget your herds,
  (CHO.)

254. THE HOLY BABY

Recorded and arranged by J. and A. Lomax, from the singing of Kelly Pace, and Negro quartet, Gould Penitentiary, Arkansas, 1942. AAFS 49 A. SEE: Greenleaf, 91; Guide and Index (*The Twelve Apostles*); JAFL LXVII, 382; Randolph IV, 34 for notes; Sears.

Fast rocking rhythm ♩ = 96 *increasing to* ♩ = 112

GUITAR— 2A, 4, 7A-B
BANJO— 1, 2 or 5

A transcription of the song with parts as sung by a folk quartet   *The rests are the main accents in every line.*

① Chil - dren, go and I___ will send thee. How shall I___ send thee? Lord,
(2-12) Chil-dren, go (etc.)   (will send thee)

① I shall send thee one by one, Well, 1. one was the Ho - ly (a-) Ba - by, Was (to ✠)
② I shall send thee two by two, Well, 2. two was the Paul and (a-) Si - las, And (to 1)
③ I shall send thee three by three, Well, 3. three was the He - brew chil - dren, And (to 2)

④ I shall send thee four by four, Well, 4. four was the four come a-knock-in' at the door, And (to 3)

⑤ I shall send thee five by five Well, 5. five was the Gos - pel wri - ters, And (to 4)
⑥ I shall send thee six by six Well, 6. six was the six that could-n't get fixed, And (to 5)
⑦ I shall send thee seven by seven Well, 7. sev-en was the seven come down from Heav'n, And (to 6)

⑧ I shall send thee eight by eight, Well, 8. eight was the eight that stood at the gate, And (to 7)

⑨ I shall send thee nine by nine, Well, 9. nine was the nine that dressed so fine, And (to 8)

⑩ I shall send thee ten by ten, Well, 10. ten was the Ten Com - mand-ments, And (to 9)
⑪ I shall send thee eleven by eleven, Well, 11. eleven was the 'leven de - rid - ers, And (to 10)
⑫ I shall send thee twelve by twelve, Well, 12. twelve was the Twelve Di - sci - ples, And (to 11)

borned by the Vir-gin Ma - ry,__ Was wrapped in the hol-low of a claw - horn, Was

laid in the hol-low of a man-ger, Was born, born, Lord - y, born in Beth-le - hem.__

1 Children, go and I will send thee.
  How shall I send thee?
  Lord, I shall send thee one by one,
  Well, one was the Holy Baby,
  Was borned by the Virgin Mary,
  Was wrapped in the hollow of a clawhorn,
  Was laid in the hollow of a manger,
  Was born, born, Lordy, born in Bethlehem.

2 Children go and I will send thee.
  How shall I send thee?
  I shall send thee two by two,
  Well, two was the Paul and Silas,
  And one was the Holy Baby, *etc.*

3 I shall send thee three by three,
  Three was the Hebrew children, *etc.*

4 I shall send thee four by four,
  Well, four was the four come a-knockin' at the door, *etc.*

5 Five was the Gospel writers, *etc.*

6 Six was the six that couldn't get fixed, *etc.*

7 Seven was the seven come down from Heav'n, *etc.*

8 Eight was the eight that stood at the gate, *etc.*

9 Nine was the nine that dressed so fine, *etc.*

10 Ten was the Ten Commandments, *etc.*

11 Eleven was the 'leven deriders, *etc.*

12 Twelve was the twelve Disciples, *etc.*

255. THIS TRAIN

FROM: p. 593 of *American Ballads and Folk Songs*, Lomax (Macmillan, N.Y., 1934).
SEE: White, 64. Recorded from singing of Negroes in South-West in 30's.
This genuine congregational spiritual was a quartet favourite.

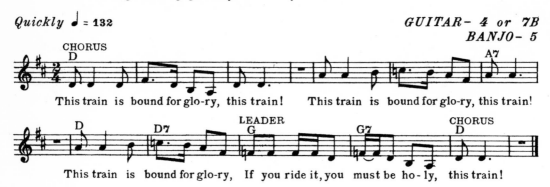

Quickly ♩ = 132

GUITAR— *4 or 7B*
BANJO— *5*

This train is bound for glo-ry, this train! This train is bound for glo-ry, this train!

This train is bound for glo-ry, If you ride it, you must be ho-ly, this train!

1 This train is bound for glory, this train! (2)
This train is bound for glory,
If you ride it, you must be holy, this train!

2 This train don't pull no gamblers, this train! (2)
This train don't pull no gamblers,
Neither don't pull no midnight ramblers, this train!

3 This train don't pull no jokers, this train! (2)
This train don't pull no jokers,
Cigarette puffers and cigar smokers, this train!

4 This train don't pull no dancers, this train! (2)
This train don't pull no dancers,
Hootchie-cootch shakers and Charleston prancers, this train!

5 This train don't pull no extras, this train! (2)
This train don't pull no extras,
Don't pull nothin' but the Heavenly Special, this train!

256. THE DOWNWARD ROAD

Recorded and arranged by John and Alan Lomax from the singing of North Carolina Negroes in 30's. Song is probably of fairly recent origin. SEE: Odum I, 73; for similar song, *see* Lomax IV, 28.

Piano arrangement by DON BANKS

With great energy ♩ = 168

GUITAR 7A-7B
BANJO- 5

CHORUS

f Well, bro-ther, the down-ward road is crow-ded, crow-ded, crow-ded, Yes, the
down-ward road is crow-ded with un-be-liev-in' souls.

VERSE

1. Now look at that old dan-cin' dea-con, Thought he was do-in' migh-ty well, But when he come to find out, He done made up his bed in Hell.
2. Just look at that crap-shoot-in' bro-ther, Thought he was do-in' migh-ty well, But when he come to find out, He was mak-in' up his bed in Hell.

Last time

CHORUS:

Well, brother, the downward road is crowded,
                                      crowded, crowded,
Yes, the downward road is crowded with
                                      unbelievin' souls.

1 Now look at that old dancin' deacon,
Thought he was doin' mighty well,
But when he come to find out,
He done made up his bed in Hell.   (CHO.)

2 Just look at that crap-shootin' brother,
Thought he was doin' mighty well,
But when he come to find out,
He was makin' up his bed in Hell.   (CHO.)

3 Here come that old backbitin' sister, *etc.*   (CHO.)

4 Here come that old whisky-drinkin' elder, *etc.*
                                      (CHO.)

5 When I was a sinner, Lord,
I loved my distance well,
But when I come to find myself,
I was hangin' over Hell.   (CHO.)

257. ALL NIGHT LONG

FROM: p. 448 of *An American Songbag*, Carl Sandburg (Harcourt, Brace, 1927).
Used by permission. SEE: Odum I, 126.

1 Paul and Silas bound in jail,
   All night long,
One for to sing and the other for to pray,
   All night long,
One for to sing, and the other for to pray,
   All night long,
Do, Lord, deliver po' me.

2 Never seen the like since I been born,
The people keep a-comin' and the train done
Do, Lord, deliver po' me.   [gone. (2)

3 Ain't but the one train on this track,
Straight up to Heaven and straight right back, (2)
Do, Lord, deliver po' me.

REELS

258. KNOCK JOHN BOOKER
(Alabama)

259. MISS MARY JANE
(South Carolina)

'For a long time I could not git a-hold of religion, because I wanted to dance . . .'

THE AFRICAN SLAVES came from a culture where the dance played a natural part in every drama and crisis of human life. They entered a culture in which the dance was, at best, a self-conscious amusement or, at worst, a sin. Some masters, regarding their slaves as animals without souls to lose, encouraged them to dance, just as the captains of the slave ships had whipped their captives until they danced, for then not so many died of heartbreak or committed suicide on the crossing from Africa. The whites looked on with pleasure as their Negroes flung themselves into the dance—leaping, clowning, miming, and, with rolling hips and bellies, expressing their joyful and erotic impulses.

In the West Indies and South America there developed Afro-American dance styles which gave rise to the modern conga, rhumba, tango, etc. The drums continued to roll for the *counjaille* in New Orleans' Congo Square until the end of the nineteenth century, long enough to leave an echo in hot jazz. On the sea islands off the Carolina coast, one could, until lately, catch glimpses of these African-style dances of the slaves. Elsewhere the Negroes renounced them, publicly at least, as they became Protestant converts.

But as dance they must, they adopted the frontier country dances, the jigging steps and the old ring games—but Africanized them and enlivened them, so that the whites soon were imitating their former pupils. Black-faced dancers were already performing Negro jigs in New York, Boston and Philadelphia by the time Cornwallis had surrendered at Yorktown.

Here, one of the creators of the Afro-American dances, a South Carolina ex-slave woman, recalls the pleasures of the ring-games of her youth . . .

I tol' you about de ole days when I could dance an' sing an' pick cotton wid de best of dem, 'cause you know I done been raise 'roun de white folks ebber since I been a leetle mite—wen I ain't but so leetle dat I can hide underneat' old Miss' rocking-chair. Den wen I gets bigger, I cum out an' hide underneat' her apern; den I get so big an' fat dat I gets to be a regular wheeligo gal: dat's our name for a big, bustin' gal.

Old Miss, she laff, an' say to Marster, ' Let them have it, let them have it, they work all the better for it.' O Lordee, dem were happy days! I always had my stomach full of vittles den. An' atter de fiel' work, I teks my ' fly-away ' (dat's my hat) an' I teks de calico dress Miss done gib, an' I go to de nigger-yard; an' glory, how I done dance.

QUOTE: *Negro Folklore in South Carolina*, Henry Davis, JAFL XXVII, 1914, No. CV., p. 252.

260. ALL FOR THE MEN

OF NECESSITY, the folk culture of the slave was a patchwork of African survivals and of scraps of custom, speech, and song picked up from the whites, the whole tacked together with his own ingenious improvisations. In the old-fashioned Virginia courting scene, reported below, we can see the slave's charming, but rather pathetic attempt to emulate the courtly manners of the old South. So far as songs were concerned, the Negro singer almost always improved upon what he learned from the whites as in this Alabama version of an old English courting game.

He: My dear, kin' miss, has you any objections to me drawin' my chair to your side and revolvin' de wheel of my conversation aroun' de axle of your understandin'?

She: I has no objection to a gentleman addressin' me in a proper manner, kin' sir.

He: My dear miss, de worl' is a howlin' wilderness full of devourin' animals, and you has got to walk through hit. Has you made up yer min' to walk through hit by yersef, or wid some bol' wahyer?

She: Kin' sir, I will reply in answer to yer'terrigation in de fus place, sence I think you is a hones' gentleman, dat I feels dat a lady needs de pertection of a bol' wahyer in dis worl', where dere's many wil' animals an' plenty of danger.

He: Den, kin' honored miss, will you condescen' to encourage me to hope that I might, some glorious day in de future, walk by yer side as a perteckter?

She: Kin' sir, ef you thinks you is a bol' wahyer, I will condescen' to let you pass under my observation from dis day on, an' ef you proves wuthy of a confidin' lady's trus', some lady might be glad to accept yer pertection—an' dat lady might be me.

QUOTE: Botkin V, 648 (Original: Frank Banks and Portia Smiley, from *Southern Workman and Hampton School Record*, Vol. 24, 1895).

261. SATURDAY NIGHT

I KNOWED a man who was free and he wanted to marry a slave girl named Carrie, and he gave himself to Carrie's master, so he could marry her. That love is an awful thing, I tell you. Of course, in them days, we never knowed about real marriage for we couldn't read. When you got ready to marry, you just go to the master and tell him you wanted somebody and if you wasn't no scrubby man and was healthy, you could just take her and start living with her.

In those days people married by jumping the broom handle or carrying a glass of water on their heads. My momma told me that she jumped the broom with a glass of water on her head, and never spilled a drop. After the war you had to do the marriage all over, and all the slaves had to go and buy a license.

On some plantations, ol' Massa did all the courting. He'd pick a wife out for one of his slaves, and they'd get a whipping if they didn't stay with her, whether they liked her or not. After the marriage, we'd have a party, and dance and sing, and maybe eat us some chicken or a hog we'd stolen . . . Then later if the women didn't have no children after two or three years, they would take 'em and marry 'em to somebody else or sell 'em. Wonder what make 'em want so many children? Make 'em rich, I guess . . .

There was plenty that married women on other plantations, and they'd go off, or slip off on Saturday nights to see their wives, maybe just go to a dance. And when they'd be coming home, the old patterollers'd get after them and run 'em. They'd scatter just like rabbits, because if them patterolls caught you away from your plantation without a pass, it meant thirty-nine licks.

488

The slave economy did little to sustain stable family life or to encourage the development of a new code of sexual morality to replace tribal patterns of conduct. The slave was a valuable work animal, whose increase enriched his owner. Powerful Negro males were used as studs on some plantations. No Negro woman dared to resist the approaches of the overseer or the owner; no man could safely protect his own wife from these advances; and pretty girls were kept by the whites as concubines, or used for casual amusement.

Divorce on the plantation was casual and fairly common, yet an amazing number of slave marriages lasted for a lifetime, and many ex-slaves formalized their unions after emancipation. However, it is not surprising that the enforced laxity of the slave system favoured the survival of the African mother-centred family, and West African permissiveness about sexual relations. When their work was done, the Negroes were encouraged to have a good time; and to some extent their easy-going, pleasure-loving, freely sensual African way, so different from the white ambivalence over sex, has survived even into our own day. This hedonistic feeling pervades their dancing songs, such as this Saturday-evening holler and banjo tune.

QUOTE: Fisk.

262. RIDIN' IN A BUGGY

By the beginning of the twentieth century Negro adults had given up the ring-plays in all but the most isolated sections of the South. Among the children, however, the old games remained still very much alive. As late as the 'thirties and 'forties at almost any rural Negro school, one could see the little girls playing together at recess, clapping and chanting in a ring, while in the centre a couple ' cut up shines ', moving so nimbly and gracefully that they seemed almost to be skimming the ground. Here an Alabama singer recalls one of the games of her youth . . .

I always did sing the play songs that we played. When there was something to be sung or led, they always want me to do it. So everybody would ring up again, and I'd start the song I loved best, *Ridin' In a Buggy*.

Well, when I tell um stop, we all stop. Then somebody step out and choose two partners. Then everybody be swinging and singing. And if I was stealing partners I'd have to dance all the way to the other bunch and then sing and act mightily and steal me a partner and take her back to *my* crowd. I'd keep on till the other bunch would be down to the main one. Then *he* gon' start stealin' his partners back, and if I don't mind, he's gonna have some of mines, too. We *did* love to play them stealin' partner games—me singin' and Bessie pattin'. Bessie *could* pat; you could hear the sounds of her feet and her hands just like a drummer in a band. When we got tired and hot, then we'd play a kissin' game . . .

QUOTE: *The Rainbow Sign*, A. Lomax.

263. STEAL, MISS LIZA

The songs and games of rural Negro children, which are so graceful, fiery, and expressive, reflect an attitude of permissiveness towards sexual pleasure quite at variance with at least the idealized behaviour of the white group. Permitted sexual activity begins earlier, as these two typical stories of the 1930's indicate . . .

A fifteen-year-old country boy . . . ' I had my first experience when I was thirteen years old. This girl was older than I was, about fifteen, and she showed me what to do. Now I ain't bothered about it much. About once a month. All you have to do is just go to a girl's house and if she says yes, you sit on the steps till everybody go to bed, and then you get a chance . . .'

A sixteen-year-old girl . . . ' We call it " breaking " around here. I can't think of a single girl, unless it's some of the real small ones, that don't " break " with boys. I do, right often, and I enjoys it, too. Mama knows, but Papa doesn't . . .'

QUOTE: Fisk

264. YOU CAIN' LOSE-A ME, CHOLLY

' I told him once that I didn't love him; I hated him. Then I told him that I loved him so much that I just loved to see him walk . . .'

OUT OF A PATCHWORK of acquired, inherited, and improvised culture, the Negro developed his own folk pattern. When springtime flamed in his blood he longed to find a wife and raise a family; and the choice of a mate was as risky and tense a business for him as it was for his white brother. Although the same tender emotion filled his heart, romantic sentiments of the sort one finds in white folk love songs do not occur in early Negro folk songs. So far as I know, the expression ' I love you ' was not found in Negro folk song earlier than the blues, and songs of a tender and sentimental cast began to appear only in the 1930's. Yet the Negro was a gay, passionate, vigorous lover ; a practical, tender, and devoted husband. When he went courting, he went laughingly, in search of pleasure . . .

After the Lord turned me around, I began to feel that I needed a wife. I said, ' Lord, I need a helpmate. Direct me to the woman who will make me a wife.'

I went down to see Sally. Her mother told her, said, ' Go fix Brother Charlie something to eat; he looks kinder hungry.' Sally jumped up and put the skillet on the fire, threw in two big pieces of shoulder meat, set the coffee on, and in no time she had the victuals on the table. All the time she was going about I was saying, 'Lord, help me, Lord, help me!' I couldn't eat a bite. I was just lookin' at her. She said, ' You are not eating. I thought you were hungry.' I said, ' The sight of you would fill any man, unless his heart was made of stone.'

I sat there at that table and talked to her until the chickens started crowing for day. I grabbed my hat and ran over three miles to work. My heart was jumping in my bosom. I plowed, sang and prayed all day long, and when night came I wasn't a bit tired. I knew that I had found my mate.

QUOTE: Fisk.

265. BLACK SHEEP

' I nussed babies till I got agin nussin' babies.'

ONE OF THE SENTIMENTAL images of the old South is that of the faithful Negro slave woman crooning tenderly to her little white charge; but when the story is told by the slaves who lived it, this picture is tinged with bitter irony and the tragic undertone of the Southern lullabies is explained.

490

In them days they would sell a baby from its mother and a mother from its baby, like cows and calves, and think no more about it. I've seen um handcuffed as long as from here to the fence out there, the women who were bein' sold down the river, screamin' an' hollerin' about leavin' their children.

After I got to be about six years old my owner sold me to some people that lived out in the country. So they bought me, and sometimes I used to go to the field; sometimes I stayed in the house and nursed the babies.

Old Miss would be settin' there, just knittin' and watchin' the babies. They had a horn, and they'd blow on that when it was time for one of the women in the field to come to the house and nurse her child. The white folks was crazy 'bout their nigger babies, 'cause that's where they got their profit. Old Miss used to just hug me up and say, ' How's my little breeder this mornin'?' An' then I'd go back to rockin' them babies. After a while I'd get tired, and 'tend like I was asleep; I'd ease the cradle over and throw the baby out. Old Miss would slap me. You don't know how hard a hand can hurt less you been slapped by old Miss, but I'd take the slap, because she would say, ' Git out of here and stay till you wake up,' and that was just what I wanted, 'cause I'd git to play then.

QUOTE: Fisk.

491

266. BUCK-EYE RABBIT

THE SECULAR SONGS of the slaves were even more circumspect and oblique in their comment on plantation life than the spirituals. Most of them deal with the common animals of the Southern woods, especially the rabbit. I suspect that there is more than a trace of the primitive hunter's magic in these charming rhymes, and perhaps a carry-over of African totemistic beliefs as well. Among the people of West Africa, the hare played an important role in folk tales, and the slaves continued to regard the rabbit with an affection tinged with awe. Ex-slaves recalled . . .

The old folks was more scared of the rabbit than anything else. If you were going along and a rabbit crossed in front of you, you would stop and go right back home . . .

. . . We used to sing to the rabbits. When we would be out playing and catch two or three, we would tell the rabbits,—' Hark, from the tomb the doleful sounds.' . . .

Yet, for the most part timid, swift, clever Brer Rabbit, with his soft, slightly bulging brown eyes, represented the slave in song and folk tales. He constantly eluded or tricked Brer Fox, Brer Dog, Brer Bar, or Brer Wolf, who stood for the powerful and aggressive white man. Perhaps the slaves hoped somehow to touch their masters' hearts with these stories. Certainly, that appears to have been one of Uncle Remus's motives in telling such tales to his little white owner.

QUOTE: Fisk.

267. SHORTENIN' BREAD

THIS OLD RING GAME tells of the longing of the slaves for the good things on their master's table. The children, of course, felt the sharpest pangs . . .

The way we fed when I was a little thing on the plantation, they had a big wooden trough, and Aunt Fanny would take that and pour pot liquor in it, or milk, and break bread up in that. Then she'd ring the bell, and we'd all come running and just kneel down and eat out of that trough, like little chickens or puppies.

I was a house gal, and Mistress would tell me, ' Go an' pick up some chips for Aunt Fan to put on the lid.' I would break out an' run to get the chips because I was crazy about white bread, and when I got back there, Mistress would give me some white bread. I liked that because Mammy and them didn't get white bread but once a week, on Sunday. The rest of the time they had corn bread. I was so foolish. When Mistress died I just cried and cried, and Mammy say, ' What's the matter with you, gal?' I said, ' Ol' Miz is dead, and I won't get no more white bread.' I thought when she died she carried all that white bread with her . . .

QUOTE: Fisk.

268. THE BLUE-TAIL FLY

IN THEIR BEST PIECES—such as *Turkey in the Straw, Dan Tucker, O Susannah, Buffalo Gals*, and this abolitionist ditty—the black-face minstrel composers closely imitated the ring games and animal jingles of the slaves; and these songs proved themselves by going back into wide oral circulation. Such minstrel hits were parodied again and again; and *The Blue-Tail Fly*, a favourite song of Abe Lincoln's, has been frequently found among Negro folk singers. It subtly reflects the repressed hostility of slave towards master which was the undercurrent of Southern plantation society.

In 1864 a Texas woman, left to look after the plantation when her husband went off to war, wrote . . .

Another four years of war and we might as well give the Negroes away. I would willingly move into a white settlement and work with my hands, for I can see that the Negroes care no more for me than if I was some old free darkie.

Another vivid glimpse of that period is caught in the dialogue of two little Southern white girls who were playing lady:

' Good evening, Madam, how are you today?'
' I don't feel very well. All of my niggers have run away and left me.'

QUOTE: *Plain People of the Confederacy*, B. I. Wiley.

269. BILE THEM CABBAGE DOWN

ALONG THE NIGER and to the north, wherever Africans came in contact with Moslem culture, they learned to play primitive lyres, fiddles, guitar- and banjo-like instruments. Thus, the slaves who were kidnapped from this region of Africa found the white settler's fiddle a familiar instrument. Soon talented slave musicians were playing for balls in the Tidewater country and Negroes were improvising variations on white fiddle tunes, often on violins they made themselves. The files of Colonial Williamsburg show that master Negro fiddlers were common in Virginia at the beginning of the 18th century. The story of this ex-slave fiddler speaks for hundreds of other Negro folk-musicians across the whole South.

I used to be a great fiddler. I first learned how to play on a long gourd with horse-hair strings. Of course, I couldn't go very high on it, but it done pretty well. That was the first of my learning to play. After a while, I bought me a fiddle for a dollar and eighty cents, and then, way after the war, I bought me a fiddle, sure enough.

Negro fiddlers played the instrument with great percussive effect, bowing heavily and developing the rough, vital and rhythmic style which one hears among both whites and Negroes in the South today. Since they came from an orchestral culture, the slaves brought a variety of their instruments into their primitive plantation orchestras—the bones (still in use even in England), the jawbone (now the wash-board), the bush-bass (the tub bass of the skiffle band), the Jew's harp, and especially the banjo (for history *see* pp. 201-2). Rural banjo playing is still fundamentally African in character. Says Pete Seeger on this score, ' A subtle, rhythmic-melodic pattern is set up which repeats itself with no change in tempo, no matter what complex variations may be introduced.'

These banjo and fiddle bands existed everywhere in the South prior to the Civil War, and their 'raggy' music inspired the minstrels (*see* p. 81-2). Soon the Negroes were listening to black-face versions of their own songs, some of which, though giving unpleasant caricatures of the blacks, were composed by talented men, truly inspired by Negro music; and these songs gave rise to new folk songs on both sides of the Jim Crow line. The hoe-down tune, *Bile Them Cabbage Down*, reflects slave, minstrel, backwoods white, and ante-bellum influences, so well blended as to form a new category of music, best called 'Southern American'.

QUOTE: Fisk.

270. LYNCHBURG TOWN

When I was a young man comin' up to be a fiddler, I mostly played four tunes—*Soldier's Joy*, *Arkansas Traveler*, *Jim Along Josey* and *Black Eyed Susan* . . .

THIS NEGRO FIDDLER had one British melody (*Soldier's Joy*), one Negro reel (*Jim Along Josey*), one white frontier breakdown (*Arkansas Traveler*), and one southern American hoe-down (*Black-Eyed Susie*) in his tune bag. Normally, one can recognize a Negro reel tune or Negro influence in the chorus of a reel. Negroid choruses are usually composed of shorter phrases, with more careful matching of speech sound and pitch than in the white mouth-music refrains. Thus the Negro refrains can be sung more easily in chorus than the white songs. The white fiddle-songs reflect the lighter, more melodic bowing of the back-woods fiddler, but are usually not such catchy *songs*.

Lynchburg Town, which was equally popular among fiddlers and banjo pickers of both races, tells of the days after the Civil War when the Negroes were cast adrift to make their own place in the world of sharecropping and the Ku Klux Klan.

QUOTE: Fisk.

271. OLD MARSE JOHN

'WHITE FOLKS do as they please: colored folks do what they can '—quipped the wise old slaves. They became expert actors. They smiled at insults, laughed to hide anger and fear and 'to keep from cryin' '. They fooled Stephen Foster and all the other white folks into believing what it was most comfortable for them to believe. Behind their hands they chuckled, vengefully and ironically . . .

When old Miss died, we all came to the house, just a-hollerin' and cryin' and holdin' our hands over our eyes. Old Uncle Albert just keeled over on the floor and looked like he was cryin', but when he saw nobody wasn't lookin' he was dyin' laughin'. When we all got outside, we just laughed and said, ' Old Miss just gone on to Hell, like a damn barrel-full of nails.

Foster's stereotype of the faithful darkey no more fits the slave group than the abolitionist image of the deeply religious and persecuted African noblemen. Some Negroes were atheists. Others feigned stupidity and drove their masters wild by their calculated sloth. They lied and stole to keep alive and they rebelled as they could . . .

The chickens on our place knew us; they would just run and hide whenever they saw a slave coming . . . I was so sassy! They would knock me and beat me, but I would sass to the last . . .

Emancipation, from which they had expected so much, left most Negroes homeless and landless, forced to work as sharecroppers for their former masters. Reconstruction, which had promised them political freedom, ended in the bloody reprisals of the Ku Klux Klan. And so the Negroes ' did what they could '. Many lived off their women, who cooked for the white folks and stole pans of food for their ' sweet-back men '. The irreverent laughed at the preacher. They saw him praying on Sunday morning and robbing hen roosts and the watermelon patch on Monday night. The rest of the week he kept quiet about the bootleggers and the white man's mulatto concubines—and called on the willing sisters of the church while their husbands were at work. Thus the venal, wenching, hypocritical preacher became a principal butt of Negro humour, as the black peasants began to realize that they would be free ' only when the good Lawd set them free '.

This song sums up the Negro disillusionment with his white folks, his church leadership, and with himself. Its pseudo-religious refrain permitted it to be sung at church sociables where no other secular song was allowed. It tickled the white folks who liked to think of their black labourers as amusing and childish clowns. Barbershop quartets rejoiced in its rowdy ironies and its rich, corny chords.

QUOTE: Fisk.

272. OLD BANGUM

ONLY A HANDFUL of the British ballads* so treasured by white pioneers were taken over by Negro singers, although ballad style eventually inspired Negro narrative songs such as *John Henry*, *Frankie*, and *Stagolee* (*see* pp. 560, 569 and 571). The white planters probably did not sing ballads to any great extent; they were the songs of the poor whites whom both the planters and their slaves scorned and avoided. More importantly, however, the romantic themes of the ballads had no great meaning or significance for the Negro.

At first glance it seems curious that Negro singers have shown considerable affection for *Old Bangum*, which is a popular adaptation of a courtly romance. In the romance Sir Eglamour does knightly battle with a wicked giant and rescues a fair lady. British country singers considerably simplified the story to create the traditional ballad, *Sir Lionel* (Child No. 18), and American Negroes further condensed the story. Their variants tell how a brave man, whose plain title is Old Bangum, rides into a dark wood and conquers a fearsome, bloodthirsty beast—a sort of bogeyman story. Crooned quietly to its sweet old tune, it is an excellent ballad for children, who must face the nightmares conjured up in their imaginations by adults. The Negro slave child, particularly, must often have felt he was facing a monster when he stood up against his white owners . . .

Whipping darkies was the joy of the white folks in them times, and we had an overseer that went round and whupped the niggers every morning, and they hadn't done a thing. So he went to my father and said, ' Bob, I'm gonna whip you this morning.' Daddy said, ' I ain't done nothin',' and he said, ' I know it. I'm gonna whip you to keep you from doing something,' and he hit him with that cowhide—you know, it would cut the blood out of you with every lick if they hit you hard—and daddy was chopping cotton, so he just took up his hoe and chopped right down on that man's head and knocked his brains out.

QUOTE: Fisk.

* *The Maid Freed from the Gallows, Barbara Allen, Lord Thomas, St. James' Infirmary, Our Goodman, Little Sir Hugh*, and the *Wily Auld Carle*.

273. THE QUEEN'S GARDEEN

AT THEIR BEGINNINGS ballads purport to recount true stories; yet the framework of fact usually carries a popular fantasy. Time wears away much of the factual detail until only a dream remains. Chaucer gives all the details of this gruesome propaganda piece in the Prioress's Tale. Little Hugh of Lincoln, after being crucified and mutilated by the Jews, was found floating in a well. The Holy Wafer, placed upon his tongue, permits him to name his murderers, and after various miracles, which a thirteenth-century chronicler relates, eighteen Jews were hanged for the supposed crime.

Little remains of this antique piece of racial propaganda in American versions. The villain's part is as often played by a gipsy, a nurse, a duke's daughter, or the queen, as by a Jew. The story is reduced in this Bahaman version to a single picture of horror—a murderess who comes from nowhere into a child's sunny day and, after playing with her small victim, viciously murders him.

Bahamans sing this sadistic ballad with quiet tenderness and in a melting three-part harmony that underscores the horror of the story. A Negro child, growing up under slavery, did not have to imagine the cruel queen of the ballad; she sometimes met her, whip in hand, in the front parlour of the plantation house . . .

As soon as Mars Bill left Ol' Miss called me in. She was sitting in a big chair and had a heavy strap in her hand. ' Come here and kneel down, you black devil, I am going to whip you half to death.' She grabbed me by the back of the head and pulled it down between her knees. She had me there and commenced to working on me.

QUOTE: Fisk, p. 107.

274. THE RICH OLD LADY

OF ALL the folk singers I have recorded in the past twenty-five years, I learned the most about style from James Baker, alias Iron Head, permanently confined on the Sugarland State Farm, Houston, Texas. Iron Head won his nickname one day in the Brazos River bottom, where he and his mates were clearing land. A dead limb fell and struck him on the head with force sufficient to have killed most men. Iron Head merely wiped the blood out of his hooded eyes and kept chopping and singing. He had been ' on the river in 1904, when you could find a dead man on every turn row '. Old Iron Head had ' made it ' and for this he was admired as a ' hard head ' by his tough prison mates and the sadistic men who guarded them.

One of his old buddies 'on the river' had been a great singer, and Iron Head treasured all the songs he had learned from this man. He sang with great intensity and concentration, in a warm, reedy baritone, decorating every tune with charming vocal flowers. From him we first heard *The Grey Goose, Go Down, Old Hannah, Shorty George, Little John Henry*, and many others; his version of *The Sailor Cut Down in His Prime* has the finest of all recorded airs. The plot of the present Scots ballad tickled him immensely. Perhaps it appealed to his professional instincts, for it contains the outlines of one of the perfect crimes.

496

258. KNOCK JOHN BOOKER

Recorded by John Lomax in 1940 and arranged by Alan Lomax from the singing of Alabama Negroes on L.C. 20B4, Harriet McClintock, Livingstone. A local song which mentions a character common among Negro and imitation Negro pieces. It also occurs in a sea shantey and as a mountain banjo piece (see *Cousin Emmy*, Brunswick OE 9258). 'Booker' is another form of *buckra*, a word of African origin meaning 'white'. Randolph II, 344 says Jeb Stuart kept a Negro banjo-player with him to pick this tune during his campaigns.

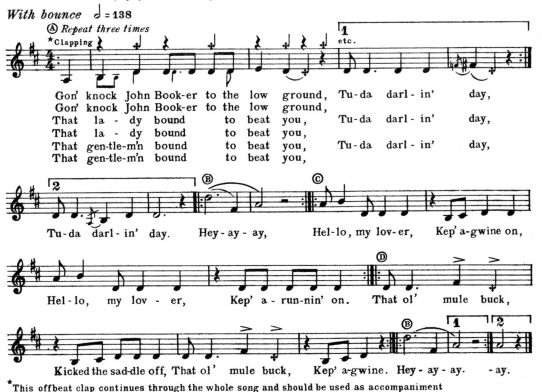

*This offbeat clap continues through the whole song and should be used as accompaniment

INTRODUCTION. (Part A)

LEADER: Gon' knock John Booker to the low ground, } (2)
CHORUS: Tu-da darlin' day,
LEADER: That lady bound to beat you, } (2)
CHORUS: Tu-da darlin' day,
LEADER: That gentlem'n bound to beat you, } (2)
CHORUS: Tu-da darlin' day.

(Part B)

CHORUS: Hey-ay-ay,
Hey-ay-ay.

(Part C)
LEADER: Hello, my lover,
CHORUS: Kep' a-gwine on,
LEADER: Hello, my lover,
CHORUS: Kep' a-runnin' on. } (2)

(Part D)
LEADER: That ol' mule buck,
CHORUS: Kicked the saddle off,
LEADER: That ol' mule buck,
CHORUS: Kep' a-gwine.

(Part B)
CHORUS: Hey-ay-ay,
Hey-ay-ay . . .

The singer may then return to the introduction and start the song again. Any of the various parts may be extended by as many repeats of lines as are desired.

The answering voice must enter just slightly ahead of the beat and while the leader is singing his final note. This overlapping effect is typical of all the Afro-American spirituals, worksongs, and reels.

259. MISS MARY JANE

FROM: p. 117 of *On the Trail of Negro Folk Songs*, Dorothy Scarborough (Harvard U.P., 1925). Used by permission. A Negro children's game song from slaves in South Carolina.

Gaily ♩ = 84

GUITAR— ANY ²/₄ STYLE
BANJO— 1-3

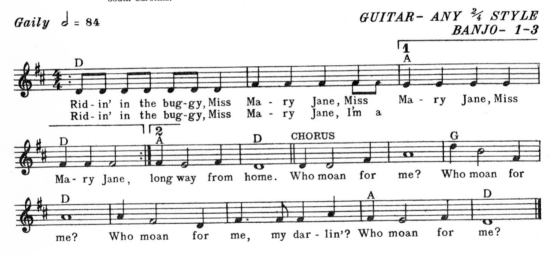

1 Ridin' in the buggy, Miss Mary Jane,
 Miss Mary Jane, Miss Mary Jane,
 Ridin' in the buggy, Miss Mary Jane,
 I'm a long way from home.
 CHORUS:
 Who moan for me?
 Who moan for me?
 Who moan for me, my darlin'?
 Who moan for me?

2 Sally got a house in Baltimo',
 Baltimo', Baltimo',
 Sally got a house in Baltimo'
 And it's three stories high. (CHO.)

3 Sally got a house in Baltimo',
 Baltimo', Baltimo',
 Sally got a house in Baltimo',
 An' it's full of chicken pie. (CHO.)

260. ALL FOR THE MEN

FROM: p. 154 of *Folks Songs of Alabama*, Byron Arnold (University of Alabama Press, 1950). Used by permission. As sung by Ruby Pickens Tartt. SEE: Brown III, 20; Gomme II, 362; Lomax III, 78. Originally an English singing game, with the addition of the ' thataway ' material, it became a popular amusement song among Negroes and whites in the South.

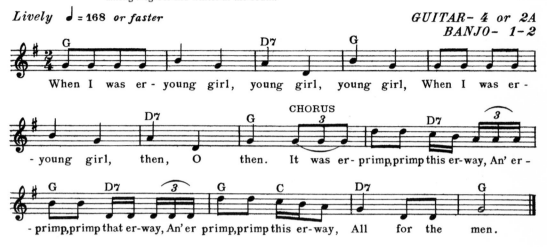

1 When I was er-young girl, young girl, young girl,
When I was er-young girl, then, O then.
CHORUS:
It was er-primp, primp this er-way,
An' er-primp, primp that er-way,
An' er-primp, primp this er-way,
All for the men.

2 The boys came er-courtin', courtin', *etc.*
CHORUS:
It was er-kiss, kiss, this er-way, *etc.*

3 Then we quarrelled, quarrelled, *etc.*
CHORUS:
It was er-yow, yow, this er-way, *etc.*

4 Pretty soon we made it up, made it up, *etc.*
CHORUS:
It was er-' my love ' this er-way, *etc.*

5 Then we married, married, *etc.*
CHORUS:
It was er-ha, ha, this er-way, *etc.*

261. SATURDAY NIGHT

Arranged by Alan Lomax from the singing of John A. Lomax. Frontier Texas background, additional stanzas from Brown III, 533. SEE: White, 175, 336. These verses hollered at intervals in long days of field labour in the South heartened the worker by reminding him of the pleasures of the weekend. Its rhythm has nothing to do with the rhythm of labour, for it is lyric in intention.

break of day, Old mas-sa's got me gwine, Old mas-sa's got me gwine.

1. Saturday night and Sunday, too,
   Pretty gals on my mind,
   Monday mornin' break of day,
   Old massa's got me gwine. (2)

2. Jaybird pull a two hoss plough,
   Sparrow, why won't you?
   'Cause my legs is little and long,
   I'm scared they'll pull in two. (2)

3. Monday morning break of day,
   White folks got me gwine,
   Saturday night when the sun goes down,
   That yaller gal am mine. (2)

4. Lightnin' is a yaller gal,
   She lives up in the clouds,
   Thunder is a black man
   And he can holler loud. (2)

5. When he kisses Miss Lightnin',
   She falls all in a wonder,
   He jumps up and grabs the clouds
   And that's what makes it thunder. (2)

6. Love it am a killin' thing,
   Beauty am a blossom,
   But if you want yo' finger bit,
   Just poke it at a possum. (2)

7. I am gwine ter die some day,
   When it comes my time,
   And the very last word I expect to say—
   Is—'I wish that gal were mine.' (2)

262. RIDIN' IN A BUGGY

Recorded and arranged by Alan Lomax and Ruby P. Tartt from the singing of Vera Hall, Livingstone, Alabama.

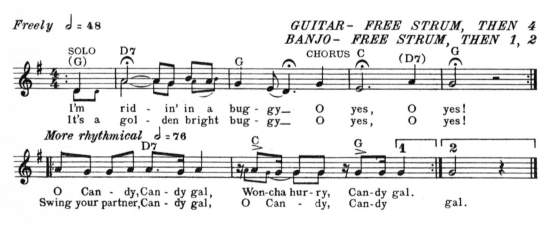

Freely ♩ = 48

GUITAR— FREE STRUM, THEN 4
BANJO— FREE STRUM, THEN 1, 2

I'm rid - in' in a bug - gy— O yes, O yes!
It's a gol - den bright bug - gy— O yes, O yes!

More rhythmical ♩ = 76

O Can - dy, Can - dy gal, Won-cha hur - ry, Can-dy gal.
Swing your partner, Can - dy gal, O Can - dy, Can-dy gal.

(Slowly and lingeringly)
SOLO: I'm ridin' in a buggy,
CHORUS: O yes, O yes!
SOLO: It's a golden bright buggy,
CHORUS: O yes, O yes!

(Fast and dancy)
CHORUS: O Candy, Candy gal,
Woncha hurry, Candy gal.
CHORUS: Swing your partner, Candy gal,
O Candy, Candy gal. (*ad. lib.*)

(Slowly and lingeringly)

SOLO: Now choose you two partners.
CHORUS: O yes, O yes!
SOLO: And I wants a good rappin'.
CHORUS: O yes, O yes!
Double Chorus is then sung.

263. STEAL, MISS LIZA

Adapted by Alan Lomax. SEE: Brown III, 522; Sears; White, 172. A widespread Negro children's dancing song which is related to the square-dance piece *Liza Jane (see* Lomax, II, 284, Sharp II, 356).

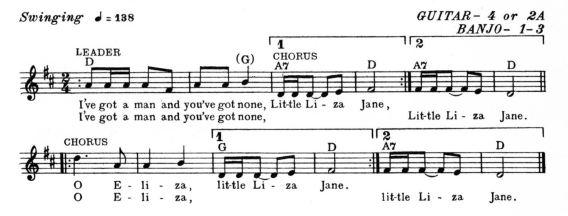

Swinging ♩ = 138

GUITAR – 4 or 2A
BANJO – 1-3

1 I've got a man and you've got none,
    Little Liza Jane,
  I've got a man and you've got none,
    Little Liza Jane.

CHORUS:
O Eliza, little Liza Jane. (2)

2 You swing mine and I'll swing yours,
  I'll swing mine and you swing yours. (CHO. 1)

3 I've got a house in Baltimo',
  Forty-'leven chillun on the flo'.

CHORUS 2:
Steal, Miss Liza, little Liza Jane. (2)

4 I steal yours and you steal mine,
  That's the way we'll get along fine. (CHO. 2)

264. YOU CAIN' LOSE-A ME, CHOLLY

FROM: p. 80 of *Negro Folk Songs as Sung by Lead Belly*, Lomax. Copyright, 1936, Macmillan, N.Y. © 1959, Folkways Music Publishers, New York. A Negro reel tune from Louisiana.

Fast dance ♩ = 126

GUITAR— 7A–B
BANJO— 5A

CHORUS:
You cain' lose-a-me, Cholly,
You cain' lose-a-me, boy.
You cain' lose-a-me, Cholly,
You cain' lose-a-me, boy.

1 Up to Willie Winston's I went a-rodin',*
   Down on my knees I was doin' a little co'tin',
     Ev'ry time she turn aroun' she says it so funny,
     'I got a pretty boy to bring me money.'

2 I went a-rowin' and my gal went, too,
   Down in the bottom where the boat broke through.
     (CHO.)

3 I got a yaller gal I can't keep,
   She use up a ba'l† of money ev'y week. (CHO.)

4 Hog and the sheep, they went to the paster,‡
   Hog tol' the sheep, 'You better git a little faster.'
     (CHO.)

5 Sheep says, ' Hog, I have a sore toe.'
   'Excuse me, sheep, I did not know.' (CHO.)

* riding   † barrel   ‡ pasture

265. BLACK SHEEP

Collected by John A. Lomax in North Carolina. SEE: Brown III, 153; Lomax II, 304; Randolph II, 345; Scarborough, 145. This is one form of the universal Negro ' mammy ' lullaby of the South.

GUITAR– 6A
BANJO– 4B

1. Black sheep, black sheep, Where'd you leave your lamb? Way down in the val - ley.

2. Bees and the but-ter-flies A - pick-in' out his eyes, Poor lit-tle thing cry-in'
4. My mo-ther told me Be - fore she went a - way To take good care of the

'Mam-my.' 3. Black sheep, black sheep, Where'd you leave your lamb? Way down in the
ba - by, But I went out to play And the

val - ley. ba-by ran a - way, And the poor lit-tle thing cry-in' 'Mam - my.'

1 Black sheep, black sheep,
Where'd you leave your lamb?
Way down in the valley.

2 Bees and the butterflies
A-pickin' out his eyes,
Poor little thing cryin' ' Mammy '.

3 Black sheep, black sheep,
Where'd you leave your lamb?
Way down in the valley.

4 My mother told me
Before she went away
To take good care of the baby,
But I went out to play
And the baby ran away,
And the poor little thing cryin' ' Mammy '.

266. BUCK-EYE RABBIT

FROM: p. 120 of *Folk Songs of Alabama*, Byron Arnold (University of Alabama Press, 1950). Used by permission. As sung by E. H. Pillans, Mobile. For references to rabbit and possum songs *see* Brown III, 206.

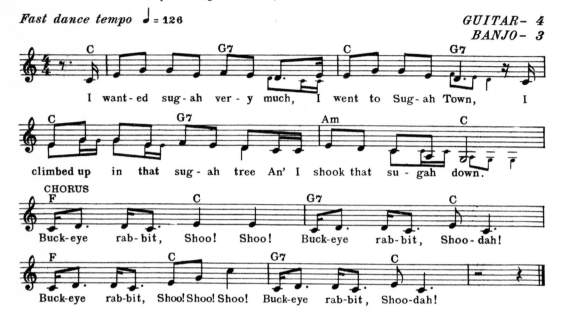

Fast dance tempo ♩ = 126

GUITAR– 4
BANJO– 3

I want-ed sug-ah ver-y much, I went to Sug-ah Town, I climbed up in that sug-ah tree An' I shook that su-gah down.

CHORUS

Buck-eye rab-bit, Shoo! Shoo! Buck-eye rab-bit, Shoo-dah!

Buck-eye rab-bit, Shoo! Shoo! Shoo! Buck-eye rab-bit, Shoo-dah!

1 I wanted sugah very much,
I went to Sugah Town,
I climbed up in that sugah tree
An' I shook that sugah down.
CHORUS:
Buck-eye rabbit, Shoo! Shoo!
Buck-eye rabbit, Shoo-dah!
Buck-eye rabbit, Shoo! Shoo! Shoo!
Buck-eye rabbit, Shoo-dah!

2 I went down to my sweetheart's house,
I ain't been dah befo',
She fed me out of an old hog trough,
And I don't go dah no mo'! (CHO.)

3 Way down yonder on Cedar Creek,
Where all them gals grow 'bout 'leven feet,
Jump in the bed but it ain't no use,
Feets stick out like a chicken roost. (CHO.)

267. SHORTENIN' BREAD

Collected and arranged by Alan Lomax. SEE: Brown III, 535; Lomax II, 234; Randolph II, 328; Scarborough, 152; Sears; White, 193. This is a genuine plantation song which became widely popular when Lawrence Tibbett and others recorded it.

Gaily ♩ = 184

GUITAR– ANY 2/4 STYLE
BANJO– 1 or 3

Three lit-tle chil-lun, ly-in' in bed, Two was sick and the
Sent for the doc-tor, doc-tor said, 'Feed those chil-lun on

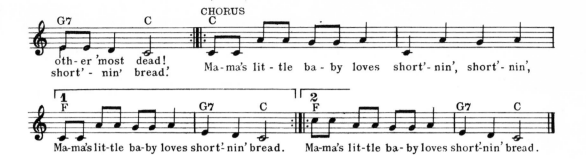

oth-er 'most dead!
short'-nin' bread!
Ma-ma's lit-tle ba-by loves short'-nin', short'-nin',

Ma-ma's lit-tle ba-by loves short'-nin' bread. Ma-ma's lit-tle ba-by loves short'-nin' bread.

1 Three little chillun, lyin' in bed,
Two was sick and the other 'most dead!
Sent for the doctor, doctor said,
' Feed those chillun on short'nin' bread.'
CHORUS:
Mama's little baby loves short'nin', short'nin',
Mama's little baby loves short'nin' bread. } (2)

2 When them chillun sick in the bed,
Heard that talk about short'nin' bread,
Popped up well and dance and sing,
Skippin' roun', cut the pigeon wing.* (CHO.)

3 So put on the skillet, slip on the led,†
Mammy gwine make us some short'nin' bread,
And that ain't all our mama gwine do,
She gwine cook us some coffee, too. (CHO.)

4 I slipped in the kitchen, I raise up the led,
I stole me a mess of that short'nin' bread.
I wunk at the pretty gal and I said,
' Baby, how'd you like some short'nin' bread?'
(CHO.)

5 They caught me with the skillet, caught me with the led,
Caught me with that gal making short'nin' bread.
Six months for the skillet, six months for the led,
Now I'm doin' time for eatin' short'nin' bread.
(CHO.)

* a frontier step dance † lid

268. THE BLUE-TAIL FLY

Collected and arranged by Alan Lomax. SEE: Brown III, 496; Scarborough, 201.
Davis mentions a number of variants. The *crack-corn* refrain was genuine slave lore.
The ballad, written by an abolitionist, was popular in North before the Civil War
—a favourite of Lincoln's; went back into folk circulation, and became a national
folk song again in 1940's.

Freely ♩ = 66

GUITAR - FREE STRUM, THEN 4
BANJO - FREE STRUM, THEN 1-2

When I was young, I used to wait On mas-ter and give him the plate,

More rhythmical ♩ = 104

And pass the bot-tle when he got dry, And brush a-way the blue-tail fly.

Jim-my, crack corn, and I don't care, Jim-my, crack corn, and I don't care,

Jim-my, crack corn, and I don't care, Old mas-sa's gone a - way.

1 When I was young, I used to wait
On master and give him the plate,
And pass the bottle when he got dry,
And brush away the blue-tail fly.
CHORUS:
Jimmy, crack corn, and I don't care, (3)
Old massa's gone away.

2 And when he'd ride in the arternoon,
I'd follow after with a hickory broom,
The pony being very shy,
When bitten by the blue-tail fly. (CHO.)

3 One day when ridin' round the farm,
The flies so num'rous they did swarm,
One chanced to bite him on the thigh,
' The Devil take the blue-tail fly!' (CHO.)

4 The pony jump, he run, he pitch,
He threw my master in the ditch,
He died and the jury wondered why,
The verdict was the blue-tail fly. (CHO.)

5 We laid him under a 'simmon* tree,
His epitaph was there to see,
' Beneath this stone I'm forced to lie—
Victim of a blue-tail fly.' (CHO.)

6 Ole massa's dead and gone to rest,
They say all things is for the best.
I never shall forget till the day I die
Ole massa and the blue-tail fly. (CHO.)

7 The hornet gets in eyes and nose,
The skeeter bites you through your clothes.
The gallinipper flies up high,
But wusser yet, the blue-tail fly. (CHO.)

* persimmon

269. BILE THEM CABBAGE DOWN

Adapted by Alan Lomax from the singing of Peggy Seeger. SEE: Brown III, 519;
Richardson, 88; Scarborough, 124, 165; White, 234, 303. See *Lynchburg Town*.
A Negro reel tune which has become universally popular among white square-
dance musicians. Verses sung depend upon the whim of the singer.

Dance tempo ♩ = 116

GUITAR } ANY 2/4 STYLE
BANJO }

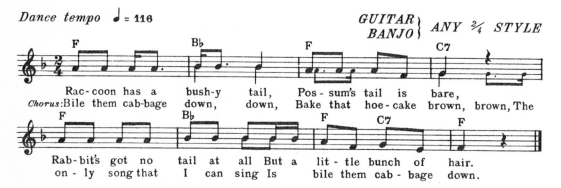

Rac-coon has a bush-y tail, Pos-sum's tail is bare,
Chorus: Bile them cab-bage down, down, Bake that hoe-cake brown, brown, The

Rab-bit's got no tail at all But a lit-tle bunch of hair.
on-ly song that I can sing Is bile them cab-bage down.

1 Raccoon has a bushy tail,
  Possum's tail is bare,
  Rabbit's got no tail at all
  But a little bunch of hair.
  CHORUS:
  Bile them cabbage down, down,
  Bake that hoe-cake brown, brown,
  The only song that I can sing
  Is—bile them cabbage down.

2 Raccoon and the possum
  Rackin' cross the prairie,
  Raccoon ax the possum
  Did she want to marry? (CHO.)

3 Possum is a cunnin' thing,
  He travels in the dark,
  And never thinks to curl his tail
  Till he hears old Rover bark. (CHO.)

4 Raccoon up a 'simmon tree,
  Raccoon on the ground,
  Raccoon say to the possum,
  ' Won't you shake them 'simmons down?' (CHO.)

5 Jaybird died with the whoopin' cough,
  Sparrow died with the colic.
  Along come the frog with a fiddle on his back,
  Inquirin' his way to the frolic. (CHO.)

270. LYNCHBURG TOWN

FROM: p. 60 of *Our Singing Country*, Lomax (Macmillan, N.Y., 1941). SEE: Brown III, 498; White, 142, 178. This song appears in pre-Civil War minstrel books. Had folk roots. First made by Negroes, then sung by minstrels. Thus renewed, the folk Negroes then passed it on to mountain whites among whom it became a common banjo and square dance piece.

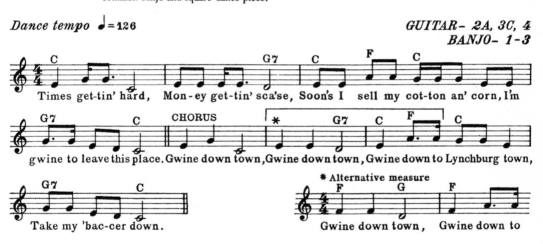

Dance tempo ♩=126

GUITAR- *2A, 3C, 4*
BANJO- *1-3*

1 Times gettin' hard,
  Money gettin' sca'se,
  Soon's I sell my cotton an' corn,
  I'm gwine to leave this place.
  CHORUS:
  Gwine down town, (2)
  Gwine down to Lynchburg town,
  Take my 'baccer down.

2 'Baccer sellin' high, (2)
  'Baccer sellin' at fifteen cents,
  Nobody there to buy. (CHO.)

3 'Baccer sellin' low, (2)
  'Baccer won't bring seven cents,
  Damn if I think I'll go. (CHO.)

507

4 Buy me a load of posts,
　Fence my grave around,
　Keep Bob Ridley's old grey sow
　From rootin' me out the ground.　(CHO.)

5 Old bee made the honeycomb,
　Young bee make the honey,
　Negro make the 'baccer crop,
　White folks git the money.　(CHO.)

6 White man goes to college,
　Negro to the field,
　White man learn to read an' write,
　Negro learns to steal.　(CHO.)

7 White man goes to meetin',
　Never see him smile,
　Negroes in the church-house
　You can hear 'em laugh a mile.　(CHO.)

8 Little piece of ashcake
　And a little piece of fat,
　White folks 'gin to grumble
　If you eat so much as that.　(CHO.)

9 I went down town,
　Bought me a jug of wine,
　Tied me up to the whippin' post
　Give me forty-nine.　(CHO.)

10 I went down town,
　Bought me a jug of gin,
　Tied me up the whippin' post
　Give me hell agin.　(CHO.)

271. OLD MARSE JOHN

Melody and part of text from p. 163 of *On the Trail of Negro Folk Songs*, Dorothy Scarborough (Harvard U.P., 1925). Used by permission. Arranged by Alan Lomax. SEE: Brown III, 508, 549; Lomax II, 254; White, 370. First stanza like *Old Horse* sea shantey. Frequently found in blackface minstrel songsters after 1836.
Piano arrangement by MATYAS SEIBER

Moderato ♩ = 160

GUITAR— 2A, 4, 5A
BANJO— 1 - 3

Old Marse John came ri-din' by, 'Say Marse John, that mule's gon-na die'.

'If he do, I'll tan his skin, And if he don't I'll ride him a-gin.' O

1 Old Marse John came ridin' by,
   ' Say, Marse John, that mule's gonna die.'
   ' If he do, I'll tan his skin,
   And if he don't, I'll ride him agin.'
   CHORUS:
   O mourner, you shall be free,
   Yes, mourner, you shall be free,
   When the good Lord sets you free.

2 My old mistis promise me,
   When she died she'd set me free,
   She lived so long, she got so po',
   She left old Sambo pullin' at his hoe. (CHO.)

3 My old mistis lyin' in the leaves,
   Head full of lice, stockin' full of fleas,
   There was old mistis dead and gone,
   But here was old Sambo a-hoein' the corn. (CHO.)

4 My gal Sal, she sho is a card,
   She works right out in the white folks' yard,
   Cooks the goose, gives me the stuffin',
   She thinks I'm workin', I ain't doin' nothin'.
                                          (CHO.)

5 She kills the turkey, saves me the bone,
   Drinks the beer, saves me the foam,
   She kills the chicken, saves me the wing,
   Thinks I'm workin', ain't doin' a thing. (CHO.)

6 I likes my wife, I likes my baby,
   I likes my flapjacks floatin' in gravy,
   I likes my coffee, I likes it strong,
   When I get to eatin', just bring the butter 'long.
                                          (CHO.)

7 Some folks say that a preacher won't steal,
   I caught two in my cornfield,
   Preachin' and prayin' all the time,
   And pullin' my melons off the vine. (CHO.)

8 I went to the river to be baptize,
   Step on a root and I got capsize,
   The water was deep and the preacher was weak,
   This mourner went to Heaven from the bottom
                 of the creek. (CHO.)

9 Now when I'm dead just bury me deep,
   Tell all the gamblers I've gone to sleep,
   Put a pair of bones in my right hand,
   And I'll throw seven in the promised land.
                    (CHO.)

272. OLD BANGUM

FROM: p. 51 of *On the Trail of Negro Folk Songs*, Dorothy Scarborough (Harvard U.P.). Used by permission. SEE: Belden, 29; Child, No. 18; Coffin, 48; Lomax IV, 149; Randolph I, 72; Scarborough, 51; Sharp I, 54. A British ballad probably derived from *Sir Eglamour of Artois*, it has wider oral currency in U.S. than Britain.

1 Old Bangum, will you hunt and ride?
   Dillum down dillum.
  Old Bangum, will you hunt and ride?
   Dillum down.
  Old Bangum, will you hunt and ride,
  Sword and pistol by your side?
   Cubbi-kee, cuddledum, killi quo quam.

2 There is a wild boar in these woods, (3)
  Eats men's bones and drinks their blood.

3 Old Bangum drew his wooden knife (3)
  And swore he'd take the wild boar's life.

4 Old Bangum went to the wild boar's den (3)
  And found the bones of a thousand men.

5 They fought four hours in that day, (3)
  The wild boar fled and slunk away.

6 Old Bangum, did you win or lose? (3)
  He swore, by Jove, he'd won his shoes.

273. THE QUEEN'S GARDEEN

Collected and arranged by Alan Lomax. SEE: Belden, 69; Child, No. 155;
Coffin, 110; Creighton I, 16; Randolph I, 148; Scarborough, 53; Sharp I, 222.
An English ballad, widely popular in U.S. especially South, with a very frequent
occurrence among Bahaman Negroes.

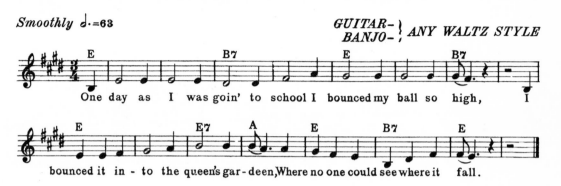

1 One day as I was goin' to school
  I bounced my ball so high,
  I bounced it into the queen's gardeen,
  Where no one could see where it fall.

2 'Come een, come een, my brave young boy,
  Come een and get your ba-all.'
  ' O no, O no, I can't come ee-een,
  Unless my school-mates follow.'

3 She showed him an apple as green as grass,
  She showed him a gay gold ring,
  She showed him a kerchief as white as snow
  So she could entice him ee-een.

4 She took him by his lily-white hand,
  She led him through the ha-all,
  She took him into the green gard-een,
  Where no one could hear when he holloaed.

5 She brought a kerchief of linen fine,
  A knife both long and keen,
  She brought a basin of marble sto-one
  To catch his lifeblood ee-en.

274. THE RICH OLD LADY

FROM: *Our Singing Country*, Lomax (Macmillan, N.Y., 1941), arranged by Alan Lomax. This story occurs in two closely related ballads, our version coming from the Scots *Wily Auld Carle*, or *The Wife of Kelso*, versions of which are found in South and southern Middle-West. SEE: Belden, 237; JAFL XXIX, 179, XLIX, 235; Reeves, 204; Sharp I, 348.
The other more popular form—*Johnny Sands*—has been printed often and was popularized by the Hutchinsons, etc. SEE: Brown II, 448; Gardner, 480; Randolph IV, 246.

Piano arrangement by MATYAS SEIBER

Dm   A7   Dm

-o,   Love my dar-lin' - o,   Love my dar-lin' - o.

Repeat Chorus 2 or 3 times

1 Once I knowed an old lady,
Round Tennessee did dwell,
She had a lovin' husband,
But she loved other mens as well.

CHORUS:
Love my darlin'-o, (4)

2 'I'm goin' down to the doctor's shop
Just as straight as I can go,
See if I can't find somethin' round that place,
That'll run my husband blind.' (CHO.)

3 She only found two marrowbones,
An'she told him to eat them all,
Says, ' Now, I'm blind, my dear young wife,
An' I jes' can't see at all. (CHO.)

4 ' Honey, I would go and drown myself,
If I only knew the way.'
Says, ' Now, my dear, come and go with me,
Mother's 'fraid you'll run astray.' (CHO.)

5 She gits way back, takes a little runnin' start,
Gonna shove her old man in;
Old man jumps just a little one side,
An' a-headlong she plunge in. (CHO.)

6 She whoops and she hollers,
Just as loud as any woman could squall;
Old man know his sweet wife's dyin'
An' cannot see at all. (CHO.)

7 Old man bein' so kind-hearted,
Knowin' his sweet wife could not swim,
Reached right back and gits a great long pole
And he shoves her further in. (CHO.)

8 Come all you young, hasty women,
An' take warnin' after me,
Don't never try to drown a po' old man
That's so blind he cannot see. (CHO.)

WORK SONGS

275. JOHNNY, WON'T YOU RAMBLE?

(An ante-bellum axe or hoeing song from the Texas penitentiary)

THE LAND of the South was cleared, ploughed, and harvested by Negro labour; the roads and the railroads were cut through mountain, forest and flat by gangs of Negroes; the levees along the muddy rivers were piled up by Negro mule-skinners; the loads on the steamboats were handled by Negro roustabouts; and the cotton bales were screwed into the holds of the ships by Negro stevedores. From the beginning, it was the white man standing in the shade, shouting orders with a club or whip or pistol in his hand—while out in the sun the blacks sweated with the raw stuff of wealth, cursing under their breath, but singing at the tops of their voices. Thus work songs flowered richly in the South. Every new job brought a fresh style with a special rhythm. Without these songs the South, as we know it, would never have come into being.

The British sailor chanteys may have influenced the American Negro work songs to some extent but, fundamentally, they are a part of an African musical tradition. Africa south of the Sahara is a continent of work songs. The Bantu peoples have always eased the pain of labour by communal songs—porters' songs, paddling songs, hoeing songs, maize-grinding songs, fishermen's songs, hunting songs, and scores of other types—the work bard rapping out a catchy dance rhythm on a piece of iron or wood and improvising satires on everything and everyone, sowing his verses with earth-rank bawdry, or vaunting the heroic achievements of his gang, while the deep-voiced chorus roars a response to every line. This solo-chorus form is the fundamental West African song-style; it shows up again and again in our Negro folk song, most clearly in the work songs and the early spirituals, and even in the blues and jazz, where the chorus speaks through the guitar or piano.

The white planters, observing that their slaves worked more cheerfully and effectively when they sang, encouraged them to sing; and the African work-song tradition found new roots in the Southern states. Travellers in the ante-bellum South were deeply impressed by the strange, wild chants the Negroes sang as they rowed or paddled in Carolina lagoons or Louisiana bayous. The Negro axeman, chopping in the virgin timber, chanted . . .

> When I was young and in my prime,   (hah!)
> Sunk my axe deep every time,   (hah!)
> Now I'm old and my heart's growing cold,   (hah!)
> Can't swing my axe to save my soul,   (hah!)
>   Come on, Mister Tree, you almost down,   (hah!)
>   Come on, Mister Tree, want to see you hit the ground.   (hah!)

Of the field songs sung by American slaves we have the scantiest records. Some fragments have been preserved in the Southern penitentiary tradition . . .

> Long summer day makes a white man lazy,
>   Long summer day.
> Long summer day makes a nigger run away, sir,
>   Long summer day.

The summer days were long, indeed, for the slaves. The hard-driving Calvinist planter paid high prices for his human work animals and saw to it that they gave him full value.

> You had to be up when day broke and be on the way to the field or you had trouble with the overseer. We worked every day from sunup to eleven and twelve at night in the summer when the days was long. Then on moonshiney nights we would just work on through the night till day clean.

Johnny, Won't You Ramble? comes straight out of this scene. Such songs persisted where peonage took the place of slavery after the emancipation proclamation of 1865. The fact is that the atmosphere of slavery persisted long after the institution itself was abolished. The attitude of the overseers on the big construction jobs and in the convict forced labour camps differed little from that of the ' nigger drivers ' under slavery. Negroes who rebelled or talked back were still beaten or killed outright. The gangs of sweating blacks still 'rolled from can to can't—from when you can just see in the morning till you can't see no more at night '. Their songs provided them with an outlet for their protests and filled their hours of toil with the deep and satisfying joy of communal creation. The songs, in a sense, stamped the railroads, the cleared land and the piled-up levees as their handiwork.

The African work-song tradition did not, therefore, die out or diminish in America. It adapted itself to a multitude of new tasks and continued to grow and ripen until machines began to replace hand labour in the early years of the twentieth century. In a very real sense the chants of Negro labour may be considered the most profoundly American of all our folk songs, for they were created by our people as they tore at American rock and earth and reshaped it with their bare hands, while rivers of sweat ran down and darkened the dust. Every line of every song defines a uniquely American experience, and the melodies are stirring and powerful adaptations of tunes drawn from the whole body of Southern tradition.

The legions of unknown bards who shaped these songs were men of talent so striking that they could make voices heard among choruses of expert and highly critical singers, trained to catch every nuance of a song by hours of music-making in church, on the job, and at dances. As the century came to a close, these rambling singers of labour composed the big Negro ballads (*John Henry, Casey Jones, Frankie*) and the early blues out of the materials of this same tradition. Then, laying their powerful and work-wise hands on the white man's guitar, piano, clarinet, and trumpet, they made them sing their way, thus laying the groundwork for the American orchestral sound that was to flower into jazz.

QUOTE: Fisk.

276. JOHN GILBERT IS DE BOAT

BY 1800 THE Ohio River was already an important highway and it remained so for a hundred years while a fantastic procession of flat boats, keel boats, and river steamers swept down its broad, smooth waters from Cincinnati towards the West. The most original singers in the river's history were the Negro roustabouts who chanted lewd and lively songs while they shifted enormous loads up and down the dipping, swaying gangways of the paddleboats. Lafcadio Hearn has left us a magnificent description of their wonderful polyphonic choruses, enlivened by drumming and dancing . . .

. . . The air is wonderfully quick and lovely, and the chorus is quite exciting. The leading singer sings the whole song, excepting the chorus. *Shiloh*, which dis-syllable is generally chanted by twenty or thirty voices of abysmal depth at the same time with a sound like the roar of twenty Chinese gongs struck with tremendous force and precision. A great part of *Limber Jim* is very profane, and some of it not quite fit to print. The chorus is frequently accompanied with that wonderfully rapid slapping of the thighs and hips known as ' patting Juba '.

The tune of *Limber Jim* is lost and gone down river with the last of the Ohio river rousters, but this song, which Mary Wheeler collected from an old-time river ruler, should be sung in the same manner.

The *John Gilbert*, built in Pittsburgh in 1881, ran the Ohio from Cincinnati to Florence, Alabama, and carried such loads of peanuts on her return trips that the rousters called her ' Peanut John '.

QUOTE: *An American Miscellany*, L. Hearn, Vol. I, p.147-60 (Dodd, Mead & Co., 1924).

277. ROCK ABOUT, MY SARO JANE

' BEFORE FREEDOM ' whites did most of the stevedoring, for the river offered the easiest road to freedom to the Negro slaves. Later Negroes took over the work. Clubbed, kicked, lashed, sometimes simply killed and dumped into the river by tough 'nigger-driving ' mates, these men were scarcely better off than slaves. As one old rouster put it, ' I'ze just nobody. I'ze the most lone man they is. 'Foh duh wah, I was a slave. Now I'ze a slave to this here steamboat.' One of their Mississippi songs runs . . .

Po' roustabout ain't got no home,
Makes his living with his shoulder-bone.

On that shoulder-bone some ' bullies ' could, for show, lift a 500-lb. bale of cotton. As for the working load, the mates defined that as what two good men could pick up and one could carry. The work went at a lope; an endless belt of rousters with loads trotting down the gangway into the boat, up the bank to the loading point, and back again, with the mate ready to fall upon the first man who lagged or weakened.

How in Hell d'yu 'spect me to hold her,
I've got no skin on either shoulder . . .

Yet, like all men who handle a hard job, the rousters were proud of being tougher than the toughest mate or the hardest job, and this virility shines through all their songs. In the oldest roustabout chants there are echoes from the Civil War days when freed Negroes worked on Yankee gunboats.

Went to the river and I couldn't get across,
Jumped on a rebel louse, thought it was a hoss,
Now some folks say that a rebel won't steal,
But I caught two in my corn field.

516

278. RILEY

ON THE low-lying islets which fringe the sea coast of Georgia and the Carolinas, one finds a Negro culture noticeably distinct from that of the inland Piedmont. Even before the Civil War runaway slaves found refuge on these islands in villages of freedmen, and, after 1864, all-Negro colonies were founded there by abolitionists.

On black bayous, deep in the shadow of live-oak groves, where the grey moss trails across palmetto leaf, these hidden villages have kept alive the oldest Negro tradition in North America. Here one sees dances like the ' Buzzard Lope' which imitate the actions of animals. Here one finds an occasional African carving. The minds of the people turn easily to stories of Brer Rabbit and the other favourite animal heroes of the Negro slave. ' Shouts ' (*see* p. 463) are common, along with chanteys, not greatly different, one would say, from the Negro work songs which so strongly influenced the sea chanteys of the early nineteenth century. In 1935 I recorded a batch of chanteys like *Riley*, which were being used even then for launching small boats, for pulling timber, or for any job of heavy lifting. ' Big John Davis ', the lead singer, could tell me nothing about ' old Riley '. He may have been an escaped slave, or a house servant who accompanied his master on a trip to England. He may have been the John Riley or the Willy Reilly of the British ballads, both voyagers and figures of romantic adventure. At any rate, he left the South, and the singer wants to follow him.

279. PAY ME

IN BRUNSWICK, Georgia, at the muddy mouth of the Savannah River, where frigates, clippers, barquentines, and steam boats have for centuries loaded Georgia indigo, rice, and cotton, I found Negro longshoremen singing at their work in the 1940's. They bellowed songs as they hoisted, heaved and screwed down their cargoes, as had twelve generations of their forebears. By the 1940's, however, their songs were no longer nostalgic or oblique. These young huskies of the docks said directly and openly what they thought, and their song has proved enormously appealing to young people all across America.

280. THE JOHN B.'s SAILS

THE SMALL BOAT piers of Nassau Harbour form the market-place of the Bahamas. The dirty, sea-scarred sloops, tethered on the pale blue water, are like so many country wagons loaded with produce for sale in the capital. A sixteen-footer stands in towards the dock, its deck only a few inches above the waves, carrying a cow, five goats, a dozen hens, four women, six children, and four or five sailors. This crowded little boat is ending a journey from an island perhaps two or three hundred miles away. As it noses into the pier, a similar craft lifts its ragged sail and departs, its deck packed with passengers and freight, for some coral islet far down the chain toward Haiti.

These vessels carry no charts, no compasses, and no auxiliary engines, yet few of them come to grief, for the Bahaman is at home in his reef-filled azure seas. They tell and believe a story about an old Negro pilot, grown blind, who could stick his finger in the water and tell precisely where the boat lay.

281. COTTON NEEDS PICKIN'

Our white folks was good to us. They didn't 'low the overseer to whip us darkies, but he would watch you good, and he always knew who wasn't working. We could talk and sing and do as we pleased, just so we picked our cotton. I couldn' pick as fast as some of 'em. Some picked as much as a hundred baskets a day, and just carried on singing' and laughin' all the while. Sometimes girls would wet in their baskets or put rocks in the bottom to make the cotton heavier. Everybody had plenty to eat, and they say there wasn't no plantation that turnt out the work like we done, real good farm work, I mean.

QUOTE: Fisk.

282. WHOA BACK, BUCK

ONE OF LEAD BELLY'S uncles was a teamster, who freighted goods into the backwoods on wagons drawn by oxen. Like all ox-drivers he hurled streams of profanity at his animals; and Lead Belly recalled how the old fellow sometimes kept the family awake cussing in his sleep. *Whoa Back, Buck*, his ox-driving song, is one form of a field work song that we have found all the way from Virginia to Texas—the Negro plough-hand's re-make of the fiddlers' *Old Joe Clark*.

283. BRING ME LI'L' WATER, SYLVIE

LEAD BELLY'S Uncle Bob was married to a woman named Sylvie. On hot days when he was ploughing at the bottom of the field a long way from the house, he used to holler to Sylvie to bring the water bucket; and out of this little field holler Lead Belly developed the song and the story.

284. PO' FARMER

THEY TELL about a Negro sharecropper who brought in his yearly crop of cotton to the plantation gin, saw it ginned into four bales, and stood watching the white manager juggle the accounts so that the price for his cotton exactly matched the total of what his family owed the plantation commissary. The cropper then remarked that he had about another bale of cotton at home. 'Hell's fire!' grumbled the white man. 'Now I'll have to figger this account of yours all over again to bring you out even!'

Then they tell about the Northern man who planned to buy a big, fine Southern farm. He had the soil tested; he went over the books; but just before he signed the cheque, he asked one of the Negro croppers on the place whether the farm was a paying proposition.

No sir, boss, you can't make no money here. If you do, you be the first man ever done it since the war. You see, de ducks eat everything up round here.'

'What do you mean by that?'

'Well, we croppers raises lots of stuff and we takes it to town, but then de white folks figgers and figgers, and dey ducks dis and dey ducks dat, and by the time they's done, de ducks done eat up everything we raised.'

QUOTE: *The Book of Birmingham*, John Horuiday (Dodd, Mead, 1921).

285. THE BOLL WEEVIL HOLLER

JOHN LOMAX remembers that the first time he ever heard of the ballad of the boll weevil was one hot Texas day in 1905. The 'phone rang in his office with Houston on the line. 'Howdy, Mister Lomas,' said a Negro voice at the other end. 'I hear tell you is lookin' for old-time ballit (ballad) songs. Well, I just composed one. And if you will kindly accept the charge, I be glad to sing it to you right now. It's all about the boll weevil, lookin' for a home . . .'

The boll weevil, a tiny cotton borer which lays its eggs in the young bud and destroys the cotton, came into Texas from Mexico in the 1890's, and spread rapidly across the whole South, bringing ruin to the cotton kingdom. As he watched the white man trying to get rid of this pest, the displaced Negro farm worker identified and sympathized with the little black bug. He knew he was unwanted, like the boll weevil, but he was equally determined to have a home. This is the theme of all the boll-weevil lore, of this holler from the red clay country of Alabama, and of these boll-weevil yarns from Northern Florida.

A boll weevil flew onto the steerin' wheel of a white man's car and says, 'Mister, lemme drive yo' car.'
De white man says, 'You can't drive no car.'
Boll weevil says, 'Oh yeah, Ah kin. Ah drove five thousand cars last year and Ah'm goin' to drive ten thousand this year.'
A man told a tale on de boll weevil again. Says he heard a terrible racket and noise down in de field, went down to see what it was, and what you reckon? It was Ole Man Boll Weevil whippin' li'l Willie Boll Weevil 'cause he couldn't carry two rows at a time.

QUOTE: Hurston, pp. 149-151.

286. GO DOWN, OLD HANNAH

After freedom, most of Master Jim Smith's niggers left him, and then he had what they call chain-gang slaves. He paid 'em out of jail to work for him. I stayed in peonage out there for 'bout forty years, 'bout forty miles south of Greenwood . . . I couldn't get away because they watched us with guns all the time. You had to ask to git water. If you didn't work in a hurry, they would whup you with a strap that had five-six holes in it. I ain't talkin' 'bout what I heard—I'm talkin' 'bout what I seed. When the levee busted, that kinda freed me . . .

In Texas, some of the big prison camps for Negroes are situated on land formerly occupied by slave and lease-labour plantations. The songs, therefore, were handed on from slave to peon to leased convict to state prisoner, and when we visited the state penal farms in the 1930's, we found this old work-song tradition still alive and growing, with choruses of trained singers ready for our recording machine.

The big prison farms were operated to produce a revenue for the state government rather than as reformatories for the criminal and socially unstable personality. If the wardens had a philosophy, it was that there ' was nothing better for a bad nigger than hard work '. The guards saw to it that every convict put forth his maximum effort all day and every day. The men rose before dawn (as early as 3 a.m. in the summer), ate a huge breakfast, were counted and divided into their work squads, and then trotted ahead of their mounted guards to the fields. They worked until darkness and then were often made to run back to their barracks. Failure to keep up with the ' lead man ' in the group brought clubbing, lashing, and pistol whipping in the fields. For more serious ' offences ', the prisoners were spreadeagled, and formally whipped by the farm supervisor, put into solitary, jammed into the ' hot-box ', or punished in one of the many other ways that cruel man has devised to torture his brothers. Only the seriously ill were excused from work. A convict who pleaded a minor complaint was ' playing sick ' and might be severely disciplined. The men who made trusty, by toadying to the guards, won considerable privileges, the most extraordinary of which was the permission to see their women visitors in private.

Heywood Patterson, in his terrifying book *Scottsboro Boy*, has told in gruesome detail the workings of this outmoded penal system and its frightful effects upon human beings. What I saw of the prison farm as a visitor sickened me. I knew how easy it was for a Negro worker to land in the county jail for some minor crime, for gambling or for ' talking back '. From the county gang his path could lead him easily to the state pen. I realized how, for almost a century, these penal farms have been a threat to every Southern Negro, especially the independent and rebellious of spirit. It was frightening to hear *Go Down, Old Hannah*, which dates back to the lease system of 1900 or earlier, still sung with topical significance in the 'thirties. *Old Hannah* is the sun; the weary convict longs for the world to end rather than see the sun rise again on another day of toil.

QUOTE: Botkin VII, from WPA ex-slave MS.

287. LONG JOHN

LIGHTNING STOOD OUT among his fellow prisoners on the Darrington Farm, like a jagged streak of fire in a stormy night. He was tall, pantherlike and blue-black; his eyes gleamed with a cold, wild light, and his unconquerable laugh rang through the gloomy prison dormitory. Southern prison life had left Lightning unbowed. As a matter of pride, he set the pace in the fields, and led the work songs all day in a voice that heartened his comrades. No other prisoner we met dared to sing so openly what he felt. His first song, *Johnny, Won't You Ramble?*, dispelled at once whatever illusions I had about the kindliness of Southern plantation life. His second song described with frightening precision how a sadistic captain whipped a prisoner in the field . . .

> Can't you hear the bully screaming,
> Great God-a-mighty?

Next, Lightning sang a Texas work-song version of *Long John Green*, the Negro criminal who ran away whenever he cared to and who was caught only when he wished to be. The song describes a prison break. A convict runs for the woods with the guards shooting at him. He reaches the shelter of the trees and someone goes for the ' dog-man ', master of a pack of bloodhounds. Then for hours the chase goes on, the man on foot using every trick he knows to cover his trail ahead of the hounds and his mounted pursuers. The song, too, is a chase—the chorus for ever running on the heels of the leader. So Lightning sang it, and at the end he said to us with a proud smile, ' I can outrun all the horses and dogs on this farm any time I gets a notion to leave, and I'm gettin' in the notion now.'

When we returned six months later to record him again, his buddies grinned and said, ' Lightnin' walked off an' left them dogs standin', just like ol' Long John.' Here was another manifestation of Ol' John, the trickster slave (*see* p. 466).

288. ANOTHER MAN DONE GONE

ON THE east coast they tell about Blue Jim, who had blue gums, red eyes, and diamonds in his teeth. When they put Blue Jim on the chain gang, he would work till about nine o'clock in the morning, and then say, ' White folks, so long, I'm goin' up town.' Off he would stroll wearing his stripes, the guards shooting at him, 'Blue Jim walkin' slow and laughin' at 'em.' From Tennessee to Texas they sing about Long John, a man they could never get their fingers on, and in the Mississippi Delta they call him the *Travelin' Man*.

> Travelin' man, he certainly was a travelin' man,
> Travelin' man that was ever in the land,
> The police took a Winchester rifle,
> Shot that boy right though the head,
> He come a-tumblin' to the ground,
> Everybody thought he was dead.
> They sent down South where his mother had gone,
> She was carried away in tears,
> They opened up the coffin for to see her son,
> And the fool had disappeared . . .
> He was a travelin' man . . .

From the red clay counties of Alabama comes this grim song of an escaped convict, lurking in the shadows of the liveoaks yonder, hungry, desperate, ready to kill anybody who does not help him. When the deputies drive up to the shack in the cotton patch and ask if anyone has seen him, nobody ever heard of the man, nobody knows anything.

289. JUMPIN' JUDY

THE STATE PENITENTIARY at Nashville was a gloomy Victorian Gothic building with tiers of cells around and above the foundries and factories where the prisoners worked. Black Samson told us, ' Boss, please help me get outa here, 'cause I just naturally don't like this place.' We were introduced to a poor, simple lad who, as his comrades said, could ' beat on a bucket sweeter than any man alive '. He sat before the mike, and his hands rippled out exquisite African rhythms on the lid of a tin lard can. Then as he listened to the play-back, he smiled to himself and said, ' Lord, I know when Mr. Roosevelt hear this in the White House, he's sure gonna turn this poor boy loose.'

Alan Prothero was the only one whom we felt we could help. He had been lead singer on a section gang in the free world. His voice flowed rich, deep, and brown like a Southern river, with big low notes like some big, black drift-logs in the stream, and sweet silver top notes like the sunlight on the ripples of the river. All of his melodies were beautifully formed, and all will become part of the American heritage of song. We resolved to try to help him win a pardon or a parole, as white men can so often do for Negro prisoners in the South. When all the legal papers were ready, a letter came from a lawyer in Tennessee saying, ' Alan Prothero died of tuberculosis last week.'

290. THE LONGEST TRAIN

A SIMILAR SONG, combining elements of the white *Turtle Dove* and the Negro *Lonesome Road*, has been three or four times discovered in the Southern mountains. Sharp recorded a beautiful fragmentary version in Kentucky . . .

> Black girl, black girl, don't lie to me,
> Tell me where did you stay last night?
> I stayed in the pines where the sun never shines,
> And shivered when the cold wind blows . . .

I feel confident, however, that this strain came into the mountains from Negro sources when the railroad and industry first brought the banjo and the blues into the region; then traditional mountain stanzas were tacked on to the Negro songs. White versions normally speak of ' the longest train I ever saw ', which was a constantly recurring element in Negro prison work songs recorded during the 1930's in all the states east of Mississippi. Many of these songs spoke of Joe Brown's coal-mine, where leased-out Negro convicts dug coal.

The story of the Negro convict miner is, perhaps, the most frightful chapter in American history, comparable in many respects to the horrors of German concentration camps. The leasing of convict to labour on private mines and plantations began after the Civil War when Southern jails were full, and when the state governments were impecunious, corrupt, and vengefully reactionary. In return for small yearly fees, the state turned over its prisoners to private individuals, who could then exploit the men as they pleased.

George Korson in his important work, *Coal Dust on the Fiddle*, described how this system of legalized slavery fed on human souls and bodies. Sheriffs and agent-provocateurs received commissions for contriving the arrest of poor people for petty offences and then shipped them off to the mines. Once there, the dangers of the job and the system of cumulative penalties made it doubtful if the prisoners ever came back alive. The prison diet hardly sustained life in men driven at their tasks for twelve hours a day. Safety precautions and ventilation were all but non-existent. Inexperienced men were required to hack out huge quantities of coal per day. In one mine in Alabama, for instance, where a well-equipped miner today produces three tons of coal in a day's work, the convicts were set daily tasks of ten to fourteen tons. If they failed their quotas the trusty-guards—convicted killers who got time off for keeping up production—could beat and torment them as they chose. The miner, struggling in the black bowels of the earth, choked with dust and the fumes from explosions, worked under a heavy pall of fear—the fear of explosions and cave-ins, and the fear of the killers who watched him in the darkness of the pit.

In Alabama, fifteen thousand convict miners, working under these concentration-camp conditions, seriously affected the standard of living of the state's twenty thousand free miners. And finally, in 1928, after fifty years of demands for reform, the last convict mine was closed down. A Negro convict, walking out of the prison stockade, burst into tears, saying, ' Lordy, slavery's over at last.' His song has one of the most plaintive of all American melodies.

SOURCE: Korson II.

291. IT MAKES A LONG-TIME MAN FEEL BAD

I got a rainbow tied all round my shoulder,
Ain't gonna rain, ain't gonna rain . . .

. . . SINGS THE SWEATING gang of convicts, as their picks slice shimmering arcs of light over their heads and then ring on the hard rock of the roadway. The leader gathers his chorus together like a fist of voices and flings them at the hot blue sky, at the faces of the guards, at the heavy, wounding green of the bottom woods. A tall yellow boy, lithe as a stalk of cane, spins his pick handle on the up-stroke till it ' shines like a diamond ', and laughs out the bass part. A stumpy man with one white eye like a dead moon in his dusty black face decorates each final cadence with a high, sweet, soprano cry. Three other old-timers fill in with rasping, syncopated unison. And just at the leader's elbow a shy young fellow sings second lead, following every phrase with a wild HANH! of exhaled breath as the picks fall on the off-beats. Thus a half-dozen or a dozen Negroes singing and working together sound like a regiment of humanity on the march; and, sounding so to themselves, the men take heart, the muscles relax and roll supplely under the sweat-cooled skin, and the heartbreaking job gets done in pride and beauty, and with a rush of communal joy. The present song is an old swampers' chant composed by the Negro axe-men who cleared the right-of-way for the Gulf and Shelf Island Railroad, which was built in the 1880's to run from Gulfport up into the soft-pine forests of Central Mississippi.

292. I GOT TO ROLL

'IT DON'T MATTER so much about a man's voice, when he's leading a song,' said the convict singers in the Mississippi pen. 'He can just practically speak the words off, if he know the song and the *time*, and if he be a real good worker and know *how the job got to be done* . . .' Thus the pace of the work and the spacing of the work blows, which the songs control, are for the workers the qualities most required in a good song leader. Matching his tempo to their muscular tone and his songs to their collective mood, giving voice to his own fantasies and to theirs and improvising comments on the happenings of the day—a good work-song leader can keep a gang of men working happily for long, hot hours. In Haiti I have seen such master singers, weaving extravagances of lewdness, keep forty or fifty men roaring with laughter while they worked at high speed in dizzying heat. During slavery white plantation owners assigned men to do nothing but sing, as did the bosses of big construction jobs in the post-bellum South. These folk poets voiced the protest of their fellow workers in satiric lines.

293. CAN'T YOU LINE IT?
294. BLACK GAL

Big bell call you, little bell warn you,
If you don't come now, I'm gonna break in on you,
Aincha gwine, aincha gwine, boys, aincha gwine . . .

. . . SANG THE SHACK-ROUSTER, who rapped on the boxcar doors and woke the men of a Southern railroad construction crew. From that early morning call to the gambling songs that accompanied the late-night coon-can games, there was a tune for every part of the rail-road worker's day and every job he did. The mule-skinners hollered the lonesome blues at their mules as they piled up the right of way. The tie-toters chanted as they trotted along with the ties on their shoulders. When the steel rails were dumped off the flat cars there was a steel caller to co-ordinate the efforts of the gang who muscled the two-ton rails . . .

All right now, boys, don't get hurt,
I want you to go home lookin' all right . . .

The gang who picked up the rails with their iron dogs and swung them into the buckles and screwed in the bolts had another persuasive, professional voice who kept them moving in rhythm, one minute to a rail, twenty rails in twenty minutes. The gravel poured round the ties from the gravel car, and along came the tamping gang to pack it in tight, tapping in syncopated rhythm, as their leader sang *Black Gal* or crooned . . .

Every Monday morning, baby, when I rise,
Got a pick and a shovel, baby, hangin' by my side . . .

Last of all, the track-lining bunch came dragging their crowbars down the new rail-road track. Yards behind, the foreman sighted along the rail, spotted the crooked place and yelled, ' Run on down to the fourth johnnyhead (joint ahead) and shove it east!'

The gang moved to the indicated spot, jammed their lining bars in under the rail and waited while their song leader chanted a verse. Then, during the chorus, they swung against their bars and inched the whole section of track into line. The leader improvised fresh verses, the bawdier the better, and the gang sang and shifted the track, until a cry from the foreman directed them on down the line.

All day long to the sound of songs so wild and sweet that the mocking birds in the nearby bushes stopped to listen, the new railroad moved into the Southern wilderness.

295. DON'T LIE, BUDDY

THE RAILROAD gang lives in boxcar houses on the siding. Sitting on the front steps in the evening, batting away the mosquitoes and gallinippers, they swap lies, joree (kid) one another to pass away an hour before bedtime . . .

' What de darkest night you ever see?'

' De darkest night ah ever see, a raindrop knock on my doorstep an' ast fer a light to see how to hit de groun'.'

' What is de tallest man you ever see?'

' De tallest Ah ever seen was gittin' a haircut in Heaven, an' a shoe-shine in Hell.'

' What is de runningest car you ever see?'

' De runningest car Ah ever see was my uncle's ole car—it run over Monday, kill Tuesday, sen' Wednesday to de hospital, cripple Thursday, an' tol' Friday to tell Saddy to be at de fun'al Sunday at 4 o'clock p.m.'

' What de strongest mule you ever saw?'

' Well, Ah saw a ol' mule so strong you hitched him to midnight an' he break daylight.'

' What's the slowest thing you ever saw?'

' A snail was crossin' de road for seben years. Just as he got across, a tree fell and barely missed him ' bout a inch or two. If he had a been where he was six months before, it would er kilt him. De snail looked back at de tree and tole de people, '' See, it pays to be fast ''.'

QUOTE: *Humorous Tales of the South Carolina Negro*, ed. J. Mason Brewer, S.C. Negro Folklore Guild, No. 1 (Orangeburg, S.C., 1945), pp. 27-30.

296. LET THE DEAL GO DOWN

SHOOTING CRAPS, dealing Georgia Skin or coon-can, the Negroes croon to their cards and dice, especially when luck is running against them and they feel miserable. In northern Florida before the game begins, they read through the deck, addressing each card as an actor in the drama to come . . .

Ace means the first time that Ah met you,
Deuce means there was nobody there but us two,
Trey means the third party, Charlie was his name,
Four spot means the fourth time you tried dat same old game,
Five spot is five years you played me for a clown,
Six spot, six feet of earth when de deal goes down.

Now, ahm holdin' de seben spot for each day in de week.
Eight spot, eight hours you sheba'ed wid yo' sheik.
Nine spot means nine hours Ah work hard every day,
Ten spot means de tenth of every month I brought you home mah pay,
De Jack is Three Card Charlie who played me for a goat,
De Queen, dat's you, pretty mama, also tryin' tuh cut mah throat,
De King, dat's hot papa Nunkie and he's gointer wear de crown,
Se be keerful y'all ain't broke when de deal goes down.

Then the dealer starts singing for the deal, slapping a card down hard at the end of every line.

QUOTE: Hurston.

297. EAST COLORADO BLUES

THE RAILS ran on west and the gangs of workers followed them, carrying their old songs and legends. The nine-pound mauls slammed down on the heads of a million steel spikes—the pick-axes rose and fell a thousand million strokes—to the rhythm of the hammer song that was already old when John Henry fell dead at the Big Bend Tunnel. Every time a ganger swung his hammer, he invoked the help of that legendary giant of the rails . . .

This is the hammer—HUNH! . . . (The hammer comes down.)
Killed John Henry—HUNH! . . . (Another blow.)
Can't kill Me—HUNH! . . . (Another stroke.)
Can't kill me—HUNH! . . . (The hammer rings on steel again).

' John Henry was a good man in his time,' the singer says, ' but his time is gone. Watch me. I've got a head like a rock and a heart like a marble stone.'

My hammer falls from my shoulder—HUNH!
Steel runs like lead—HUNH! . . .

Out of this work song some music-' physicians ', some rambling hobo guitar picker made this plaintive blues, asking his guitar strings to speak to him between every phrase . . .

275. JOHNNY, WON'T YOU RAMBLE?

FROM: p. 460 of *Our Singing Country*, Lomax (Macmillan, N.Y., 1941). Arranged by Alan Lomax from singing of Lightning, Darrington State Farm, Texas, 1934. Once published.

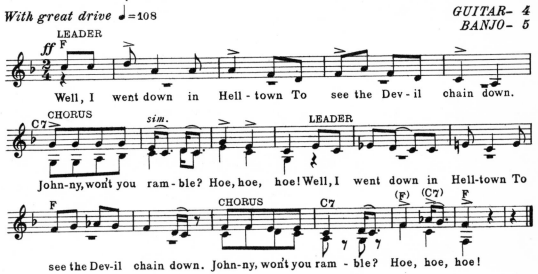

With great drive ♩=108

GUITAR– 4
BANJO– 5

Well, I went down in Hell-town To see the Dev-il chain down. John-ny, won't you ram-ble? Hoe, hoe, hoe! Well, I went down in Hell-town To see the Dev-il chain down. John-ny, won't you ram-ble? Hoe, hoe, hoe!

1. Well, I went down in Helltown
   To see the Devil chain down.
   Johnny, won't you ramble?
   Hoe, hoe, hoe!
   Well, I went down in Helltown
   To see the Devil chain down.
   Johnny, won't you ramble?
   Hoe, hoe, hoe!

2. Ol' massa an' ol' missis,
   Sittin' in the parlour.
   Jus' fig'in' an' a-plannin'
   How to work a nigger harder.

3. Ol' massa kill a fattenin' calf,
   You oughta heard those bullies laugh,
   Ol' massa kill a Jersey bull
   To give those bullies a bellyfull.

4. I looked on the hill
   And I spied ol' massa ridin',
   Had a bullwhip in-a one hand,
   A cow-hide in the other.

5. ' Ol' massa, ol' massa,
   I'll give you half a dollar.'
   ' No, no, bully boy,
   I'd rather hear you holler.'

276. JOHN GILBERT IS DE BOAT

FROM: *Roustabout Songs of the Ohio River*, Mary Wheeler. Copyright 1939 by Remick Music Corp. Used by permission.

Quietly jazzy ♩= 116

GUITAR– 6A
BANJO– 4B

John Gil-bert is de boat, Dy-de-o,— dy-de-o,— John—

527

Gil-bert is de boat, Dy - de - o,___ Run-nin' in de Cin-cin-na-ti trade.___

VERSE

You see dat boat a-com-in', She's com-in' roun' de ben',

to Chorus without pause

An' when she gits in, She'll be load-ed down a-gain.

CHORUS:
John Gilbert is de boat,
Dy-de-o, dy-de-o,
John Gilbert is de boat,
Dy-de-o,
Runnin' in de Cincinnati trade.

1 You see dat boat a-comin',
   She's comin' roun' de ben',
   An' when she gits in,
   She'll be loaded down again.   (CHO.)

2 She hauled peanuts an' cotton
   An' she hauled so min' (many)
   When she got to Johnsonville
   Her wuk would jus' begin.   (CHO.)

3 She hauled so many peanuts
   Her men would run out on 'o (her),
   Dey done run out in de wilderness
   An' neber come back no mo'.   (CHO.)

4 Lee P. Kahn wuz de head clerk,
   Cap'n Duncan wuz de cap'n,
   Billy Evitt wuz de head mate,
   Runnin' in de Cincinnati trade.   (CHO.)

5 See that boat a-comin',
   She comin' roun' de ben',
   Loaded to the bottom, Lawd,
   Wid Lou'siana men.   (CHO.)

6 Hear her bells a-ringin',
   Hear her old whistle blow,
   She's loaded down with peanuts, man,
   An' she's comin' back for mo'.   (CHO.)

277. ROCK ABOUT, MY SARO JANE

FROM: p. 133 of *Folk Song : U.S.A.*, Lomax (Duell, Sloan and Pearce, 1947).
Arranged from singing of Uncle Dave Macon.

Rowdy ♩=104

GUITAR– 4
BANJO– 3

I've got a wife an'-a five l'il' chil-lun, Be-lieve I'll take a trip on the

big Mac-Mil-lan, O Sa-ro Jane! O there's noth-ing to do but to sit down an' sing An' rock a-bout, my Sa-ro Jane. O rock a-bout, my Sa-ro Jane, Rock a-bout, my Sa-ro Jane.

1 I've got a wife an'-a five li'l' chillun,
   Believe I'll take a trip on the big MacMillan,
   O Saro Jane!
   CHORUS:
   O there's nothing to do but to sit down an' sing
   An' rock about, my Saro Jane.
   O rock about, my Saro Jane,
   Rock about, my Saro Jane,
   O there's nothing to do but to sit down an' sing
   An' rock about, my Saro Jane.

2 B'iler busted an' the whistle done blowed,
   The head cap'n done fell overboa'd,
   O Saro Jane!   (CHO.)

3 Engine give a crack an' the whistle give a squall,
   The engineer gone to the Hole-in-the-wall,
   O Saro Jane!   (CHO.)

4 Yankee build boats for to shoot them rebels,
   My musket's loaded an' I'm gonna hold her level,
   O Saro Jane!   (CHO.)

278. RILEY

Recorded and arranged by Alan Lomax from the singing of John Davis, Frederica, Georgia, 1935. For an earlier version of this song SEE: *Parish*. Possibly related to *Stormalong*.

With a shout ♩=72

GUITAR-
BANJO-} FREE STRUM

Ri-ley, Ri-ley, where are you? Wo, Ri-ley! Wo, ma-an! Ri-ley, Ri-ley, where are you? Bye-bye, my Ri-ley, wo!

1 Riley, Riley, where are you?
   Wo, Riley! Wo, ma-an!
   Riley, Riley, where are you?
   Bye-bye, my Riley, wo!

2 Riley's gone to Liverpool!
   Wo, Riley! Wo, ma-an!
   Riley's gone an' I'm goin' too!
   Bye-bye, my Riley, wo!

3 Wish I were Cap'n Riley's son,
Wo, Riley!   Wo, ma-an!
I'd lay around and drink good rum,
Bye-bye, my Riley, wo!

4 Thought I heard my cap'n say,
Wo, Riley!   Wo, ma-an!
Tomorrow is our sailin' day,
Bye-bye, my Riley, wo!

279. PAY ME

Recorded and arranged by Alan Lomax from the singing of Negro roustabouts,
Savannah, Georgia, 1944. SEE: Lydia Parrish, *Slave Songs of the Georgia Sea Islands*
(Creative Press, N.Y.).

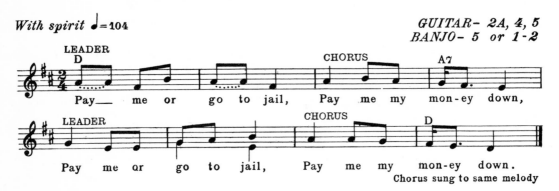

With spirit ♩=104

GUITAR- 2A, 4, 5
BANJO- 5 or 1-2

1 Pay me or go to jail,
Pay me my money down,
Pay me or go to jail,
Pay me my money down.
CHORUS:
Pay me, O pay me,
Pay me my money down,
Pay me, O pay me,
Pay me my money down.

2 Pay me, mister stevedore,
Pay me my money down,
Pay me, mister stevedore,
Pay me my money down.   (CHO.)

3 *This is not the end of the song;
the remaining stanzas will
be left to the reader's devising.*

280. THE JOHN B.'s SAILS

Recorded and arranged by Alan Lomax from the singing of Bahaman Negroes,
Nassau, 1935. SEE: Sandburg, 22.

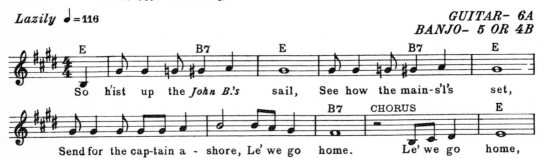

Lazily ♩=116

GUITAR- 6A
BANJO- 5 OR 4B

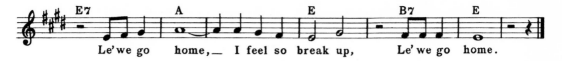

Le' we go home,— I feel so break up, Le' we go home.

1 So h'ist up the *John B.'s* sail,
See how the mains'l's set,
Send for the captain ashore,
Le' we go home . . .
CHORUS:
Le' we go home,
Le' we go home,
I feel so break up,
Le' we go home.

2 The cap'n an' the mate got drunk,
They broke up the people's trunk,
Send for the captain ashore,
Le' we go home . . . (CHO.)

3 The cook took runnin' fits
An' broke up all my grips,
Send for the captain ashore
Le' we go home . . . (CHO.)

281. COTTON NEEDS PICKIN'

Adapted from a Florida song brought to Hampton Institute in Virgina and transcribed by Natalie Curtis-Burlin, *Negro Folk Songs*, Book 3, page 10 ff. Copyright, G. Schirmer, 1918. The intermediate source was the singer-teacher Charity Bailey.

Gaily ♩=160

GUITAR- 2A, 4
BANJO- 5

Cot-ton needs pick-in' so bad, Cot-ton needs pick-in' so bad,—
Cot-ton needs pick-in' so bad, I'm gon-na pick all o-ver this world.
Verses sung to same melody

CHORUS:
Cotton needs pickin' so bad, (3)
I'm gonna pick all over this world.

1 One twentieth of May morning,
Under that barnyard tree,
Them Yankees read them papers
An' sot them darkies free. (CHO.)

2 I been workin' in a contract
Ever since that day
And just found out this year
Why it didn't pay. (CHO.)

3 When boss sold that cotton
I asked for my half,
He told me I done chopped out
My half with the grass. (CHO.)

4 Boss said, ' Uncle Billy,
I think you done right well
To pay your debts with cotton
And have your seeds to sell.' (CHO.)

5 I sold them seeds this mornin'
For five cents a peck
And bought this here red handkerchief
You see around my neck. (CHO.)

6 Boy, stop goosin'* that cotton,
You better take care,
Make haste, you lazy rascal,
And bring that row from here—Oh! (CHO.)

* carelessly picking

531

282. WHOA BACK, BUCK

FROM: p. 85 of *Negro Folk Songs as Sung by Lead Belly*, Lomax. Copyright Macmillan, N.Y., 1936. © Folkways Music Inc., 1959. This is Lead Belly's variant of a Negro ploughman's song, which occasionally satirizes the poor whites; known from Texas to Miss. SEE: Lomax IV, 284, V, 232.

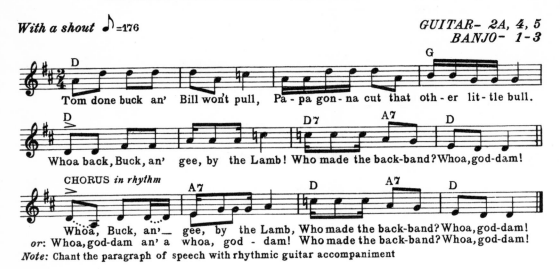

Note: Chant the paragraph of speech with rhythmic guitar accompaniment

This man was drivin' twenty yokes of oxen. He was a long ways from home an' it was a slow, drizzlin' rain and the man was cold. He was tryin' to git his oxens to hurry up a little faster, so ev'y once in a while he'd cut down on um—TI-YOW! he'd pop that long blacksnake whip. But you know about how much speed oxen has got. 'Stead of them gettin' faster, they was speedin' up slower . . .

1 Tom done buck and Bill won't pull,
   Papa gonna cut that other little bull.
   Whoa back, Buck, an' gee, by the Lamb!
   Who made the back-band? Whoa, goddam!
   CHORUS:
   Whoa, Buck, an' gee, by the Lamb!
   Who made the back-band? Whoa, goddam!
           (or)
   Whoa, goddam, an'-a whoa, goddam!
   Who made the back-band? Whoa, goddam!

2 Eighteen, nineteen, twenty years ago,
   I taken Sal to the party-o,
   I taken Sal to the party-o,
   Wouldn' let her dance but a set or so.   (CHO.)

3 Me an' my gal come walkin' down the road,
   Wind from her feet knockin' *Sugar in the Gourd.*
   Sugar in the gourd and the gourd on the ground,
   Want to get the sugar gotta roll the gourd around.   (CHO.)

4 Chicken in the bread-tray, mighty good stuff,
   Mama cook him chicken an' he never get enough,
   Jawbone eat an'-a jawbone talk,
   Jawbone eat with a knife an' fawk.   (CHO.)

283. BRING ME LI'L' WATER, SYLVIE

FROM: p. 89 of *Negro Folk Songs as Sung by Lead Belly*, Lomax. Copyright Macmillan, N.Y., 1936. © Folkways Music Inc., 1959.

This man was in the field ploughin' in the two hottest months of the year, which is July and August. He called his wife, Sylvie, the first time and she didn't hear him, so he called her again, a little louder.

> Bring me li'l' water, Sylvie,
> Bring me li'l' water now,
> Bring me li'l' water, Sylvie,
> Ev'ry li'l' once in a while.

That second time Sylvie heard him. She grab her bucket and fill it with cool water from the well, and she went runnin'. Down through the field, the little bucket knockin' against her legs and a little water spillin' out on the cotton dress she wore. She holler back at him to let him know she comin' . . .

> Don't you see me comin'?
> Don't you see me now?
> Don't you see me comin'?
> Ev'ry li'l' once in a while?

It was hot down there and when that man look up and saw li'l' Sylvie comin' trottin' along, he begin to feel good. He commenced to blowin' his horn . . .

> Bring me li'l' water, Sylvie,
> Bring me li'l' water now,
> Bring me li'l' water, Sylvie,
> Ev'ry li'l' once in a while.

533

Sylvie was just skippin' 'long now, and when she got up near her husban' she hollered again to show him how glad she was to see him . . .

> Don't you hear me comin'?
> Don't you hear me now?
> Don't you hear me comin'?
> Ev'ry li'l' once in a while?

Well, the man he retch for that bucket and he dip in the dipper an' have him a big, long draught of that cool well-water, look like it do him good right down to his toes. Sylvie just laugh to see him satisfied. Then he tol' her, ' Now, look here, darlin', you better open up your ears a little wider so you can hear me when I holler. I'm burnin' down here in this bottom, and when I wants my water I wants you to come in a hurry. So you listen next time when I holler.'

> Bring me li'l' water, Sylvie,
> Bring me li'l' water, now,
> Bring me li'l' water, Sylvie,
> Ev'ry li'l' once in a while.
>
> Lawd, Lawd, Sylvie,
> Lawd, Lawd, now!
> Lawd, Lawd, Sylvie,
> Ev'ry li'l' once in a while.

284. PO' FARMER

FROM: p. 280 of *Our Singing Country*, Lomax (Macmillan, N.Y., 1941). For similar songs, see Brown III, 244.

Slow and driving ♩=112

GUITAR– 4, 7A–B
BANJO– 5

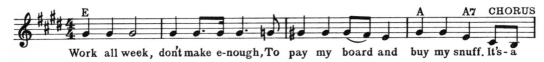

1 Work all week, don't make enough,
To pay my board and buy my snuff.
CHORUS:
It's-a hard, it's-a hard,
It's-a hard on we po' farmers, it's-a hard.

2 Every mornin' when I get up,
It's hitch my horse and it's all day cut. (CHO.)

3 It's every night when I get home,
Peas in the pot and an old jaw-bone. (CHO.)

4 Work all week in the noonday sun,
Fifteen cents when Sat'dy come. (CHO.)

285. THE BOLL WEEVIL HOLLER

Recorded and adapted by J. and A. Lomax and R. P. Tartt from the singing of
Vera Hall and Rich Amerson, Livingstone, Ala. SEE: Brown III, 245; Laws, 241;
Lomax II, 112, V, 225; Scarborough, 77; White, 351. This is the Alabama
bluesy version of the ballad found in Texas and Miss.
Piano arrangement by DON BANKS

1 First time I seen the boll weevil
He's settin' on the square,*
Next time I seen him
He had his family there, (3)
Next time I seen him
He had his family there.

2 'Tell me, boll weevil,
Where is your native home ?'
'Way down in the bottom†
Among the cot'n an' corn.' *etc.*

3 'Tell me, boll weevil,
How'd you get yo' great long bill ?'
'Way out in Te———xis,
Among the western hills.' *etc.*

4 Boll weevil here,
Boll weevil everywhere,
They done ate up all the cotton and the corn,
All but the new-ground square. *etc.*

5 Well, the farmer asked the merchant,
For some meat and meal.
'Tain't nothin' doin', old man,
Boll weevil's in your field.' *etc.*

6 'Tell me, boll weevil,
What make yo' head so red ?'
'Been workin' on yo' cotton
Till I'm almost dead.' *etc.*

* the square-shaped cotton bud   † river-bottom land

286. GO DOWN, OLD HANNAH

FROM: p. 356 of *Our Singing Country*, Lomax (Macmillan, N.Y., 1941). Recorded and arranged by John and Alan Lomax from the singing of Ernest Williams, Sugarland, Texas, 1933. SEE: Lomax III, 118, L.C. 38B. This is certainly a Texas prison (slave?) song, found in no other state.
Piano arrangement by DON BANKS

Note: This melody must be freely adapted to the remaining stanzas.

1 Go down, old Hannah, well, well, well!
Doncha rise no mo',
If you rise in the mornin',
Bring Judgement Day.

2 You ought come on this Brazos,* well, well, well!
Nineteen and four,
You could find a dead man
On every turn row.†

3 You ought come on this Brazos, well, well, well!
Nineteen and ten,‡
They was drivin' the women
Like they do the men.

4 Moon in the mornin', well, well, well!
'Fore the sun does rise,
Well, I thought about my woman,
Hang my head an' cry.

5 Well, the sun was shinin', well, well, well!
An' the men was flyin',
Ol' Captain was hollerin',
We was almost dyin'.

6 Well, I looked at old Hannah, well, well, well!
She was turnin' red,
And I looked at my partner,
He was almost dead.

7 One of these mornin's, well, well, well!
An' it won't be long,
That man's gonna call me,
An' I'll be gone.

8 So go down, old Hannah, well, well, well!
Doncha rise no mo',
If you rise in the mornin',
Set the world on fire.

* Brazos River, location of state prison farms.
† Where teams with ploughs can be turned at the end of the field.
‡ The days of the convict lease system.

287. LONG JOHN

FROM: p. 75 of *American Ballads and Folk Songs*, Lomax (Macmillan, N.Y., 1934).
Adapted and arranged by John and Alan Lomax. SEE: Odum I, 227: Scarborough,
268. This Negro axeman's song is related to *Lost John*, copyrighted by Handy, 1912.

Racing ♩ = 208
♩ upstems sung by leader
♩ downstems sung by group

GUITAR – 7A
BANJO – 5

Says-uh 'Come on, gal,(Says-uh, Come on, gal,) An'-uh, shut that do','(An'-uh

shut that do',) Says,'The dogs is com-in',(Says, The dogs is com-in',) An'
I've got to go, (An' I've got to go.) Well-a two, three min-utes,
(Two three min-utes,)Let me catch my win', (Let me catch my win',) In-a
two, three min-utes, (In-a two, three min-utes,)I'm gone a-gin, (I'm
gone a-gin.)'It's-a Long John (It's a Long John.)He's long gone. (Long gone.)Like a
tur-key through the corn, (Like a tur-key through the corn,) With his
long clothes on, (With his long clothes on,) He's gone, gone,(He's gone, gone.)

1 Says-uh, ' Come on, gal,
An'-uh shut that do','
Says, ' The dogs is comin'
And I've got to go.
Well-a two, three minutes,
Let me catch my win',
In-a two, three minutes,
I'm gone agin.'

CHORUS:
It's-a Long John,
He's long gone.
Like a turkey through the corn
With his long clothes on,
He's gone, gone.

2 Well, my John said,
  On the fourth day,
  Well, to ' Tell my rider
  That I'm on my way.
  Gonna call next summer
  Ain't gon' call no mo',
  If I call next summer,
  Be in Baltimore.'   (CHO.)

3 Well, John made
  A pair of shoes.
  Funniest shoes
  That ever was seen.
  Had a heel in front
  And a heel behind,
  Till you couldn't tell where
  That boy was gwine.   (CHO.)

4 Well, my John said
  In the ten chap ten,
  ' If a man die,
  He will live again.'
  Well, they crucified Jesus
  And they nailed Him to the Cross.
  Sister Mary cried,
  ' My child is lost.'   (CHO.)

288. ANOTHER MAN DONE GONE

FROM: p. 326 of *Folk Song : U.S.A.*, Lomax (Duell, Sloan and Pearce, 1947).
Adapted and arranged from the singing of Vera Hall and Rich Amerson, Livingstone, Ala., by J. Lomax, A. Lomax and R. P. Tartt.

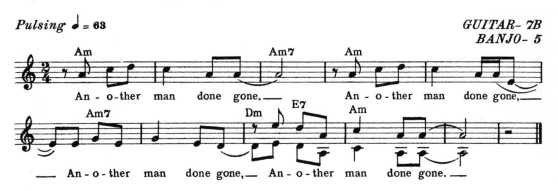

Pulsing ♩ = 63   GUITAR- 7B
                                                            BANJO- 5

1 Another man done gone.   (4)   4 He killed another man.   (4)

2 I didn't know his name.   (4)   5 I don't know where he's gone.   (4)

3 He had a long chain on.   (4)   6 Another man done gone.   (4)

289. JUMPIN' JUDY

FROM: p. 82 of *American Ballads and Folk Songs*, Lomax (Macmillan, N.Y., 1934).
Arranged by John and Alan Lomax from the singing of Allan Prothero, Nashville
Penitentiary, 1933. This is a unique version of a Negro work song found in
Tenn., Miss., and Ark. penitentiaries. SEE: Lomax IV, 392; L.C. 14B1.
Piano arrangement by DON BANKS

1 Jumpin' Judy, jumpin' Judy,   (3)
   Was a mighty fine gal.   (2)

2 Little Judy brought jumpin'   (3)
   To this whole roun' worl'.   (2)

3 Yonder come little Rosie,　(3)
　　How'n the worl' do you know ?　(2)

4 She wore a Mother Hubbard,　(3)
　　Like a mournin' gown.　(2)

5 The lace on her apron,　(3)
　　How it do hang down.　(2)

6 Heard her tell the sergeant,　(3)
　　' Come after my man.'　(2)

7 ' He's been here rollin'　(3)
　　For the States so long.　(2)

8 ' I know he's sorry　(3)
　　That he ever done wrong.'　(2)

9 Well, you kick an' stomp an' beat me,　(3)
　　An' you call that fun.　(2)

10 If I catch you in my home town,　(3)
　　Gonna make you run.　(2)

290. THE LONGEST TRAIN

Adapted and arranged by Alan Lomax. SEE: Brown III, 332, 347, 355; Gordon,
83; Sharp II, 278. Song has many forms and is principally sung from Alabama,
east.
　　　　　　　　　　Piano arrangement by DON BANKS

Mournfully, with a beat ♩ = 104

GUITAR- 2A, 4, 5A, 7A-B
BANJO- 5

1 The longest train I ever did see
　Ran around Joe Brown's coal mine.
　The head light passed at six o'clock,
　The cab come by at nine.

2 The prettiest girl I ever saw,
　Was on that train and gone,
　Her eyes were blue and her cheeks were brown
　And her hair it hung way down.

3 That train it wrecked at the four mile hill,
And killed my Evaline,
Her head was found in the drivin' wheel,
Po' body ain't never been seen.

4 The longest day and the longest night
Was the day Evalina died,
I walked the track the whole day long,
Hung down my head and cried.

5 The long steel rail and the short cross tie
They carried me away,
Was transportation brought me here,
But I'll make it home some day.

291. IT MAKES A LONG-TIME MAN FEEL BAD

Recorded and arranged by Alan Lomax from the singing of Negro prisoners, Parchman, Miss., 1947.
Piano arrangement by DON BANKS

long - time man ____ feel bad, ____ my Law-dy, Law-dy, ____ When he

can't - a can't - a get a let - ter, my Law-dy, from home. ____

CODA

1 It makes a long-time man feel bad, (2)
   It makes a long-time man feel bad, my Lawdy, Lawdy,
   When he can't-a can't-a get a letter, my Lawdy, from home.

2 There's a wreck out on the road somewhere, (3)
   On the Gulf, O Lawdy, Lawdy, Ship Island Road.

3 Captain George, don't you drive me all the time, (3)
   You'll drive me, drive me till I go, my Lawdy, stone blind.

4 Hattie Belle, don't you cry about a dime, (2)
   If you cry about a nickel, you'll die about a dime,
   Hattie Belle, O Belle, don't you cry, don't cry about a dime.

292. I GOT TO ROLL

FROM: p. 390 of *Our Singing Country*, Lomax (Macmillan, N.Y., 1941). Recorded and arranged by John and Alan Lomax from the singing of Black Samson, Nashville, Tenn., 1937.

Piano arrangement by DON BANKS

Slow ♩ = 88

GUITAR- 7
BANJO- 5

Note: This is never sung to a note of fixed pitch, but is a loud half shout half grunt.

1 Ham and eggs, pork and beans,
I would-a et more, but the cook wasn't clean . . .

CHORUS:
I got to roll—roll in a hurry,
Make it on the side of the road.

2 If I'd-a knowed my cap'n was blind,
   I wouldn'-a went to work, boys, till the clock struck nine.   (CHO.)

3 If I'd-a knowed my cap'n was bad,
   Wouldn'-a sold that pistol that I once did have.   (CHO.)

4 If I'd-a knowed my cap'n was mean,
   I never would-a left St. Augustine.   (CHO.)

293. CAN'T YOU LINE IT?

Recorded and arranged by Zora N. Hurston and Alan Lomax from Negroes in
northern Florida, 1935. SEE: Hurston.
Piano arrangement by DON BANKS

When I get in Il-li-nois, I'm gon-na spread the news a-bout the
nickel's worth-a ba-con and a dime's worth-a lard, I would buy more___ but the

Flor-i-da boys.}___ Shove it o - ver! Hey, hey! Can't you
time's so hard.}___

line it? A - shack-a lack-a lack-a lack-a lack-a lack-a boo! Can't you

1 When I get in Illinois,
I'm gonna spread the news about the Florida boys.
CHORUS:
Shove it over!
Hey, hey! Can't you line it?
A-shack-a lack-a lack-a lack-a lack-a lack-a boo!
Can't you move it?
Hey, hey! can't you try?

2 A nickel's wortha bacon and a dime's wortha lard,
I would buy more but the time's so hard. (CHO.)

3 Here come my woman across the field,
Her mouth exhaustin' like an automobile. (CHO.)

4 I heard a big noise round the river bend,
Must be the Southern* crossin' the L and N.* (CHO.)

5 Jack the Rabbit, Jack the Bear,
Can't you move it just a hair? (CHO.)

* two railroads

294. BLACK GAL

FROM: p. 13 of *American Ballads and Folk Songs*, Lomax (Macmillan, N.Y., 1934).
Adapted by Alan Lomax. A composite of versions of this railroad and prison work
song from all over the South. Known from Va. to Miss. For many similar songs,
see Odum I and II.

With a shout ♩ = 184

GUITAR– 7A–B, 5A
BANJO– 5A

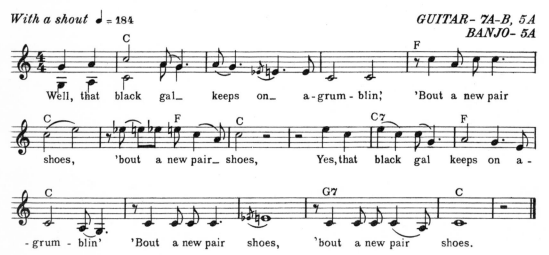

Well, that black gal keeps on a-grum-blin', 'Bout a new pair shoes, 'bout a new pair shoes, Yes, that black gal keeps on a-grum-blin' 'Bout a new pair shoes, 'bout a new pair shoes.

A sudden rainstorm has softened up the road bed and the rails are no longer level. The foreman sends his gang down the line with a jack and their tamping tools.

Foreman: J'int ahead!
Track caller: How you like that?
Foreman: That's all right.
Caller: Gittin' away!   (*The jack clicks as the rail is lifted.*)
Foreman: Set down one.   (*The jack is lowered one notch.*)
Caller: All right.   Catch it.   (*The men pack gravel in under
    the tie as the caller sets the rhythm with . . .*)

1 Well, that black gal keeps on a-grumblin'
    'Bout a new pair shoes, 'bout a new pair shoes,
    Yes, that black gal keeps on a-grumblin'
    'Bout a new pair shoes, 'bout a new pair shoes.

2 Well, I give her ten silver dollar
    Just to buy some shoes, just to buy some shoes,
    And she came back 'hoopin' and a-hollin',
    With a bottle of booze, with a bottle of booze.

Caller: Got that one caught.   What you lookin' at now?
Foreman: Centre ahead.
Caller: How you like that for centre?
Foreman: All right.
Caller: Gittin' away!   (*The jack clicks.*)
Foreman: All right!
Caller: Gone again!   (*He sings . . .*)

3 Well, that black gal keeps on a-squabblin',
    'Bout her some clothes, 'bout her some clothes.
    An' I give her fifty silver dollars
    To buy some clothes, to buy some clothes.

4 Then she came back 'hoopin' an' a-hollin',
    With a mouthful of gold, with a mouthful of gold.
    I got a bulldog weighs nine hundred,
    In my back yard, buddy, in my back yard.

Foreman: You not gettin' on that tamper, boy.
Caller: I was thinkin' about Rosie that time.
Foreman: Okay, let's have a little tampin' at
    the third j'int ahead.
Caller: How you like that?
Foreman: Git down behind it.
Caller: Gittin' away!   (*The jack clicks.*)
Foreman: Shake that a little.   Now tamp it!
(*The caller sings . . .*)

5 An' when I hear that bulldog barkin',
    Somebody round, buddy, somebody roun'.
    But when you hear my pistol shootin',
    Another man dead, buddy, another man dead.

6 When you hear my old hammer ringin',
    Steel runnin' like lead, buddy, steel runnin' like lead.
    This old hammer killed John Henry,
    Can't kill me, buddy, can't kill me.

295. DON'T LIE, BUDDY

Collected and re-composed by Josh White. The tune is common in South-East, and often carries very vulgar stanzas.

1 Mammy Logan, she had a daughter,
   And she run a cook shop, down in Florida.
   How I know ?   God knows I been there,
   An' I bought fo' po'k chops—for a quarter.

   CHORUS :
   A-don't lie, buddy, don't lie,   (3)
   Don't, buddy, don't, don't lie. (*Repeat chorus.*)

2 Jack the Rabbit-got a mighty bad habit,
   Eatin' up my corn an'-my cabbage,
   I went down-to the low ground.
   And I cured that fool of—his bad habit.   (CHO.)

3 I got a quarter, I got a half,
   I got a pretty gal-at last,
   She bring me coffee, she bring me tea,
   She don't love nobody—but me.   (CHO.)

296. LET THE DEAL GO DOWN

Recorded and arranged by Zora N. Hurston and Alan Lomax, N. Florida. See notes: *Can't You Line It?*

CHORUS: Let the deal go down, boys, (WHAP!)
(*Slap the table to indicate that a card is dealt.*)
Let the deal go down . . . (WHAP!)

1 If your cards ain't lucky, wo, partner!
  Y' oughta be in a rollin' game. (WHAP!) (CHO.)

2 I wanta win for my sweet mama, Wo, partner!
  She needs a new pair of shoes. (WHAP!) (CHO.)

3 But ol' bullin' Jack o' Diamonds, Wo, partner!
  Gonna make me lose. (WHAP!) (CHO.)

297. EAST COLORADO BLUES

Arranged from Folkways American Folk Music Album, Record No. 80. *Spike Driver's Blues*, Mississippi John Hurt. A Negro hammer song associated with John Henry ballad, possibly its root. Common among Negroes and whites in Appalachian area. SEE: Lomax IV, 380; Scarborough, 220; Sharp II, 42; White, 261.

Piano arrangement by DON BANKS

With drive ♩ = 92

GUITAR- 5C

1 It's a long ways from East Colorado,
Honey, to my home. (3)
It's a long ways from East Colorado,
Honey, to my home. (3)

2 This is the hammer that killed John Henry,
But it won't kill me, (2)
No, it won't kill me. } (2)

3 Well, John Henry he left his hammer,
Lyin' 'side the road, (3) } (2)

4 This old hammer fallin' from my shoulder,
The steel goin' down, (3) } (2)

5 When you hear my hammer ringin',
Steel runnin' like lead, (3) } (2)

6 Take this hammer, carry it to the captain,
Tell him I'm gone,
Yes, tell him I'm gone,
Lawd, tell him I'm gone. } (2)

BALLADS

298 and 299. JOHN HENRY

To write about John Henry is to tell two stories—the facts about his contest with the steam drill, so far as we know them, and the origins of the song, so far as we can summarize them. Both these accounts must be kept separate from the legend of John Henry, which has spread, together with his ballad, as far west as Shanghai and run somewhat wild in London, where a young English jazz fan informed me—' John Henry worked on the Rock Island Line that runs from New York to New Orleans. He died when somebody hit him on the head with a hammer.'

As to the facts, we owe everything to Professor L. W. Chappell who, in his book *John Henry*, came as near tracing a major folk hero to his roots as anyone ever will. Chappell established that John Henry had *not* been a rouster on the Mississippi, an Arkansas spike driver, a pile driver on the docks, or a tunnel worker in Jamaica, Alabama, or Michigan. He pinpointed the scene of the ballad at the Big Bend Tunnel on the C. & O.R.R. in the West Virginia Mountains about 1870. A mile and a quarter long, the Big Bend was the biggest tunnel job attempted by man up to that date. Chappell describes a terrifying and barbaric scene. Far in the bowels of the mountains, lamps burn dimly in the foul air. Rock falls are frequent and ventilation is primitive. In the oppressive heat the workers strip down to the merest rags. Two men work in each steel-driving team. The shaker sits on the tunnel floor, the six-foot drill between his straddled thighs, twisting it by hand a quarter turn every time the driver strikes it. The driver, standing five to six feet away from the drill, swings his 10 lb. sheep-nose hammer through a nineteen foot arc, and comes down on the head of the drill like a man-made thunderbolt. Many stanzas of the John Henry ballad allude to the Rabelaisian jokes to which this scene gives rise—jokes bawled out by these half-naked, sweating men, who are thinking of the women in the railroad camp. A roar of laughter greets the double-entendre verse.

> This old hammer—WHAM!
> Killed my buddy—WHAM!
> Can't kill me—WHAM!
> Can't kill me—WHAM!

John Henry—a six foot tall, 200 lb. black man ' of pure African blood '—could out-sing and out-drive any other man on the job. When the newly invented automatic steam drill was brought to the Big Bend, what was more natural than to stage a contest between this man and the machine? They say that John Henry swung 20 lb. hammers, one in each hand, and never missed a stroke for the thirty-five minutes of the test. He beat the machine handily, drilling two holes seven feet deep, while the steam drill only made one of nine feet.

He probably did not die from the effects of his victory, as the song says, but later on in one of the frequent cave-ins that made the Big Tunnel the grave of so many workers. The work went on but a grim note now sounded in the bawdy lines—

This old hammer—WHAM!
Killed John Henry—WHAM!
Can't kill me—WHAM!
Can't kill me—WHAM!

The point of the jest, of course, was that John Henry died not from overwork at the tunnel, but from too much love-making. Thus genuine pagan humour gave rise to a heroic legend which continued to develop as the song was diffused. Like most Negro ballads, *John Henry* is seldom sung by Negro folk singers as a connected narrative but occurs, rather, as a loose collection of stanzas, from which one may infer the story. Along with John Henry's defiance of his captain (9) and the ' little piece of steel' stanza (5), and the lines about the little woman dressed in red, the most common stanzas in my experience are the well-known floating fragment of the Scots ballad, *The Lass of Roch Royal*, ' Who gonna shoe your feetses?' etc. (*see* p. 216). In fact, these are frequently sung to the John Henry tune with no mention of John Henry. Two derivative stanzas, reporting a cynical exchange between a Negro worker and his woman (1 and 2), sometimes take the place of the old Scots stanzas.

> ' Where did you get your slippers from,
> And the dress you was wearin' so fine?' etc.

Such rowdy verses about the railroad camp followers were probably sung before the contest with the steam drill and John Henry's death. Indeed, Chappell concurs with this idea. As in the case of Casey Jones, a new story was tacked on to an existing framework, the theme coming from the old hammer song. Similarities of the tune structure, metre, and poetic style incline me strongly to believe that the two *Lass of Roch Royal* stanzas were the framework of the work ballad. No other Negro song conforms so closely to classical ballad style.

John Henry, then, with its list of his numerous female admirers, its account of steel-driving so violent it shook the mountain (a phallic image), probably began as a testament to the erotic prowess of John Henry and his fellows. The ballad was born of the marriage of the hammer song with the most beautiful of Scots songs of illicit love. Hence it derives its almost magic power.

John Henry, a descendant of Old John, the trickster slave, became the hero of the hard-working, hard-hitting, hard-boiled guys who opened up the modern South. An unknown bard gave him lines to speak which assert that men are always more important than the machines they build. Every singer knows, consciously or unconsciously, that John Henry could prove this by night as well as by day.

300. LITTLE JOHN HENRY

THE EVERGREEN MEMORY of great John Henry of the Smoky Mountains fades out in the South-West. Arkansas and Mississippi know him as a section hand, not a tunnel worker. In Texas his story dwindles by the side of western legends. So far as I am aware, his name occurs rarely in Texas folk song—in this tender little section-gang song, given us by the prisoner, Iron Head. His refrain croons over the name, John Henry, as if the hero were somebody to be pitied and protected, while his succinct and perfect verses are a collage of the disconnected thoughts that roll through a section-hand's mind, while he is tamping ties down on the Gulf and Colorado, pardner, or the Santa Fe.

301. CASEY JONES

THE FAMOUS ENGINEER was born in south-eastern Missouri on March 14, 1864 and christened John Luther Jones. In his teens the family moved across the Mississippi River to Caycee, Kentucky, whence comes the nickname he later chose to distinguish himself from the numerous other John Joneses working for the Illinois Central Railroad. Casey became an engineer at the age of twenty-six, and his skill soon won him a crack passenger run on the Cannonball Express between Memphis, Tennessee and Canton, Mississippi.

Schedules were flexible in those early days and an engineer lived by the maxim—' Get her there and make time or come to the office and get your time.' This system suited Casey, who was happiest when he could peep out of his cabin window and see the side rods of his engine moving so fast they looked solid. Then Casey would grin and blow his whistle till it sounded like a big whippoorwill singing in the Mississippi night. The country Negroes along Casey's route loved his whistle. For them, the big, handsome, laughing Irishman, who drove his monstrous black machine so recklessly past their fields, symbolized freedom and power. Thus, when Casey was killed in a spectacular wreck in the early hours of the morning on April 30, 1906, the stage was already set for the acceptance of his ballad. Sim Webb, his fireman, told Eldon Roark the story of what happened.

We were whittling that lost time away to nothing, and Mr. Casey was still in high spirits. As we left Durant, he stood up and hollered to me over the boiler head, ' Oh, Sim! The old girl's got her high-heeled slippers on tonight. We ought to pass Way on time.'

Way was just six miles north of Canton, and he had it figured out that we'd be back on time when we hit there, and we would coast on in. We hadn't received any more orders. Down the track we went, approaching Vaughan, which is twelve miles above Canton. Vaughan was at the lower end of a double S curve. The north switch was just about the middle of the first S, and as we roared down on it we saw two big red lights. They appeared to me as big as houses. I knew it was a train not in the clear. I could see the lights, but Mr. Casey couldn't because there was a deep curve to the fireman's side. I yelled to Mr. Casey, ' Look out! We're gonna hit something!'

' Jump, Sim!' he shouted, and these were his last words. I heard him kick the seat out from under him and apply the brakes. About that time I swung down as low off the engine as I could, and hit the dirt. When I came to, half an hour later, Mr. Casey was dead. Our engine had ploughed through the caboose of the freight, and two other cars—a car of shelled corn and a car of hay! . . . . When Casey's body was found in the wreckage, an iron bolt was driven through his neck, and a bale of hay rested on his chest . . .

Wallace Saunders, who worked in the Canton roundhouse, began the composition of the ballad as he wiped Casey's blood off what was left of Engine No. 382. This Negro folk poet had just returned from a visit to Kansas City where he had picked up a barrel-house ballad that ran . . .

> On a Sunday mornin' it began to rain,
> Round the bend spied a passenger train,
> On the pilot lay po' Jimmie Jones
> He's a good old porter, but he's dead an' gone,
> Kaze he's been on the Cholly so long . . .

To make a new ballad he had to do no more than put *Casey* where *Jimmie* had stood. Saunders's two or three verses, flowing through the folk imagination of the Yazoo Delta, soon burgeoned into a number of ditties so suggestive, and having so little to do with the real Casey, that the friends of his widow would start a fight if anyone even whistled the tune in the Memphis roundhouse. The implications of this song were pleasant, but hardly respectable.

Was a woman, named Alice Fly,
Said she would ride with Mr. Casey or die.
' I ain't good lookin', but I takes my time,
I'm a ramblin' woman with a ramblin' mind.'

I left Memphis to spread the news,
Memphis women don't wear no shoes,
Had it written on the back of my shirt
Nachul born easeman don't have to work . . .

The idea that Casey was a rounder* crept into the vaudeville version of the song, which became a hit tune in the years before World War I. Mrs. Casey Jones sobbed and sued in vain. Americans wanted a railroad hero with real hair on his chest; the folk singers noodled away on their guitars and muttered . . .

Casey Jones was long an' tall,
He pulled the throttle on the Cannonball,
Pulled the whistle and he gave a squawl,
Said, ' I'm gonna ride the scoundrel to Niag'ra Falls.'

The internationally known and copyright Newton and Siebert version was based on the vulgar Mississippi ditty, but transferred Casey's activity to the western railroads. In turn it has produced its own oral variants, including this one from Southern Illinois.

QUOTE: *Casey Jones, Fireman*, Eldon Roark (*Railroad Magazine*, Vol. 19, March 1936, No. 4).
* Roué.

302. REUBEN

Reuben OR *The Reuben Blues* is a harmonica blower's tune and a favourite piece among country banjo-pickers and fiddlers in the South, especially in Virginia and the Carolinas. Occasionally one meets a singer who knows a few verses of the song, but I have never heard it sung in ballad form. This version is a mixed bag of stanzas—some gathered from Virginia-born Willie Johnson of the Golden Gate Quartet, and others picked up through the years along the song-hunting trail.

The truth about Reuben may lie buried in the memory of an old-timer along the East Coast, but so far no one has found the man who knows or will tell the whole story. However, perhaps one may reconstruct it from the vagrant stanzas here collected. Negroes are not permitted to drive engines on Southern railroads; they can rise no higher than the post of fireman in the trade. After the Civil War, however, when the South was policed by Northern troops and governed by ex-slaves, there were Negro engineers on Southern railroads, among them Reuben . . .

Perhaps Reuben drank too much; perhaps he bragged too much as well. At any rate, when the Federal troops marched north and the whites fought their way back into power, Negroes lost their good jobs. It would have been typical of that violent period if Reuben had been lynched or run out of town or simply skedaddled for Mexico. One way or another, he disappeared, but the sound of his whistle still echoed in the hearts of the patient black workers of the South.

303. PO' LAZARUS

I'm goin' out west, way out west among the robbers,
Be a robber, too, wo—Lawdy, be a robber, too . . .

SO BEGINS one version of *Po' Lazarus*.   The West referred to was the Delta land opened up for cultivation when the great levees were built along the Mississippi late in the nineteenth century. Negroes from Georgia, Alabama, and Eastern Mississippi poured into the new land. The swampers, roustabouts, mule-skinners, gandy-dancers (railroad workers), peons, and convicts, who pioneered this country, lived a life in gun-ruled camps that made the ructions of Dodge City and Deadwood look like Sunday School picnics. Most men carried pistols. The gangs were ruled by the bullies of the camps and gun-toting white bosses. When a man was ' blowed down ' his body was buried in the rising levee, and the work and the songs rolled on. This territory and this epoch gave rise to innumerable work songs, to ballads like *Stagolee*, *Brady*, and *Po' Lazarus*, and to the blues.

The ballad of *Po' Lazarus* is always sung as a work song, by a gang of men swinging picks, axes, or hammers and joining their leader after he gives the first phrase. As with most Negro ballads, every performance produces a fresh version, the stanzas occurring in the same order only by chance. This is ballad in its primal stage, communally recreated with each performance, the song being merely one member of an extended family of work songs including *This Old Hammer*, *Ham and Eggs*, *East Colorado Blues*, etc. I have never been able to find out anything definite about the origin of the ballad or the identity of its hero ; Negroes in the Deep South do not gossip freely with white men about such matters ; but its setting is clearly described in the following conversation between two Delta levee camp workers . . .

Natchez: You could kill anybody down there so long as he was a Negro, and you could work better than him.
Leroy: But don't kill a good worker.
Natchez: I've heard boss man come around and say, ' If you boys keep outa the graveyard, I'll keep you outa jail.' And that's just what they'll do. If one of his good teamsters kill up somebody an' they put him in jail, the old man will just go down there and talk to the sheriff and bring him home again.

Next day, he'll be out there on the job.

Leroy: That was what we called a bad Negro—a man that would kill his own people.

Natchez: But if he'd fight a white man, they'd say he gone crazy like that feller they sing the old song about
           —Po' Lazarus. He walked the table one day but he didn't stop.

Leroy: No, he took that old .45 and stuck it in the pay car window—

Natchez: Collected all *his* back pay and *ours*, too.

Leroy: That's the kind they call bad *and* crazy.

QUOTE: *Blues in the Mississippi Night*, ed. Alan Lomax, on Nixa and United Artists labels.

304. RAILROAD BILL

RAILROAD BILL was the folk hero of the turpentine workers in the Red Hills of Alabama. These ' woods-riders ' bleed the trees on great slash-pine plantations, collect the resin, and manufacture turpentine in crude stills. Living in camps far out in the piney woods, turpentiners were often held to their poorly paid jobs by a system of peonage.

Morris Slater decided to buck the racket and came to town with his rifle. A deputy sheriff made the mistake of asking him to hand it over, whereupon Slater put a bullet hole in the officer's head. Then he took to the woods. For years he lived by breaking open boxcars on lonely sidings, stealing canned goods, axes, shotgun shells and selling them to his Negro neighbours at low prices. Some folks were afraid to talk; the rest admired and protected their local hero. They named him Railroad Bill and began to rhyme a ballad . . .

> Talk about your five and ten dollar bill,
> You ain't never seed a bill like Railroad Bill . . .

Sheriff Culpepper came after him, but Railroad Bill beat him to the draw. Then Sheriff Macmillan, who had been Slater's friend, swore he would get the outlaw. One morning Macmillan found a crude note on his desk . . . ' I love you and do not want to kill you so do not come after me. Bill.'

Sheriff Macmillan was a brave man. He cornered Slater in a lonely cabin but the outlaw out-gunned and shot him dead. A reward was offered for Railroad Bill, dead or alive. Again and again he outwitted his pursuers, until at last one day in 1896 a phoney message lured him into a crossroad country store. There two hidden gunmen cut him down.

When the notorious boxcar bandit was laid out on the cooling board, folks came from as far away as Pensacola to look at him. Most Negroes breathed easier when they knew he was dead, for Bill had made trouble for the whole race; yet, after he was gone, they liked to remember how one coloured man had done as he pleased and was smart and too dangerous to be stopped. His ballad travelled out of Alabama into the mountains, becoming a guitar-picker's show piece.

305. FRANKIE

AMERICA's two most popular ballads—*Frankie* and *Barbara Allen*—share a common theme— the revenge of woman on man (*see* note on *Barbara Allen*, p. 170). Bonny Barbara, without consciously willing it, broke her lover's heart, while the less inhibited Frankie ' dropped

557

.ier man like a hunter drops a bird '. Frankie had her greatest vogue during the suffragette period. She also took direct action—she cut down the predatory male with her smoking .44. Feminine listeners revenged themselves through little Frankie on a predominantly patriarchal society which treated them as second-class citizens and disapproved of their erotic life. Men sang this song to women in a spirit of guilt, anxious to prove that they were not, like Albert, vain, promiscuous, and unappreciative. Middle-class performers had the thrill of vicarious participation in the sexually uninhibited and violent life of the demi-monde.

For the Negro folk audience, however, the song touched upon even more painful social problems. After Reconstruction and until World War II, Negro men were, by and large, surplus labour in America. Last hired and first fired, they were forced to roam from town to town and job to job. Meanwhile, Negro women could usually get some sort of work as domestics. Temporary liaisons and casual divorce by desertion became common at a certain social level. This is what the blues tell us about. Men of charm and talent could always find a hard-working woman to keep them. As a natural consequence, the ladies protected their honour with razors, pistols, and poison.

A mountain woman named Frankie Silvers chopped up her no-account husband with an axe on Toe River, North Carolina, in 1831, and became the heroine of a good ballad, though probably not the direct ancestor of this one. One expert opines that Federal troops before Vicksburg in 1863 sang the Frankie ballad. Another claims that it was known along the Mississippi in 1888. Orick Johns in *Time of our Lives* writes that the song was popularized by a coloured blues singer named Mammy Lou who entertained at Babe Connor's high-brown bawdy house in St. Louis in the '90s. Other accounts attribute other dates to the ballad, but all of these dates fall between 1850 and 1914, the majority in the mauve decade. My guess is that a number of Frankie-type ballads may have been composed by Negroes and whites in the Mississippi Valley, during this period, about a number of similar incidents. For the reasons already discussed, no other theme had such importance. George Milburn says that he has a hundred such ballads in his collection which mention neither Frankie, Albert, nor Johnny. ' Albert ', by the way, seems to be the name of the hero in the majority of older versions, ' Johnny ' having been introduced by the Leighton Brothers in the jazzy variant that became a favourite American college song.

The present ballad tells the story of a murder that took place during the 1890's in either St. Louis or Kansas City, Missouri, then the headquarters of ragtime. Here the relatively relaxed racial attitudes, typical of Missouri, brought about frequent contacts between whites and Negroes in sporting-house areas, and thus a number of Missouri Negro ragtime songs (*Bill Bailey, Ta-ra-ra-boom-de-ay, Frankie*, etc.) became known to the whole country.

Two women have turned up claiming to be the original Frankie. In 1938 a proprietress of a shoe-shine parlour in Portland sued Republic Pictures for $200,000 damages when the song was used in a film. She testified that the ballad referred to her murder of her lover Allen Britt in St. Louis in 1899. My present informant, Palmer Jones, says that this version was sung to him in Omaha in 1908, by one Frankie Baker who swore that she had killed her man in Kansas City some years previously, and then had composed this ballad.

306. STAGOLEE

THE MEN who ran the river were hard guys. Memphis was their capital city, and the murder rate in Memphis has been one of the highest in the world as long as there have been comparative statistics in this field. No one can be quite certain just who the original Stagolee was, whether black or white, whether a Memphis gambler or a hard-headed river runner. Shields McIlwaine in *Memphis Down in Dixie* tells of Stack Lee, a dashing Confederate cavalryman, son of a Mississippi river captain, a skull-cracking steamboat officer, and the father of many mulatto babies; one of his Negro sons, Jim Stack Lee, was, according to McIlwaine, the bad-eyed killer about whom the rousters sang . . .

> Stack-o-Lee's in the bend,
> Ain't doin' nothin' but killin' good men . . .

Others say that the bad man was a rouster named after the famous steamboat *Stack-o-Lee* —others that he was a tough Memphis sport, who had sold his soul to the Devil in return for a magic Stetson hat. However, the facts are less important than the legend of the Negro bully and killer, who proves the virility of the group by defying all the conventions of the society which imprisons him. To a dying man who begs for mercy, Stagolee responds, ' Die, damn it and prove it!' There was only one destination for such a hero . . .

> Stagolee went down to Hell, lookin' mighty curious,
> The Devil says, ' Here's that sport from East St. Loui-ous.'

But Stagolee felt right at home in Hell. After all, he had lived there all his life. He passed out ice-water to everybody in the place and turned the dampers down to make it more comfortable for all his ex-Memphis pals. Then he romped on to West Hell, where it was hot enough to suit him, snatched up the Devil's pitchfork and hollered . . .

> ' Listen, Tom Devil, you an' me's gonna have some fun,
> You play on your cornet, and, Black Betty, you beat the drum.'

298. JOHN HENRY - I

Adapted and arranged by Alan Lomax. SEE: Brown II, 623 (gives references); Brown III, 355 (for occasional first stanzas in mountain song); Laws, 231; Lomax II, 3; White, 189; 52 versions in the L.C. Archive. Two books on John Henry, one by G. B. Johnson and the other by Lewis Chappell (JENA, 1933). The Johnson version is valuable for its texts and tunes. Chappell, however, thoroughly studied all field sources and presented a profound and brilliant picture of how a ballad arises in a particular environment. A model study, unique in folk song literature.

Vigorous ♩ =126

GUITAR- 5B-C, 7A
BANJO- 1-2

1 Well, it's honey an' it's darlin' when I'm here,
   An' it's big nasty man when I'm gone,
   An' when you see me comin' with a twenty-dollar bill,
   It's ' Baby, where you been so long, long, long? '
   It's ' Baby, where you been so long? '

2 ' It's where did you get yo' slippers from,
   And the dress you are wearin' so fine? '
   ' I got my slippers from a railroad man, Lawd, Lawd,
   And my dress from a driver in the mine'. *etc.*

3 ' Who's gonna shoe your little feetses,
   Who's gonna glove your hand,
   Who's gonna kiss your red, ruby lips, Lawd,
   And who's gonna be your man? ' *etc.*

4 ' My mama gonna shoe my little feetses,
   My papa gonna glove my hands,
   My sister gonna kiss my red, ruby lips, Lawd,
   And John Henry gonna be my man.' *etc.*

5 John Henry was just a li'l baby,
  Settin' on his daddy's knee,
  He pint his finger at a little piece of steel, Lawd.
  ' Steel gon' be the death of me.' *etc.*

6 They took John Henry to the mountain,
  That mountain was so high,
  Mountain so tall and John Henry so small, Lawd, Lawd,
  He lied down his hammer and he cried. *etc.*

7 Captain told ol' John Henry,
  Says, ' I believe this mountain's sinkin' in ? '
  Says, ' Stand back, captain, and doncha be afraid, Lawd,
  It's nothin' but my hammer catchin' wind.' *etc.*

8 Captain told John Henry,
  ' Gonna bring my steam drill around,
  Gonna take my steam drill out on the job, Lawd, Lawd,
  Gonna beat John Henry down.' *etc.*

9 John Henry told his captain,
  Says, ' A man ain't nothin' but a man,
  And before I'd let your steam drill beat me down, Lawd,
  I'd die with this hammer in my hand.' *etc.*

10 John Henry spoke to his shaker,
  Says, ' Shaker, boy, you better pray,
  Cause if I miss with my nine-pound maul, Lawd, Lawd,
  Tomorrow'll be you' buryin' day.' *etc.*

11 John Henry hammerin' on the right-hand side,
  Steam drill drivin' on the lef',
  John Henry beat that steam drill down, Lawd, Lawd,
  But he hammered his fool self to death. *etc.*

12 The woman in the west heard of John Henry's death,
  Couldn't hardly stay in bed,
  Stood in the rain, caught the east-bound train, Lawd,
  ' Goin' where John Henry's dead.' *etc.*

13 John Henry had a little woman,
  Just as pretty as she could be,
  The only objection I'ze got to her, Lawd, Lawd,
  She want every man she see. *etc.*

14 John Henry had another woman,
  The dress she wore was blue,
  She went walkin' down the track and she never look back,
  And I wish my wife was true. *etc.*

15 They took John Henry to the tunnel,
  And they buried him in the sand.
  Every little woman come down the road, Lawd, Lawd,
  Say, ' There lays my steel-drivin' man.' *etc.*

299. JOHN HENRY—II

FROM: p. 123 of *John Henry*, G. B. Johnson (University of North Carolina Press, 1929). Used by permission.

Smoothly and strongly ♩=104

GUITAR— 2A, 4
BANJO— 1-2

John Hen-ry was a lit-tle boy, And he set on his fa - ther's

knee, Said, 'Be - fore I'd let this drive me down, Lawd, I'm goin'

die wid dis ham-mer in my hand,___ I'm goin' die wid dis ham-mer in my hand.'

1 John Henry was a little boy,
And he sat on his father's knee,
Said, ' Before I'd let this drive me down,
Lawd, I'm goin' die wid dis hammer in my hand,
I'm goin' die wid dis hammer in my hand.'

2 John Henry said to his captain,
' Captain, w'en you go to town,
Won't you bring me back a nine-pound hammer?
I'm goin' drive dis steel on down.' (2)

3 Oh, w'en I want good whisky,
Oh, w'en I want good corn,
Baby, w'en I sing dat lonesome song,
Honey, down de road I am gone,
Honey, down de road I am gone.

4 John Henry had a little woman,
And de dress she wear was red,
And she went down de road and she never look
' I'm goin' weh my man fall dead.' (2)   [back.

300. LITTLE JOHN HENRY

FROM: p. 198 of *American Ballads and Folk Songs*, Lomax (Macmillan, N.Y., 1934).
Recorded and arranged from the singing of James Baker, Sugarland, Texas, 1933.
Piano arrangement by DON BANKS

Quiet blues ♩=96

GUITAR— 7B
BANJO— 5

It was ear-ly one_ morn - in'   An' it looked like

1 It was early one mornin'
   An' it looked like rain,
   Way roun' that curve, Lord,
   I spied a gravel train.
   CHORUS:
   O my little John Henry, ⎱
   Godamighty knows.   ⎰ (2)

2 Now where'd you get your learnin'?
   Please tell it to me.
   On the Gulf and Colorado,*
   Partner, and the Santa Fe.* (CHO.)

* two western railroads

3 Now when you get a section,
  Lemme be your straw,*
  And when you get a daughter,
  Lemme be your son-in-law. (CHO.)

4 I got a woman in Dallas
  Work in the Baker Hotel.
  Some call her Maggie,
  Her name Katie Belle. (CHO.)

* strawboss, or assistant

301. CASEY JONES

1 Come all you rounders, I want you to hear
  The story of a brave engineer;
  Casey Jones was the rounder's name,
  On a big eight-wheeler of a mighty fame.
  CHORUS:
  Casey Jones, he pushed on the throttler,
  Casey Jones was a brave engineer,
  Come on, Casey, and blow the whistler,
  Blow the whistle so they all can hear.

2 Now Casey said, ' Before I die
  There's one more train that I want to try,
  And I will try ere many a day
  The Union Pacific and the Santa Fe.'

3 Caller called Casey about half past four,
  He kissed his wife at the station door,
  Climbed in his cab and was on his way,
  ' I've got my chance on the Santa Fe.'

4 Down the slope he went on the fly,
  Heard the fireman say, ' You've got a white eye.'
  Well, the switchman knew by the engine's moan
  That the man at the throttle was Casey Jones.

5 The rain was a-pounding down like lead,
  The railroad track was a river bed,
  They slowed her down to a thirty-mile gait,
  And the south-bound mail was eight hours late.

6 Fireman says, ' Casey, you're running too fast,
  You run the black board the last station you passed.'
  Casey says, ' I believe we'll make it through,
  For the steam's much better than I ever knew.'

7 Around the curve comes a passenger train,
  Her headlight was shining in his eyes through the rain,
  Casey blew the whistle a mighty blast
  But the locomotive was a-comin' fast.

8 The locomotives met in the middle of the hill,
  In a head-on tangle that's bound to kill,
  He tried to do his duty, the yard men said,
  But Casey Jones was scalded dead.

9 Headaches and heartaches and all kinds of pain
  They all ride along with the railroad train,
  Stories of brave men, noble and grand,
  Belong to the life of the railroad man.

302. REUBEN

Collected and arranged by Alan Lomax from the singing of Willie Johnson,
Newport, Va., 1939. SEE: Brown III, 264, 560; Lomax V, 254.
Piano arrangement by DON BANKS

With a slow rock ♩=112

GUITAR— *ANY ¾ STYLE*
BANJO— *5 or 1-2*

CHORUS

Cry-in', Reu - ben, Cry-in', Reu - ben, po'

boy, Tell me where have you been so long? _____ Lor-dy,

where have you been so long? long? _____

1. When old Reuben left home,
   He wasn't but nine days old.
   When he come back he was a full grown man, O Lordy,
   When he come back he was a full grown man.
   CHORUS:
   Cryin', Reuben,
   Cryin', Reuben, po' boy,
   Tell me where have you been so lo—o—ong?
   Lordy, where have you been so long?

2. Well, old Reuben had a train
   Run from Boston down to Maine,
   You could hear the whistle blow a hundred miles,
       O Lordy, etc.

3. Now you ought to been in town,
   When old Reuben's train went down,
   You could hear that whistle blow a hundred miles, etc.

4. Well, they got old Reuben down
   And they took his watch and charm.
   It was ev'rything that po' boy had, O Lordy, etc.
   CHORUS:
   Cryin', Reuben,
   Cryin' Reuben, po' boy,
   I wonder where that po' boy's go-o-one,
   Now I wonder where that po' boy's gone.

5. Now old Reuben had a wife
   She was tired of her life,
   'Cause old Reuben didn't have no home,
       O Lordy, etc.

6. Now I don't know for sho,
   B'lieve he's gone to Mexico,
   Nine hundred miles from his home, O Lordy, etc.

7 If I die a railroad man,
　Want you to bury me in the sand,
　So I can hear the special when she blow,
　　　　　　　　　　　　　　　O Lordy, *etc.*

8 I don't like no railroad man,
　He gonna kill you ef he can,
　And drink down your blood like wine,
　　　　　　　　　　　　　　　O Lordy, *etc.*

303. PO' LAZARUS

FROM : p. 308 of *Folk Song: U.S.A.*, Lomax (Macmillan, N.Y., 1947). Arranged and adapted by John and Alan Lomax from many Mississippi Valley recordings.
SEE: Laws, 238; Lomax II, 91, IV, 342.

With great drive ♩=92

GUITAR— 7A-B
BANJO— 5

High Sheriff,—— he tol' the dep-u-ty, (Hunh-unh!) he says,
'Go—— out an' bring—— me—— Laz-'us.' (Hunh unh!) High
Sher-iff,—— he tol' the dep-u-ty, (Hunh unh!) he says——
'Go out an' bring me Laz-'us, (Hunh unh!) Bring him dead or a-live,
Wo, Law-dy, bring him dead or a-live.' (Hunh unh!)

1 High Sheriff, he tol' the deputy, he says, ' Go out an' bring me Laz'us.' (2)
　Bring him dead or alive, Wo, Lawdy, bring him dead or alive.'

2 Oh the deputy 'gin to wonder, where in the worl' he could fin' him, (2)
　' Well, I don't know, Wo, Lawdy, I jes' don' know.'

3 Oh they found po' Laz'us 'way out between two mountains, (2)
　An they blowed him down, Lawd, Lawd, an' they blowed him down.

4 Ol' Laz'us tol' the deputy he had never been arrested, (2)
　By no one man, Wo, Lawdy, by no one man.

5 So they shot po' Laz'us, shot him with a great big number, (2)
　Number forty-five, Wo, Lawdy, number forty-five.

567

6 An' they taken po' Laz'us an' they laid him on the commissary counter, (2)
   An' they walked away, Wo, Lawdy, an' they walked away.

7 Laz'us tol' the deputy, ' Please gimme a cool drink o' water (2)
   Jes' befo' I die, Wo, Lawdy, jes' befo' I die.'

8 Laz'us' sister run an' tol' her mother, (2)
   ' Po' Laz'us dead, Wo, Lawdy, po' Laz'us dead.'

9 Laz'us' mother, she laid down her sewin', (2)
   She begin to cry, Wo, Lawdy, she begin to cry.

10 Laz'us' mother, she come a-screamin' and' a-cryin', (2)
   ' That's my only son, Wo, Lawdy, that's my only son.'

11 Laz'us' father, he sho' was hard-hearted, (2)
   Didn't say a word, Wo, Lawdy, didn't say a word.

12 Laz'us' sister, she couldn't go to the funeral, (2)
   Didn't have no shoes, Wo, Lawdy, didn't have no shoes.

(A pause—then the gang sings:)

13 Cap'n, did you hear about—all yo' men gonna leave you? (2)
   Nex' pay-day, Wo, Lawdy, nex' pay-day.

304. RAILROAD BILL

FROM: p. 118 of *American Ballads and Folk Songs*, Lomax (Macmillan, N.Y., 1934).
Collected and arranged by John A. and Alan Lomax. An Alabama Negro Ballad—
widespread in central South and found among mountain whites. SEE: Laws, 239;
Odum I, 198; Scarborough, 251.

Smoothly and steadily ♪=184 (*or faster*)

GUITAR- 5B-C
BANJO- 1-3

1 Railroad Bill, Railroad Bill,
   He never worked and he never will,

CHORUS:
They lookin' for that bad Railroad Bill,
or
O ride, ride, ride.

2 Railroad Bill was a mighty bad man,
  Shot the light out the brakeman's hand. (CHO.)

3 Railroad Bill cut a mighty dash,
  Shot MacMillan by a lightnin' flash. (CHO.)

4 Mrs. MacMillan she whooped and squawled,
  'That's my husband, for I heard him fall.' (CHO.)

5 I went down on No. 1,
  Railroad Bill had just begun. (CHO.)

6 I come back on No. 2,
  Railroad Bill had just got through. (CHO.)

7 An' just as I caught ol' No. 4,
  Somebody let fly with a 44. (CHO.)

8 I come back on No. 5,
  Gonna git him dead or alive. (CHO.)

9 Railroad Bill was a mighty spo't,*
  Shot all the buttons off the sheriff's coat. (CHO.)

10 Railroad Bill, goin' down the hill,
   Lightin' cigars with a five-dollar bill.
   CHORUS:
   Ride on, Railroad Bill.

11 Railroad Bill say, before he died,
   He would build a railroad for the bums to ride.
   CHORUS:
   Ride on, Railroad Bill.

* sport

305. FRANKIE

FROM: Collection of G. Legman, as recorded in Kansas City by Palmer Jones.
Tune set by Alan Lomax. SEE: Belden, 330; Brown II, 589; Laws, 232; Randolph
II, 125; Scarborough, 80.

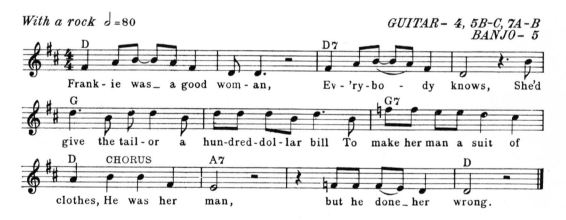

With a rock ♩=80   GUITAR- 4, 5B-C, 7A-B
                                              BANJO- 5

Frank-ie was_ a good wom-an, Ev-'ry-bo-dy knows, She'd
give the tail-or a hun-dred-dol-lar bill To make her man a suit of
clothes, He was her man, but he done_ her wrong.

1 Frankie was a good woman,
  Ev'rybody knows,
  She'd give the tailor a hundred-dollar bill
  To make her man a suit of clothes,
  He was her man, but he done her wrong.

2 Frankie was a good woman,
  Ev'rybody knows,
  Every time she gave Albert a hundred-dollar bill,
  He'd spend it on those parlour house who(r)es,
  He was her man, but he done her wrong.

3 Frankie went down to the bar-room
  And called for a glass of gin,
  She asked the man called the bartender,
  'Has my cheatin' man been in?
  He's my man, I b'lieve he's doin' me wrong.'

4 Says, 'Frankie, I'll tell you no story,
  Good gal, I'll tell you no lie,
  I saw your man pass here an hour ago,
  With a girl called Alice Fry,
  He's your man, I b'lieve he's doin' you wrong.

5 Frankie went back to the crib house,
  This time she didn't go for fun,
  Under her blue silk kimono
  She brought her Johnnie's* forty-four gun
  To kill her man, 'cause he done her wrong.

6 Frankie went down to the hop joint,
  And knocked on the hop-joint door,
  She said, ' Open up, you Chinese ——— ,
  Or you'll run this joint no more,
  I'm lookin' for my man, cause he's done me wrong.'

7 Frankie went down to the coke joint
  And she rung the coke-joint bell,
  She says, ' If I find that mistreatin' bastard in here,
  I'm going to kill him, sure as hell,
  Because he's my man, and he's been doing me wrong.'

8 She crept up an old dark alley,
  She heard her pet bulldog bark,
  Lookin' up the stairway,
  She spied Albert sneaking through the dark,
  He was her man, but he's done her wrong.

9 Now when Albert, he saw Frankie,
  The poor boy started to run;
  She says, ' You might as well stop, you ——— ,
  I'm going to shoot you (dead) with your own gun,
  Because you was my man, but you done me wrong.'

10 When Albert saw Frankie meant it,
  He started off as fast as he could,
  But she squeezed that .41 four times
  And he dropped like a stick of wood,
  'Cause he was her man, but he done her wrong.

11 ' Turn me over, Frankie,
  Turn me over slow,
  Turn me over on my left side, baby,
  Your bullet wound me so,
  I was your man, but I done you wrong.'

12 Now the cops they got Frankie
  And put her in a cell,
  The very first word I heard her say—
  ' I wonder will my man get well ?
  I love my man, though he done me wrong.'

13 The doctor was to operate on Albert
  With a great big surgeons' knife,
  Frankie offered the doctor a thousand dollars cold
  To save her Albert's life,
  'Cause he was her man and he done her wrong.

14 Frankie went to the hospital
  About three o'clock next day,
  She got there just five minutes late,
  Albert had passed away,
  He was her man and he done her wrong.

15 Frankie went to Albert's mother
  And she fell down on her knees
  And she cried, ' Mother, mother,
  Forgive me, won't you, please!
  He was your son and the only one.'

16 Mother says, ' Frankie, I forgive you,
  But forget I cannot,
  You killed my one and only son,
  The only support I got,
  He was my son and the only one.'

17 The judge, he says to Frankie,
  ' Here you stand before me,
  We've got you charged with an awful crime,
  Murder in the first degree,
  You shot your man, 'cause he done you wrong.'

18 Frankie says, ' Judge, I'm sorry,
  This thing has come to pass,
  I never shot him in the first degree,
  I shot him in his trifling ——— ,
  'Cause he done me wrong, 'cause he done me
                        wrong.'

19 The jury went out on Frankie,
  And sat under an electric fan,
  Come back and said, ' You're a free woman,
  Go kill yourself another man,
  If he does you wrong, if he does you wrong.'

20 Rubber tire the buggies,
  Rubber tire the hacks,
  Frankie even rubber tire the horses' feet
  To bring poor Albert back,
  Though he was her man and he done her wrong.

21 Frankie went out to the graveyard
  And fell down on her knees,
  And she prayed to the good Lord
  To give poor Albert ease
  Because he was her man, now he's dead and gone.

ENVOI:
22 I looked down the street, Lord,
  Far as I could see,
  All I could hear was a two-string bow
  Playing *Nearer, My God, to Thee*,
  He was her man, and he done her wrong.

* Boy-friend's—may have replaced ' Albert ' as the ballad's hero.

306. STAGOLEE

Recorded and arranged by Alan Lomax from the singing of Negro prisoners in the
Mississippi Penitentiary. SEE: Laws, 240; Lomax II, 93; Odum II, 196; Scar-
borough, 92. Folkways American Folk Music Album, No. 19.
Piano arrangement by DON BANKS

Slow pulsing blues ♩ = 84

GUITAR- 4-5
BANJO- 5

1. It was ear-ly,____ ear-ly one morn-in',____ When I heard_ my bull-dog bark,
lee____ told Bil-ly Ly-ons, ____ 'What do____ you think of that?

Stag-o-lee and Bil-ly Ly-ons Was squab-blin' in the
You win all my mon-ey, Bil-ly, Now you spit in my Stet-son

dark.
hat.'

2. Stag-o-

Note: For higher voices this is most effective played in E major

1 It was early, early one mornin',
When I heard my bulldog bark,
Stagolee and Billy Lyons
Was squabblin' in the dark.

2 Stagolee told Billy Lyons,
' What do you think of that?
You win all my money, Billy,
Now you spit in my Stetson hat.'

3 Stagolee, he went a-walkin'
In the red-hot, broilin' sun—
Says, ' Bring me my six-shooter,
Lawd, I wants my forty-one.'

4 Stagolee, he went a-walkin'
Through the mud and through the sand.
Says, ' I feel mistreated this mornin',
I could kill most any man.'

5 Billy Lyons told Stagolee,
  ' Please don't take my life,
  I've got three little helpless chillun
  And one poor, pitiful wife.'

6 ' Don't care nothin' about your chillun,
  And nothin' about your wife,
  You done mistreated me, Billy,
  And I'm bound to take your life.'

7 He shot him three times in the shoulder,
  Lawd, and three times in the side,
  Well, the last time he shot him
  Cause Billy Lyons to die.

8 Stagolee told Mrs Billy,
  ' You don't believe yo' man is dead;
  Come into the bar-room,
  See the hole I shot in his head.'

9 The high sheriff told the deputies,
  ' Get your pistols and come with me.
  We got to go 'rest that
  Bad man Stagolee.'

10 The deputies took their pistols
  And they laid them on the shelf—
  ' If you want that bad man Stagolee,
  Go 'rest him by yourself.'

11 High sheriff ask the bartender,
  ' Who can that bad man be? '
  ' Speak softly,' said the bartender,
  ' It's that bad man Stagolee.'

12 He touch Stack on the shoulder,
  Say, ' Stack, why don't you run? '
  ' I don't run, white folks,
  When I got my forty-one.'

13 The hangman put the mask on,
  Tied his hands behind his back,
  Sprung the trap on Stagolee
  But his neck refuse to crack.

14 Hangman, he got frightened,
  Said, ' Chief, you see how it be—
  I can't hang this man,
  Better set him free.'

15 Three hundred dollar funeral,
  Thousand dollar hearse,
  Satisfaction undertaker
  Put Stack six feet in the earth.

16 Stagolee, he told the Devil,
  Says, ' Come on and have some fun—
  You stick me with your pitchfork,
  I'll shoot you with my forty-one.'

17 Stagolee took the pitchfork,
  And he laid it on the shelf.
  Says, ' Stand back, Tom Devil,
  I'm gonna rule Hell by myself.'

BLUES

307. I'M ALL OUT AN' DOWN

STAGOLEE began as a ballad and ended as an eight-bar blues, which probably explains why it is the only ballad still widely sung by modern Negro folksingers. This is the age of the blues. The blues are as essential to jazz as red pepper is to the Mexican dish *chile* or okra to gumbo. Torch-singers or crooners cannot make the grade if they do not have a hint of the blues in their voices. The blue notes (the minor seventh, diminished fifth, and minor third), the descending cadences ornamented with Negroid slurs and other vocal tricks—the 8-10-12 or 16- bar formula—have become national musical trade-marks with which Americans stamp any music they are really fond of. The blues have crept in everywhere—into Carnegie Hall and cowboy song, into spirituals and symphonies, into hillbilly and the hit parade.

Seventy years ago, however, the blues lived in the wild and melancholy cries of the mule-skinners and roustabouts of the Mississippi Valley. As Jelly Roll Morton disdainfully put it, the blues was the music of ' the inferior longshoremens along the river, folks that didn't even bathe from one week to the next '. A levee camp worker, to keep his mules surging against their collars, would give a long, plaintive cry . . .

O—o, wo—o—, Lawd,
I looked all over the whole corral,—
And I couln' find a mule with his shoulder well,
Oo—Lawd, with his shoulder well.

Oo—, Lawd—,
Hamestring's poppin' and the collar cryin',—
Captain's holl'in' and I'm almos' dyin',
O well, well, my Lawd, I'm almos' dyin' . . .

Every skinner had his own tune and his own verses. Their voices rang like bugles and moaned like trombones. They could improvise new stanzas until the sun went down. Their wayward country melodies cannot be written down, for they are all movement, all soaring or gliding from one note to another. They must be studied on records. (*See* Lomax items in the record appendix.) But when country guitar players tied them to repeated chord sequences, they began to assume a form that could be performed by the rest of us. Such a song is this old levee camp blues, which Lead Belly learned as a boy in Louisiana and arranged for guitar. It begins with a long country whoop, and goes on to an elaborate 10-bar blues. Lead Belly punctuated it here and there with an explosive TI-YOW! imitative of the pop of the skinner's blacksnake whip.

573

308. HATTIE BELLE

Natchez: Some people say that the blues is a cow wanta see her calf, but I don't say it that way. I say it's a man that's got a good woman and she turns him down, and that gives you the blues.

Leroy: That's right. When I have troubles, blues is the only things that helps me. For instance, the rent situation . . .

Natchez: The thing I think about the blues is—it didn't start in the North, it didn't start in the East, it started in the South.

Leroy: It started from slavery.

Natchez: I worked on levee camps, extra gangs, road camps and every place, and I hear guys singing *Um-mmp* this and *Um-mmp* that, and I believe they was really singing from their heart, expressin' how they felt to the people.

Natchez: I've known guys that wanted to cuss out the boss and was afraid to go up to his face, and I've heard them sing those things. He make like the hoss or mule stepped on his foot and say, ' Get off my foot, goddam it!' He really be talkin' to his boss—' You sonofabitch you, you got no business . . .'

Leroy: Yeah, blues is a kind of revenge.

Natchez: I been around where they have prisoners chained together. Some of them have great big balls hangin' on their legs or some be tied to a stake.

Leroy: I remember a friend of mine were in a much badder place than that what you're talkin' about. It were so tough down there that they didn't put those chains on um. They let them go. They tell um to run, you know,—' RUN!' The dogs is there to catch you or track you whatsonever you run to.

Natchez: The point is that those fellers have the blues, too.

Leroy: That's right. All blues originated from stuff like that.

Natchez: You singin' from your heart—the way you feel. It's not for nobody to play behind you . . . Of course, there's some people haven't had no hardships, they don't understand how it is with the poor man.

Leroy: For instance, classics and stuff like that. They can't play the blues even if they wanted to. I mean, it takes a man that have *had* the blues to *play* the blues.

We found this blues relative of *Lonesome Road* sung as a work song in the North Carolina penitentiary.

QUOTE: *Blues in the Mississippi Night*, ed. Alan Lomax.

309. CARELESS LOVE

You know what they say—a man can calkerlate his life till he get mixed up with a woman or straddle a cow . . .

THE EARLIEST BLUES consisted of lines from work songs and hollers repeated four times to a steady beat on the guitar.

> Had a good-lookin' woman, but the fool laid down and died. (4)
> I don' see no fire, but I sho am burnin' down. (4)
> Good-lookin' woman make a bulldog break his chain. (4)

Although they were solo songs, they conformed to the Negro choral pattern, with the guitar giving antiphonal responses. Big Bill Broonzy and Handy both say that the earliest tune in the Yazoo Delta country was about a white prison official named Joe Turner . . .

> They tell me Joe Turner been here and gone. (3 or 4)

Other old-timers in the Delta say the first blues was . . .

Make me a pallet on your flo'   (3)
So your good man will never know . . .

In metre and tune both these songs strongly resemble *Careless Love*, which mountain singers claim as an old song, and which seems to be derived from such southern English fragments and couplets as . . .

It was in the month of sweet July
When I first listened to your lies.
And now my apron, it won't tie,
And I wished I'd never heard your lies.

In my opinion mountain songs like *Careless Love* provided the mould into which the Delta singers poured their free, bluesy hollers. Thus the blues, like the Negro hoe-downs, spirituals, and ballads, used Anglo-American song-forms as their starting point. No song could have been more appropriate, since the majority of the blues tell of the careless love of wandering Negro workers. Left-Wing Gordon, the strolling poet of the blues, says . . .

I'm leavin' here, walkin' an' talkin' to myself, an' I won't be satisfied nowhere I go. Take me till tomorrow night and about a dozen books to tell about all the jobs I had and the places I been. I had some mighty fine women. First was Abbie Jones in Ioway Street. Next was in Missouri, next one St. Louis, next one East St. Louis, nex' in Memphis—she took my money and gone. Next woman I had was at Columbia, South Carolina. These is just the finer ones, 'scusin' them that I married. Never did get no divorce. Too much trouble and don't seem no need. Other kinds of sweethearts I can git when I have plenty money. Had so many of them I can't count um. Take me till day after tomorrow to tell about um. Just look like I never can feel satisfied. I got the 'fo-day blues, can't keep um off my mind. I got the railroad blues, ain't got no fare . . .

QUOTE: Odum III.

310. ONE DIME BLUES

THE FIRST and finest of Negro folk blues composers to make commercial recordings was Blind Lemon Jefferson, who had earned his living for many years, playing in the joints up and down the Frisco railroad track in Dallas, Texas. His high, country voice rang through the murk of the barrelhouse like the call of a country rooster, and his guitar supplied a delicate tracery of comment that no one has since matched. His records sold so fast that the Paramount Record Company gave them a special label, trimmed in lemon. In the end, they say a jealous woman poisoned the blind bard, but his blues, composed with honesty and wit, will keep him long in memory.

Perhaps the best of his songs is this portrait of the unemployed casual labourer. Lemon hit the dead centre of realism in his lyrics, as one can see in this Negro housewife's story from the 1930's.

Ain't nobody really workin' here now. My husband picks up what he can, but he can't get nothin' steady. Can't hardly say what he makes—just enough to get by and pay the rent and give us a little food, but ain't none of us ever get enough to eat . . . Now you may not believe that, but it's true. Why, just a little over two weeks ago, he caught a bad spell and couldn't find no work at all. On Friday I had a little flour left and some syrup.

575

Well, I made biscuits and we ate that. The next day was Saturday, and one or two folks in the house come up and brung me a little of their food, but they was all poor and couldn't keep it up. By Monday we didn't have not one piece of nothin' to eat in the house. Poor little Catherine, was around here just as hungry as she could be, but she's a sweet-natured child and wouldn't complain a bit. On Tuesday, my husband pawned his only suit for three dollars, and we ate then, the first time for a week . . .

QUOTE: Fisk.

311. GOOD MORNIN', BLUES

When you lie down at night, an' it ain't too hot an' ain't too cold, but you turnin' from side to side, what's the matter? The blues got you. When you get up in the mornin', the blues is walkin' round your bed. Your friends may be all around you, but you don't want any talk out of them. What's the matter? The blues got you !

THE ELIZABETHANS described melancholy as ' the blue devils '. The American pioneers, coming from park-like, village-organized, custom-ordained Europe, set adrift on the vast sea of the American wilderness, suffered from the blue-devils of homesickness. They felt lost and lonely in the raw and unfinished spaces of the new world. Thomas Wolfe, who has come closer than any other writer to the spirit of the American man, speaks of him as ' lost and wind-grieved '. The slave found that ' there was no hiding-place round here ', and the Negro of Reconstruction felt his kinship with the little boll weevil who ' was lookin' for a home, just a-lookin' for a home '.

Round the turn of the century when the Negro left the farm and went north, he found the blues waiting for him at every station down the line. He had the *Alabama Blues*, *The Atlanta Blues*, *The New Orleans Hop Scop Blues*, *The Fort Worth Blues and the Dallas Heart Disease*, *The St. Louis Blues* (like a rock cast in the sea), *The Michigan Water Blues*, *The Wabash Blues*, *The State Street Blues* (in Chicago), *The Harlem Blues*, even *The London Blues*. The blues dominated ocean and land—*Salt Water Blues*, *Deep Sea Blues*, *Mountain Top Blues*, *Lowland Blues*. Even the weatherman had his blues—*Thunderstorm Blues*, *Wind Howling Blues*, *Rain Falling Blues*.

Early in the 'twenties a recording director for one of the big companies experimented with a folk blues record—*I'm Gonna Move to Kansas City* by banjo-framming Jim Jackson. The singer and composer was paid ten dollars for the song; its sales ran to about a half million copies. Companies formed to exploit this new field. As no organized way of reaching the Southern Negro market existed at that time, Pullman porters carried batches of blues records on their Southern runs and sold them for fancy prices. In those days, sweet Mama expected sweet Papa to bring the latest blues record home on Saturday night along with his weekly pay.

Blues singers and guitar pickers from all over the South blew into the studios of Chicago and Indianapolis and Detroit. Folk singers with fancy monikers like Pinetop Smith, Big Bill, Texas Alexander, Memphis Minnie, The Devil's Son-in-Law, Georgia Tom, became major recording artists. Big Bill, for instance, began recording in 1926 and since then has waxed over three hundred songs, and played in scores of other sessions. If all the verses of the recorded blues were laid end to end, it would make a lonesome moan that could be heard on the moon. These songs speak plainly, pithily, and powerfully about the emotional disturbances of urban society in the west. The jobless, dispossessed, unwanted, predatory Negro male was the first character in our civilization to experience and express these feelings. Now we are all aware of them, and the big, sad wind of the blues sings through heart-strings from Memphis to Moscow. When Negroes perform these verses they laugh for they have learned to swallow their tears and live on the salt.

312. CORINNA

IN THEIR NATIVE Southern setting, the blues, like Spanish flamenco, function largely as dance music. A worker who hums the blues on the job is thinking of the Saturday night dance. There the blues will roll all night from a broken-down upright piano or from a little orchestra which may include harmonica, mandolin, fiddle, guitar, washboard, tub-bass, and jug in any combination—or simply a pianist or a solo guitar player-singer. The lone guitar player was the entire orchestra at most of the dances I attended in the Deep South during the 'thirties and 'forties. Some wretched wooden shack far out in the country was the dancing house. By 10 p.m. it was packed with couples, dancing belly to belly, their feet barely moving in a slow-drag step that made the whole house reverberate like a great drum. In one corner of the room sat the guitar player, both feet whamming out the rhythm, the left hand frailing the strings of his battered guitar, the right whining out the blue notes between chords. Meanwhile, his powerful, sobbing voice cut through the noise and carried the bitter and ironic verses of the blues to the ears of every dancer.

The dance was new as well. The practice of couple dancing (waltz, polka, schottische, etc.)—which had become the rage in the cities and the scandal of most rural areas towards the close of the nineteenth century—stimulated the worldly folks of the Negro community to create the far more erotic dances of blues and jazz, which have since become internationally popular. In rural areas these dances were quite African in character, involving freely sensual movements of shoulders, breasts, belly, and hips. Dancing in this way, the 'Devil's chillun' of the Negro community defied the preacher and his respectable following.

What the local blues-man sang was his own resetting of traditional couplets, which commented bitterly and realistically on the actual emotional problems of the dancers. These people were the flotsam at the far edges of America's emotional and social whirlpool, and the blues told their story, sang of the sorrows of their degraded and insecure lives. Their response was not to weep, but to laugh, to shout approval and encouragement, to dance with more abandon and more evident sensual pleasure, and, for the women, to run to the singer and to fling their arms round his neck and kiss him all over his sweating face. He was their bard, the mouthpiece for their agony, and the more he squawled, moaned, sobbed, and violently beat his guitar, the happier they felt. Here, in the blues, the feelings of frustration and agonized conflict masked in the white love songs and the Negro spirituals were shouted out with the force of a work song; in these songs the double burden of Calvinist conflict and racial degradation was frankly exposed.

A tender little blues with a touch of jazz and a flavour of hillbilly, this folk song of the 1920's has been so often resung by whites and Negroes in the South that it is now impossible to say on which side of the Jim Crow line it was born.

313. TROUBLED IN MIND

'The thing has come to a showdown now, and we really want to know why and how come a man have the blues,' said Natchez.

THAT THE NEGRO has been often humiliated, has been consistently denied education and opportunity—these are contributing causes to the blue feeling, of which we are all aware. Yet there is another, perhaps more pervasive source of torment, which arises from the Negro's unconscious acceptance of our standards of beauty. A bitter verse of the blues puts it this way.

> I don't want no black woman puttin' sugar in my tea,
> For they black is evil, I'm scared she might pizen me.

The contrast between 'black' and 'white' burns into the mind of most Negro children. White signifies power, wealth, freedom, opportunity, prestige, social mobility, education, cleanliness, and so on. Black is perversely and wrongly associated with poverty, servility, ignorance, slavery, irresponsibility, lack of opportunity, shame, and a host of negative prohibitions—blacks not allowed to enter here, blacks not allowed to sleep here, blacks not allowed to eat here, to study here, to live here. 'To them,' cried out one blues singer, 'we nothin' but a face, a black face.'

To some considerable degree American Negroes, confronted with these negative attitudes, accepted them as their own. Charles Johnson's sociological research in the South in the '30s defined this phenomenon with horrifying accuracy. A sizable sampling of Southern Negro school-children tended to assess their own skin colour as a couple of shades lighter than it actually was. Admired teachers and friends were rated a couple of shades lighter than their actual colouring, while enemies were described as several shades darker than they were in fact. Between light and dark-skinned children yawned a gulf of colour prejudice almost as unreasoning and strong as among racist white Southerners and their coloured workers.

One brown-skinned seventeen-year-old Tennessee girl said, 'I select my friends on the basis of colour. All my friends are either light or brown-skin. I just can't get along with dark people. It just seems to me that black people are evil . . . The best colour is white. You have many more privileges and there is more chance for advancement in life. Black people just have a hard time; nobody really likes them. I don't suppose I should be so hard on them, but I just can't help it' . . .

The black and evil blues will roll on and on, troubling the minds of many American citizens until we all join in expunging this guilty stain from the hearts of our countrymen.

QUOTE: Fisk.

314. HOW LONG BLUES

PERHAPS the most remarkable advance in music during the twentieth century has been the development of solo and ensemble playing among American Negro jazz musicians. Until the turn of the century, few Negroes had access to European orchestral instruments; but once the popularity of ragtime and jazz guaranteed them a professional status, the jazz men soon found new ways of playing every instrument that fell into their hands. Trumpets, trombones, saxophones, guitars, and pianos all spoke a new and more colourful language at the behest of the uninhibited natural musicians of the Mississippi Valley. Virtuosi of great brilliance appeared who not only could improvise superbly in solo and in ensemble, but played so well together that the music sounded as if it were produced by one man. These players developed one new orchestral idiom after another; in fact, Negro jazz style is still changing so rapidly that white musicians can scarcely keep pace with it, for as fast as the white musicians absorb one musical innovation of their Negro masters, a new sound comes belting out of Harlem or the South Side of Chicago.

The most difficult of all the problems solved by the Negro folk musicians was that of adapting piano technique to his special musical needs. Guitar strings could be pushed or pulled to follow his vocal patterns, horns and reeds could be overblown or muted, but the piano, tuned rigidly to a tempered scale, resisted innovation. However, Negro musicians taught even this stiff and elegant drawing-room instrument to sing the blues and to beat out the complex drum-rhythms of ragtime and boogie-woogie. In Negro churches untaught pianists accompanied spirituals so that their expressiveness was enhanced and folk singing was encouraged. Honky-tonk pianists learned to slur so subtly that they seemed to be playing notes in between the keys. Under their powerful left hands the bass registers resounded like two or three tuned African drums.

Among the most talented of these piano naturals was Jimmy Yancey, who was born in the slums of Chicago in 1896 and who died in the same neighbourhood in 1951. He shunned the limelight, seldom played professionally, and recorded only late in life. During the week he worked as grounds tender for the Chicago White Sox Baseball Team. At weekends he liked to play the piano for his friends. One evening I took a bottle of whisky round to Yancey's flat and spent one of the most enjoyable evenings of my life listening to that timid, rather fragile little old man make his piano sing blues, while his wife rocked and knitted in the background. I came away feeling that I had heard the master blues pianist.

Pinetop Smith, Meade Lux Lewis, Albert Ammons—the best of the boogie-woogie virtuosi—all learned ' under ' Jimmy Yancey. These younger men made records, played in night clubs, became famous. Jimmy preferred to stay at home, experiment on the piano and play at private parties on the South Side of Chicago . . .

> ' Wear your dress above your knees,
> And strut your stuff with who you please.'

SOCIAL WHIST PARTY
at
Slamfoot and Mama Jackson's
Apartment at the back above Joe's shine Parlor
Professor Yancey will officiate at the piano

For those who want to learn how to play blues piano, Peggy Seeger has transcribed (and condensed) the way Jimmy Yancey played the *How Long Blues*, accompanying his wife, Mama Yancey.

315. IRENE

THE ARCHIVE of American Folk Song, which now numbers some 60,000 songs in its files of field recordings, came into actual being one broiling summer day in the State Penitentiary in Angola, Louisiana. The first recording we took on our new portable equipment was of the state's prisoner, Lead Belly, singing *Irene Goodnight*.

We were powerfully impressed by his panther-like grace and his extraordinary good looks: his already snow-white hair set off the aquiline features and the proudly gazing eyes inherited from his African and Cherokee Indian ancestors. We were amazed by his mastery of his great, green-painted twelve-string guitar, but we were deeply moved by the flawless tenor voice which rang out across the green cotton fields like a big sweet-toned trumpet. We believed Lead Belly when he said, ' I'ze the king of all the twelve-string guitar players of the world.'

My father and I had come to the penitentiary hunting folk songs. In Lead Belly we found a great folk artist, who not only stamped the songs with his own strong personality, but at once involved us in his life. Before the recording session had ended, Lead Belly had what he wanted from us—the promise to ask the Governor of Louisiana to pardon this two-time murderer. We stopped off at Baton Rouge the next day and left a recording of Lead Belly's ballad appeal for a pardon in Governor O.K. Allen's office . . .

> I left my wife wringing' her hands an' cryin',
> ' Governor O.K. Allen, save this man of mine.
>
> Had you, Gov. O.K. Allen, like you got me,
> I'd wake up in the morning, and set you free . . .'

Whether because of this song or for another reason, Lead Belly was paroled to my father a year later, and joined him on a long tour through the Southern prisons, where Lead Belly's performances for the convicts demonstrated just the kind of songs we wanted to record. At the Christmas meeting of the Modern Language Association, Lead Belly sang at the final smoker and drew an ovation from an audience of two thousand staid college professors. Newspaper and magazine stories led to a series of concert engagements where, despite the fact that few of his listeners could understand his Louisiana dialect, Lead Belly triumphed again and again with his brilliant performances. His wedding was filmed for the ' March of Time ' and covered by the New York Press.

In the years that followed Lead Belly recorded his songs for a number of companies, though never so beautifully as he had first sung them for us in Louisiana; his voice grew thinner and harder in the smoke and tension of New York City yet, even in his late recordings, he sang with so much force and with such great style that he has become the model for hundreds of young folk singers in Britain and the U.S.A. Everywhere he performed, he sang *Irene*, his most beloved song. Instinctively, he must have guessed that one day it would be a hit, and so it happened.

Death came to him slowly and painfully in the form of a creeping paralytic disease, that stilled his sinewy limbs one after another, like an army cautiously besieging and capturing some great fortification. He had been unable to sing for many months, before he finally told his wife, Martha Promise Ledbetter, goodbye on the night of December 6, 1949. Six months later, *Irene Goodnight* became the hit of the year and sold about two million records. It was translated into every European language and has become a folk song in a dozen countries. Today, the songs of this violent, talented man, whom life had tempered to a steely hardness; are sung by an ever-widening circle of people round the world; and it looks very much as if this Louisiana farm-labourer and convict will emerge as one of the important musical figures of the twentieth century.

316. BLACK, BROWN, AND WHITE

JIM CROW roosts everywhere. He rides the trains. He sits in the jury in court. He goes into politics and is elected to the State Board of Education. He runs the biggest real estate office in the U.S.A. He has the doorman's job at restaurants, hotels, and the movies. He loves to hang around places that the public patronizes, like drinking fountains, toilets, and hospitals.

He makes such a fool of himself sometimes that you can't help but laugh at him, wicked as he is. The South is full of tales about him. Down in Arkansas, if you're Negro and need tobacco, don't ask the storeman for Prince Albert tobacco. Why not? Because of that white man on the can. Ask for *Mister* Prince Albert!

A Negro painter fell off the scaffold one time. His partner yelled, ' Stop, Bob, don't fall.' Bob replied, ' How can I stop, man, when I'm already falling?' ' Okay then, Bob, but you're fallin' right on a white lady.' Bob, he stopped in mid-air and fell up! He was about to drop spang on Mister Jim Crow.

A Southern cop blew his whistle and stopped a country Negro who had driven through a red light. The coloured man apologized, ' Lordy, mister policeman, I saw all the white folks movin' on with the green light, so naturally I thought the red one was for us coloured people to drive ahead on.'

You laugh long and hard at these stories, but the laughter is the kind described in the blues . . .

> You don't know, you don't know my mind,
> When you see me laughin', I'm laughin' to keep from crying . . .

Big Bill Broonzy was raised by Mister Jim Crow in Mississippi. When he came north to escape his dark shadow, he met him again on the job in the steel mills of Gary. Thereupon, he composed this blues, which speaks out plainly about the problems his ancestors had faced since they came to America.

317. SOUND OFF

IN MY BASIC TRAINING camp at Missouri they had us count the rate of steps in close formation marching. We shouted out of parched throats and cursed the sergeant under our breath. Then round the corner came the Negro battalion, marching as one man, with somehow a hint of syncopation in its step. When the big, handsome, coloured sergeant counted the steps, every one of those hundreds of left feet hit the road on the off-beat. Every throat opened on the chorus. Big, four-part blues chords roared over our heads. For just a moment, army life and basic training seemed almost a pleasure.

World War II was the first time that a great number of Negroes had been accepted on something like an equal basis in the American Army. The process of expelling Jim Crow from the armed forces was not complete, but discrimination was on its way out, and you could hear it between the lines of this virile folk song of World War II. *Sound Off* is cynical, disillusioned, and touched with blue cadences, but it contains a note of confidence and a joyful acceptance of the nature of life and love that is new in American folk song.

307. I'M ALL OUT AN' DOWN

FROM: p. 131 of *Negro Folk Songs as Sung by Lead Belly*, Lomax. Copyright 1936, Macmillan Company, N.Y., © 1959 Folkways Music Publishers, New York.

Slow blues ♩ = 84

GUITAR— 7C
BANJO— 5

(*Begin the blues rhythm now and chant the prose passages between stanzas.*)

This man was a long old ways from home an' he got a brownskin woman, an' he know payday's comin' pretty soon an' that woman is shoutin' 'cause it's most payday an' she gonna git his money. Ol' mules is hongry an' de sun is goin' down. He wish payday would move off a little further so he wouldn' have to give the woman nothin'. He look way back yonder an' gin' to blow his horn . . .

1 Honey-ay-ay,
I'm all out an' down,
Honey-ay-ay,
I'm broke, babe, an' I ain't got a dime,
Ev'ry good man gets in ha'd luck sometime,
Don' they, baby,
Don' they, baby?
(*The final two lines should be repeated ad lib.*)

2 Honey,
I'm all out an' down,
Honey,
Oh, the mules an' the hosses nicklin' for their corn and hay,
Women on the levee shoutin' 'cause it's most pay day,
Cryin', ' Daddy,
Sweet Daddy.'
Aw, the women on the levee, honey, holl'in' ' Whoo, haw, gee,'
The mens on the levee holl'in' ' Doncha murder me.
Please, baby,
Don' murder.'

3 Honey,
   What you want me to do?
   Honey,
   I'm down in the bottom in the mud up to my knees,
   Workin' for my baby an' she's so hard to please,
   Ain't you, baby? (2)
   Yallow woman make a preacher lay his Bible down,
   Jet-black woman make a jack-rabbit hug a houn',
   Tell me, baby. (2)

That man was workin' a long way from home, tryin' to rake and scrape a little money together to please that woman. He was one of the best skinners on the levee. But his boss, Mister Ryan, had made this man mad. 'Stead o' takin' it out on Mister Ryan, dis man was takin' it out on the mules. Every time he hit the mule wid his blacksnake, he cut the hair right off and write his 'nitials on the mule's hide . . .

4 Honey,
   I'm all out an' down,
   Honey,
   Worked all the summer and part of the fall,
   Had to take my Christmas in my overall,
   O Lawdy! (2)
   I'm down in the bottom, skinnin' for Johnny Ryan,
   Puttin' my 'nitials, honey, on the mule's behin',
   Wid my line, babe (2)
   Honey . . .

308. HATTIE BELLE

FROM: p. 404 of *Our Singing Country*, Lomax (Macmillan, N.Y., 1941). Recorded and arranged by John and Alan Lomax in North Carolina Penitentiary, 1934. SEE: Brown III, 347; Scarborough, 73; White, 300; L.C. 14B1. This Negro work song shows the roots of the popular song *Lonesome Road*. It is one of the relatives of the song family described in note for *Longest Train*.

1 Look down, look down,
That long, lonesome road,
Hang down——
Your head, head, and cry——.

2 The best of friends
Must part, part some day,
So why——
Not you, you and I——?

3 Hattie Belle, Hattie Belle,
She's my own, own true love,
What e——vil
Have, have I done——?

4 Stand back, stand back,
All you five and ten cent men,
Got a man——
Knockin' on, on your door.

5 Well, you cause me to weep,
And you cause me to moan,
And you cause—— ·
Me to leave, leave my home——.

6 Look down, look down,
That long, lonesome road,
Where you——
And I, I must go. . . .

7 Hattie Belle, Hattie Belle,
She's my own, own true love,
Darlin'——
My time, time's so long.

309. CARELESS LOVE

A version of blues lyrics universal among Negro and white Southern folk singers, arranged by Alan Lomax. SEE: Randolph III, 306. For related songs, see *Dink's Blues* (Lomax II, 193); *Every Night When the Sun Goes In* (Sharp II, 268); *Make Me a Pallet on the Floor*, etc. (Reeves, 90) for one of English roots. The ' apron high ' verses occur in *A Brisk Young Soldier Courted Me*, according to Vaughan Williams.

Slow blues ♩ = 100

GUITAR- ANY ²/₄ STYLE
BANJO- 5

Love, O love, O care-less love,—— Love, O love, O care-less love,

Love, O love, O care - less love, You see what care-less love can do.——

Note: The top part may be used in last stanzas as melody or throughout as harmony.

1 Love, O love, O careless love, (3)
You see what careless love can do.

2 When I wore my apron low, (3)
You followed me through frost and snow.

3 Now my apron strings won't pin, (3)
You pass my door, and you won't come in.

4 How I wish that train would come, (3)
Take me back where I come from.

5 You see what careless love will do, (2)
You see, don't you see what careless love will do,
Make you leave your mama and your papa, too.

6 You see what careless love have done, (3)
Make a gran'mama marry her oldest son.

310. ONE DIME BLUES

Arranged by Alan Lomax from the singing of the composer, Blind Lemon Jefferson, Dallas, Texas, 1920's. One of the *Careless Love* family.

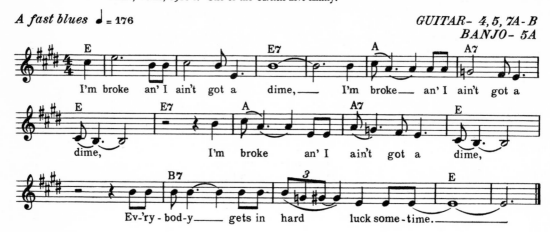

A fast blues ♩ = 176

GUITAR- 4, 5, 7A - B
BANJO- 5A

I'm broke an' I ain't got a dime, ___ I'm broke ___ an' I ain't got a dime, I'm broke an' I ain't got a dime, Ev-'ry-bod-y ___ gets in hard luck some-time. ___

1 I'm broke an' I aín't got a díme, (3)
  Ev'rybódy gets in hard luck sometime.

2 I was standin' on East Cairo Street one dáy, (2)
  Standing on East Cairo Street one dáy,
  One díme was áll I had.

3 Máma, don't treat your daughter mean, (3)
  That's the méanest woman a mán most ever séen.

4 You want your friend to be bad like Jesse Jámes, (3)
  Git twó six shooters, highway some passenger train.

5 One díme was all I hád, (3)
  That was méal befó' the lást.

6 I bóught that mórnin' néws, Lord,
  I bóught that mórnin' néws, (2)
  Then I bóught a nickel séegar, too.

311. GOOD MORNIN', BLUES

Adapted and arranged by Alan Lomax from folk sources. Based on Lead Belly's *Good Morning, Blues.* © 1959, Folkways Music Inc.
Piano arrangement by DON BANKS

Medium blues ♩ = 110

GUITAR- 7C
BANJO- 5

mf

1. I woke up ___ this morn-in' ___

1 I woke up this mornin' with the blues all round my bed,
Yes, I woke up this morning with the blues all round my bed,
Went to eat my breakfast, had the blues all in my bread.

2 ' Good mornin', blues, blues, how do you do ? ' (2)
' I'm feelin' pretty well, but, pardner, how are you ? '

3 Yes, I woke up this morning, 'bout an hour 'fore day, (2)
Reached and grabbed the pillow where my baby used to lay.

4 If you ever been down, you know just how I feel, (2)
Feel like an engine, ain't got no drivin' wheel.

5 If I feel tomorrow, like I feel today, (2)
I'll stand right here, look a thousand miles away.

6 If the blues was whisky, I'd stay drunk all the time, (2)
Stay drunk, baby, just to wear you off my mind.

7 I got the blues so bad it hurts my feet to walk, (2)
I got the blues so bad, it hurts my tongue to talk.

8 The blues jumped a rabbit, run him a solid mile, (2)
When the blues overtaken him, he hollered like a newborn child.

312. CORINNA

Collected and arranged by Alan Lomax from oral Negro sources in the 30's. A
bluesy piece widely popular among blues and hillbilly singers. Also occurs as
Alberta or *Roberta*.

Hillbilly blues ♩ = 184

GUITAR- 4, 5, 7B
BANJO- 5

1 Corinna, Corinna, where'd you stay last night?
Tell me, Corinna, where'd you stay last night?
Your shoes ain't buttoned, girl, don't fit you right.

2 Corinna, Corinna, where you been so long? (2)
Ain't had no lovin' since you been gone.

3 Corinna, Corinna, what's the matter now? (2)
You done gone bad, babe, ain't no good nohow.

4 Corinna, Corinna, way cross the sea, (2)
Ain't done no good, babe, since you left me.

5 I love Corinna, God knows I do, (2)
And I hope some day, she come to love me, too.

313. TROUBLED IN MIND

Jones was a New Orleans jazz man and arranger who played an important part in the development of jazz and blues in Chicago from early 20's onwards. The song is now in wide oral circulation among Southern whites and Negroes, with many versions.

1 Troubled in mind, I'm blue, but I won't be blue always,
The sun's gonna shine in my back do' some day.

2 I'm gonna lay my head on some lonesome railroad line,
Let the 2:19 ease my trouble in mind.

3 I love all you pretty women, I love you all the same,
Don't love none of you enough, enough to change your name.

4 Troubled in mind, I'm blue, but I won't be blue always,
Wind's gonna rise and blow my blues away.

314. HOW LONG BLUES

Carr was the most popular of all blues recording artists during 30's. He came from the Yazoo Delta country in Miss. This blues, which shows jazz influence, specifically from *Hesitation Blues*, is now in wide oral circulation among Negro blues singers.

Piano as played by JIMMY YANCEY, transcribed by PEGGY SEEGER.

Note: Variations may be made in the accompaniment of singing. The following figures may be substituted for the above piano accompaniment; only the first few measures, from ✱ onwards, are given, as the notes vary according to harmony changes (indicated in letters above the staff.)

① The right hand carries triplets against the bass figure.

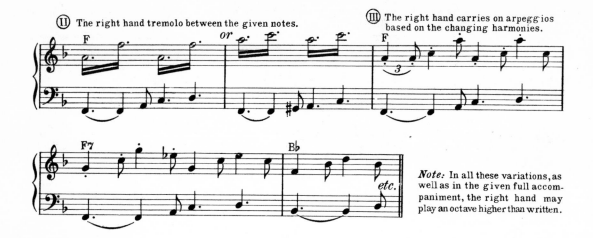

CHORUS :
How long, how long,
Has that evenin' train been gone?
How long, how long,
Tell me how long?

1 Tell me how long, how long,
Tell me how long, how long,
How long will it be
Before you'll ever learn to|quit mistreatin' me?

2 I've been down|down in the Delta,
Down in the Delta|and I've done been tried,
I can stand more trouble
Than any little woman of my size.

3 I tried to|teach my baby,
I talked to him the whole night long,
I was only just|tryin'
To teach that man|right from wrong.

4 He did not love,|he did not love me,
An' I knew|that from the start,
But I was just|tryin'
To bring that man|into my heart.

5 I would wake up|in the mornin',
I was tryin' to tell him|right from wrong,
When I'd look for my baby,
My baby,|he'd be gone.

6 That's why I cry|*how long?*
How long,|how long will it be
Before you'll ever learn
To quit mistreatin' me?

(*Note :* Bar lines indicate Mama Yancey's caesurae—when she broke the metre of the verse for musical reasons.)

592

315. IRENE

FROM: p. 235 of *Negro Folk Songs as Sung by Lead Belly*, Lomax. Copyright Macmillan, N.Y., 1936. Copyright Ludlow Music, 1950, as *Goodnight Irene*. Composed by Huddie Ledbetter, arranged by John and Alan Lomax.

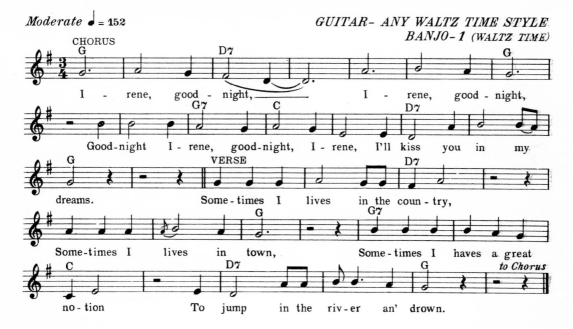

CHORUS:
Irene, goodnight,
Irene, goodnight,
Goodnight, Irene, goodnight, Irene,
I'll kiss you in my dreams.

1 Sometimes I lives in the country,
Sometimes I lives in town,
Sometimes I has a great notion
To jump in the river an' drown. (CHO.)

2 Last Sat'dy night I got married,
Me an' my wife settled down,
Now me an' my wife have parted,
Gonna take me a stroll uptown. (CHO.)

3 I loves Irene, God knows I do,
I loves her till the sea runs dry,
An' if Irene turns her back on me,
I'll take morphine an' die. (CHO.)

4 Quit your ramblin', quit your gamblin',
Quit your stayin' out late at night,
Go home to your wife an' your fam'ly,
Sit down by the fireside bright. (CHO.)

316. BLACK, BROWN, AND WHITE

Composed by Big Bill Broonzy in the 40's. Copyright Wm. Broonzy, 1946.

Fast narrative blues ♩ = 126

GUITAR– 4, 5, 7B
BANJO– 5

Just lis-ten to the song I'm sing-in,' bro-ther, You'll know it's true. If you're black and got to work for a liv-in,' boy, This is what they'll say to you: Now, if you're white, you're right, And if you're brown, stick a-round, But if you're black,——— O bro-ther, 'Get back, get back, get back.'

1 Just listen to the song I'm singin', brother,
  You'll know it's true.
  If you're black and got to work for a livin', boy,
  This is what they'll say to you:
  CHORUS :
  Now, if you're white, you're right,
  And if you're brown, stick around,
  But if you're black, O brother,
  ' Get back, get back, get back.'

2 I 'member I was in a place one night,
  Everybody was having fun,
  They was all drinkin' beer and wine,
  But me, I couldn't get none. (CHO.)

3 I was in an employment office,
  I got a number and got in line.
  They called everybody's number
  But they never did call mine. (CHO.)

4 Me an' a man was workin' side by side,
  And this is what it meant.
  He was gettin' a dollar an hour
  And I was gettin' fifty cents. (CHO.)

5 I helped build this country,
  I fought for it, too,
  Now what I want to know is,
  What you gonna do about Jim Crow? (CHO.)

317. SOUND OFF

Collected and arranged by Alan Lomax from Negro soldiers in Missouri, 1945.
In many variants this was sung by all Negro outfits in World War II.

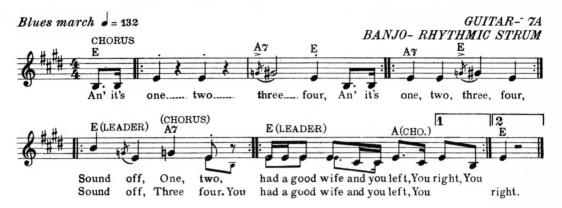

CHORUS:
An' it's one—two—three—four,
An' it's one—two—three—four,
An' it's one, two, three, four,
One, two, three, four,
Sound off,
One, two,
Sound off,
Three, four. } (2)

1 You had a good wife and you left,
You right.
You had a good wife and you left,
You right. (CHO.)

2 Jody's got my gal and gone,
Left me here a-singing this song. (CHO.)

APPENDIX I. BOOK LIST

The list of books that follows is the most informal sort of bibliography, containing only a handful of volumes out of the hundreds devoted to American folk song and folklore. For a complete survey of everything published in American folklore in recent years, the two best sources are : Dr. Ralph Bogg's bibliography published serially in *The Southern Folklore Quarterly*, by the University of Florida, and the remarkable bibliography of Dr. Charles Haywood (cited below). This journal can be consulted, together with most of the other volumes comprising this list, in the Library at Cecil Sharp House, London ; in the British Museum ; and in the folklore section of the Library of the University of London. The reference libraries in the U.S.A. are simply too numerous to mention.

The reader interested in examining comparative versions of the songs in this volume can find a plenitude of references in the sources cited in the headnotes. The headnotes give page references, each collection being designated by the surname of its principal editor, or, in some cases, by abbreviated titles. These key words are arranged in alphabetical order, with full titles given in the following list.

BOOK KEY

ABBOTT E. C. (' Teddy Blue ') and H. H. Smith, *We Pointed Them North* (University of Oklahoma Press, 1954). The best single book about the American cowboy and his life, told by a man who rode the trail from Texas to Wyoming in the 'seventies and 'eighties.

ANDREWS Edward D. *The Gift to be Simple* (J. J. Augustin, 1940).

ARNOLD Byron. *Folk Songs of Alabama* (University of Alabama Press, 1950).

BARRY Phillips. *British Ballads From Maine* (Yale University Press, 1929). Child ballads only. Fine scholarship.

BAYARD S. P. *Hill Country Tunes* (Memoir 39, American Folk Lore Society, Philadelphia, 1944). Collection of South-western Pennsylvania fiddle tunes with excellent notes and bibliography.

BECK E. C. *Songs of the Michigan Lumberjacks* (Michigan University Press, Ann Arbor, 1941). A fine lumberjack collection currently in print.

BELDEN H. M. *Ballads and Songs collected by the Missouri Folklore Society*. (University of Missouri, Columbia, Mo, 1940). This is the best inexpensive single book with general references to the whole Anglo-American folk song field. It can be ordered directly from the University of Missouri Press.

BLAIR Walter. *Native American Humor* (American Book Company, 1937). A source book of salty regional sketches of Southern folk life.

BOTKIN I. *The American Play-Party Song*, ed. B. A. Botkin, (Lincoln, Nebraska, 1937). Fundamental reference source for American mouth music and game-song tunes.

BOTKIN II. *Treasury of American Folklore*, ibid. (Crown Publishers, New York, 1944).

BOTKIN III. *Treasury of New England Folklore*, ibid. (1947).

BOTKIN IV. *Treasury of Southern Folklore*, ibid. (1949).

BOTKIN V. *Treasury of Western Folklore*, ibid. (1951).

BOTKIN VI. *Treasury of Mississippi Lore*, ibid. (1955).

BOTKIN VII. *Lay My Burden Down*, ibid. (University of Chicago Press, 1945).

BOTKIN VIII. *Treasury of Railroad Lore*, with A. Harlow (Crown, 1953).
These invaluable compilations of American folk-say and regional writing give the whole panorama of American folklore and have been of the utmost importance in the preparation of this volume.

BRONSON Bertrand. *The Traditional Tunes of the Child Ballads* (Princeton University Press, 1959). The first volume of a series which brings together all published melodies of the Child ballads, together with exhaustive comparative and analytic notes.

BROWN II. *North Carolina Folklore*. Volume II, *Folk Ballads from North Carolina*, edited by H. M. Belden and A. P. Hudson (Duke University Press, Durham, North Carolina, 1952--). Rich collection of British and native American ballads.

BROWN III. *North Carolina Folklore.* Vol. III, *Folk Songs from North Carolina*, ibid. Two parts of a five-volume series devoted to the folk songs and folklore collected by the late Frank C. Brown, and edited by Newman White, H. M. Belden and others. A fundamental reference book, supplementing Belden. Volume IV contains the tunes.

CALHOUN A. W. *A Social History of the American Family from Colonial Times to the Present* (Barnes and Noble, N.Y., 1945).

CAZDEN Norman. *The Abelard Folk Song Book*, New York State ballads edited and arranged for piano and guitar (Abelard-Schuman, N.Y., 1958).

CHILD F. J. *English and Scottish Popular Ballads* (Houghton Mifflin, Boston, 1883-). Source book of information for 305 of the best British ballads. The original multi-volumed Child was re-published in 1957 by the Folk Lore Press in N.Y.C.

COFFIN Tristram. *The British Traditional Ballad in North America* (The American Folklore Society, 1950). Survey of all published American versions of the Child canon.

COLCORD Joanna. *Songs of American Sailormen* (W. W. Norton, Inc., New York, 1938). The classic work on chanteys and sea ballads, to whose editor this author owes many debts of gratitude.

CREIGHTON I Helen. *Songs and Ballads from Nova Scotia* (Dent and Sons, Toronto, 1933).

CREIGHTON II Helen. *Traditional Songs of Nova Scotia*—collected by H. Creighton and Doreen Senior (The Ryerson Press, Toronto, 1950). Helen Creighton has uncovered a new world of folk songs in her area.

DAVIDSON M. B. *Life in America* (Houghton Mifflin Co., Boston, 1951). A magnificent popular history of the U.S., in two volumes, profusely illustrated with period paintings, engravings, and photographs. An essential companion work and the source for many ideas in this book.

DAVIS A. K. *Traditional Ballads from Virginia* (Harvard University Press, 1929).

DOERFLINGER William. *Shanty Men and Shanty Boys* (Macmillan, 1951). The most thorough study of sea songs in English to date.

DORSON Richard. *Jonathan Draws the Long Bow* (Harvard University Press, 1946). Excellent source for New England folk tales.

ECKSTORM, Fanny and Mary Smyth. *Minstrelsy of Maine* (Houghton Mifflin, 1927). The story of how folk songs were made and sung in this neck of the woods.

FISK. *Unwritten History of Slavery*, Volume I. *God Struck Me Dead*, Volume II of Social Science Source Documents, published in mimeograph by the Social Science Institute, Fisk University, Nashville, Tennessee, 1945. Vol. I is edited by O. S. Egypt, J. Masuoka, and Charles S. Johnson. Vol. II is edited by Paul Radin and C. S. Johnson.

FLANDERS I Helen Hartness. *New Green Mountain Songster* (Yale University Press, 1939).

FLANDERS II. *Ballads Migrant in New England* (Farrar and Strauss, New York, 1953).

FLANDERS III. *Vermont Folk Songs and Ballads* (Stephen Daye Press, Brattleborough, 1931). The work of Mrs. Flanders and George Brown in their Vermont folk song archive excellently surveys the ballad tradition of New England.

FRIEDMAN A. B. *The Viking Book of Folk Ballads* (Viking Press, N.Y., 1956). A very interesting comparative survey of ballads in English from the British Isles, America, and Australia.

GARDNER Emelyn, with Geraldine Chickering. *Ballads and Songs of Southern Michigan* (University of Michigan Press, 1939).

GOMME Alice. *The Traditional Games of England, Scotland and Ireland* (David Nutt, London, 1894). Two volumes of the dictionary of British folklore.

GORDON Robert. *Folk Songs of America* (National Service Bureau Publication, W.P.A., N.Y., 1938). An out-of-print but important survey of the whole field.

GREENLEAF E. and G. MANSFIELD. *Ballad and Sea Songs from Newfoundland* (Harvard University Press, 1933).

GREENWAY John. *American Songs of Protest* (University of Pennsylvania Press, 1953). A study of the topical songs, the strike songs, and songs of protest produced in urban and rural America in the last seventy-five years.

GREIG Gavin. *Last Leaves of Traditional Ballads*, edited by Alexander Keith (Aberdeen, 1925). The best survey of the Scottish Child Ballads.

GUIDE. *A Guide to English Folk Song Collections*, 1822-1952, Margaret Dean-Smith (University Press of Liverpool, 1954). A fundamental, though incomplete, bibliographical index of folk songs in the English publications.

HAMPTON. *Religious Folk Songs of the Negro as sung at the Hampton Institute*, edited by Nathaniel Dett (G. Schirmer, 1927). One of the handiest compilations, with 165 songs.

HAYWOOD Charles. *A Bibliography of North American Folk Lore and Folk Song* (Greenburg, N.Y., 1951). 1,292 pp.; maps included. A 40,000 item bibliography organized by regions and types.

HOLBROOK Stewart H. *Holy Old Mackinaw* (Macmillan, N.Y., 1938). A riproaring history of the lumbering industry and the men who made the lumberjack ballads.

HURSTON Zora N. *Mules and Men* (Kegan Paul, London. Lippincott, Philadelphia, 1935). The best single book on Negro folklore in the U.S.

INDEX. An Index to the songs published in the *Journal of the English Folk Dance and Song Society* since 1888. An invaluable reference book.

JACKSON I George P. *White Spirituals of the Southern Uplands* (University of North Carolina Press, 1933).

JACKSON II. *Spiritual Folksongs of Early America* (J. J. Augustin, N.Y., 1937).

JACKSON III. *Down East Spirituals* (ibid , 1941).

JACKSON IV. *White and Negro Spirituals* (ibid., 1944). Dr. Jackson in these volumes has done the greatest single job in American folk-song scholarship.

JAFL. *Journal of American Folklore*, 1888—various editors, now published in Philadelphia, University of Pennsylvania. Scholarly articles on every phase of American folklore.

JEFSS. *Journal of the English Folk Dance and Song Society*, various editors (Cecil Sharp House, Regents Park Road, London, 1899 onwards).

JOHNSON T. W. and R. *The Book of American Negro Spirituals* (Viking Press, 1925). The best standard collection with most of the finest songs.

JOYCE P. W. *Old Irish Folk Music and Songs* (Longmans, London, 1909). A large collection of Irish tunes, many versions of which are sung in the U.S.A.

KEPHART Horace. *Our Southern Highlanders* (Macmillan, N.Y.C., 1922). A sympathetic and colourful study of the Southern mountaineer, in the days before railroads and roads had disturbed old-fashioned mountain life.

KOLB S. and J. *A Treasury of American Folk Songs* (Bantam Books, N.Y., 1948).

KORSON I. *Minstrels of the Mine Patch*, ed. George Korson (University of Pennsylvania Press, Philadelphia, 1938).

KORSON II. *Coaldust on the Fiddle* (University of Pennsylvania Press, 1943). In these and other books George Korson completely surveys the folk-song tradition of the American coal-miner.

LAWS G. M. (Jr.) *Native American Balladry, A Bibliographical Survey* (American Folklore Society, Philadelphia, 1950). A study of American ballads parallel to the Coffin study of the Child ballads.

LEACH Maria. *Standard Dictionary of Folklore, Mythology and Legand* (Funk and Wagnall, 1949). A superb two-volume encyclopædia covering the whole field.

LINSCOTT E. H. *Folk Songs of Old New England* (Macmillan, N.Y., 1939).

LOMAX I. *Cowboy Songs*, ed. John A. and Alan Lomax (Macmillan Publishing Co., N.Y., 1938).

LOMAX II. *American Ballads and Folk Songs* (ibid., 1934).

LOMAX III. *Negro Folk Songs as Sung by Lead Belly* (ibid., 1936). Out of print. The songs now appear in *Leadbelly* (Ludlow Publishing Co., N.Y., 1959).

LOMAX IV. *Our Singing Country* (ibid., 1941). Out of print.

LOMAX V. *Folk Song: U.S.A.*, ibid., (Duell, Sloan & Pearce, 1947). Also *Best Loved American Ballads* (Grosset & Dunlap).

MACKENZIE I W. Roy. *Ballads and Sea Songs from Nova Scotia* (Harvard University Press, 1928). A fine collection with exhaustive reference notes to British sources.

MACKENZIE II. *The Quest of the Ballad* (Princeton University Press, 1919). The best account of collecting ballads.

MASTERSON James R. *Tall Tales of Arkansas* (Chapman and Grimes, Boston, 1943).

NEWELL W. W. *Games and Songs of American Children* (Harper Bros., N.Y., 1883-1911). A fine collection of Anglo-American games with good references to British sources.

ODUM I H. W. with G. B. Johnson. *The Negro and his Songs* (University of North Carolina Press, Chapel Hill, N.C., 1925).

ODUM II ibid. *Negro Workaday Songs* (1926). Two invaluable collections of texts from the South-East.

ODUM III. *Rainbow Round My Shoulder* (Bobbs Merrill, Indianapolis, 1928). A fabulous autobiography of a wandering Negro worker, singer, and guitar player, giving the setting for work songs and blues.

OPIE Peter and Iona. *Oxford Dictionary of Nursery Rhymes* (Oxford University Press, 1951). The best reference work in this field, exhaustive notes.

ORD John. *The Bothy Songs and Ballads of Aberdeen, etc.* (Alexander Gardner, Glasgow, 1930). A fine collection of farm-workers' ballads from north-east Scotland, with many American parallels.

PARRISH Lydia. *Slave Songs of the Georgia Sea Islands* (Creative Age Press, N.Y., 1942). Excellent collection skilfully transcribed. Important background information on songs plus good bibliography.

PEATTIE Roderick. *The Great Smokies and the Blue Ridge* (Vanguard Press, 1943). The best single book on the richest region for American folk songs, much used in the preparation of this volume.

RANDOLPH I-IV. *Ozark Folk Songs*, collected and edited by Vance Randolph in four volumes (State Historical Society, Columbia, Missouri, 1946-50). The best edited, most complete, and best documented of the regional collections. Hundreds of songs. An invaluable work.

RANDOLPH V. *Ozark Superstitions* (Columbia University Press, N.Y., 1947). In this as in his many other works on the Ozarks Mr. Randolph gives us a complete and mature picture of his subject.

REEVES James. *The Idiom of the People* (Heinemann, London, 1958). An edition of unpublished texts from the Sharp MSS, throwing an entirely new light on the frankly erotic character of southern English songs.

RICHARDSON E. A. with S. Spaeth. *American Mountain Songs* (Greenburg, N.Y., 1927, new edition, 1955). An excellent collection of unfamiliar songs, well arranged.

RICKABY Franz. *Ballads and Songs of the Shantey Boy* (Harvard University Press, 1926). The first and best of lumberjack ballad collections.

RITCHIE Jean. *Singing Family of the Cumberlands* (Oxford University Press, 1955). A beautifully written family history, by a mountain girl who grew up with the Kentucky mountain songs and thoroughly explains their setting.

SANDBURG Carl. *The American Songbag* (Harcourt, Brace & Co., N.Y., 1927). The first, the saltiest, and the most charming general anthology.

SCARBOROUGH Dorothy. *On the Trail of Negro Folk Songs* (Harvard University Press, 1925). An account of folk-song collecting in the deep South with many little-known songs.

SEARS. *The Song Index*, and its supplement (H. W. Wilson Co., N.Y., 1926). A bibliographical survey of a wide variety of songbooks of all types, including some folk song collections. An invaluable guide to semi-popular folky songs of the recent past.

SHARP I and II Cecil, with Maud Karpeles. *English Folk Songs of the Southern Appalachians*, 2 vols. (Oxford University Press, 1932). The finest collection of the most beautiful of the Appalachian songs. Sharp's collections of songs from the southern counties of England are equally important. *See* Guide.

THOMPSON Harold W. *Body, Boots and Britches* (J. B. Lippincott, Philadelphia, 1940). A delightful, scholarly survey of this field.

WEBB W. P. *The Great Plains* (Ginn & Co., 1931). The best book on the development of this area and source for many of the ideas in the western section.

WELLS Evelyn. *The Ballad Tree* (The Ronald Press, N.Y., 1950). A sympathetic and scholarly study of the background of the Child ballads in Britain and the U.S.

WHALL W. B. *Sea Songs, Ships, and Shanties* (James Brown, Glasgow, 1920). Perhaps the best single English publication on sailor folk songs. Valuable notes.

WHITE Newman I. *American Negro Folk Songs* (Harvard University Press, 1928). Good references to printed sources of Negro minstrel types.

APPENDIX II. GUITAR AND BANJO GUIDE

THE GUITAR

by ALAN LOMAX

TUNING

Tune your guitar to a piano as follows: First string to E above middle C; 2nd to B below middle C; 3rd to next G below that B; 4th to next D below that G; 5th to next A below that D; 6th and thickest string to bass E below that A. Or use a guitar pitch pipe.

THE CHORDS

In Diagram I the black dots indicate where the strings are to be pressed down (or fretted). The numbers above each chord indicate which fingers are to be used. Broken lines indicate that a finger is pressed flat across one or more strings. X's mark strings *not* to be played in the chord. Unmarked strings are to be played open (i.e. *not* fretted).

You will find on the diagram the main major, minor, modal and blues chords used in the keys of F, C, G, D, A, E, Dm, Am, Em, Bm, F#m and C#m. The principal chords in the keys of G and Em are indicated by arrows. The principal chords for the other keys lie around their key chords in the same spatial relationship. Note: To find the chord family for any key draw the arrows from that chord, in the same pattern as on the diagram for G or Em.

DIAGRAM I   Guitar Chords

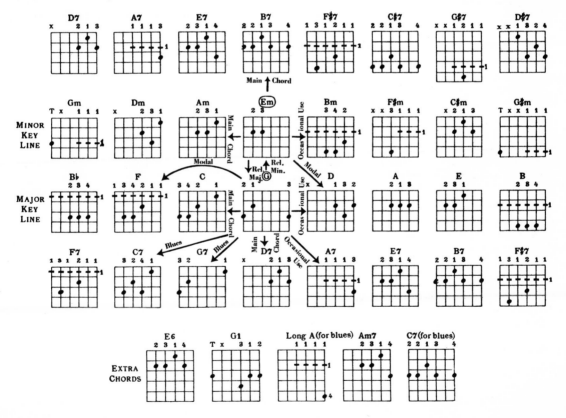

In order to play other keys, or if you wish to avoid learning all the chords in the diagram, use a capo. The capo fits round the neck of the guitar and clamps across the finger board so that all the strings are fretted at once. Each time you move it up a fret, you change the pitch of all the strings a semitone. Clamp it down at the back of the first fret and play C position chords. Actually you will be playing in the difficult key of C♯. Play your D chords, and you will be playing in E♭. Play the key of E positions and you will be playing in F.

RIGHT HAND STYLES.

1 *Strumming*

Thumb alone ; thumb and three fingers ; or thumb and first finger.

(a) The thumb plucks or strokes the first string of the chord. In Em, this is E. (b) The thumb (or three fingers or first finger) moves down across the remainder of the strings for the second beat of the measure. Repeat ad lib., using the three bass strings of the chord in turn for step (a).

The rhythm is $\frac{2}{4}$ with two beats of equal length, that is, *bump-di* (♩ ♩). For waltz-time (or $\frac{3}{4}$, with three equal beats), repeat step (b) twice.

NOTE : Strumming can also be free. Let the melody and chord changes determine where you support the song with casually strummed chords.

2A *Plucking.* Simple $\frac{2}{4}$ and $\frac{3}{4}$.

(a) Pluck one of the bass strings with a downward motion of the thumb. (b) The index, middle and ring fingers pluck up on the three treble strings all together. For $\frac{3}{4}$ time, repeat step (b).

2B $\frac{3}{8}$ *and* $\frac{6}{8}$ *time*

(a) Pluck down with thumb on a bass string. (b) Pluck up with all three fingers on three treble strings together. Step (b) is short and quick. The rhythm is *bump-iy* (♩ ♪).

NOTE : In slower $\frac{3}{8}$ and $\frac{6}{8}$ tunes, waltz-time rhythm is often effective.

3A *Arpeggio or Rippling Styles.* Simple $\frac{2}{4}$

(a) Pluck down on a bass string with thumb. (b) Index finger plucks up on G string. (c) Middle finger plucks up on B string. (d) Ring finger plucks up on E string ; in the rhythm *bump-uh-di-di* (♫ ♫)

3B Simple $\frac{3}{4}$ *or waltz time*

(a) Pluck down with thumb on bass string. (b) Play the above steps in the following sequence : b-c-d, c-d ; or b-c-d, b-c. The rhythm then becomes *bump-uh-di-di-di-di* (♫ ♫ ♫) .

3C *Woody's Lick*

Woody Guthrie, the Okie balladeer, sings many of his best long ballads to a combination pluck and arpeggio. You play alternate strokes of 2A and 3A, or, for waltz time, 2A waltz and 3 B.

4 *The Scratch*

This is the most useful, easy lick for hillbilly songs, square-dance tunes, and lots more.

$\frac{2}{4}$ *time*. Start counting four equal beats. (a) The thumb plucks down on bass string and accounts for the first two beats. (b) The index finger, held almost perpendicular to the strings, takes the third beat, by moving down across the three treble strings, ' scratching ' them with the back of the nail. (c) Once down, the index finger immediately scratches back up across several of the treble strings for the fourth beat. The second half of the measure is thus split in two and the rhythm is *bump-dĭ-dĭ* (♩ ♫).   Be sure to accent the thumb and the down scratch.

$\frac{3}{4}$ *or waltz time.*   (a) The thumb plucks down on bass string.   (b) Index finger scratches down-up, down-up.   The rhythm is thus *bump-dĭ-dĭ-dĭ-dĭ* (♩ ♫♫) .

5A *Carter Family Lick*

(a) Start a good scratch going, as above.   (b) With index finger keeping up the rhythm, pick out the melody on the bass strings with the thumb.   This is very easy to do in the keys of C and G. There are various devices that make this style even more interesting.

Hammering on.   What you actually do here is to split the rhythm of the (a) or bass part of any measure.   For instance, in the E minor chord, you can pluck the A string open, then strike it with the second finger of the left hand on the second fret, sounding the note B.   Then scratch the treble strings.   Next pluck the D string open, then strike it with the ring finger on the second fret, sounding the note E.   Then scratch the treble string.   You can hammer on, inside any chord.   The effect is to add a bit of syncopation.   The rhythm of the $\frac{2}{4}$ scratch is changed to *bump-ŭh-dĭ-dĭ* (♫ ♫).

Pulling off is just the reverse of hammering on.   For instance, if you are scratching in E minor chord, pluck the second bass string to sound B, then pull the second finger off quickly and slightly to the side of the string, sounding an open A.   This device, too, can be applied anywhere in the chord.

NOTE: You can *hammer on* or *pull off* any string, whether first plucked by the right hand or not.

5B *Clawhammer Picking*

In this style, the melody is picked out on the treble strings against a constantly moving bass.

(a) The thumb plucks down on the first bass string, as, simultaneously, the index finger plucks *up* on one of the treble strings.   (b) The thumb then strums down alone across all the strings.   (c) Step (a) is repeated, with thumb and index finger picking different strings as the melody requires.   (d) The thumb strums down across all the strings.   The rhythm is $\frac{2}{4}$ *bump-dĭ* (♩ ♩) .

NOTE :   When you have mastered the mechanics of this stroke, you can start playing tunes on the treble strings.

The index finger may pluck a treble string with any thumb stroke—in between the thumb strokes, if the melody requires it.

5C *Single-string Picking*

This is a variation on the exchange between bass and treble strings, between thumb and index finger, as shown in 5B, but performed entirely on single strings.

(a) With the E chord, for instance, play first low E (string 6 open), then the E above (on fretted 4th string).   Keep the thumb plucking these two notes one after another, swinging easily and regularly from one to another in $\frac{2}{4}$ rhythm *bump-dĭ* (♩ ♩) .   (b) Then pick out the melody with the index finger thus :   with every thumb pluck, pick a note of the tune with the index finger on a treble string.   Keep the bass rocking as above.   (c) If you wish the melody to be played off-beat, the index finger may pluck after the thumb, instead of with it.   The rhythm will be *bump-ŭh-dĭ-dĭ* (♫ ♫).

6A *The Lullaby Lick*

This is another variation on the $\frac{2}{4}$ arpeggio, which sounds nice with lullabies, and soft, gentle tunes.

(a) Pluck down with thumb on bass string. (b) Pluck G with index finger. (c) Pluck B and E with two fingers together. (d) Repeat step (b). Then repeat the pattern to the rhythm *bump-uh-di-di* (♪♪ ♪♪). For $\frac{3}{4}$ time, simply repeat steps (c) and (d) : a-b-c-d-c-d.

6B *Arpeggio in $\frac{3}{8}$ and (or) $\frac{6}{8}$*

(a) Pluck a bass string with the thumb. (b) Pluck up with index finger on G string. (c) Pluck up with one or two fingers on one or two top strings. Repeat ad lib. with varying combinations of bass and treble strings. The rhythm is *bump-uh-iy* (♩♩♩). This smooth stroke may be alternated with measures of 2B.

7A *Slow Rock*

This is a simple strum with a damp added. In order to damp a string, you stop the sound by touching the heel or palm of your right hand on that string. This adds 'rock' to the rhythm. Damping is indicated by letters 'mmmp'.

(a) Stroke down across one or several strings with the thumb. (b) Strum down across all treble strings with the backs of the fingers, then damp all strings instantly. Both beats are strongly accented. The rhythm is *bump-bummmp* (♩ ♩).

7B *Fast rock*

This is a scratch with damping added.

(a) Thumb strokes across some bass strings. (b) Scratch down *hard* to make the strong accent in the measure, then damp instantly. (c) Scratch back up again. The rhythm is *bump-dmmmp-di* (♩ ♩♪). Hammering on and pulling off may be added.

7C *Blues Lick*

Good for blues and work songs.

(a) Strum down with strong accent across the first four or five strings, using the thumb. Damp instantly. (b) Strum back up across two or three of the treble strings with the ball of the index finger. The rhythm is *UMP - di* (♩. ♩). Sometimes the player begins on the offbeat (*di*), but *UMP* remains the main beat of each measure. In this stroke, as in others, rhythmic interest will come by splitting the beats up in various ways.

THE FIVE-STRING BANJO
by PEGGY SEEGER

TUNING

There are three common tunings :

(a) 'G' *tuning* (Diagram IIA). Beginning with the shortest string, and strumming away from you, you tune them as follows: 5th is G above middle C on the piano; 4th is D below middle C; 3rd is G below middle C ; 2nd is B below middle C ; 1st is D above middle C.

(b) 'G minor' *tuning* (Diagram IIB). This is the same as 'G' tuning, except that the 2nd string is tuned down to B♭ below middle C.

(c) 'C' *tuning* (Diagram III). This is the same as 'G' tuning, except that the 4th string is tuned down to C below middle C.

604

DIAGRAM IIA Chords For G Tuning (Banjo)   IIB Chords For G Minor Tuning

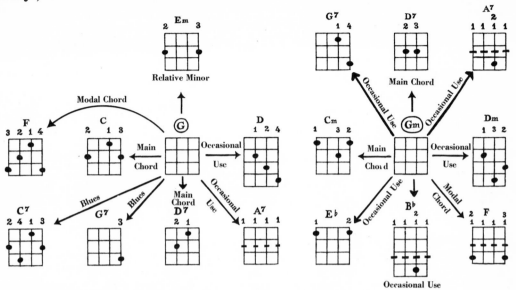

THE CHORDS

In the chord diagrams, the black dots indicate where the strings are to be fretted. The numbers above each chord indicate which fingers are to be used. The dashes indicate where a finger (usually the index finger) is pressed flat across one or more strings. The chords are ranged in families with related chords grouped around them, and marked by labelled arrows.

USE OF THE CAPO

The capo is a clamp which fits around the banjo neck and frets all the strings at once. When you move it up one fret, you raise the pitch of the capoed strings by a semitone. Each time you capo up, you must re-tune the 5th string accordingly. The capo facilitates playing in other keys than the C(m) and G(m) positions given.

To play in the key of D minor, capo up to the second fret, play C minor position; tune 5th string to A or D. For Am, capo to 2nd fret, play Gm position; 5th string to A or E. For Em, capo to 4th fret, play Cm position; 5th string to B or E. For D, capo to 2nd fret, play C position; 5th string to A or D. For A, capo to 2nd fret, play G position; 5th string to E or A. For E, capo to 4th fret, play C position; 5th string to B or E. For songs in other keys, such as F, it will be easier for the singer to modulate up or down to another key.

NOTE : To work out the chord families, consult the layout of chords in the guitar manual.

THE RIGHT HAND STYLES

1 *The Basic Strum*. In $\frac{2}{4}$ time. Count four equal beats.

(a) The Index finger plucks up on 3rd or 4th string. Count two beats. (b) The other three fingers brush down across 1st, 2nd, and 3rd strings together for the third beat ; (c) thumb plucks

5th string for the 4th beat. Repeat ad lib. to a rhythm of *bump-did-di* (♩ ♫)

In $\frac{3}{4}$ *or waltz time.* The rhythm, *bŭmp-dĭd-dĭ-dĭd-dĭ* (♩ ♫ ♫). Play as before, but repeat (b) and (c) (i.e., a-b-c-, b-c.).

There are two variations on basic strum (melodic and rhythmic) ($\frac{2}{4}$ and $\frac{3}{4}$).

Hammering On, is an addition made by the left hand.   For instance, in the key of C :   Pluck 3rd string with index finger. Then with 2nd finger of left hand strike or hammer down on the 2nd fret of the same string. Complete strum as above. The resulting rhythm is *bŭmp-ă-dĭd-dĭ* (♫ ♫).

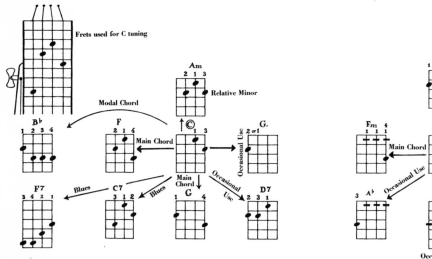

DIAGRAM IIIA   C Tuning with C Major Chord Family
(Banjo)

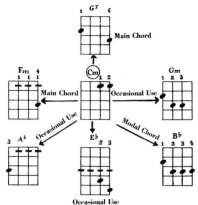

IIIB   C Tuning with C Minor Chord Family

Pulling Off, is the reverse.   Fret a C chord with the 2nd finger already *on* the 3rd string 2nd fret. (a) Pluck 3rd string with index finger.   (b) Pull 2nd finger down off that string to the side, so that the string sounds the unfretted note.   Complete strum as before.   You can hammer on or pull off from any note *within* the chord played.

2A *Double-thumbing* (Simple).   Count 4 equal beats.

(a) Index finger plucks 1st string. (b) Thumb plucks 2nd string.   (c) Fingers brush across all strings. (d) Thumb plucks 5th string.

2B *Complex double-thumbing.*   Count 4 equal beats.

(a) Index finger plucks 1st string. (b) Thumb plucks 2nd string.   (c) Index finger plucks 1st or 2nd string. (d) Thumb plucks 5th string. The rhythm for both 2A and 2B is *bŭmp-ă-dĭd-dĭ* (♫ ♫).

NOTE : this style can also be played ' backwards ' : (a) thumb plucks 3rd ; (b) index finger plucks 1st ; (c) thumb plucks 5th ; (d) index finger plucks 1st.

3 *Frailing*

This is the same rhythm as the basic strum (1) but it makes a rougher sound. (a) Move the slightly clenched hand down across all strings, striking the first string with the back of the nail of the

606

index finger. (b) Still with hand clenched, brush all the strings with downward movement. (c) Play 5th string with thumb. You can apply double-thumbing techniques here, too.

4A $\frac{3}{8}$ and $\frac{6}{8}$ time

   i   (a) Pluck with thumb on *any* string (5th included). (b) Hammer on or pull off *any* string. (c) Brush down across all strings. Repeat, playing different string in step (a). The rhythm is

bŭmp-ŭh-tў (♩♩♩).

   ii   (a) Pluck any low string (e.g., 4th) with thumb. (b) Pluck an adjacent higher string (e g. 3rd) with index finger. (c) Pluck with 2nd finger (or 2nd and 3rd fingers) the next adjacent higher string (or strings, if two fingers used). As before, the string used in step (a) must be varied.

Rhythm is *bŭmp-ŭh-tў* (♩♩♩).

   NOTE : These two strokes may be mixed for variety.

4B *Lullaby Style*

   (a) Thumb plucks 4th string ; (b) Index finger plucks 3rd string. (c) 2nd and 3rd fingers simultaneously pluck 2nd and 1st strings. (d) Repeat step (b), usually on same string. Repeat smoothly to rhythm of *bŭmp-ă-dĭd-dĭ* (♩♩♩♩).

5A *Whamming* (Good for songs with a heavy beat)

   (a) Brush fingers down over strings. (b) Hammer on or pull off any string with left hand. (c) Repeat step (a). (d) Brush fingers *back* across all strings. Steps (a) and (c) should be accented.

The rhythm is *bŭmp-ŭh-dĭd-dĭ* (♩.♩♩.♩).

5B To elaborate this :

   (a) With slightly clenched hand brush down across all strings. (b)Repeat step (a). (c) Repeat step (a) again. (d) The hand then brushes back up across all strings once. This should give the same rhythm as in 5A but this is a slightly more energetic stroke, i.e., *bŭmp-dĭ bŭmp-dĭ* (♩.♩♩.♩).

   NOTE : in both styles of whamming, waltz time may be obtained by repeating the final two motions of the right hand, the desired rhythm being *bŭmp-dĭ bŭmp-dĭ bŭmp-dĭ* (♩.♩♩.♩♩.♩).

APPENDIX III. DISCOGRAPHY

A Selected List of LPs
of American Folk Songs

The best way to learn to sing or to understand folk music is to study authentic recordings. The singing styles and the playing techniques of traditional singers and musicians carry at least half of the emotional and aesthetic messages of folk song. Students or would-be performers who neglect these stylistic features, because they are too strange or difficult, will never reach their goals. It is far better to become thoroughly acquainted with one body of material at a time than to try to swallow too much at once. And, in my belief, it is a waste of time to learn songs in the manner of one of the urban singers of folk songs. Better go straight to the source.

The majority of recommended records in this list are by traditional singers. Of these perhaps the best are: *Anglo-American Ballads,* Library of Congress No. 1; *Mississippi Prison Songs; Spirituals* by Dock Reed and Vera Hall; and *Anthology Of American Folk Music,* Folkways. I also commend for your pleasure some of the contemporary urban folk music to be found on the items labelled blue grass, modern blues and gospel. Here folk music is still growing from its traditional roots, but with urban influence. Among these try LITTLE WALTER or MUDDY WATERS for blues; *Knee Deep in Blue Grass* by Bill Monroe and any of the Scruggs records for blue grass; and *The Ward Concert* on Savoy for gospel. Finally, I have included a number of the most interesting records made by the folkniks—the urban singers of folk songs—where these singers have learned to perform with some folk feeling or where they present songs otherwise unavailable on record.

The list follows the general plan of this book, with four main sections, SONGS FROM THE NORTH, SONGS FROM THE WHITE SOUTH, SONGS FROM THE WEST, NEGRO SONGS, followed by an introductory section, called GENERAL. Under the latter fall the records whose contents cross regional lines, along with a number of British and Canadian albums, important for background. The records within each section are arranged alphabetically by title or main singer and brief descriptive comments accompany each entry.

A catalogue of the records issued by the *Archive of American Folk Song,* Library of Congress, Washington, D.C., may be obtained by writing the Librarian and then the items must be sent for by mail. *Folkways Records,* 117 West 46th Street, New York City, publishes an even larger catalogue, also available by mail, although these records may be bought in the stores as well. Popular records labels, such as Columbia, Vanguard and Elektra may be obtained through your local record dealer, although he may not have them in stock. He will certainly be unfamiliar with many of the labels such as Chess, Starday, and Folkcraft. For these records try the specialty stores in your area, or apply to the following shops:

For hillbilly and blue grass: Melody Lane Record Ranch, 73 Franklin Square, L.I., New York. For blues and gospel, Kenny's, 148 West 125th Street, New York City. For square dance records: Frank Kaltman, 1159 Broad Street, Newark, N.J., publisher of *Folkcraft.*

This list is based in part on a title catalogue published in *Folksingers and Folksongs In America,* Ray M. Lawless, Duell Sloane and Pearce, 1960.

GENERAL

Records which touch one or more regions, historical records, British records.

ALMANAC Singers, The: Deep Sea Ballads and Sod Buster Ballads; Commodore—COM DL 30002 12″; Woody Guthrie, Lee Hays, Pete Seeger sing genuine songs with moving power.

AMERICAN History, Songs and Ballads of; (D. Emrich) Lib. of Cong.—AAFS L 29 12″; Topical ballads, folk performers; amusing but of secondary interest.

ANGLO-American Ballads; (A. Lomax ed.); Lib. of Cong.—AAFS L 1 12″; The best record in the field. Texas Gladden, our finest singer, along with others almost as good.

ANGLO-American Songs and Ballads; (D. Emrich ed.); Lib. of Cong. AAFS: L 12, L 14, L 20, L 21; Four good records presenting interesting cross-sections of many types and from many regions; authentic singers.

ANGLO-American Shanties, Lyric Songs, Dance Tunes, and Spirituals; (A. Lomax ed.); Lib. of Cong. AAFS L 12″; Star performances by the best folk artists; a must.

ANTHOLOGY of American Folk Music: American Ballads; Part 3 (H. Smith ed.) Folkways FA 2953 (FP 253) 12″; Dubbings from the best early commercial recordings by great southern Negro and white performers; the best single collection.

BADEAUX, Ed: *American Guitar;* Folkways FG 3534 12″; illustrates several guitar styles with appropriate songs.

BAHAMAN Songs, French Ballads and Dance Tunes, Spanish Religious Songs and Game Songs; Lib. of Cong. AAFS L 5 12″; First field recordings from Bahamas, Cajun Louisiana, Texas—Mexicans.

BALLAD Hunter, The: John A. Lomax talks and plays his field recordings. Lib. of Cong.: AAFS L 49: *Cheyenne;* Western songs; *Blues, and Hollers;* L 50: *Chisholm Trail;* Country songs; *Rock Island Line,* Negro railroad and work songs; L 51: *Two Sailors,* clipper ship and canal songs; *Boll Weevil,* seven boll weevil songs; L 52: *Spirituals,* Negro; *Railroad Songs,* Negro railroad work songs; L 53: *Jordon and Jubilee,* Negro spirituals; *Sugarland,* Texas Negro prison songs.

BARRY, Margaret: *Songs of An Irish Tinker Lady;* Riverside RLP 12-602 12″; Barry, a virtuosic gypsy street singer performs modern come-all-ye's.

BRAND, Oscar: *GI American Army Songs* (assist. by F. Hellerman); Riverside RLP 12-639 12″; *The Wild Blue Yonder,* Elektra EKL-178; *Tell It To The Marines,* EKL-174; *Every Inch A Sailor,* EKL-169; Brand has assembled the modern topical songs of the services and sings them with pleasure.

CARAWAN Sings; Folkways FG 3544 12″; A serious city singer with a good voice who cares about folk song style and content.

CLANCY Brothers and Tommy Makem, *The Rising Of The Moon,* Tradition TLP 1006 12″; *Come Fill Your Glass With Us,* Tradition TLP 1032 12″. Born in Ireland the Clancy Brothers rant Irish songs of drink and rebellion in grand style. Tommy Makem is superb.

ELLIOT, Jack and Derroll Adams: *The Rambling Boys;* Topic Records 10 T 14 10″; Jack, the unique folknik, has absorbed completely the style and mannerisms of the field singer and performs with a fine California banjo player.

ENGLAND; A. Lomax and Peter Kennedy (col. and ed.);

Columbia KL-206; Field recordings of genuine folk singers from all parts of England.

ENGLISH And Scottish Popular Ballads, The: sung by Ewan MacColl and A. L. Lloyd. Vol. 1; Riverside RLP 12-621 12″; The classic British ballads recorded by two accomplished city singers; some dull patches.

ENNIS, Seamus: *The Bonny Bunch Of Roses;* Tradition TLP 1013 12″; The finest British singer-musicologist sings and plays Uileann pipes. Beautiful.

FOLK MUSIC, USA: (collection edited by Moses Asch and Harold Courlander) Folkways FE 4530 12″; field recordings and old commercials blended to make a fine picture of genuine American balladry. Important.

FOLKSAY: Six Volumes: Stinson SLP-5, 6, 9, 11, 12, 13; these early recordings featuring Pete Seeger, Cisco Houston, Leadbelly, Bess Lomax, Woody Guthrie and others are a must for collectors.

GIBSON, Bob: *Carnegie Concert;* Riverside RLP 12-816; a vigorous youngster with a good voice and banjo, moving toward commercial success.

IRELAND, (collected and edited by Seamus Ennis and Alan Lomax) Columbia KL-4941; field recordings in which superb Gaelic English language singers sing exquisite tunes.

IVES, Burl: *The Wayfaring Stranger,* Stinson SLP 1 12″; The first and the best Ives recording with his Indiana folk-song background still showing. Recommended later Ives records on Columbia and Decca.

KINGSTON TRIO: From The Hungry i; Capitol CAP T-1107 12″; the first and best of the commercial college-boy folk groups. Genuine enthusiasm and humor.

LARK In The Morning, The: (col. and ed. Diane Hamilton); Tradition TLP 1004 12″; lovely songs and dances of Ireland sung by polished and genuine folk singers. Important.

LOMAX, Alan with Peggy Seeger and Guy Carawan: *Folksong Saturday Night;* Kapp-1110.

LISTEN To The Story: (A. Lomax ed.) Coral CLP 59001 10″; reprints of early and important commercial folk recordings of American Ballads.

LOMAX, John A. Jr.: *Sings American Folksongs;* Folkways FG 3508 12″; a straightforward presentation of favorite ballad songs from Texas.

LLOYD, A. L.: *Australian Bush Songs;* Riverside RLP 12-606 12″; the best of Lloyd who learned the ballads while working sheep in Australia.

LONESOME Valley: Pete Seeger, Lee Hays, Woody Guthrie, others; Folkways FA 2010 10″; a good early recording of these singers.

MacCOLL, Ewan and Peggy Seeger: *Bad Lads And Hard Cases,* Riverside RLP-12-632; *Bless 'Em All,* Riverside RLP 12-642; *British Industrial Folk Songs,* Stinson SLP 179 12″; *Classic Scots Ballads,* Tradition TLP 1015 12″; *Matching Songs of The British Isles And America,* Riverside RLP 12-637; *Shuttle And Cage,* Topic Records 10-T13 10″; *Scots Drinking Songs,* Riverside RLP 12-605. Manchester born of Scots working-class ballad singing parents, MacColl became poet and actor, then turned to ballad singing and is now without peer in dramatic presentation of British folksongs. Peggy, raised on Library of Congress field recordings, inheriting great musicality from her parents, has become the most sensitive musician of all city singers of folk songs.

McCURDY, Ed: "THE DALLIANCE SERIES": *When Dalliance Was In Flower* (Vol. 1–3); *Son Of Dalliance;* Elektra EKL- 110, 140, 160, 170; a trained voice, but a salty and perceptive person, Ed is perfect for these 18th century bawdy ballads.

NEW LOST CITY RAMBLERS, The: The New Lost City Ramblers; Folkways FA 2396 12"; three young folkniks have seriously studied 20th century mountain music for years and the result is charm, fine music and fun. Old Timey Songs For Children, Folkways FC 7064 12"; Songs From The Depression, Folkways FH 5264 12".

ODETTA: Ballads And Blues; Tradition TLP 1010 12"; a Chicago girl with a good voice. New, to Negro folk tradition, Odetta, occasionally rings the bell.

O'HARA, Mary: Songs Of Erin, London LL1572 12"; Songs Of Ireland, Tradition TLP 1024 12"; lovely fine-art performance of beautiful songs.

PLAY And Dance Songs and Tunes; (B. A. Botkin ed.) Lib. of Cong. AAFS L9 12"; fiddle, dulcimer, and banjo tunes with play-party games; good but secondary.

ROBERTSON, Jeannie: Songs Of A Scots Tinker Lady; Riverside RLP 12-633 12"; an Aberdeen Scots gypsy woman who is one of the great ballad singers of today.

ROBERTS, Robin: Fair And Tender Ladies (acc. on banjo by Erik Darling) Tradition TLP 1033 12"; tasteful singing of interesting Irish and American songs.

SANDBURG, Carl: Ballads And Songs: Lyrichord LL 66 12"; Swedish American ex-farmhand and hobo with poetic perception of folk essences.

SCOTLAND, (A. Lomax, H. Henderson, and others, col. and ed.) Columbia SL 209; field recordings of genuine singers from all parts of Scotland.

SEEGER, Peggy: Animal Folksongs For Children; Folkways FC 7051 10"; with Barbara and Penny Seeger: American Folksongs for Christmas, Folkways FC 7053 10"; Folksongs of Courting And Complaint, Folkways FA 2049 (FP 49); first class. See note on Ewan MacColl.

SEEGER, Pete: American Ballads, Folkways FA 2319 12"; American Folksongs For Children, Folkways FC 7001 12"; American Industrial Ballads, Folkways FH 5251 12"; At Carnegie Hall With Sonny Terry, Folkways FA 2412 12"; Darlin' Corey, Folkways FA 2003 (FP 3); Nonesuch And Other Folk Tunes, Folkways FA 2439 12"; 5-String Banjo Instructor, Folkways FI 8203; The Folksingers Guitar Guide, Folkways FI 18354; A wonderful musician, tireless worker for folk music, true idealist and leader—Pete sings straight and his honesty and charm are winning America. For Folkways he has recorded a huge catalogue of songs. Fabulous mass-song leader—see FA 2412. Instructions records difficult but basic.

SEEGERS: American Folk Songs Sung By The Seegers, Penny, Barbara and Mike Seeger; Folkways FA 2005 10"; my favorite city folksinger record.

SONGS Of Work And Freedom; Washington 460; Union songs, songs of democracy.

STAFFORD, Jo: American Folk Songs, with orchestra; Capitol H-75 10"; a "pop" singer with a warm feeling for folksong.

SQUARE DANCE Group, American: Running Set and Longways Dances; (Margot Mayo leader), Decca DL 8012 12"; Miss Mayo was the founder of the American folk dance revival and the New York City folksong revival. Basic instruction record. For other square dance records see the Southern and Western sections.

TALKING UNION: Pete Seeger, Woody Guthrie, Josh White . . . Folkways FH 5285 12"; the classic recording of American folksongs of protest.

WARNER, Frank: American Folksongs and Ballads; Elektra EKL-3 10"; Our Singing Heritage (acc. by Billy Faier), Elektra EKL 153 12"; Frank sings more like his field informants than they do themselves. My favorite male ballad singer.

WEAVERS At Carnegie Hall, The: Vanguard, VRS 9010 12"; The first of the city folksong groups and in many ways the best.

WHITE, Josh: Ballads and Blues, Decca DL 8665 12"; Josh White Sings, Stinson SLP 15 10"; urbanized folksinger; fantastic guitar; romantic and moving singer.

WOOD, Hally: American Folk Songs Of Sadness And Melancholy, Elektra EKL 10 10"; faithful to the letter of folk sources Hally catches the essence of the lonesome song tradition.

THE NORTH

THE NORTH, including New England, Nova Scotia, Newfoundland, Canada, sea and lumberjack songs.

ALLEGHENY Mountains, Folksongs of the: Sung by Patrick Gainer; Folk Heritage Recording DB 2122-3 12"; straight urban performance of universal material.

AMERICAN Revolution, Story Of The: two singers, chorus, fife and drum band performing unusual topical songs of the period. See also House and Ives.

BLUESTEIN, Gene: Songs Of The North Star State: (Minnesota) Folkways FA 2132; spirited performance of unusual material in several languages.

CANADIAN Northwoods Ballads: Sung by Wade Hemsworth; Folkways FW 6821 (FP 821) 10"; straight urban performance of unusual material.

CANADIAN FOLKSONGS: (edited with notes by M. Barbeau) Vol 3 Columbia Lib of Folk and Primitive Music SL 211 12"; field recordings in English, Scots, French and Indian. Important.

CAPE BRETON ISLAND, Songs From The: (Recorded by S. R. Cowell) Folkways FE 4450 (P450); field recordings of fine Gaelic and other material.

CLAYTON, Paul: Bay State Ballads (Massachusetts) Folkways FA 2106 (FP 4722) 10"; sympathetic treatment of some rare songs by a good collector-singer. Whaling And Sailing Songs From The Days Of Moby Dick; Tradition TLP 1005.

ESKIN, Sam: Shanty Men; Folkways FA 2019 (FP 19) 10"; Eskin is near to the bone; recommended.

HAWES, Bess and Mickey Miller: American Folksongs; Folkways FA 2393; gentle, musical and lovely.

HUNTINGTON, E. G.; Folk Songs Of Martha's Vineyard; Folkways FA 2032 10"; straight urban performance of interesting material.

HOUSE, Wallace: Ballads Of The Revolution (1776–1781); Folkways FH 2152 (FP 48/2) 10"; good topical songs of the period.

IVES, Burl: Songs Of The Revolution; Encyclopedia Britannica Films; EBF Album II; good topical songs of the period.

LLOYD, A. L. and Ewan MacColl: Thar She Blows!, Riverside RLP 12-635 Blow Boys Blow (with Alf Edwards, Ralph Rinzler, Steve Benbow) Tradition TLP 1026 12"; Haul On The Bowlin', Stinson SLP 80 10", The best shanty records, spirited reconstruction, exciting.

LOY, Lawrence with the Pokeberry Promenaders HAR 7035; square dancing New England style.

LUMBERJACK Songs: sung by Ellen Stekert; Folkways FA 2345 12"; spirited collector-singer performs fresh material. See *Wolf River, Ontario, Canadian, Eskin* for other Lumberjack songs.

MacCOLL, Ewan: See LLOYD, A. L.

MILLS, Alan: *Folk Songs Of Newfoundland*, Folkways FW 6831 (FP 831); FW 8771; with the Shantymen: *Songs Of The Sea*, Folkways FA 2312 12"; Canada's most popular folksinger, virile and easy to listen to. Newfoundland record especially recommended.

MINERS, Songs and Ballads Of Anthracite: (G. Korson ed.), Lib of Cong AAFS L 16; miner bards singing their own stuff. Important but secondary.

NEW ENGLAND, British-American Ballads Of: Flanders Ballad Collection 12" lp; Child ballads sung by field singers. Good though dry.

NEWFOUNDLAND—See *Mills, Canadian*.

NEW YORK CITY: 1, 2, 3 And A Zing, Zing, Zing (Childrens' street songs collected by Tony Schwartz) Folkways FC 7003; *Music In The Streets* (col. Tony Schwartz), Folkways FD 5581; *Sounds Of My City* (T. Schwartz-col.), Folkways FP 7341; folksay and song imaginatively documented.

NOVA SCOTIA, Folk Music From: (recorded by H. Creighton), Folkways FM 4006 (P 1006) 12"; *Nova Scotia Folk Music From Cape Breton*, (recorded by Diane Hamilton), Elektra EKL 23 10"; *ONTARIO: Ontario Folksongs*: (recorded by Edith Fowke) Folkways FM 4005 12"; three important collections of field recordings that show the Canadian background of our Northern ballads.

SEA Songs and Shanties, American (D. Emrich ed.) (I, II) Lib of Cong I-AAFS L 26 12"; II-AAFS L 27 12"; recordings of the last of the clipper ship sailors. Important. See also: *Clayton, Lloyd, Eskin*.

WOLF RIVER Songs: (recorded by S. Robertson Cowell); Folkways FW 4001 (F 1001) 12"; genuine lumberjack singing from the middle west. Important.

WOODHULL, Floyd: *Woodhull's Old Tyme Masters*; Camden 220; The master of the New England Square dance style.

THE WHITE SOUTH, including Southern Appalachians, white spirituals, square dance music, banjo and guitar music, blue grass, hillbilly, gospel . . .

ACUFF, Roy: *Songs Of The Smoky Mountains*: Columbia HL 9004 10"; the most popular and genuine hillbilly singer of the '40s; a Tennessee "wailer".

BANJO In The Hills: Starday SLP 104 12"; a good cross-section of contemporary southern white entertainment music. Features blue grass and hillbilly (Stanley Bros., Carl Story . . .)

BANJO Songs Of The Southern Mountains: (Ken Goldstein, col.) Riverside RLP 12-610 12"; field recordings of folk banjo pickers from the southern mountains. Recommended.

CASH, Johnny: *Johnny Cash*; Sun Records LP 1220 12"; an original songmaker from Arkansas, popular in style but with folk roots. Recommended.

CARLISLE Brothers: *Fresh From The Country*: King 643; nice hillbilly.

CLAYTON, Paul: *Cumberland Mountain Folksongs*: Folkways FA 2007 10"; good material by a tasteful collector-singer.

COUNTRY Express: Starday SLP 109 12"; See note *Banjo In The Hills*.

COUNTRY Gentlemen: The Country Gentlemen; Folkways Fa 2409 12"; charming hillbilly trio in blue grass style. Recommended.

COUNTRY And Western Jamboree: King 697 12"; see note: *Banjo In The Hills*.

FLATT, Lester and Earl Scruggs with the Foggy Mountain Boys: *Country Music*, Mercury MER 20358 12"; *Foggy Mountain Jamboree*, Columbia CL 1019 12"; *Lester Flatt and Earl Scruggs*, Columbia HL 7250 12"; *Songs Of Glory*, Columbia CL 1424 12"; Scruggs started blue grass banjo and is still its finest exponent. Hillbilly ballads, gospel, original instrumentals performed at the peak of blue grass style. Try CL 1019.

JACKSON, Tommy: *Popular Square Dance*, Dot 3085; *Do Si Do*, Dot 3015 Dot 3163; master of the hot modern square dance fiddle.

JONES, Grandpa: *Grandpa Jones Sings His Greatest Hits*, King 554 12"; half comic, half folksinger; amusing.

KAZEE, Buell H.: *His Songs and Music*, (recorded by G. Bluestein), Folkways FS 3810 12"; a master folksinger and banjo picker from Kentucky. Strongly recommended.

LOMAX, Alan, Collector and Editor. Field recordings to be released in 1960–61 in stereo by Atlantic: *Blue Ridge Mountain Music* (blue grass); *Animal Folk Songs For Children* (ballads, lullabys, game songs, etc.); *White Spirituals*, E. C. Ball (with guitar and gospel quartet and Sacred Harp); childrens' record is pure folk; the others—modern mountain music. Acoustically exciting.

LOUVIN Brothers: *Tragic Songs Of Life*, Capitol EAP 3-769; fine folk hillbilly.

LUNSFORD, Bascom Lamar: *Minstrel Of The Appalachians*, Riverside RLP 12-645 12"; *Smoky Mountain Ballads*, Folkways FA 2040 (FP 40) 10"; great material; authentic and salty performance.

MAINER, J. E.: with Mountaineers: *J. E. Mainer*, King 666 12"; fine example of folk hillbilly of the last generation.

MAPHIS, Joe: *Fire On The Strings*, Columbia CL 1005 12"; the wildest, hottest, and fastest of mountain string musicians.

MARLIN, Sleepy: Folkcraft X-45-1324-5-6-7; Folkcraft X-45-1149-52; good southern mountain fiddling.

MARTIN, Jimmy: *Good N' Country*, Decca DL 4016; blue grass singer in the Bill Monroe style.

MONROE, Bill: with his Blue Grass Boys: *I Saw The Light*, Decca DL 8769 12"; *Knee Deep In Blue Grass*, Decca DL 8731 12"; *Bill Monroe and His Blue Grass Boys*, Decca ED2353 ext ply 45 rpm, ED 2354 ext ply 45 rpm; the leader of the first blue grass orchestra and still its most exciting singer DL 8731 is a must.

MOUNTAIN MUSIC Blue Grass Style: (recorded by M. Seegar), Folkways FA 2318 12"; little known and interesting blue grass musicians.

MOUNTAIN MUSIC Of Kentucky, (recorded by John Cohen); Folkways FA 2317 12"; fine documentary of eastern Kentucky folk music. Recommended.

NEW LOST CITY RAMBLERS, The: See *General Section*.

NILES, John Jacob: *American Folk Songs*, RCA Camden CAL 245 12"; talented collector-arranger; incredible counter-tenor.

OLD HARP SINGERS: Folkways FA 2356 12"; country

singers performing folk hymns in four-part shape notes. Interesting. See SACRED.

OSBORNE BROTHERS and Red Allen: MGM 3734; modern blue grass band with a special sound.

PALEY, Tom: Folk Songs From The Southern Appalachians, Elektra EKL 12 10"; one of the talented members of the New Lost City Ramblers.

PEGRAM, George and Walter Parham: Pickin' And Blowin'; Riverside RLP 12-650 12"; marvelous raw-boned mountain music with banjo and mouth harp. A must.

RAMSAY, Obray: Banjo Songs Of The Blue Ridge And Great Smokies, Riverside RLP 12-649 12"; a really fine contemporary southern mountain folk performer.

RENO, Don and Red Smiley: Reno and Smiley, King KEP 384; a favorite blue grass group; modern.

RITCHIE, Jean: American Folk Tales and Songs, (with Richard Chase and Paul Clayton); Tradition TLP 1011 12"; Field Trip, Collector Limited CLE 1201 12"; Kentucky Mountain Songs, Elektra EKL 125 12"; The Ritchie Family Of Kentucky, Folkways FA 2316 12"; Saturday Night And Sunday Too, Riverside RLP 12-620 12"; Songs From Kentucky, Westminster WP 6037 12"; Southern Mountain Children's Songs And Games, Folkways FC 7054 (FC 754) 12"; Traditional Songs Of Her Kentucky Mountain Family, Elektra EKL 2 10"; heritor of a rich family folk song background, Jean brings true artistry and refinement to her performances to make them the finest contemporary records of traditional Kentucky songs.

RODGERS, Jimmie: My Rough And Rowdy Ways, RCA Victor LPM 2112 12"; Never No Mo, Victor LPM 1232 12"; Train Whistle Blues, Victor LPM 1640 12"; yodeler and blues guitar picker, this Texas brakeman established hillbilly in national affections.

SACRED Harp Singing (G. P. Jackson and A. Lomax, col.) Lib. of Cong. AAFS L 11 12"; great music, marvelously sung; the folk hymns of the southern pioneers in four-part polyphony.

SCRUGGS, Earl: See Flatt

STANLEY BROTHERS, The: Country Pickin' And Singin', Mercury MG 20349 12"; Hard Times—I Worship You, Mercury 70546-X45 (45 rpm); The Stanley Brothers, Starday SLP 106 12"; Stanley Brothers, King 615 12"; closest blue grass group to mountain tradition. See MG 20349 and 70546-X45 expecially. A must.

SOUTHERN MOUNTAINS: See also under General Section— the Library of Congress records and The Folkways Anthology and Folk Music: USA.

STEELE, Pete: Banjo Tunes and Songs (recorded and edited by E. Kahn); Folkways FS 3828 12"; a fine folk performer from Kentucky; excellent material, but a little feeble.

STONEHAM FAMILY, The: American Banjo Tunes and Songs; Folkways FA 2315 12"; one of the first mountain singing families on commercial records, here recorded again and nice to listen to.

STONEY MOUNTAIN BOYS, The: Folk Songs From The Blue Grass, United Artists UAL 3049 12"; wild, wonderful, folky blue grass, poorly recorded but recommended.

TRAVIS, Merle: Back Home, Capitol T 891 12"; a hillbilly singer who has kept his love for genuine mountain balladry; lovely guitar. Five stars.

WEST, Harry and Jeanie: Gospel Songs, Folkways FA 2357 12"; Smoky Mountain Ballads, Esoteric ES 545 12"; More Southern Mountain Folk Songs, Stinson SLP 74 10";

Southern Mountain Folk Songs, Stinson SLP 36 10"; two Kentuckians now living in New York City recreate the authentic artistry of their backgrounds. Fine style and good listening.

THE WEST

From the Ozarks and Texas, on to the Pacific . . .

BENDER, Bill: Frontier Ballads and Cowboy Songs, Stinson SLP 18 10"; straight western; early recording; good.

BOUND FOR GLORY, Folkways FA 2481 (FP 78/1) 12"; Will Geer reads capsuled Guthrie life story with dubbings of Guthrie singing.

CAJUN Songs From Louisiana: Folkways FE 4438 FP 438 12"; interesting little-known Americana from southwest Louisiana.

CASENER, Bill: A Large Measure of Square Dance, Old Timer 2002; the California Square dance style.

COWBOY DANCES: Lloyd Shaw with orchestra, Decca DL 9003 12"; spectacular modern western square dance style, elaborate instruction set.

COWBOY Songs, Ballads, And Cattle Calls From Texas (recorded by John A. Lomax): Lib of Cong AAFS L28 12"; the real McCoy. Some great items and some not so great.

DRIFTWOOD, Jimmy: Jimmy Driftwood and the Wilderness Road, RCA Victor LPM 1944 12"; Newly Discovered Early American Folk Songs, RCA Victor LPM 1635 12"; The Westward Movement, RCA Victor LPM 2171 12"; descendant of the folk poets who wrote "Jesse James" and "Joe Bowers," Driftwood is America's wittiest contemporary folk bard. Fine, salty, sometimes corny, singing. The first mouth bow recording. 1635 strongly recommended.

ENGLISH, Logan: The Days Of '49, Folkways FH 5255 12"; spirited performance of little-known, but important, material.

FOSTER, Pat: with Dick Weissman: Gold In California, Riverside RLP 12-654 12"; spirited performance of important, but little-known, material.

GILMORE, Ed: Square Dance Party, Decca DL 9052; Learn Square Dancing, Decca DL 9051; Modern California square dancing.

GUTHRIE, Woody: Cowboy Songs (with Cisco Houston), Stinson SLP 32 10"; recommended; Folk Songs—Vol. I, Stinson SLP 44 10"; the first of a series of salty folk anthologies. Recommended; Songs To Grow On, Folkways FC 7015 (FP 715); the Oklahoma folk bard rhymes up delightful rib-ticklers for the kids. A must; Talking Dust Bowl, Folkways FA 2011 (FP11), a re-issue of the great Guthrie Dust Bowl Ballads from the 1937 Victor recordings. A must. See also Folksay in General Section.

HILTON, L. M.: Mormon Folk Songs, Folkways FA 2036; a Mormon ballad singer, a bit stuffy, but appealing.

HOUSTON, Cisco and Bill Bender: Traditional Songs Of The Old West, Stinson SLP 37 10"; good Western stuff.

JACKSON, Harry: The Cowboy, Folkways FHS 723 12"; a Wyoming ex-cowboy singing wild and free. The real McCoy. Recommended.

JONSEY: A Selection Of The Most Popular Calls, MacGregor 1204; the founder of California square dance calling. Good.

KRABER, Tony: Chisholm Trail, Mercury Mer 20008; a Montana singer gives a spirited performance.

LET'S SQUARE DANCE, Hollywood LPH 21; square dance, California style.

LOMAX, Alan, with Guy Carawan (banjo and guitar), *Texas Folk Songs*, Tradition TLP 1029 12".

LOUIS, Joe; *Square Dance Message*, Joe Louis 3301; California square dance style.

MORMONS, Songs Of The, and *Songs And Ballads Of The West*, (D. Emrich) Lib. of Cong. AAFS L 30 12"; field recordings from Utah. See also *Hilton*.

OSTER, Harry, collector and editor: *A Sampler Of Louisiana Folksongs*, Folk Lyric LSS 1201; Old French, French-Negro and English songs, field recordings: *Louisiana Folksong Jambalaya*, Folk Lyric LS A-2; field recordings.

RUFF, Bob: *The Student Dancers*, Sets in Order 4002/4005; square dance instruction.

STONE, Cliffie: *Promenade*, Capitol T 1286; the best of the square dance records.

WOOD, Hally: *Texas Folk Songs*, Stinson SLP 73; a Texas girl with a great feeling for the authentic sound. Very moving.

NEGRO SONGS, including spirituals, ring games, work songs, blues, jazz, modern blues, gospel and rock and roll.

AFRO-American Blues And Game Songs, (A. Lomax ed) Lib of Cong AAFS L 4; One of the most important field recordings.

AFRO-American Spirituals, Work Songs and Ballads (A. Lomax ed) Lib of Cong AAFS L 3 12"; Field recordings. A must.

ALABAMA, Negro Folk Music Of (Harold Courlander ed.), Six Volumes. Folkways FE 4417 (P 417), FE 4418 (P 418), FE 4471 (P 471), FE 4472 (P 472), FE 4473 (P 473), FE 4474 (P 474); spirituals, ring games, blues, hollers, folk tales from rural Alabama. Some fine things.

B. B. King: *Singin' The Blues*, Crown CLP 5020; the most popular modern blues singer in the South.

BECK, Elder Charles D., *Urban Holiness Service*, Folkways FR 8901 12"; exciting preaching, singing, trumpet blowing; recorded in church.

BLUES In The Mississippi Night (Col and ed by A. Lomax), United Artists UAL 4027; interview between three country blues musicians with illustrations of work songs, hollers and spirituals. A must.

BLUES, Riot In The, with Ray Charles, Hopkins, Sonny Terry, Brownie McGhee and others. Time-7006; good selection of modern blues.

BO DIDDLEY: *Have Guitar, Will Travel*, Checker U 2816; old country blues style with some rock and roll. Delightful.

BRADFORD, Alex: *Too Close To Heaven*, Specialty SP 2108 12"; a striking dynamic modern gospel singer. Recommended.

BROONZY, Big Bill: *Big Bill's Blues*, Columbia WL 111 12"; *Country Blues*, Folkways FA 2326 12"; *His Story*, (interview with Studs Terkel) Folkways FG 3586 12"; with Pete Seeger: *Folk Songs And Blues* (interview with Studs Terkel; with songs) Folkways FS 3864 12"; a great Mississippi blues singer who succeeded in the commercial record world. Always moving.

CARAVANS; Mary Don't You Weep—I'm Not Tired Yet, Gospel MG 3005 (45 rpm); exciting gospel chorus; recommended.

CAT IRON; Folkways FA 2389 12"; a fascinating Natchez folk blues performer. Recommended.

CHARLES, Ray: *In Person*, Atlantic 8039 12"; *Ray Charles At Newport*, Atlantic 1289 12"; the most exciting contemporary performer, pianist, singer, composer; uses religious folk for great rock and roll hits. A must.

COOKE, Sam: *The Soul Stirrers*, Specialty SP 2106 12"; A great modern gospel quartet. A must.

COTTON, Elizabeth: *Negro Folk Songs And Tunes*, Folkways FG 3526 12"; folk Negro guitar player; interesting style, early blues. Recommended.

COUNTRY Blues, The, (S. B. Charters ed.); Folkways RF 1 12"; re-issues of early commercial blues records. A classic.

DAVIS, Reverend Blind Gary: *The Singing Reverend*, Stinson SLP 56 10"; *Harlem Street Spirituals*, Riverside RLP 12-611 (disc also contains *Carolina Street Ballads* sung by Pink Anderson) like Ray Charles, but subtle, and pure folk. SLP-56, five stars.

DAVIS Sisters: *Shine On Me;* Savoy MG 14007 12"; swinging female gospel quintet.

DIXIE Hummingbirds: A Christian Testimonial, Peacock PLP 100 12"; considered by Negroes as the finest quartet today. A must.

DOGGETT, Bill: *On Tour*, King 667; one of the many recordings of this vital, rocking, modern singer.

DOMINO, Fats: *The Fabulous "Mr. D.";* Imperial LP 9055; a rock and roll piano man from New Orleans, loaded with charm. Modern folk jazz. Many good records.

EAGLIN, Snooks: *Snooks Eaglin*, Folkways FA 2476 12"; New Orleans street blues man with jazzy style. Nice.

FULLER, Jesse: *Working On The Railroad*, World Song EG 10-027 10"; *Work Songs, Blues, Spirituals*, Good Time Jazz L 12031 12"; Southern folk instrumentalist living in San Francisco. A fascinating original.

GATE CITY Singers: *Prayer Is The Key*, Mercury MG 3004 12"; rocking gospel chorus.

GOLDEN GATE Quartet: *Golden Gate Spirituals*, Columbia CL 6102 10"; fine folk tunes and texts swung in the manner of the '30s.

GOSPEL Caravan: *Gospel Caravan*, Revelation PLP 5001 12"; rocking gospel chorus.

GOSPEL Songs: Sung by the Missionary Quintet (recorded in the Bahamas); Folksways FW 6824 (FP 824) 10"; Negro spirituals, Bahaman style.

HARMONIZING Four: *Harmonizing Four*, Vee Jay LP 5002 12"; fine gospel quartet.

HIGHWAY QC'S, Vee Jay LP 5005; Rivals of the Hummingbirds and the Silvertones. Recommended.

HOOKER, John Lee: *The Country Blues*, Riverside 12838 12"; *The Blues*, Crown CLP 5157; *I'm John Lee Hooker*, Vee Jay 10007 12"; *Highway Of The Blues*, Audiolab 1520; Mississippi born country blues man now making hit records. Recommended.

HOPKINS, Lightnin': *Autobiography In Blues*, Tradition TLP 1040 12"; *Country Blues*, Tradition TLP 1035 12"; *Lightnin' Hopkins*, Folkways FS 3822 12"; *Lightnin' And The Blues*, Harold 1012; electrifying Texas blues guitarist and composer.

HOWLIN' WOLF: Howlin' Wolf, Chess LP1434; Great country blues man from Arkansas.

JACKSON, Mahalia: *Mahalia Jackson*, Columbia CL 644 12"; *Bless This House*, CL 899; two choice records among many by the grand diva of gospel. Recommended.

JAZZ, History of, (Frederic Ramsey Jr. ed.), 11 Volumes; Folkways FJ 2801, 2811; dubbings from all levels of

Afro-American records from work songs to Chicago jazz period. A wonderful set.

JAZZ, Riverside History Of: Riverside, 4 LPs 12-113-116; Another similar series but with more accent on "pop" jazz.

JEFFERSON, Blind Lemon: *Classic Folk-Blues,* Riverside RLP 12-125; *Folk-Blues,* Riverside RIV 1014 10"; One of the first and still the greatest of all Negro blues singer-composers, unmatched as a guitarist. Five Stars.

JOHNSON, Blind Willie: *His Story,* (recorded by S. B. Charters), Folkways FG 3585 12"; street singer of spirituals, and for me the most moving of them all.

JOHNSON, Lonnie: *Blues By Lonnie Johnson,* Prestige 1007; the great guitarist of New Orleans jazz, turned blues singer in the '30s, still great in retirement.

KNIGHT, Marie: *Songs Of The Gospel,* Mercury MG 20196 12"; the best female gospel shouter today. Recommend.

LEADBELLY: Last Sessions, Folkways 2941-2 4-12"; *Leadbelly's Legacy* Vol. 3 (earliest known commercial recordings) Folkways FA 2024 (FP 24) 10"; *Memorial,* Volumes I–IV, Stinson SLP 17, 19, 48, 51 10"; *Rock Island Line,* Folkways FA 2014 10"; *Take This Hammer,* Folkways FA 2004 10"; Texas-Louisiana born and raised, Leadbelly spanned the recent history of Negro secular song from work songs and square dances to raggy ballads, early blues and jazz blues. He has left a heroic mark on his age. FA 2004 and FA 2224 especially recommended.

LEWIS, Furry: *Furry Lewis,* Folkways FS3823 12"; Samuel B. Charters discovers and beautifully documents one of the first commercially recorded blues singers.

LITTLE WALTER: *The Best Of Little Walter,* Chess LP 1428; Harmonica player and singer extraordinary. One of the finest modern records.

LOMAX, Alan: Collector and editor. Field recordings to be released in 1960–61 by Atlantic. *Sounds Of The South* (Primitive dance music, spirituals, hollers, etc); *Roots Of The Blues* (Old Mississippi blues); *The Blues Roll On* (Modern Mississippi blues); *Negro Spirituals* (Old and new); the best recording I've done to date.

McGHEE, Brownie: *Blues,* Folkways FA 2030 10"; *Brownie McGhee Sings,* Folkways FG 3567 12"; with Sonny Terry: *Songs,* Folkways FA 2327 12"; *Traditional Blues* Vol. I, Folkways FA 2921 12"; a Tennessee blues man of great charm and talent who made his home in the East and now sings for everyone. See also: *Terry, Sonny.*

MEMPHIS SLIM: *Memphis Slim And The Real Boogie Woogie,* Folkways FG 3524 12"; *Memphis Slim And The Real Honky Tonk,* Folkways FG 3535 12"; the most accomplished folk-blues pianist alive. Recommended.

MORTON, Jelly Roll: A 12" LP documentary recorded in the Library of Congress by Alan Lomax. Jelly talks, plays and sings. Riverside 9001–9012.

MUDDY WATERS: Muddy Waters Sings Big Bill, Chess 1444, interesting; *The Best Of Muddy Waters,* Chess 1427. My favorite modern blues record. A Mississippi folk-blues man turning sophisticate.

NEW ORLEANS, Music Of: (recorded by S. B. Charters). 5 Volumes; Folkways FA 2461-5; A fine and elaborate documentary.

OSTER, Harry: Collector and Editor: *Angola Prisoners' Blues,* (Negro Prison blues) Folk Lyric LSS A-3; *Prison Work Songs* (From La. Prison) Folk Lyric LSS A-5; *Angola*

Prison Spirituals, Folk Lyric LSS A-6; *Rev. Pearly Brown— Georgia Street Singer,* (with R. Allen as Ed.) Folk Lyric FL-108; *Those Prison Blues,* (sung by Robert Pete Williams, La. Prison singer), Folk Lyric FL-109; Fine documentary recordings by able Louisiana collector.

PRICE, Lloyd: *The Exciting Lloyd Price,* ABC Para 277; The rocking blues singer who put "Stagolee" at the top of the hit parade.

PRISON Camp Work Songs, Negro, (recorded at Ramsey and Retrieve State Farms—Texas) Folkways FE 4475 12"; *Prison Songs From The Mississippi State Penitentiary* (Collected by A. Lomax), Tradition TLP 1020 12"; not as good as the Lib of Cong records, but still highly recommended, especially the Tradition album which is a must.

RAGTIME, piano roll classics by S. Joplin, S. Turpin, others; Riverside RLP 12-126;

RAMSEY, Frederic Jr., *Been Here And Gone* (Col. and ed. by F. Ramsey Jr.) Folkways 2659 12"; a good cross-section of this collector's field recordings.

REED, Dock and Vera Hall: *Spirituals,* Folkways FA 2038 (FP 38); *Spirituals,* Folkways FE 4473 12"; two marvelous country singers from Alabama. Five stars.

RELIGIOUS Songs And Services, Negro: (B. Botkin) Lib of Cong AAFS L 10 12"; good document of authentic material.

RING GAMES From Alabama: (H. Courlander) Folkways FC 7004 12"; good document of authentic material.

ROCK 'N ROLL, The Greatest, with Ray Charles, Ruth Brown, The Clovers, etc.; Atlantic 8001. A good cross-section of the best Negro rock and roll. See also *Charles, Price.*

RURAL BLUES, The: (col. and ed. by S. B. Charters), Folkways RF 202 (2-12"); excerpts important early blues recordings from commercial records. Recommended.

SONGS of Praise, Sung by the Sensational Nightingales; Peacock PLP 101 12"; Fine gospel quartet.

SOUTH, Music From The; (col. and ed. by F. Ramsey Jr.), nine LPs of field recordings from Ala., Miss., N. Orleans; Folkways FA 2651-58.

STAPLE Singers, The, Uncloudy Day, Vee Jay LP 5000; Mississippi guitar and street singing style, a bit dressed up, but moving.

SWAN Silvertones, The: Vee Jay LP 5003; rivals of the Dixie Hummingbirds.

TERRY, Sonny: *Sonny Terry,* Folkways FA 2035 10"; *City Blues,* Elektra EKL 15 10"; *Folk Blues,* Elektra EKL 14 10"; *Sonny Terry And His Mouth Harp,* Riverside RLP 12-644 12"; *Sonny Terry's Washboard Band,* Folkways FA 2006 10"; Blind Sonny Terry from Durham, North Carolina brings harmonica playing to a peak of folk refinement. Solid singer. Non-pareil.

THARPE, Sister Rosetta: *Gospel Train,* Decca 8782 12"; Originator of gospel song style; the best guitarist. Five stars.

WARD, Clara: *Gospel Concert,* Dot 3138; the most spectacular of the gospel groups.

WARD, L. Robert and his Rasberry Singers: *He's Got The Whole World In His Hands,* Savoy MG 14027 12"; cross-section of good gospel groups.

WASHBOARD Band, Country Dance Music, Folkways FA 2201 (FP 601); Sonny Terry, Pete Seeger produce one of the most delightful sounds on records.

WILLIAMSON, Sonny Boy (2nd): *Down And Out Blues,* Checker 1437; Rough and exciting Arkansas heir to the crown of the late, great Sonny Boy from Tennessee. Solid.

WORK Songs And Calls, Negro, (B. Botkin ed), Lib of Cong AAFS L 8 12″; Important document; see also *Prison Songs, Blues In The Mississippi Night, Alabama.*

YANCY, Jimmy, *Yancy's Getaway,* Riverside 12-124; the great boogie composer, the subtle pianist. Recommended.

INDEX OF SONG TITLES

KEY : Bold type indicates reference to song, roman type indicates reference to song note

INDEX OF FIRST LINES

High Sheriff, he tol' the deputy, he says, 'Go out an' bring me Laz'rus,' 567
Hog drovers, hog drovers, hog drovers we air, 399
Hold the wind, hold the wind, 474
Honey, 583
How came that blood on your shirt sleeve? 25
How do you think I began in the world? 31
How long, how long, 589
'How old are you, my pretty little miss?' 212
Hudson River steamboat, steaming up and down, 85
Hurrah for the choice of the nation, 97

I am a noted highwayman, Cole Younger is my name, 350
I am a poor and a ramblin' boy, 192
I am looking rather seedy now while holding down my claim, 397
I been a-havin' some hard travellin', 435
I been to the North and I been to the South, 255
I don't want your millions, Mister, 292
I got a gal at the head of the creek, 232
I have two sons and a son-in-law, 43
I rode to church last Sunday, 209
I wanted sugah very much, 504
I was down along the river, just sittin' on a rock, 442
I went up to London town, 188
I wish't I had a-heard ye when ye called me, 248
I woke up this mornin' with the blues all round my bed, 586
If you don't quit monkeying with my Lulu, 342
If you want to go to Heaven let me tell you what to do, 433
I'll give my love an apple without e'er a core, 27
I'll sing you a true song of Billy the Kid, 387
I'll tell you all a story about Omie Wise, 268
I'm a lonely bull-whacker, 333
I'm a-ridin' old Paint and I'm a-leadin' old Fan, 378
I'm bound to follow the longhorn cows until I git too old, 368
I'm broke an' I ain't got a dime, 586
I'm goin' away to Texas, 320
I'm ridin' in a buggy, 500
I'm troubled, I'm troubled, 208
In eighteen hundred and forty-nine, 61
In eighteen hundred and ninety-two, 115
In eighteen hundred and sixty-one, Skiball, 98
In good old colony times, 11
In the days of eighteen and one, 283
Irene, goodnight, 593
It is of a fearless highwayman, a story I will tell, 347
It makes a long-time man feel bad, 542
It ofttimes has been told, 49
It was early, early one mornin', 571
It was early one morning, 562
It was late last Saturday evening, 312
It was on the drive in eighty, 119
It was out in old West Texas in the Spring of '83, 380

It'll be Lawd, Lawd, Lawd, when I'm gone, 471
It's a long ways from East Colorado, 549
It's all out on the old railroad, 237
It's do you know those horse traders, 323
It's four long years since I reached this land, 338
I've been a moonshiner for sev'nteen long years, 257
I've been wand'rin' early, 418
I've got a man and you've got none, 501
I've got a wife an' a-five li'l' chillun, 528
I'ze the bye that builds the boat, 149

John Gilbert is de boat, 527
John Hardy was a brave little man, 271
John Henry was a little boy, 562
Johnson boys, raised in the ashes, 223
Jumpin' Judy, jumpin' Judy, 540
Just listen to the song I'm singin', brother, 594

Keep a-inchin' along, inchin' along, 456
Kind friends, you must pity my horrible tale, 339

Let the deal go down, boys, 548
'Let's go a-huntin',' says Risky Rob, 311
Look down, look down, 584
Lord Lovel, he stood at his castle gate, 401
Love, O love, O careless love, 585

'Madam, I have come for to court you,' 314
Mammy Logan, she had a daughter, 548
Maximilian's daughter has my love, 54
Me an' my wife an' my wife's pap, 162
Me father's a lawyer in England, 134
'Mother, I would marry and I would be a bride,' 213
My last ole dollar is gone, 288
My Lord called John while he was a-writin', 480
My Lord, what a mornin'! 454
My love is a rider, wild horses he breaks, 383
My name is Charley Brennan, from Charlestown I come, 322
My name is Joe Bowers, I have a brother Ike, 336
My name was Robert Kidd, 15
My sweetheart's a mule in the mines, 131

No more auction block for me, 455
Not a thing on the river McClusky did fear, 110
Now, didn't it rain, chillun, 477
Now some people say a man's made out of mud, 294

O a raftsman's life is a wearisome one, 112
O Cape Cod girls they have no combs, 51
O come, all you hearty haddockers, who winter fishing go, 144
O, David, 250
O fare thee well, my own true love, 145
O I had a bird and the bird pleased me, 440
O, I ride with my slicker and I ride all day, 370
O I'm a good old rebel, 256
O Johnny dear has gone away, 47